Ripon Patgiri · Anupam Biswas ·
Pinki Roy
Editors

Health Informatics: A Computational Perspective in Healthcare

Springer

Editors
Ripon Patgiri
Department of Computer Science
and Engineering
National Institute of Technology Silchar
Silchar, Assam, India

Anupam Biswas
Department of Computer Science
and Engineering
National Institute of Technology Silchar
Silchar, Assam, India

Pinki Roy
Department of Computer Science
and Engineering
National Institute of Technology Silchar
Silchar, Assam, India

ISSN 1860-949X ISSN 1860-9503 (electronic)
Studies in Computational Intelligence
ISBN 978-981-15-9734-3 ISBN 978-981-15-9735-0 (eBook)
https://doi.org/10.1007/978-981-15-9735-0

This Springer imprint is published by the registered company Springer Nature Singapore Pte Ltd.
The registered company address is: 152 Beach Road, #21-01/04 Gateway East, Singapore 189721, Singapore

Preface

Computing technique is one of the key technologies that is being currently used to perform medical diagnostics in the healthcare domain, thanks to the abundance of medical data being generated and collected. Nowadays, medical data is available in many different forms like MRI images, CT scan images, EHR data, test reports, histopathological data, doctor–patient conversation data, etc. This opens up huge opportunities for the application of computing techniques, to derive data-driven models that can be of very high utility, in terms of providing effective treatment to patients. Moreover, machine learning algorithms can uncover hidden patterns and relationships present in medical datasets, which are too complex to uncover, if a data-driven approach is not taken. With the help of computing systems, today, it is possible for researchers to predict an accurate medical diagnosis for new patients, using models built from previous patient data. Apart from automatic diagnostic tasks, computing techniques have also been applied in the process of drug discovery, by which a lot of time and money can be saved. Utilization of genomic data using various computing techniques is other emerging areas, which may in fact be the key to fulfilling the dream of personalized medications. Medical prognostics is another area in which machine learning has shown great promise recently, where automatic prognostic models are being built that can predict the progress of the disease as well as can suggest the potential treatment paths to get ahead of the disease progression. Our book on *Health Informatics: A Computational Perspective in Healthcare* presents at attracting research works, to demonstrate the potential and the advancements of computing approaches to utilize healthcare centric and medical datasets.

Silchar, India

Dr. Ripon Patgiri
Dr. Anupam Biswas
Dr. Pinki Roy

Contents

About the Editors

Dr. Ripon Patgiri is currently working as an Assistant Professor at the Department of Computer Science & Engineering, National Institute of Technology Silchar. He has received his B.Tech., M.Tech. and Ph.D. degree from the Institutions of Electronics and Telecommunication Engineers, Indian Institute of Technology Guwahati and National Institute of Technology Silchar, respectively. His research interests are big data, bioinformatics and distributed systems. He has published several papers in reputed journals, conferences and books. Also, he was General Chair of 6th International Conference on Advanced Computing, Networking and Informatics. Currently, he is General Chair of International Conference on Big Data, Machine Learning and Applications to be held during 16–19 December 2019 at National Institute of Technology Silchar. Moreover, he is an organizing chair of 25th International Symposium Frontiers of Research in Speech and Music (FRSM 2020), to be held during 08–09 October 2020. He is also an organizing chair of International Conference on Modeling, Simulations and Optimizations (CoMSO 2020), to be held during 3–5 August 2020. Furthermore, he is a Guest Editor of "Big Data: Exascale computation and beyond" in EAI Transaction on Scalable Information Systems and Guest Editor of "Internet of Things: Challenges and Solutions" in "EAI Transactions on Internet of Things". He reviewed many research articles from KSII Transactions on Internet and Information Systems, Electronics Letters, EAI Endorsed Transactions on Energy Web, EAI Endorsed Transactions on Scalable Information Systems, ACM Transactions on Knowledge and Data Engineering, IET Software, International Journal of Computational Vision and Robotics, Journal of Computer Science, International Journal of Advanced Computer Science and Applications and IEEE Access. Also, he served as TPC member in many conferences. He is a senior member of IEEE, member of ACM, EAI and ACCS and associate member of IETE.

Dr. Anupam Biswas is currently working as an Assistant Professor at the Department of Computer Science & Engineering, National Institute of Technology Silchar. He has received his B.Tech., M.Tech. and Ph.D. degree from Dibrugarh University, Motilal Nehru National Institute of Technology Allahabad and Indian

Institute of Technology (BHU) Varanasi respectively. His research interests are social networking, review mining, sentiment analysis, machine learning and soft computing. He has received the Best Paper Award for the paper titled "Community Detection in Multiple Featured Social Network using Swarm Intelligence" in International Conference on Communication and Computing (ICC-2014), Bangalore. Also, he has received Reviewer Award from Applied Soft Computing Journal (IF 3.541), Elsevier, 2015 and 2017, and Physica A: Statistical Mechanics and its Applications (IF 2.243), Elsevier, 2016. He has published several papers in reputed journals, conferences and books. He is a reviewer of IEEE Transactions on Fuzzy Systems (TFS), IEEE Transactions on Evolutionary Computation (IEEETEVC), IEEE Systems Journal (IEEE-SJ), IEEE Transactions on Systems, Man and Cybernatics: System (IEEE TSMC), Applied Soft Computing (ASOC), ACM Transactions on Knowledge Discovery from Data (TKDD), ACM Transactions on Intelligent Systems and Technology (TIST) and Physica A: Statistical Mechanics and its Applications and Information Sciences.

Dr. Pinki Roy is currently working as an Assistant Professor at the Department of Computer Science & Engineering, National Institute of Technology Silchar. Dr. Pinki Roy received her B.Tech. degree in Computer Science & Engineering from Dr. Babasaheb Ambedkar Technological University, Lonere, Maharashtra (2002, First class with distinction) and M.Tech. degree (2004, First class with distinction) from Dr. Babasaheb Ambedkar Technological University, Lonere, Maharashtra. She has received her Ph.D. degree in the year 2014 in the field of Language Identification from National Institute of Technology, Silchar, Assam-788010, India. She was working as a Lecturer in Naval Institute of Technology, Colaba, Mumbai, India. (from February 2004 to August 2004). Her research interests include language identification, speech processing, machine intelligence and cloud computing. She has published several papers in reputed journals, conferences and books. She has received several awards which are listed below—1. "Distinguished Alumnus Award", Dr. Babasaheb Ambedkar Technological University, Lonere, Maharashtra, 2014. 2. "Young Scientist Award", Venus International Foundation, Chennai, 2015. Awarded for major contribution in research during Ph.D. 3. "Rastriya Gaurav Award", India International Friendship Society, New Delhi, 2015. 4. "Bharat Excellence Award", Friendship Forum, New Delhi, 2016. 5. "Best Golden personalities Award", Friendship Forum, New Delhi, 2016. 6. "Global Award for Education", Friendship Forum, New Delhi, 2016. 7. Honoured as one of the "Most Distinguished Lady Alumni" by Computer Engineering Department of Dr. Babasaheb Ambedkar Technological University, Lonere, Maharashtra, India.

6G Communication Technology: A Vision on Intelligent Healthcare

Sabuzima Nayak and Ripon Patgiri

Abstract 6G is a promising communication technology that will dominate the entire health market from 2030 onward. It will dominate not only health sector but also diverse sectors. It is expected that 6G will revolutionize many sectors including healthcare. Healthcare will be fully AI-driven and dependent on 6G communication technology, which will change our perception of lifestyle. Currently, time and space are the key barriers to health care and 6G will be able to overcome these barriers. Also, 6G will be proven as a game changing technology for healthcare. Therefore, in this perspective, we envision healthcare system for the era of 6G communication technology. Also, various new methodologies have to be introduced to enhance our lifestyle, which is addressed in this perspective, including Quality of Life (QoL), Intelligent Wearable Devices (IWD), Intelligent Internet of Medical Things (IIoMT), Hospital-to-Home (H2H) services, and new business model. In addition, we expose the role of 6G communication technology in telesurgery, Epidemic and Pandemic.

Keywords 6G communications · Smart healthcare · Intelligent healthcare · Quality of services · Quality of experience · Quality of life · Intelligent internet of medical things · Intelligent wearable devices · Hospital-to-home service · Telesurgery · Edge computing · Artificial intelligence

1 Introduction

6G communication technology is attracting many researchers due to its prominent features and its promises. It will revolutionize diverse fields and we will evidence the revolution from 2030 onward. Many features of 6G have already been discussed in premier forum and continuously gathering various requirements of 6G communi-

S. Nayak · R. Patgiri (✉)
National Institute of Technology Silchar, Silchar, India
e-mail: ripon@cse.nits.ac.in

S. Nayak
e-mail: sabuzimanayak@gmail.com

R. Patgiri et al. (eds.), *Health Informatics: A Computational Perspective in Healthcare*, Studies in Computational Intelligence 932,
https://doi.org/10.1007/978-981-15-9735-0_1

cation technology [5, 10, 12, 35]. Also, Nayak and Patgiri [28] exposes issues and challenges of 6G communication technology. Many countries have already started 6G communication technology for timely deployment. Firstly, Finland initiated 6G project in 2018[19]. Secondly, United State, South Korea and China have started 6G project in 2019 [7]. Recently, Japan has also initiated 6G research project in 2020 [8]. In addition, many algorithms have been developed for 6G [9, 24]. Now, it is essential to initiate 6G project to not be left behind by other countries. On the contrary, 5G communication technology is yet to deploy in full scale over worldwide and B5G yet to be developed. 5G and B5G will have various drawbacks for revolutionize modern lifestyle, society and business. For instance, unable to support holographic communication due to lower data rate. Therefore, it is the peak time to envision future possibilities of 6G communication technology. Also, it is necessary to envision the future healthcare for well-being of peoples of the society.

The current healthcare system is providing basic facilities and the key barrier of the current healthcare system is time and space. This is unavoidable in the current scenario, however, it will not be a barrier in the near future. Moreover, ambulance service is just a transporter of patients with oxygen facility and road traffic priority which can be served by a normal car too. Besides, the elderly service is very unsatisfactory in current scenarios. The elderly service requires intensive care from medical staffs. However, it is unavailable till date. Most of patient dies in ambulance while travelling from home to hospital or before ambulance reaching the spot. Also, the accident detection system is unavailable in current healthcare systems. The accident detection system requires real-time detection to provide medical services on time and on the spot. Furthermore, Epidemic and Pandemic outbreaks, for instance, COVID-19, cannot be controlled due to lack of advanced infrastructure. A similar kind of virus will again arise in future. Thus, it is utmost important to develop the intelligent healthcare system.

The requirements of 6G communication technology for future healthcare are high data rate ($\geq$ 1 Tbps), high operating frequency ($\geq$ 1 THz), low end-to-end delay ($\leq$ 1 ms), high reliability (10^{-9}), high mobility ($\geq$ 1000 km/h) and wavelength of $\leq$ 300 μm [5]. In particular, telesurgery requires real-time communications. Also, holographic communication and augmented/virtual reality will boost up the intelligent healthcare systems. However, 5G and B5G will be unable to support intelligent healthcare. In the 5G communication era, intelligent healthcare will be implemented partially which will push forward a step ahead. However, the rural connectivity is still a challenge for 5G communication technology [43] as well as healthcare. Communication technology boost up the performance of health service and a landscape of intelligent health service is depicted in Fig. 1.

It is expected that 6G communication technology will revolutionize the healthcare completely and the healthcare will fully depend on communication technology. We will evidence the paradigm shift in healthcare due to the advent of communication technology. Current state-of-the-art healthcare system is unable to provide telesurgery due to communication issues. Moreover, ambulance service is to be replaced. Wearable devices need to be redefined. The hospital is required to restructure. The health services should be provided in real-time. Health monitoring and

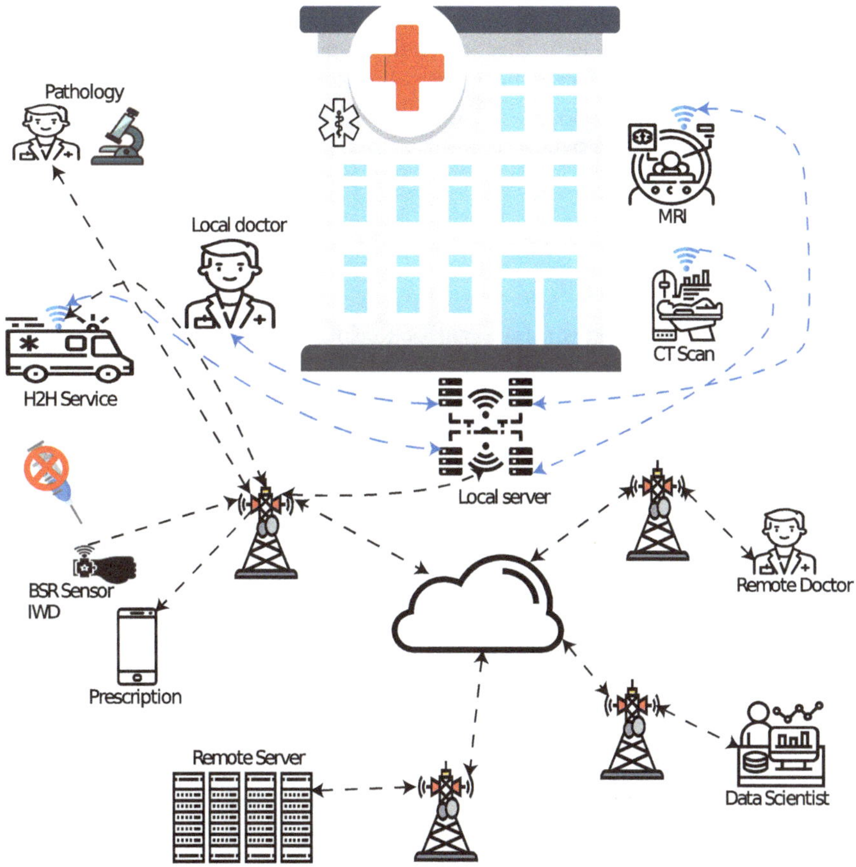

Fig. 1 A landscape of intelligent healthcare systems. This figure includes Intelligent Internet of Medical Things (Blood Sample Reader (BSR) sensor, Intelligent Wearable Devices (IWD), Online Prescription, MRI, CT Scan), Hospital-to-Home (H2H) Services implements mobile hospital, Pathology, Local Doctors, Remote Doctors, and Data Scientist

elderly services need to be redefined. Therefore, in this perspective, we envision the future healthcare using 6G communication technology. We brief the required parameters of 6G communication technology and its prime technologies. Also, we focus on Quality of Services (QoS), Quality of Experiences (QoE) and Quality of Life (QoL). Moreover, we envision the requirement of Hospital-to-Home (H2H) services, Blood Sample Reader (BSR) sensor, and Intelligent Wearable Devices (IWD). Moreover, the role of Artificial Intelligence (AI) and Edge technology in healthcare is exposed. Thus, Sect. 2 surveys detail parameters of 6G communication technology to establish the understanding of the article. In addition, Sect. 3 reviews the enabling technology for 6G to meet intelligent healthcare in near future. Sections 4, 5 and 6 expose the role of holographic communication, augmented and virtual reality, and tactile Internet in intelligent healthcare. Moreover, the parameters of intelligent healthcare are envisioned in Sects. 7, 8 and 9. This article also exposes the role of communication in handling Epidemic and Pandemic in Sect. 10. Most importantly, intelligent healthcare requires security, secrecy and privacy which are addressed in Sect. 12. Finally, this article is concluded in Sect. 13.

2 6G Technology

6G will be using the terahertz (THz) signal for transmission [12]. THz signal increases bandwidth and data rate. Moreover, it will provide bandwidth three times higher than 5G signal, i.e., mmWave [6]. 6G will have a data rate of 1 TBPS or more. 5G and B5G follow 2-dimensional communication structure, whereas the 6G will follow 3-dimensional, i.e, time, space and frequency. 6G will provide the 3D services with the support of emerging technology such as edge technology, AI, cloud computing and blockchain. The 6G communication network will be ubiquitous and integrated [1]. 6G will provide deeper and broader coverage through device to device, terrestrial and satellite communication. 6G aims to merge computation, navigation and sensing to the communication network. In the area of security, 6G will cover security, secrecy and privacy of the Big data generated by billions of smart devices. However, there will be a transition from smart device to intelligent device.

2.1 Requirements

The requirements of 6G communication are gathered and discussed by various researchers [20, 32, 39, 45–48, 50]. The key requirements of 6G communication technology are 1 THz operating frequency, 1 Tbps data rate, 300 μm wavelength, and 1000 kmh mobility range [28, 35]. The 6G architecture is 3D with consideration of time, space and frequency. The end-to-end delay, radio delay and processing requirements are $\leq$ 1 ms, $\leq$ 10 ns and $\leq$ 10 ns respectively to provide real-time communication [12, 33]. Moreover, 6G will be truly AI-driven communication technology [28]. It is expected that 6G will be fully backed by satellite. The NR-Lite will be replaced by Intelligent Radio (IR) [21]. Also, the core network the Internet of Things (IoT) will be replaced by the Internet of Everything (IoE). It is expected that 6G will enable and revolutionize many technologies in coming future. We will evidence the transitions of IoT to IoE, Smart Devices to Intelligent Devices, and other numerous possibilities.

2.2 Terahertz Communication

6G will use terahertz radiation (THz) also called submillimeter radiation. It is electromagnetic waves with wavelengths in 1–0.1 mm, hence called submillimeter radiation. THz has many advantages making it suitable for 6G communication such as high bandwidth, high data rate (upto several Gbps), high capacity and high throughput [5]. Efficiency of THz signals is possible to increase by spectrum reuse and sharing. Some techniques already exist for spectrum reuse such as cognitive radio (CR). It helps many wireless systems to access the same spectrum through spectrum sensing and interference management mechanisms [5]. In case of spectrum sharing, temporally underutilized or unlicensed spectrum is utilized to maintain availability and reliability. Symbiotic radio (SR) is a new technique to support intelligent, heterogeneous wireless networks. It will help in efficient spectrum sharing. However, deploying these techniques in the 6G wireless network are still big challenges. Moreover, continuous THz signal generation is strenuous due to requirement constraints regarding size. Designing an antenna/transmitter is also complex. In addition, the signal gets attenuated to zero after short distance transmission. It occurs due to energy loss, i.e., molecular absorption and spreading loss [13].

2.3 Transition from Smart to Intelligent

6G is expected to be truly AI-driven communication technology and hence, it will be able to introduce intelligent era [28]. Therefore, all smart devices will be converted to intelligent devices in the era of 6G [30]. The advent of AI along with mobile communication, we will evidence many transitions from smart things to intelligent things. From 2030 and onward, the IoT will be intelligent and will be replaced by IoE. The smart phone will be replaced by intelligent phones. Intelligent devices will be AI-driven devices that are able to connect to the Internet. Thus, the intelligent device (may be tiny device) will be able to predict, make a decision and share their experience with other intelligent devices. Therefore, there is a paradigm shift from smart to intelligent era using 6G communication technology.

2.4 Quality of Services

The Quality of Services (QoS) parameters of 6G technology are higher than 5G and B5G. For instance, QoS includes high data rates, extremely reliable and low latency communication (ERLLC), further-enhanced mobile broadband (FeMBB), ultra-massive machine-type communications (umMTC), long-distance and high-mobility communications (LDHMC) and extremely low-power communications (ELPC) [48]. Also, QoS includes mobile broad bandwidth and low latency (MBBLL), massive broad bandwidth machine type (mBBMT), massive low latency machine type (mLLMT) [12]. This QoS service parameters enables diverse applications to revolutionize. Thus, the 6G technology will be proven as a revolutionary technology in many fields along with healthcare.

2.5 Quality of Experiences

The Quality of Experiences (QoE) defines a high QoS and user-centric communications. QoE will be achieved by holographic communications, augmented reality, virtual reality, and tactile Internet which requires high data rate with extremely low latency. Moreover, QoE is expected to be revolutionary in intelligent cars, intelligent devices, intelligent healthcare, intelligent drones and many more. A high QoE can be achieved only when all desired parameters are implemented by 6G technology. 6G technology will be truly AI-driven communication technology [28], and thus, we will evidence many changes in our lifestyles, societies and businesses. Also, 6G promises to provide five sense communication to provide rich QoE. Thus, 6G communication will be a major milestone for healthcare. Healthcare requires high QoE for critical operations, intelligent hospitals and intelligent healthcare.

2.6 Quality of Life

The Quality of Life (QoL) is defined as enhanced lifestyle with QoS and QoE in healthcare. 6G technology will enable high QoL using communication technology. The QoL is not a core parameters of 6G communication technology, however, it will be core parameters of the intelligent healthcare systems. 6G will be able to provide high QoE along with desired parameters of QoL. The key parameters of QoL are remote health monitoring of patients, including elderly persons, connection to intelligent wearable devices (IWD), intelligent accident detection, telesurgery, precision medicine, and many parameters will be included in future. Also, another prominent feature of QoL is Hospital-to-Home (H2H) services. H2H service will be implemented using mobile hospital in an intelligent vehicle. The mobile hospital will have minimum requirements to be a hospital including medical staffs. This service is essential in QoL to improve the modern lifestyle and emergency services.

3 Enabling Technology for 6G

6G communication technology requires supporting technologies to fulfill the promises. 6G is truly AI-driven communication technology [28], and thus, it requires AI to integrate its communication technology. Moreover, 6G will enable Internet of

Everything (IoE), and it will boost up many fields. Also, edge technology is necessary for 6G technology for bringing the Cloud features closer to intelligent devices. Thus, 6G communication technology comprises of many technologies.

3.1 Internet of Everything (IoE)

6G follow 6C's for communication [12]. 6C's are capture, communicate, cache, cognition, compute, and control. High level sensing is capturing. It is essential for holographic communication in healthcare. The captured data are converted to digital data, stored in a local cache and transmitted to remote locations in real-time. In some cases, digital data are further converted to signals and transmitted to other devices for processing. But before computing, cognition helps in formulating feasible determinations based on input digital data. These are intelligent determinations which helps in making the computing easy. The computed data are transmitted to smart devices to help in controlling the action taken by smart devices for healthcare [12]. For example, raising an alarm on Epidemic and Pandemic. It will use the core services of combined and enhanced eMBB and mMTC. It will require high data rates to support touch experiences in the intelligent devices for healthcare. IoE will be required by 6G to have a huge capacity to connect millions of intelligent devices, collect tactile sensations and convert to digital data [12]. Huge capacity to connect the sensors and actuators in healthcare communication. And, low latency to maintain seamless integration among them [12]. When 6G will be commercial, it will not be the era of Big data but rather Big data 2.0. Big data 2.0 require a supercomputer to compute and analyze massive scale of small-sized data produced by healthcare devices [30].

3.2 Edge Intelligence

6G will rely on Cloud computing for storage, computing and analysis of Big data [28]. Data produced by the intelligent devices are transferred to Cloud for storage, however, it consumes communication resources and bandwidth. Nowadays, the technologies are brought closer to the data source due to the exponential growth of data. This technology is Edge technology. 6G is claiming to have a high capacity to provide smooth services to billions of intelligent devices [40]. 6G will rely on Edge technology to provide the smooth and high speed Internet services to the intelligent devices which is vital for healthcare. Edge technology collects, computes and analyses the health data in real time in its Edge nodes [24]. These nodes are located closer to the intelligent medical devices. The data generated by the user are transmitted to the Edge nodes. Also, the Edge nodes compute the health data. Then, Edge nodes analyze the data to decide the appropriate action. For example, Edge node will receive user health data transmitted from the intelligent medical devices and determines whether the user is suffering from any deficiency. The health data are constantly transmitted to Edge nodes. The Edge node monitors the health related data. Edge node also filters the health related data and transmits the important information to the Cloud for storage. Edge technology reduces cost of communication and computation [17]. Some other advantages of Edge technology are low latency, reliability, privacy, scalability and adaptability. The massive number of intelligent devices will connect to 6G Internet, hence, all the advantages of Edge technology will greatly help 6G to meet its requirements to provide high QoS in healthcare.

"The marriage of edge computing and AI gives the birth of Edge intelligence [49]." Edge intelligence is implemented using AI algorithms for analysis in Edge nodes called Edge analytics. Edge nodes receive a huge volume of health related data and AI is used to find patterns or compute them for analysis. With the help of AI, Edge nodes are capable of developing image, data and video Edge analytics. GigaSight [36] is a video Edge analytics with a decentralized hybrid cloud architecture. Xie et al. [42] proposed a video analytics that has lightweight virtualization by implementing container technology. For filtering of data in Edge nodes, Nikolaou et al. [31] proposed a predictive Edge analytics. Similarly, Cao et al. [3] proposed a descriptive analytics for mobile Edge nodes. However, AI algorithms are computationally intensive. Currently, AI algorithms execution requires high computational resources, and power consumption, which is limited in the Edge nodes. Hence, they depend on the Cloud for execution. However, Edge nodes will be one of the network nodes in 6G. All 6G network nodes will be AI-enabled for providing intelligence services to the healthcare systems. Moreover, 6G will have real-time intelligent Edge which will dramatically boost up the healthcare system. It will perform computing and analysis on live data [15]. Therefore, it is very important to execute the AI algorithms in Edge nodes instead of Cloud to reduce latency in providing the services [1].

3.3 *Artificial Intelligence*

6G will be a truly AI-driven communication network [27, 28]. 6G will make every aspect of network communication intelligent to make the system self-aware, self-compute and self-decide on a situation. The goal of 6G is to provide global coverage, including space-air-water. This is achievable only by making the different aspects of communication "intelligent". Implementation of AI algorithms is generating high accuracy and performance in communication networks. Truly AI-driven communication can offer real-time communication which is very important for modern healthcare. AI-driven healthcare improves clinical diagnosis and decision making [44]. The healthcare requires AI to perform tasks in real-time. Deep learning (DL) does not require data preprocessing. It takes original health data and performs the computation, thus, real-time data can be given as input. Moreover, it shows high accuracy while computing a large number of network parameters[25]. Similarly, another AI algorithm that is currently explored on health data is Deep Reinforcement Learning (DRL). In reinforcement learning, the system first develops a few decisions, then observes the results. Based on the observation the decision is again computed to obtain an optimal decision. DRL combines both reinforcement learning and deep neural networks algorithms and combines the advantages of both [23]. Thus, DRL gives high performance within small computation time. In addition, federated AI will share their knowledge among the intelligent devices which will booster healthcare. AI algorithms have shown high performance. AI algorithms require expensive infrastructure. The AI is also preferred for proactive caching. For Big Data, parallelism in training should be explored. All AI algorithms perform high computation task. The high computation task takes a long time and consumes more power. Whereas, 6G is unable to provide such relaxation. The AI algorithms that will be implemented in 6G will have their own issues. For example, large numbers of layers in Neural Network. However, research is performed to improved AI algorithms with less computation time and less energy consumption to improve the performance of 6G which leads to increase in efficiency in healthcare.

4 Holographic Communication

"Hologram is a physical recording of an interference pattern that uses diffraction to generate a 3D light field [14]". The image generated has parallax, depth and other properties of the original object. Holographic communication uses cameras from different angles to create a hologram of the object. It will use the core service of combined and enhanced eMBB and URLLC. It will require high data rates to provide good quality of service and streaming high definition videos. Moreover, very low latency is required for real-time voices and immediate control responses [12]. Holographic communication will be a major breakthrough for healthcare. And, 6G is capable of providing this service. 6G Holographic communication will help connect people. In case of emergence, in some cases the doctors have to wait for the expert doctor(s) for a diagnosis. However, using holographic communication the expert doctor(s) can diagnose the patient while travelling. And, can supervise the doctor for an early medical treatment. Many times the patient has to travel to many doctors for a correct diagnosis or the treatment is unavailable in that hospital. The patient may have to travel to different states or to different countries. In such cases, it becomes an economical and physical burden for the patient. Also, travelling in bad health is very stressful for the patient. However, using holographic communication the doctors can diagnose remotely. The patient can only visit the hospital for treatment. Holographic communication will also help the expert doctors provide services in rural areas while staying in cities or towns. Similar to 6G global coverage, the 6G holographic communication will help in global connectivity of healthcare. Upon request the expert doctor can instantly provide services without having to adjust their schedule and travel. Moreover, it will be possible to connect different doctors around the world to discuss/supervise in complex medical cases.

5 Augmented Reality and Virtual Reality

Augmented reality (AR) helps to include virtuality to real objects. Moreover, it is combined with multiple sensory abilities such as audio, visual, somatosensory, haptic etc. AR also provides real-time interaction, and presents 3D images of virtual and real objects accurately. Virtual reality (VR) refers to presenting an imaginative or virtual world where nothing is real. AR and VR will use the core service of combined and enhanced eMBB and URLLC. It will require high data rates to provide good quality of service and to stream high definition videos. In addition, very low latency is required for real-time voices and immediate control responses [12]. AR and VR require a peak data rate of 1 Tbps and user experience of >10 Gbps with >0.1 ms latency which can be provided by MBBLL [12]. Currently, both AR and VR are developing. However, 6G will open new windows for their usage in the field of healthcare. AR will help to view the inside of the body of a patient without any incision. Moreover, doctors can adjust the depth of the specific location in the body [2]. The specific body area can also be enlarged for better visibility. 6G will help the doctors to view a patient remotely. The AR and holographic communication can be combined for better diagnosis. Using VR the doctors can practice medical procedures without any patient. It will be very helpful in case of practicing complex procedures/surgery having high risk. All these devices will be intelligent devices and connected to 6G Internet. As discussed above using 6G a smooth and high resolution presentation can be created for remote medical learning or diagnosis.

6 Tactile/Haptic Internet

Haptic technology creates a virtual touch using force, motion or vibration on the user. Tactile Internet is used to transfer the virtual touch to another user, maybe human or a robot. Tactile Internet requires high speed of communication and ERLLC to grab the tactile in real-time. This technology will be used for remote surgery, i.e., telesurgery. It will also help doctors for diagnosis using touch without being physically present. Haptic human-computer interaction (HCI) is classified into three types, namely, desktop, surface, and wearable [41]. In desktop HCI, the remote doctor will be able to use a virtual tool for surgery or diagnosis. In surface HCI, the movement is not 3D, but 2D. The device to give command has a flat screen such as a mobile or tablet. As moving the hand on the screen the robot can be given a command to interact with the patient. In wearable HCI, for instance a haptic glove, is used by the remote doctor. Tactile/haptic technology will also help in providing healthcare during disaster time. For example, the COVID-19 when all countries are under lockdown and interaction with outside of the state and country is closed or natural disasters. During such situations, tactile/haptic technology will help in healthcare. Expert doctors can perform complex surgery remotely using robots. In addition, during epidemics and pandemics, the medical personnel are at great risk. A little carelessness may expose them to the deadly/contagious disease. Using tactile/haptic technology robots can be used to interact or care for the patient while medical personnel will be present remotely. All this is achievable by using 6G high speed and low latency Internet.

7 Intelligent Internet of Medical Things

In 6G communication paradigm, Intelligent Internet of Medical Things (IIoMT) will evolve and serve many purposes for well-being of humankind. IIoMT are intelligent devices that are AI-driven that makes its own decision using communication technology. IoE will also emerge along with IIoMT, and thus, medical things can connect to the Internet. For instance, MRI and CT scan. The scanner will scan the devices and send the data to remote locations through 6G technology as depicted in Fig. 1. These data can be analyzed by a pathologist in real-time. Almost all medical things will be able to connect to the Internet and instant decision can be taken. Therefore, IIoMT will be able to overcome the barrier of time, space and money. Another example, cancer patients can easily be treated by remote doctors. Currently, it takes time to detect whether the cancer patients having benign or malignant. However, cancer can be detected in real time in the near future using 6G communication technology. Also, the doctors and patients do not have to visit specialist hospitals. It takes time and money. Therefore, remote doctors will treat the cancer patients in collaboration with local doctors. Early detection of cancer patients can reduce the mortality rate to nearly zero. However, such sensors need to be invented. This scenario not only applies to cancer, but also applies to many diseases. For instance, cardiovascular treatments.

7.1 Sample Reading Sensors

Blood is vital for the human body and most of the diseases can be detected from blood. Conventional blood sampling requires needles to inject to sample the blood from the human body. However, numerous research is being conducted for needle-free blood sampling devices. For instance, Lipani et al. devices new needle-free method for glucose monitoring for diabetic patients [22]. Sample Reader Sensors (SRS) will be needle-free intelligent wearable device. The SRS sensors will revolutionize the health industry. SRS will correctly read every parameters of blood, for instance, WBC, RBC, etc. This SRS sensor will remain connected to the 6G Internet. A blood sample will be transmitted to a testing center for test results periodically, automatically or with permission from the patient. Hence, no manual intervention will be required for testing Blood sample. This device will play vital role in intensive care on elderly service and monitoring. Moreover, COVID-19 outbreak could be easily stopped using SRS, because this kind of sensor can not only reading blood, but also various samples, for instance, thyroids, stools and urine sample. With the number of cases crossing millions, countries are running out of medical gears. Taking the blood sample using needle exposes the medical staff to the disease. This SRS sensor can easily track the spread of COVID-19 virus in real-time. Thus, it will be a huge help during Epidemic and Pandemic. Therefore, SRS sensor will be the most demanded medical devices in the future.

7.2 Intelligent Wearable Devices

Intelligent Wearable Devices (IWD) are connected to the Internet and transmit psychological and physical data to test centers and monitoring centers. This devices will monitor heartbeat, blood pressure, blood tests, health conditions, body weight and nutrition. The test result will be received quickly. Also, IWD learn from the personal body history and advise the person for the next action, for instance, advising for walk or running. IWD will maintain a personal history of health, nutrition, and habits. Thus, IWD can advise what to eat in case of any deficiency. Detection of minor body issues such as deficiency will reduce the frequency of hospital visit. So, it will reduce hospital bill and hospital can focus on more complex diseases. In addition, IWD will read blood sample and the blood sample will be transmitted to pathological results. Thus, early detection of cancer can be possible using IWD. Therefore, IWD can improve health conditions and increase human life span. Also, it is vital in elderly services because elderly service requires intensive cares. Future IWD will combine multiple features in a single device. All features will be packed into a single device. The initial release of such devices will be expensive, however, over a time period cost will decrease and the common people can afford.

8 Hospital-to-Home Services

Currently, the ambulance services are just a transporter of patients with oxygen and road traffic priority. It does not serve the purpose of emergency service due to absence of intelligence. Therefore, the ambulance services are not impacting on our lives. Any normal car can also solve the same purposes if we keep oxygen and emergency signal. Therefore, a new kind of ambulance service is required to improve lifestyle.

To replace ambulance services, the Hospital-to-Home (H2H) services will be emerging. Due to the advent of communication technology, hospital can reach to home on demand and in an emergency situation. The future vehicles will be fully AI-driven to make intelligent vehicles [38]. Therefore, H2H will be implemented upon mobile hospital on an intelligent vehicle platform that will have a minimum dependence on hospitals including doctors and nurses. This mobile hospital will replace ambulance services. For instance, mobile hospital detects an accidents in real-time and reaches the spot. Then, the mobile hospital will start treating the patients before reaching the hospitals. Moreover, mobile hospital can detect any emergency situation in real-time and reach the spot to save lives. It will also enhance modern lifestyles. Specially, it is immensely necessary in elderly services. Thus, 6G communication revolutionizes modern lifestyle through the H2H services.

9 Telesurgery

The telesurgery is emerging and it is a concept for the future. It is defined as remote surgery by the doctor(s) [4]. Telesurgery requires robots, nurses and mediator of remote doctors. Communication plays a key role in telesurgery. Also, it requires a very high data rate and URLLC. 5G and B5G are unable to provide these requirements due to requirement of virtual reality. Hence, telesurgery requires the support of 6G technology. Moreover, the success of telesurgery requires real-time communication. For telesurgery, the doctor can provide guidance through verbal, telestration or tele-assist [16]. Due to 6G, more interactive verbal guidance can be provided using holographic communication. In holographic communication, the doctor can be present in the surgery for guidance and also can also move to have a better visual of the surgery area. Telestration is showing the surgery procedure remotely, for instance using video. In intelligent healthcare, AR and VR can be used for telestration. In addition, the doctor(s) can tele-assist the surgery using tactile/haptic technology. The requirements of telesurgery can be fulfilled by 6G communication technology and 6G will prove that surgery can be perform beyond boundaries.

10 Epidemic and Pandemic

Communication technology will play a vital role in epidemic and pandemic. Mostly, epidemic and pandemic are human to human transmission disease. Therefore, medical staffs are at high risk and often termed as "suicide squad". Recently, COVID-19 has taken thousands of lives, including the medical staffs. COVID-19 outbreaks could easily be stopped using IIoMT. For instance, blood sample of each person is transmitted to testing center using BSR sensor without exposing themselves to the outer worlds and the result will be received at their own home. A blood sample will be taken by intelligent wearable technology (BSR sensor) and transmit the sample data to the test centers. Thus, human chain can easily be stopped and the outbreak can be tracked in real-time. Now, millions of COVID-19 positives have been detected and billion of testing has to be conducted. This global tragedy demands intelligent healthcare systems and IWD.

11 Precision Medicine

Precision medicine is developing a customized medicine or treatment for providing better treatment to a patient [29]. For the development of precision medicine the doctors/researchers conduct research by grouping the people based on some common parameter. 6G technology can greatly help in the development of precision medicine. Also, it requires AI to provide personalized healthcare [34]. Better development of treatment requires health data of the clinical trial people. For instance, cell therapy research is carried out for critical disease treatment [18, 37]. The doctors and researchers can collect the data using IWD. This data will be collected in real-time which helps in providing accurate health data. Moreover, the research can be conducted globally. Geographical condition influence a person's immunity system. Hence, moving the people under observation to a single location will change their environment. And, this will influence the research. Therefore, through IIoMT the doctor/researcher will observe the people under observation across the globe.

12 Security, Secrecy and Privacy

The key focus of 6G technology is security, secrecy and privacy [7]. Therefore, 6G requires secure URLLC (sURLLC) to have an enhanced secure communication. 6G communication technology promises the highest level of security. It will defend the attacks using federated AI, Quantum Machine Learning, Quantum Computing and THz communication. THz communication is eavesdropping and jamming proof [28]. Healthcare requires a high level of security for data transmission over the network. Any alteration of health data can kill a patient. Therefore, it is crucial to protect health data from attackers. Moreover, 6G communication technology also focuses on secrecy of the most sensitive data. Sensitive data are protected from anyone excepts owner of the data. Also, administrators are not permitted to view these sensitive data. For instance, family history. In addition, 6G also focuses on privacy which is crucial parameters of healthcare. To increase privacy, 6G will also rely on Edge technology. The Edge nodes are located closer to smart devices. The computed data are also analyzed in the same Edge nodes. Edge nodes have small memory, hence, all data are not concentrated in one location. Therefore, Edge maintains the privacy of the user. Another important point is filtering of data by Edge nodes. Edge nodes filter the data and transmit only important information to the Cloud. It also leads to storage of less information about the user in the Cloud. Thus, it is easier for Cloud to provide security for lesser data. In the current scenario, Blockchain provides a high degree of privacy for health data [26]. It provides a secure infrastructure for handling the health data [11]. In the future, Blockchain with more advanced techniques will be very helpful in intelligent halthcare.

13 Conclusion

Intelligent healthcare must enhance QoL. Precisely, intelligent healthcare comprised of IIoMT, IWD, and H2H. All IIoMT requires high quality mobile communication, AI integration, and support from Edge computing and Cloud Computing. A key IIoMT is BSR sensors. BSR sensors are yet to be devised. BSR will be able to solve many issues in healthcare. Thus, BSR sensor needs extreme attention from the research community. Also, another prominent IIoMT is IWD. IWD will be a revolutionary technology for healthcare and it will be equipped with many sensors including BSR. It will help in diagnosis of many diseases automatically and improve drastically the health of a person. Also, a person does not require to visit hospital for regular check up, for instance, blood test, blood pressure, sugar level, etc. IWD sends the personal health data periodically to the health monitoring center for detection of any kind of abnormality. Also, an elderly person can be monitored without intervention of medical staffs. Elderly service requires intensive care, and the integration of IWD with the healthcare system will automatically take care of the person without intervention of medical staffs. In addition, IWD will learn personal medical history, food habit, body structure, environmental pollution level, and any other abnormality. Current ambulance service is just a transporter of patients with limited medical kits. This service should be replaced by H2H services. H2H service will be able to save billion of lives, and thus, it requires immediate implementation on intelligent vehicle. In addition, the mortality rate of accident can be reduced using H2H service.

References

1. Al-Eryani, Y., & Hossain, E. (2019). The D-OMA method for massive multiple access in 6G: Performance, security, and challenges. *IEEE Vehicular Technology Magazine*, *14*(3), 92–99.
2. Blum, T., Stauder, R., Euler, E., & Navab, N. (2012). Superman-like x-ray vision: Towards brain-computer interfaces for medical augmented reality. In *2012 IEEE International Symposium on Mixed and Augmented Reality (ISMAR)* (pp. 271–272).
3. Cao, H., Wachowicz, M., & Cha, S. (2017). Developing an edge computing platform for real-time descriptive analytics. In *2017 IEEE International Conference on Big Data (Big Data)* (pp. 4546–4554).
4. Challacombe, B., Kavoussi, L., Patriciu, A., Stoianovici, D., & Dasgupta, P. (2006). Technology insight: Telementoring and telesurgery in urology. *Nature Clinical Practice Urology*, *3*(11), 611–617.
5. Chen, S., Liang, Y., Sun, S., Kang, S., Cheng, W., & Peng, M. (2020). Vision, requirements, and technology trend of 6G: How to tackle the challenges of system coverage, capacity, user data-rate and movement speed. In *IEEE Wireless Communications* (pp. 1–11). https://doi.org/10.1109/MWC.001.1900333.
6. Chen, Z., Ma, X., Zhang, B., Zhang, Y., Niu, Z., Kuang, N., et al. (2019). A survey on terahertz communications. *China Communications*, *16*(2), 1–35.
7. Dang, S., Amin, O., Shihada, B., & Alouini, M. S. (2020). What should 6G be? *Nature Electronics*, *3*(1), 2520–1131. https://doi.org/10.1038/s41928-019-0355-6.

8. DOCOMO, N. (2020). White paper 5G evolution and 6G. Accessed on 1 March 2020 from https://www.nttdocomo.co.jp/english/binary/pdf/corporate/technology/whitepaper_6g/DOCOMO_6G_White_PaperEN_20200124.pdf.
9. Dong, W., Xu, Z., Li, X., & Xiao, S. (2020). Low cost subarrayed sensor array design strategy for IoT and future 6G applications. *IEEE Internet of Things Journal*, p. 1.
10. Giordani, M., Polese, M., Mezzavilla, M., Rangan, S., & Zorzi, M. (2020, March). Toward 6g networks: Use cases and technologies. *IEEE Communications Magazine*, *58*(3), 55–61. https://doi.org/10.1109/MCOM.001.1900411. March.
11. Gökalp, E., Gökalp, M. O., Çoban, S., & Eren, P. E. (2018). Analysing opportunities and challenges of integrated blockchain technologies in healthcare. In S. Wrycza & J. Maślankowski (Eds.), *Information systems: Research, development, applications, education* (pp. 174–183). Cham: Springer International Publishing.
12. Gui, G., Liu, M., Tang, F., Kato, N., & Adachi, F. (2020). 6G: Opening new horizons for integration of comfort, security and intelligence. *IEEE Wireless Communications*, pp. 1–7. https://doi.org/10.1109/MWC.001.1900516.
13. Han, C., & Chen, Y. (2018). Propagation modeling for wireless communications in the terahertz band. *IEEE Communications Magazine*, *56*(6), 96–101.
14. Holocenter: What is a hologram? Accessed on 1 March 2020 from http://holocenter.org/what-is-holography.
15. Huang, T., Yang, W., Wu, J., Ma, J., Zhang, X., & Zhang, D. (2019). A survey on green 6G network: Architecture and technologies. *IEEE Access*, *7*, 175758–175768. https://doi.org/10.1109/ACCESS.2019.2957648.
16. Hung, A. J., Chen, J., Shah, A., & Gill, I. S. (2018). Telementoring and telesurgery for minimally invasive procedures. *The Journal of Urology*, *199*(2), 355–369. https://doi.org/10.1016/j.juro.2017.06.082.
17. Illa, P. K., & Padhi, N. (2018). Practical guide to smart factory transition using IoT, big data and edge analytics. *IEEE Access*, *6*, 55162–55170.
18. Ioannidis, J. P., Kim, B. Y., & Trounson, A. (2018). How to design preclinical studies in nanomedicine and cell therapy to maximize the prospects of clinical translation. *Nature Biomedical Engineering*, *2*(11), 797–809. https://doi.org/10.1038/s41551-018-0314-y.
19. Katz, M., Matinmikko-Blue, M., & Latva-Aho, M. (2018, November). 6genesis flagship program: Building the bridges towards 6G-enabled wireless smart society and ecosystem. In *2018 IEEE 10th Latin-American Conference on Communications (LATINCOM)*, (pp. 1–9). Guadalajara, Mexico: IEEE. https://doi.org/10.1109/LATINCOM.2018.8613209.
20. Katz, M., Pirinen, P., & Posti, H. (2019, August). Towards 6G: Getting ready for the next decade. In *2019 16th International Symposium on Wireless Communication Systems (ISWCS)* (pp. 714–718). Oulu, Finland: IEEE. https://doi.org/10.1109/ISWCS.2019.8877155.
21. Letaief, K. B., Chen, W., Shi, Y., Zhang, J., & Zhang, Y. A. (2019, August). The roadmap to 6g: Ai empowered wireless networks. *IEEE Communications Magazine*, *57*(8), 84–90. https://doi.org/10.1109/MCOM.2019.1900271.
22. Lipani, L., Dupont, B. G. R., Doungmene, F., Marken, F., Tyrrell, R. M., Guy, R. H., et al. (2018). Non-invasive, transdermal, path-selective and specific glucose monitoring via a graphene-based platform. *Nature Nanotechnology*, *13*(6), 504–511. https://doi.org/10.1038/s41565-018-0112-4.
23. Luong, N. C., Hoang, D. T., Gong, S., Niyato, D., Wang, P., Liang, Y., et al. (2019). Applications of deep reinforcement learning in communications and networking: A survey. *IEEE Communications Surveys Tutorials*, *21*(4), 3133–3174.
24. Mao, B., Kawamoto, Y., & Kato, N. (2020). AI-based joint optimization of QOS and security for 6G energy harvesting internet of things. *IEEE Internet of Things Journal*, p. 1.
25. Mao, Q., Hu, F., & Hao, Q. (2018). Deep learning for intelligent wireless networks: A comprehensive survey. *IEEE Communications Surveys Tutorials*, *20*(4), 2595–2621.
26. McGhin, T., Choo, K. K. R., Liu, C. Z., & He, D. (2019). Blockchain in healthcare applications: Research challenges and opportunities. *Journal of Network and Computer Applications*, *135*, 62–75. https://doi.org/10.1016/j.jnca.2019.02.027.

27. Nawaz, S. J., Sharma, S. K., Wyne, S., Patwary, M. N., & Asaduzzaman, M. (2019). Quantum machine learning for 6G communication networks: State-of-the-art and vision for the future. *IEEE Access*, *7*, 46317–46350. https://doi.org/10.1109/ACCESS.2019.2909490.
28. Nayak, S., & Patgiri, R. (2020). 6G: Envisioning the Key Issues and Challenges. CoRR https://arxiv.org/abs/2004.04024.
29. Nayak, S., & Patgiri, R. (2020). A study on big cancer data. In A. Abraham, A. K. Cherukuri, P. Melin, & N. Gandhi (Eds.), *Intelligent systems design and applications* (pp. 411–423). Cham: Springer International Publishing.
30. Nayak, S., Patgiri, R., & Singh, T. D. (2020). Big computing: Where are we heading? EAI endorsed transactions on scalable information systems. https://doi.org/10.4108/eai.13-7-2018.163972.
31. Nikolaou, S., Anagnostopoulos, C., & Pezaros, D. (2019). In-network predictive analytics in edge computing. In *2019 Wireless Days (WD)* (pp. 1–4).
32. Piran, M. J., & Suh, D. Y. (2019, August). Learning-driven wireless communications, towards 6G. In *2019 International Conference on Computing, Electronics Communications Engineering (iCCECE)* (pp. 219–224). https://doi.org/10.1109/iCCECE46942.2019.8941882.
33. Rappaport, T. S., Xing, Y., Kanhere, O., Ju, S., Madanayake, A., Mandal, S., et al. (2019). Wireless communications and applications above 100 GHz: Opportunities and challenges for 6G and beyond. *IEEE Access*, *7*, 78729–78757. https://doi.org/10.1109/ACCESS.2019.2921522.
34. Reddy, B., Hassan, U., Seymour, C., Angus, D., Isbell, T., White, K., et al. (2018). Point-of-care sensors for the management of sepsis. *Nature Biomedical Engineering*, *2*(9), 640–648. https://doi.org/10.1038/s41551-018-0288-9.
35. Saad, W., Bennis, M., & Chen, M. (2019). A vision of 6G wireless systems: Applications, trends, technologies, and open research problems. IEEE Network, pp. 1–9. https://doi.org/10.1109/MNET.001.1900287.
36. Satyanarayanan, M., Simoens, P., Xiao, Y., Pillai, P., Chen, Z., Ha, K., et al. (2015). Edge analytics in the internet of things. *IEEE Pervasive Computing*, *14*(2), 24–31.
37. Scheetz, L., Park, K. S., Li, Q., Lowenstein, P. R., Castro, M. G., Schwendeman, A., et al. (2019). Engineering patient-specific cancer immunotherapies. *Nature Biomedical Engineering*, *3*(10), 768–782. https://doi.org/10.1038/s41551-019-0436-x.
38. Tang, F., Kawamoto, Y., Kato, N., & Liu, J. (2020, February). Future intelligent and secure vehicular network toward 6G: Machine-learning approaches. *Proceedings of the IEEE*, *108*(2), 292–307. https://doi.org/10.1109/JPROC.2019.2954595.
39. Tomkos, I., Klonidis, D., Pikasis, E., & Theodoridis, S. (2020, January). Toward the 6G network era: Opportunities and challenges. *IT Professional*, *22*(1), 34–38. https://doi.org/10.1109/MITP.2019.2963491.
40. Ullah, S., Higgins, H., Braem, B., Latre, B., Blondia, C., Moerman, I., et al. (2012). A comprehensive survey of wireless body area networks. *Journal of medical systems*, *36*(3), 1065–1094.
41. Wang, D., Guo, Y., Liu, S., Zhang, Y., Xu, W., & Xiao, J. (2019). Haptic display for virtual reality: Progress and challenges. *Virtual Reality & Intelligent Hardware*, *1*(2), 136–162. https://doi.org/10.3724/SP.J.2096-5796.2019.0008.
42. Xie, Y., Hu, Y., Chen, Y., Liu, Y., & Shou, G. (2018). A video analytics-based intelligent indoor positioning system using edge computing for IoT. In *2018 International Conference on Cyber-Enabled Distributed Computing and Knowledge Discovery (CyberC)* (pp. 118–1187).
43. Yaacoub, E., & Alouini, M. (2020). A key 6G challenge and opportunity–connecting the base of the pyramid: A survey on rural connectivity. *Proceedings of the IEEE*, pp. 1–50. https://doi.org/10.1109/JPROC.2020.2976703.
44. Yu, K. H., Beam, A. L., & Kohane, I. S. (2018). Artificial intelligence in healthcare. *Nature Biomedical Engineering*, *2*. https://doi.org/10.1038/s41551-018-0305-z.
45. Zhang, L., Liang, Y., & Niyato, D. (2019, August). 6G visions: Mobile ultra-broadband, super internet-of-things, and artificial intelligence. *China Communications*, *16*(8), 1–14. https://doi.org/10.23919/JCC.2019.08.001.
46. Zhang, S., Xiang, C., & Xu, S. (2020). 6G: Connecting everything by 1000 times price reduction. *IEEE Open Journal of Vehicular Technology*, p. 1. https://doi.org/10.1109/OJVT.2020.2980003.

47. Zhang, Y., Di, B., Wang, P., Lin, J., & Song, L. (2020). HetMEC: Heterogeneous multi-layer mobile edge computing in the 6G era. *IEEE Transactions on Vehicular Technology*, p. 1. https://doi.org/10.1109/TVT.2020.2975559.
48. Zhang, Z., Xiao, Y., Ma, Z., Xiao, M., Ding, Z., Lei, X., et al. (2019, September). 6g wireless networks: Vision, requirements, architecture, and key technologies. *IEEE Vehicular Technology Magazine*, *14*(3), 28–41. https://doi.org/10.1109/MVT.2019.2921208.
49. Zhou, Z., Chen, X., Li, E., Zeng, L., Luo, K., & Zhang, J. (2019). Edge intelligence: Paving the last mile of artificial intelligence with edge computing. *Proceedings of the IEEE*, *107*(8), 1738–1762.
50. Zong, B., Fan, C., Wang, X., Duan, X., Wang, B., & Wang, J. (2019, September). 6G technologies: Key drivers, core requirements, system architectures, and enabling technologies. *IEEE Vehicular Technology Magazine*, *14*(3), 18–27. https://doi.org/10.1109/MVT.2019.2921398.

Deep Learning-Based Medical Image Analysis Using Transfer Learning

Swati Shinde, Uday Kulkarni, Deepak Mane, and Ashwini Sapkal

Abstract There is a wide spectrum of different deep learning (DL) architectures available for medical image analysis. Among this convolution networks (CNN) found to be more efficient for variety of medical imaging task including segmentation, object detection, disease classification, severity grading, etc. In medical image analysis, accuracy of prediction is of utmost importance. In machine learning or deep learning, quantity and quality of medical image dataset plays a important role for ensuring the accuracy of future prediction. Otherwise because of less number of poor quality images, machine or deep learning models fail to predict accurately. This limitation of less quantity and less quality medical image dataset is almost removed to major extent by the transfer learning concept of deep learning. Transfer learning concept of deep learning makes the pertained models available for customization to specific application needs. Either pre-trained models are fine-tuned on the underlying data or used as feature extractors. As these pertained models are already trained on large datasets, the accurate set of generic features can be extracted to improve the overall performance and computational complexity. Because of transfer learning, limitation of large dataset requirement is removed to a greater extent and also the training cost in terms of number of parameters to be learned, training time, hardware computing cost is reduced. Plenty of pre-trained models are available including AlexNet, LeNet, MobileNet, GoogleNet, etc. Currently, many researchers are applying DL to obtain promising results in a wide variety of medical image analysis for almost all diseases including all types of cancers, pathological diseases,

S. Shinde (✉)
Pimpri Chinchwad College of Engineering, Pune, India
e-mail: swati.shinde@pccoepune.org

U. Kulkarni
SGGS Institute of Engineering & Technology, Nanded, India

D. Mane
Rajershi Shahu College of Engineering, Tathawade, India

A. Sapkal
Army Institute of Technology, Pune, India

R. Patgiri et al. (eds.), *Health Informatics: A Computational Perspective in Healthcare*,
Studies in Computational Intelligence 932,
https://doi.org/10.1007/978-981-15-9735-0_2

orthopedic diseases, etc. The proposed chapter covers introduction to deep learning, transfer learning, different award winning architectures for transfer learning, different resources for medical imaging research. This is followed by a brief case study of use of transfer learning for malaria diagnosis. The chapter also highlights on the future research directions in the domain of medical image analysis.

Keywords Medical image analysis · Deep learning · Transfer learning

1 Introduction

Artificial intelligence (AI) is the broad domain having machine learning as a sub-domain that focuses on the study of different algorithms to bring intelligence in the machines. Machine learning (ML) enables the computers to learn without being explicitly programmed that makes them to resemble like humans. There are number of machine learning algorithms including linear regression, logistic regression, naïve Bayes, decision tree, random forest, support vector machines, artificial neural networks, etc. Among these algorithms, artificial neural networks inspired by the structure and functioning of the human brain [1–3]. Deep learning (DL) is a branch of machine learning which is completely based on artificial neural networks. It is the fast growing and most emerging field that captivating up several challenges of applications. The relationship among AI, ML and DL is as shown in Fig. 1. In contrast to the artificial neural networks used in machine learning, deep learning uses artificial neural networks with many layers. These artificial neural networks with many layers are called deep neural networks and the branch to study these deep neural networks is called as deep Learning.

These traditional artificial neural networks used in machine learning were successfully used for image recognition in many application areas. However, these fully connected neural networks have following two drawbacks:

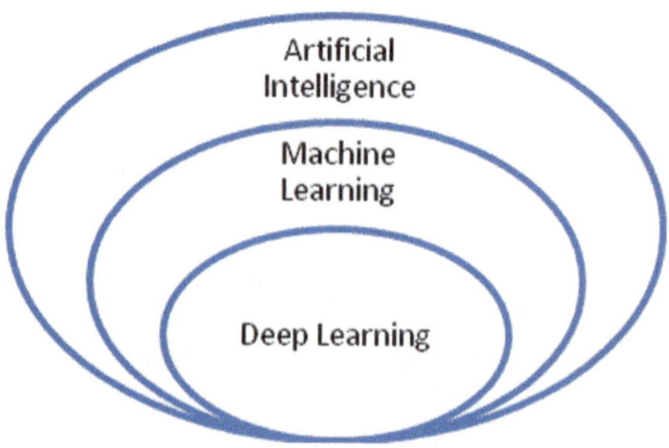

Fig. 1 Relationship between AI, ML and DL

1. Large number of parameters: In fully connected neural networks, numbers of weight parameters are more so these networks suffer from the curse of dimensionality issue. Due to this, they could not scale better for higher resolution images. For an RGB image of size, 1000 × 1000 has 3 million pixel values resulting into 1000*1000*3 = 3 million weights per neuron in the first hidden layer.
2. In addition to the above drawback, the fully connected networks do not consider the spatial structure of image. For it, the pixels at closer distances are identical to those that are at far distance from each other. Thus, it ignores the locality of reference information in the images.

2 Deep Learning in Medical Imaging

Since 1990s, it is common to extract handcrafted features and train the statistical machine learning classifier for computer aided diagnosis and has found to be the base of many commercial medical diagnosis systems. This is proved to be a major shift from manual diagnosis toward automated diagnosis. The success of these AI-based automated diagnosis lies in the accurate extraction of handcrafted features from large amount of training data. Afterward, since 2012, deep learning started gaining lot of popularity in medical applications because of its ability to learn optimal features from the data of given problem. In deep neural network, once image is given as an input, it passes through layer by layers by transforming image into abstract-level features to deeper-level features and finally classifying these features into predefined classes.

The most popular deep learning model for medical image analysis is the convolution neural network (CNN). CNN is proposed early in year 1980 but it has gain the momentum in 2012, after its successful application in 2012 to ImageNet challenge. This CNN model is referred AlexNet, who won the ImageNet challenge. Since then many advancements are made to this model, each one is developed with some different characteristics and named differently like Google Net, Mobile Net, etc.

Following are some of the CNN architectures succeeded inImageNet Large-Scale Visual Recognition Challenge (ILSVRC) that runs ImageNet project to correctly classify and detect objects and scenes.

i. **LeNet-5 (1998)**: It is a seven-level convolutional neural network proposed in 1998 and proposed by LeCun et al., so named as LeNet-5. This network was primarily designed for handwritten digit recognition. It was used in banks for recognition of digits on cheques. The input to this neural network is of 32 × 32 gray-scale images and it classifies this image into one of the ten predefined classes of digits. But this architecture limits the processing of large and high resolution images which actually needs more convolutional layers.

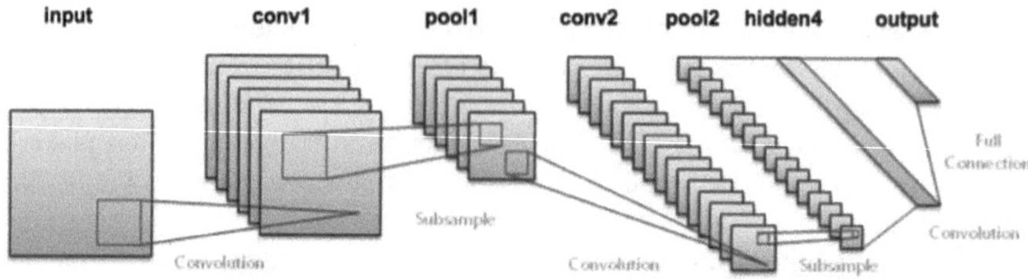

ii. **AlexNet (2012)**: AlexNet has won the ImageNet challenge in 2012 by reducing error rate to 15.3%. Its architecture is similar to that of LeNet with many stacked convolution layers resulting into deeper architecture having more filters per layer. The filter sizes used in this architecture are of 11 × 11, 5 × 5 and 3 × 3. In addition to the convolution layers, it has max pooling layers and other network optimization parameters include drop out, ReLU activation function, data augmentation, stochastic gradient descent with momentum. The training of AlexNet took six days with two NVidiaGeForce GTX 580 GPUs running concurrently resulting into two pipelines. The SuperVision group consisting of Alex Krizhevsky, Geoffrey Hinton, and IlyaSutskever has designed the AlexNet.

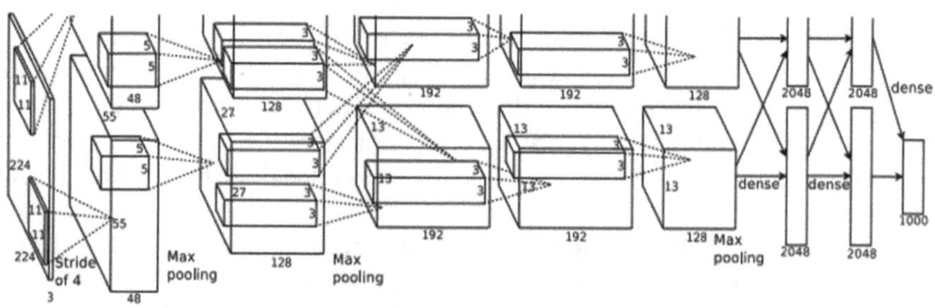

iii. **ZFNet (2013)**: ZFNet has won ImageNet challenge in 2013. Its architecture is same as that of AlexNet with different hyperparameters. This has resulted into the error rate of 14.8%.

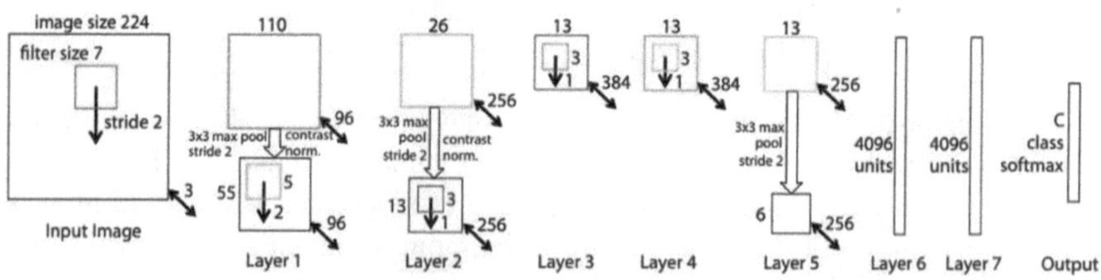

iv. **GoogleNet/Inception V1 (2014)**: GoogleNet won the ILSVRC 2014 challenge with much reduced error rate of 6.67%. This error rate is closer to human-level performance. As it was the extraordinary achievement, the creators of GoogleNet have performed the human evaluation. The human expert—Andrej

Karpathy—has achieved the error rate of 5.1% and of 3.6% with ensemble model. GoogleNet is the implementation of CNN with the structure as like LeNet dubbed with the inception module. The hyperparameters used are batch normalization, image distortions, and RMSprop. The architecture of GoogleNet has 22 layers but reduced number of parameters from 60 million of AlexNet to 4 million of GoogleNet.

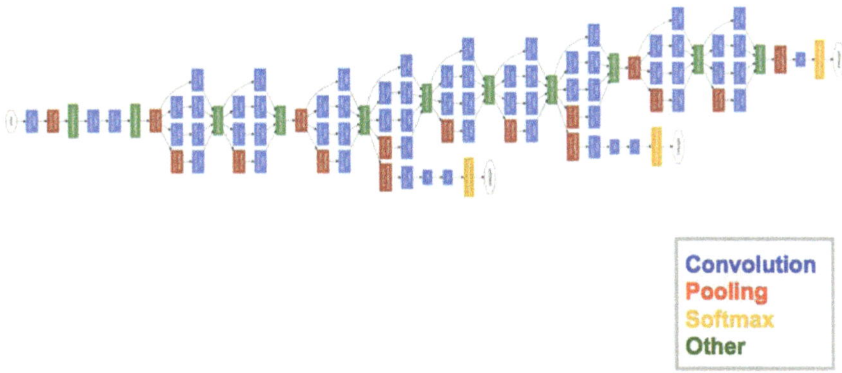

v. **VGGNet (2014)**: The runner up of ILSVRC 2014 challenge was VGGNet having 16 convolutional layers with a uniform architecture. The filter size used here was of only 3 × 3 with more number of filters. Its training took almost three weeks on 4 GPUs. The most appealing feature of VGGNet was its architectural uniformity. This makes VGGNet most suitable for feature extraction from images. Due to this reason, it is made publically available and mostly accepted pre-trained neural network for many applications and challenges as the feature extractor. But this network suffers with the large number of parameters of 138 million which makes it challenging and difficult to handle.

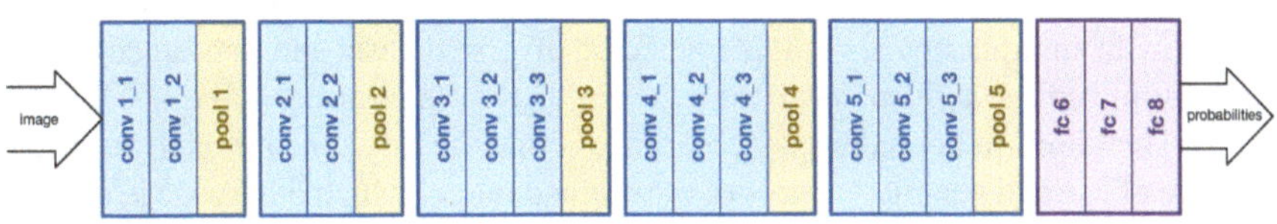

vi. **ResNet (2015)**: ResNet won the ILSVRC 2015 challenge with the error rate of 3.57% by beating the human-level performance on the given dataset. It uses the skip connections and heavy feature batch normalization which makes it unique. These skip connections are referred as gated recurrent units and they are similar to the successful elements applied in RNNS. The architecture of ResNet consists of 152 layers and a reduced complexity comparable to VGGNet.

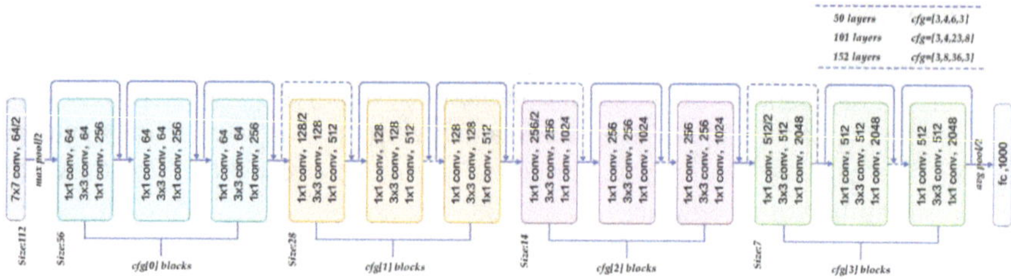

3 Transfer Learning

The transfer learning is an important technique of deep learning where the model is trained for one application and can be reused for other application. Here, the extension term signifies that earlier capability of the model is further updated and not replaced for its use to another task [4–7].

There can be many definitions of transfer learning found in the literature but all have the same meaning. Some of them are given below [13] -

"Transfer learning and domain adaptation refer to the situation where what has been learned in one setting ... is exploited to improve generalization in another setting". –Deep Learning (Adaptive Computation and Machine Learning series) by Ian Goodfellow.

"Transfer learning is the improvement of learning in a new task through the transfer of knowledge from a related task that has already been learned."–Handbook of Research on Machine Learning Applications and Trends: Algorithms, Methods and Techniques (2 Volumes) 1st Edition

In transfer learning, usually the neural network is initially trained on some large benchmark datasets having variety of labels like ImageNet [4]. This trained model is called pre-trained model and it is made available for further task specific training, called fine-tuning. Pre-trained model is capable to extract generic features accurately from input images as it is trained on diverse dataset and fine-tuned models are customized for a given task.

The intuition behind transfer learning is that the fine-tuned model get the advantage of learned generic features of pre-trained model which otherwise is not possible only with task specific smaller dataset.

Any pre-trained classification model using CNN has two parts—first part extracts features and second part does the image classification. First part of feature extraction consists of series of convolution and pooling layers and second part is a fully connected neural network. In transfer learning, based on how these two parts are carried further in fine-tuned model, following two ways of using a pre-trained model are suggested-

1. Feature Extraction: In this method, first part of pre-trained neural network is kept as it is and second part is added newly for classifying target task specific images. So here, trainable parameters for the first part are zero and only second

part is trained from scratch. This allows model to extract features based on the learned knowledge of pre-trained model and classify them into the classes by using customized model. Here, there is a huge saving on computing resources.

2. Fine-Tuning: In this method of using a pre-trained model, some earlier layers of first part of pre-trained model are kept as it is and last layers are unfreeze along with second part of fully connected classifier is customized for target task specific data. This allows the fine-tuning of the abstract-level features of pre-trained model with deeper-level task specific features of newly added layers.

4 Datasets and Other Resources in Medical Imaging

Deep learning is considered as data hungry technique and it is critically an important obstacle especially in medical domain. Most of the researchers working in this domain either use the datasets that are publically available datasets or the locally available anonymized datasets. Limited numbers of datasets are available on public platforms and that too limited in size. Building the models on these datasets belonging to different continents, having different distribution and expecting this model to work for local real-world situations is not realistic as it will not develop the required generalization ability.

Transfer learning is the solution for the above problem of limited amount of data and for generalization performance of the model. Additionally, data augmentation is a technique that solves the problem data by applying different transformations to data by preserving its labels.

Data augmentation Data augmentation is a technique used for generating the more data based on existing data. Different transformations including zooming, rotating, cropping, shearing, etc. are applied to the existing data to create more data. The technique of data augmentation [8] was used to avoid over fitting and making the model more robust.

Data synthesis This technique generates the data through programming. So here, real-world data is not collected. The main purpose of data synthesis is experimentation by which machine learning model is trained for different tasks.

Many medical datasets can be obtained from -

http://camma.u-strasbg.fr/datasets for large medical and healthcare datasets

An overview of all challenges that have been organized within the area of medical image analysis can be found on hrps://grand-challenge.org/all_challenges/and it is summarized in Table 1. Table 2 lists the code links which are openly available for research on ML in medical imaging.

Table 1 List of competitions/challenges in medical imaging domain

Disease	Name	Summary	Image modality
Many diseases	Grand challenges	Grand challenges in biomedical image analysis. Hosts and lists a large number of competitions	All
Pneumonia	Pneumonia Detection challenge-RSNA	Lung opacities on chest radiographs are located automatically	NIH chest X-ray dataset
Cardiac	HVSMR 2016 challenge	3D cardiovascular MRI-based segmentation of the blood pool and myocardium	3D cardiovascular MRI
Heart	Ischemic Stroke lesion segmentation 2018 challenge	Acute CT perfusion data-based segmentation of stroke lesions	Acute stroke MRI
Brain	BRATS-2014 BRATS-2015	Segmentation of brain tumors in multimodal MRI scans	MRI
	ISLES-2015		MRI
	MRBrains-2013		MRI
Breast cancer	CAMELYON17 CAMELYON16 TUPAC DREAM	Histopathology-based automated breast cancer detection and classification of cancer metastases in whole-slide images lymph nodes	Histopathology and mammography
Skin cancer	ISIC 2018	Melanoma detection by skin lesion analysis	Dermoscopy
Cancer, heart, chronic, pulmonary, Alzheimer's, diabetes, etc	2018 Data Science Bowl by Kaggle	Detection of nuclei in histopathology images	Histopathology
Lung cancer	• 2017 Data Science Bowl • By Kaggle LUNA16 • ANODE09	Lung cancer diagnosis by using machine intelligence	CT scan
Heart disease	• Kaggle's 2016 Data Science Bowl • SLIVER07	Heart disease diagnosis	MRI
Bone Abnormality	MURA	Prediction of bone X-ray abnormality	3D CT scan

(continued)

Table 1 (continued)

Disease	Name	Summary	Image modality
Diabetic Retinopathy	Kaggle-2015	Prediction of diabetic retinopathy	Retinal images
Chest	• LUNA16 • ANODE09	Detection of pulmonary nodules from chess scan	CT scan
Digital pathology and microscopy	• EM segmentation challenge 2012 • Mitosis detection challenges in ICPR 2012 • Mitosis detection-AMIDA 2013 • CAMELYON16 • TUPAC • GLAS-Gland instance segmentation	Cancer detection and grading	Histopathology

Table 2 List of openly available code for ML in medical imaging

NiftyNet-It is an open-source platform of convolutional neural networks for medical image analysis-related guided therapy	http://niftynet.io/
DLTK- It is the standard implementation for deep learning network on medical images	https://github.com/DLTK/DLTK
Diabetic retinopathy	https://github.com/arcaduf/nature_paper_predicting_dr_progression
DeepMedic	https://github.com/Kamnitsask/deepmedic
sU-Net: It is the CNN implementation for segmentation of biomedical images	https://lmb.informatik.uni-freiburg.de/people/ronneber/u-net
Diagnosing pneumonia based on an X-ray image	https://gist.github.com/5ed9261408db9dd76c0a73210e3f69de
V-net	https://github.com/faustomilletari/VNet
SegNet: It labels the image pixel-wise by using a deep convolutional encoder decoder architecture	https://mi.eng.cam.ac.uk/projects/segnet
Brain lesion synthesis using GANs	https://github.com/khcs/brain-synthesis-lesion-segmentation
GANCS: It is the deep generative adversarial network for compressed sensing MRI	https://github.com/gongenhao/GANCS
Reconstruction of deep MRI	https://github.com/js3611/Deep-MRI-Reconstruction

5 Medical Image Modalities

Medical imaging is one of the significant tools for disease diagnosis which shows anatomical structure of different body organs of human being. There are different modalities of medical images including radiographs, computer tomography (CT), magnetic resonance imaging (MRI), positron emission tomography (PET), skeletal scintigraphy (bone scan) [9], histopathological [10], endoscopy, thermography, nuclear images, etc. These images provide clues for diagnosis and prognosis of different diseases and also decide the further treatment plan [11, 12].

- **An X-ray** takes a picture of the inside of your body.
- **CT scan test** allows scanning and seeing body from inside by using a combination of X-rays images taken from different angles around your body and a computer processing of these. It gives more detailed information than X-ray and can be used to scan any part of your body [12].

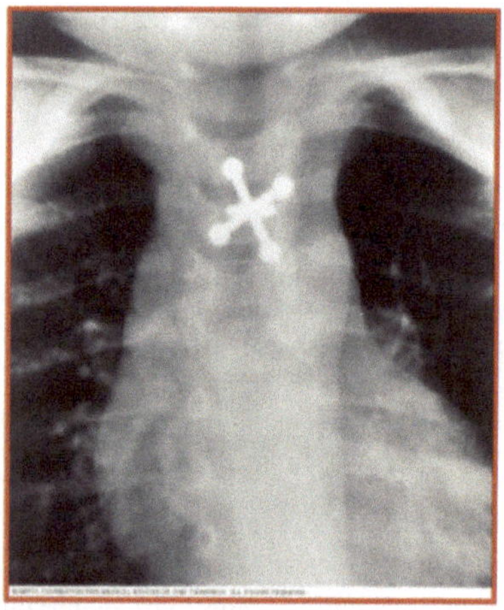

Chest X-ray

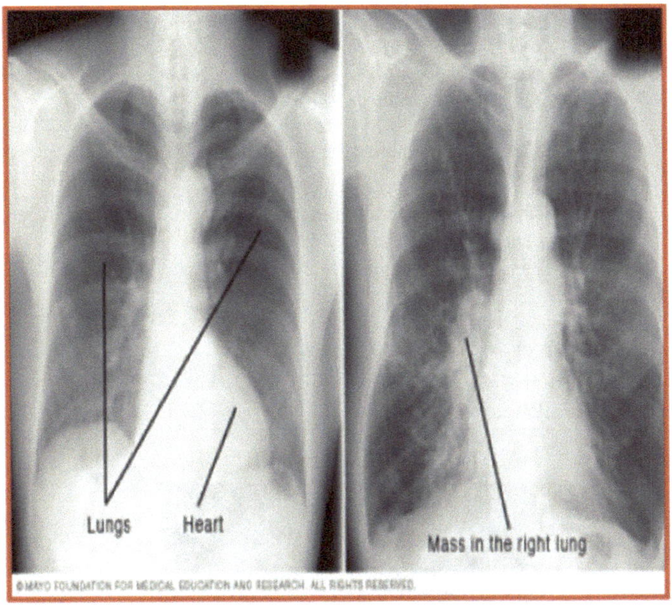

X-ray of swallowed jack

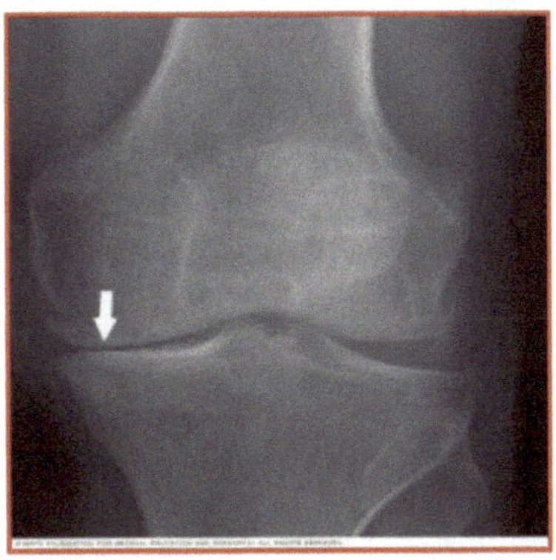

X-ray of knee arthritis

Table 3 gives information about organ-wise diseases where X-ray or CT scan imaging modality is preferred.

- **Magnetic resonance imaging (MRI)** test is used for clear visualization of human body images without the use of X-rays. MRI is recommended if X-rays or a CT scan does not show conclusive results. MRI is efficient for brain, spine and at the level of the neck [14, 15].

Table 3 Diseases where X-ray or CT scan imaging modality is preferred

X-ray/CT scan imaging	
Bones and teeth	• Fractures and infections in bones and teeth arthritis • Dental decay • Osteoporosis to measure bone density. • Bone cancer
Chest	• Lung infections or conditions as an evidence of pneumonia, tuberculosis or lung cancer • Breast cancer mammography • Enlarged heart • Blocked blood vessel • Heart diseases
Abdomen	• Digestive tract problems • Swallowed items

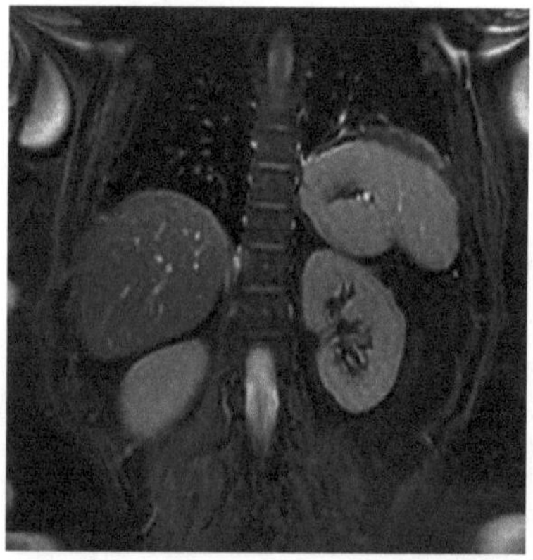

Abdomen MRI

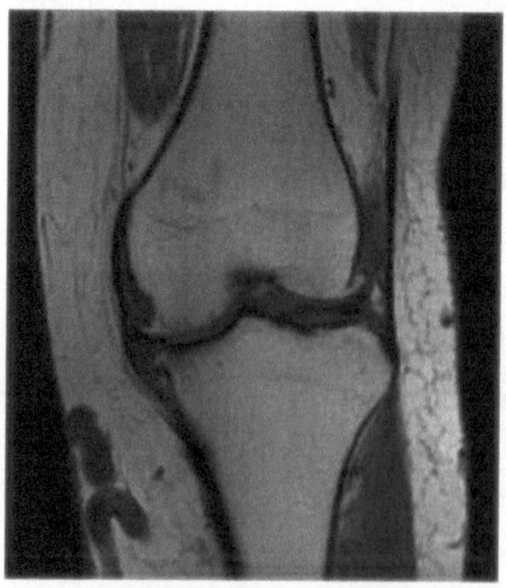

Knee MRI

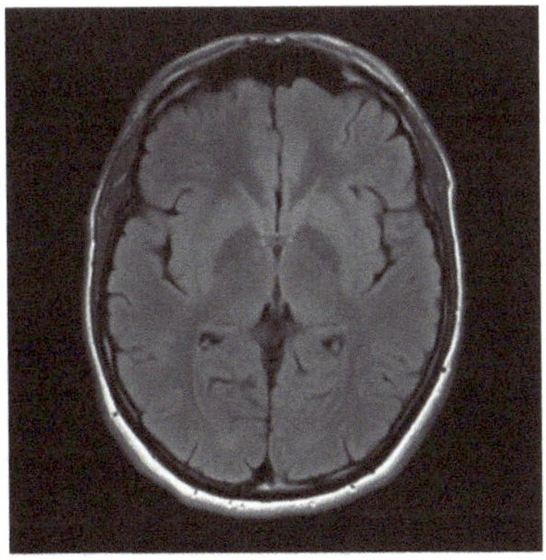

Brain MRI

Table 4 gives information about organ-wise diseases where MRI imaging modality is preferred.

- **A positron emission tomography (PET) test** scans the functioning of tissues and organs. It uses radioactive tracer which is injected in a body. This imaging can detect disease earlier in some cases than other imaging techniques. This imaging is useful in many cancers, heart diseases and brain disorders. It is useful in following diseases. Table 5 gives information about organ-wise diseases PET imaging modality is preferred [16].

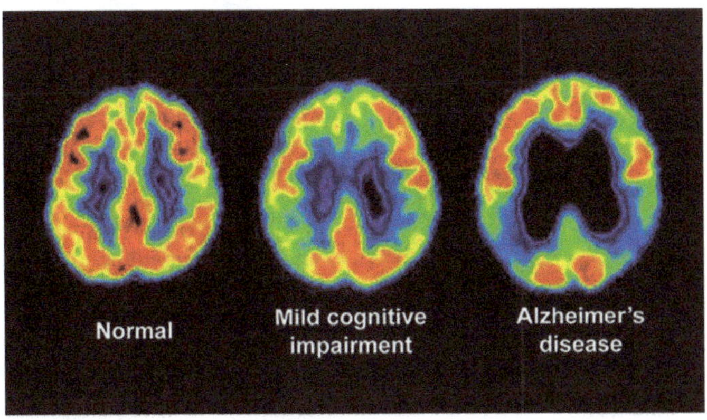

PET scans in Alzheimer's diagnosis

- **Histopathology** is the imaging technique where biopsy or surgical specimens are examined under microscope and processed using glass slides in order to identify the signs of the diseases. In order to identify the different components of the tissue

Table 4 Diseases where MRI imaging modality is preferred

MRI imaging	
Brain	• Brain tumor • Weakened blood vessel • Damage to nerve cells • Injury to brain • Eye problem • Spinal cord problem • Stroke
Heart	• Heart attack • Blockage or swelling in blood vessels • Problems with arota • Other heart-related problems
Bone	• Damage to joints, such as torn cartilage, ligaments, or tendons • Bone infections • Tumors involving the bones or joints • Herniated discs or spinal cord compression • Arthritis • Fractures that cannot be seen on X-rays
Breast	• Breast cancer • Breast cancer recurrence • See whether implants have ruptured
Liver	• Hepatitis • Cirrhosis • Liver cancer • Liver failure • Ascites • . Gallstones • Hemochromatosis • Primary sclerosing cholangitis • Primary biliary • Cirrhosis
Kidneys	• Pyelonephritis (infection of kidney pelvis) • Glomerulonephritis due to an overactive immune system • Kidney stones (nephrolithiasis) • Nephrotic syndrome • Polycystic kidney disease • End-stage renal disease (ESRD) • Papillary necrosis • Hypertensive nephropathy • Renal cyst • Acute renal failure (kidney failure) • Chronic renal failure • Diabetic nephropathy • Kidney cancer • Interstitial nephritis • Nephrogenic diabetes insipidus

(continued)

Table 4 (continued)

MRI imaging	
Pancreas	• Diabetes, type 1 • Diabetes, type 2 • Cystic fibrosis • Pancreatic cancer • Pancreatitis • Pancreatic pseudocyst • Islet cell tumor • Enlarged pancreas
Prostate gland	• Prostatitis • Enlarged prostate • Prostate cancer
Spleen	• Enlarged Spleen (Splenomegaly) • Ruptured spleen • Sickle cell disease • Thrombocytopenia (low platelet count) • Accessory spleen

Table 5 Diseases where PET imaging modality is preferred

PET imaging	
Organ	Diseases
Different types of cancers	• Cancer Brain • Cervical • Pancreatic • Colorectal • Lung • Lymphoma • Melanoma • Esophageal • Thyroid • Prostate • Head and neck
Heart	• Heart diseases- • Clogged heart arteries (angioplasty) • Coronary artery bypass surgery • Decreased blood flow in the heart
Brain	• Brain disorders- • Brain tumors • Alzheimer's disease • Seizures

under microscope, they are dyed with different stain colors [17]. Table 6 gives information about organ-wise diseases where histopathology imaging modality is preferred [18].

Table 6 Diseases where histopathology imaging modality is preferred

Histopathology imaging	
Heart and arterial system	• Arterial and venous diseases • Atherosclerotic cardiovascular disease • Myocardial infarction • Pericarditis • Cardiomyopathies • Myocarditis • Congenital heart disease • Arterial dissection • Infective endocarditis • Non-infective endocarditis • Neoplasia • Miscellaneous cardiac diseases
Brain and spinal cord	• CNS Hemorrhage • Infarction • Edema and herniation • Infections • Congenital malformations • Acquired and congenital degenerative diseases • Dementias • Neoplasms
Thyroid, parathyroids, adrenal, pituitary, and endocrine pancreas.	• Thyroid • Pituitary • Parathyroid • Adrenal • Islets of Langerhans
Female reproductive system	• Cervix, vagina, and vulva • Endometrium • Uterus • Fallopian tube • Ovary
Digestive tract from esophagus to rectum	• Esophagus • Stomach • Small intestine • Inflammatory bowel disease • Colon and appendix
Peripheral blood, bone marrow, lymph nodes, and spleen.	• RBC and bone marrow disorders • Myeloma • Lymph nodes and non-Hodgkin's lymphomas • Standard peripheral blood and marrow findings • leukemias • Hodgkin's disease

(continued)

Table 6 (continued)

Histopathology imaging	
Liver	• Steatosis • Cirrhosis • Pigmentary disorders • Neoplasms • Viral hepatitis • Miscellaneous parenchymal diseases
Male reproductive system	• Prostate • Penis • Testis
Respiratory tract, including lungs and pleura.	• Pneumonias • Granulomatous diseases • Obstructive diseases • Vascular diseases • Neoplasms • Interstitial diseases
Kidney	• Obstructive and vascular diseases • Interstitial diseases • Cystic diseases • Neoplasms • Glomerulonephritis • Infectious and inflammatory diseases

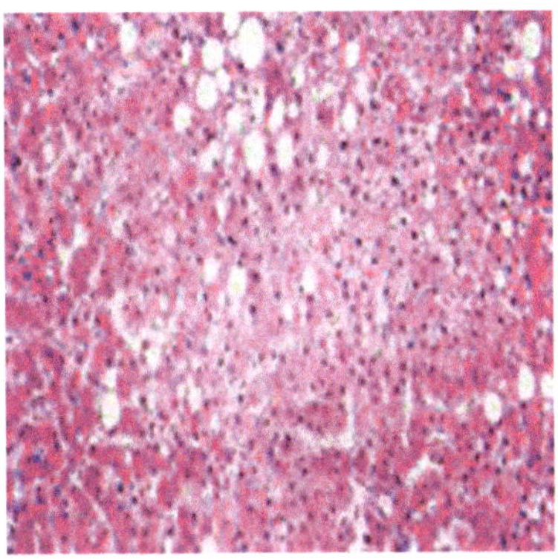

Liver steroids

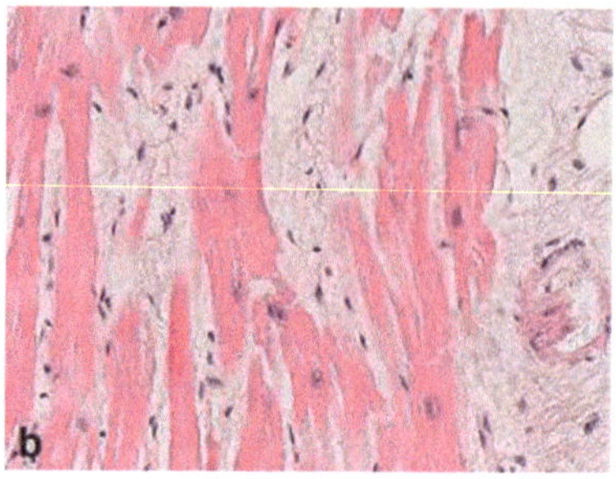

Chronic appendicitis

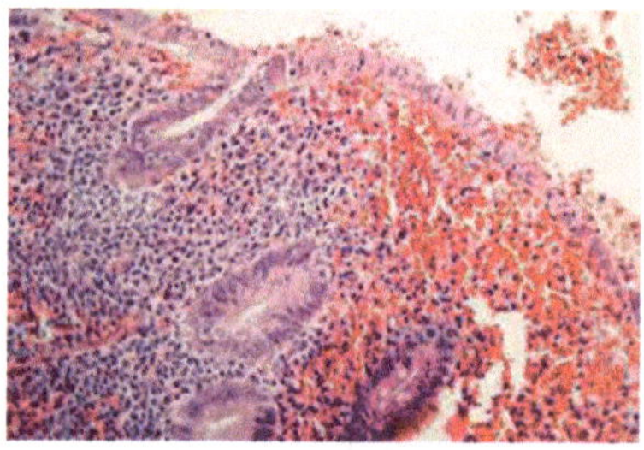

Chronic appendicitis

- **Additional imaging modalities**

Endoscopy: Endoscopy examines a digestive tract of the person. In endoscopy, the hollow organ or cavity of the body is examined by inserting the endoscope which directly into the organ. In endoscopy, a flexible pipe with a light beam and camera attached to it inserted directly into the organ. Endoscopy is used to examine over-sedation, infection, tear lining, perforation, and bleeding in urinary tract, gastrointestinal tract, ear, respiratory tract, etc. Endoscopy is recommended in following problems-gastritis, stomach pain, digestive tract bleeding, polyps or growths in the colon., ulcers, or difficulty swallowing, changes in bowel habits.

Thermography: Thermography is a test that uses an infrared camera that detects and convers the infrared radiations emitted from body into temperature and displays image of temperature distribution. Digital infrared thermal imaging (DITI) is used in diagnosis of breast cancer. It highlights the variations in the temperature on the surface of the breast for the diagnosis of the breast cancer.

Nuclear medicine imaging: In nuclear medical imaging, radioactive tracer is injected into patient's body mostly through veins or mouth and images are produced by detecting radiation from different parts of the body. This is reverse of X-rays where radiations are passed through the body from outside but in nuclear medicine imaging, the gamma rays are emitted from inside the body.

Tomography: It is also known as single photon emission computed tomography (SPECT) and it uses gamma rays for medical imaging. It is similar to nuclear imaging.

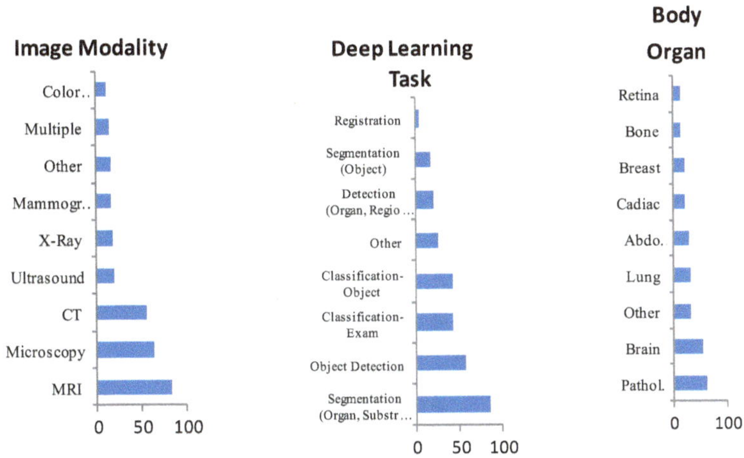

Fig. 2 Breakdown of 300 papers in terms imaging modality, deep learning task, and considered body organ

It shows the blood flow through the tissues and organs and used to help diagnose stroke, seizures, infections, stress fractures, and tumors in the spine [18].

In addition to the above imaging modalities, there are some medical imaging techniques like magnetoencephalogy (MEG), electroencephalogy (EEG), electrocardiography (ECG) which provides the patient's health information in the form of a graph with respect to time. Although these techniques carry important information buy cannot be considered as medical imaging modality.

In [19], authors have analyzed 300 research publications related to medical imaging. The breakdown of these 300 papers in terms of imaging modality, deep learning task considered in the paper, body organs targeted for study is given in Fig. 2.

6 Case Study—Medical Image Classification of Malaria Disease Images Using Transfer Learning

This disease is caused due to mosquito bites and for its diagnosis thick and thin blood smears are examined under microscope. The accuracy of such diagnosis is heavily depending upon the expertise of the pathologist and it is largely impacted by inter-observer variability. Due to the advances in digital pathology, digitized blood smear pathology images are easily available as given in Fig. 3. Subsection-a describes about dataset and subsections b and c describes the use of pre-trained model for malaria image classification and for feature extraction, respectively.

Dataset: The dataset consists of 27,588 images belonging to two separate classes with equal number of 13,794 images in each class. **One of the class is parasitized**

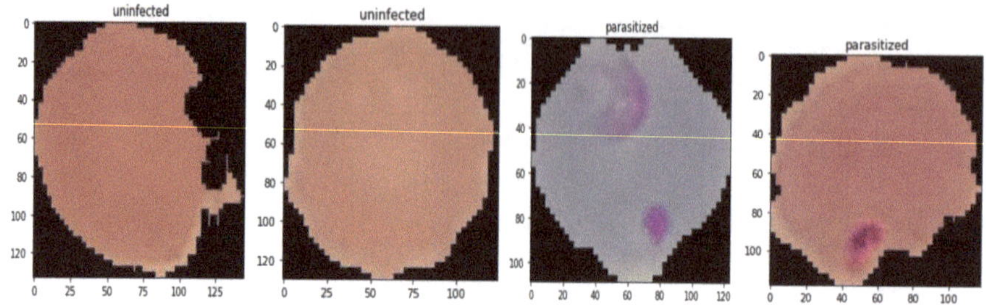

Fig. 3 Microscopic images of malaria diagnosis study

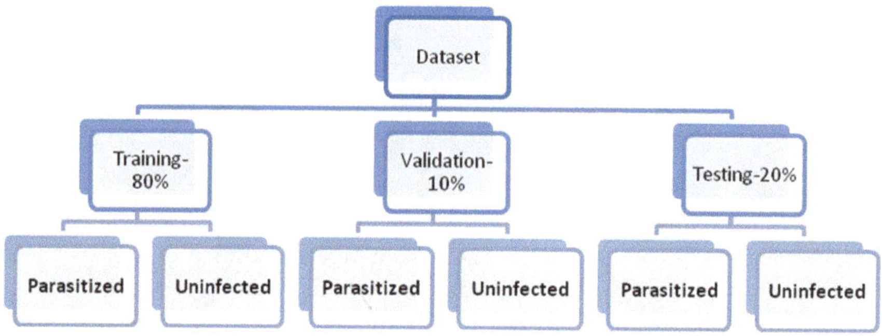

Fig. 4 Malaria dataset split

that implies the image contains malaria and other is **uninfected which implies** no evidence of malaria in the image as shown in Fig. 4. This dataset is taken from https://www.tensorflow.org/datasets/catalog/malaria.

a. **Pre-trained model for classification of malaria images**

In this paper, award winning model of ILSVRC competition VGG16 is used as a pre-trained model. The VGG 16 model accepts the input image size of 224*224*3 and produces the feature set of 7*7*512 which then can be used by any classifier or fully connected part of VGG16 as in Fig. 6. It has five blocks of layers consisting of two or three convolutions layers followed by maximum pooling layer. These layers sequentially process the input image and extract features from abstract to deeper level. For experimentation, Python, Tensorflow, and Keras framework is used with the GPU- single 12 GB NVIDIA Tesla K80 GPU.

Figure 5 depicts the performance of VGG model wrt. epochs. Model is run for 20 epochs only, still the performance given by the model is 90%. Further performance can be improved by image augmentation, fine-tuning of the model, more number of epoch, etc. by resulting into more training time.

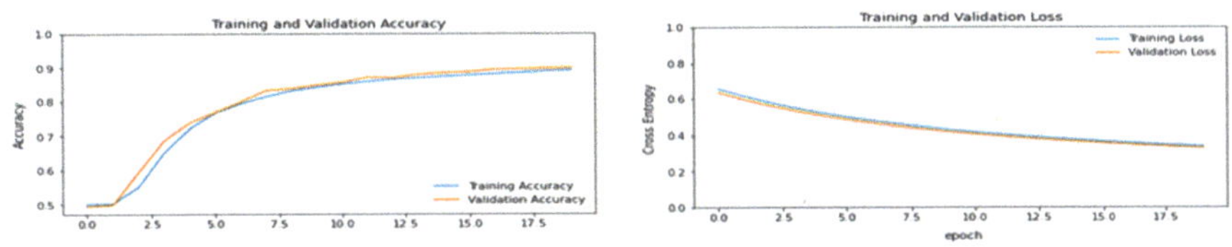

Fig. 5 VGG16 model performance on validation data

b. **Pre-trained model for feature extraction**

Machine learning needs hand crafted feature to be extracted from these images. Deep learning eases this task by extracting the spatial features from these images. The VGG16 pre-trained model is used here for extracting features. These features are fed as a input to different machine classifier. The performance of these classifiers is depicted in Table 7. Totally 19,015 instances are used for this experimentation of which 80% for training and 20% for testing. From this table, it is observed that all the classifiers have given the performance of almost 90% and above except KNN classifier. The accuracy given by random forest classifier is the highest among all. Also, the Kappa statistics for all the classifiers is close to 0.9 that represents the good performance of all the classifiers for both the classes. These performances are plotted in Fig. 6.

7 Conclusion

This paper has demonstrated the importance of deep learning in medical image analysis. For this, the role of deep learning has became of utmost importance. Many deep learning architecture are predominantly suitable for imaging applications. Transfer learning has raised the potential of application of deep learning algorithms for medical domain. Transfer learning can be used in different modes either for feature extraction or for classification. This can be achieved either by using the model as it is or by fine tuning it. Also this paper has highlighted different datasets available and the competitions in healthcare domain. This paper has also explained different image modalities used in different disease. This explanation is well accompanied by the case study of malaria disease images. Finally, this paper has listed the possible future directions of research.

Table 7 Performance comparison of different classifiers

Machine learning classifiers	Accuracy	Kappa statistic	TP rate	FP eate	Precision	Recall	F-measure	MCC	ROC area	PRC area
SVM	93.24	0.86	0.93	0.07	0.93	0.93	0.93	0.87	0.93	0.90
Logistic regression	93.66	0.87	0.91	0.04	0.96	0.91	0.94	0.87	0.98	0.98
Multilayer perceptron	92.95	0.85	0.93	0.07	0.93	0.93	0.93	0.86	0.97	0.97
KNN	88.69	0.77	0.89	0.11	0.89	0.89	0.89	0.77	0.89	0.84
Random forest	**94.16**	0.88	0.94	0.06	0.94	0.94	0.94	0.88	0.98	0.98
Decision tree	91.90	0.83	0.92	0.08	0.92	0.92	0.92	0.84	0.93	0.91

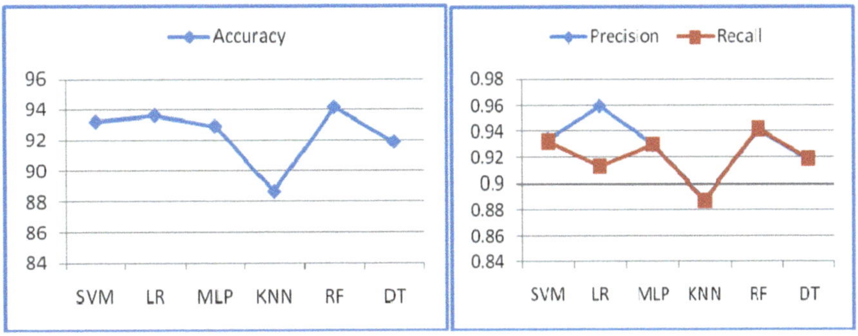

Fig. 6 Performances of different machine learning classifiers on the feature set extracted from pre-trained model VGGNet16

References

1. Suzuki, K. (2017). Overview of deep learning in medical imaging. *Radiological Physics and Technology, 10,* 257–273. https://doi.org/10.1007/s12194-017-0406-5.
2. Shinde, Swati. (2016). UdayKulkarni: Extracting classification rules from modified fuzzy min–max neural network for data with mixed attributes. *Applied Soft Computing, 40,* 364–378.
3. Swati, S., & Uday, K. (2017). Extended fuzzy hyperline-segment neural network with classification rule extraction. *NeuroComputing, 260,* 79–91.
4. Raghu, M., & Zhang, C., Kleinberg, J., & Bengio, S. (2019). Transfusion: Understanding transfer learning with applications to medical imaging. In *33rd Conference on Neural Information Processing Systems (NeurIPS 2019).* Vancouver, Canada.
5. Pan, S. J., & Yang, Q. (2010). A survey on transfer learning. *IEEE Transactions on Knowledge and Data Engineering, 22,* 1345–1359.
6. https://ai.googleblog.com/2019/12/understanding-transfer-learning-for.html.
7. https://machinelearningmastery.com/transfer-learning-for-deep-learning/.
8. Alexander, S., & Lundervold, A. L. (2019). An overview of deep learning in medical imaging focusing on MRI. *Zeitschrift für Medizinische Physik, 29,* 102–127. https://doi.org/10.1016/j.zemedi.2018.11.002.
9. Papandrianos, N., Papageorgiou, E., Anagnostis, A., & Feleki A. (2020). A deep-learning approach for diagnosis of metastatic breast cancer in bones from whole-body scans. *Applied Science, 10,* 997. https://doi.org/10.3390/app10030997.
10. Manabu, T., Noriko, Y., Hiroshi, K., Akiko, C., Shoichi, S., Masashi, U., et al. (2020). Prediction of early colorectal cancer metastasis by machine learning using digital slide images. *Computer Methods and Programs in Biomedicine, 178,* 155–161. https://doi.org/10.1016/j.cmpb.2019.06.022. ISSN 0169-2607.
11. Kim, H., Choi, Y., & Ro, Y. (2017). Modality-bridge transfer learning for medical image classification. In: CISP-BMEI 2017.
12. https://www.webmd.com/cancer/what-is-a-ct-scan#1.
13. Emilio, S. O., Jose D., Martin, G., & Marcelino, M. S. *Handbook of research on machine learning applications and trends: Algorithms, methods and techniques* (1st ed).
14. https://www.nhs.uk/conditions/mri-scan/.
15. Alexander S. L., & Arvid, L. (2019). An overview of deep learning in medical imaging focusing on MRI. *Zeitschriftfür Medizinische Physik, 29*(2), 102–127. https://doi.org/10.1016/j.zemedi.2018.11.002. ISSN 0939-3889.
16. https://www.healthline.com/health/pet-scan.
17. https://dx.doi.org/10.1109%2FRBME.2009.2034865.

18. https://mayfieldclinic.com/pe-spect.htm.
19. Geert, L., Thijs K., et.al. (2017). A survey on deep learning in medical image analysis. *Medical Image Analysis, 42*, 60–88. https://doi.org/10.1016/j.media.2017.07.005. ISSN 1361-8415.

Wearable Internet of Things for Personalized Healthcare: Study of Trends and Latent Research

Samiya Khan and Mansaf Alam

Abstract In this age of heterogeneous systems, diverse technologies are integrated to create application-specific solutions. The recent upsurge in acceptance of technologies such as cloud computing and ubiquitous Internet has cleared the path for Internet of Things (IoT). Moreover, the increasing Internet penetration with the rising use of mobile devices has inspired an era of technology that allows interfacing of physical objects and connecting them to Internet for developing applications serving a wide range of purposes. Recent developments in the area of wearable devices has led to the creation of another segment in IoT, which can be conveniently referred to as Wearable Internet of Things (WIoT). Research in this area promises to personalize healthcare in previously unimaginable ways by allowing individual tracking of wellness and health information. This chapter shall cover the different facets of WIoT and ways in which it is a key driving technology behind the concept of personalized healthcare. It shall discuss the theoretical aspects of WIoT, focusing on functionality, design and applicability. Moreover, it shall also elaborate on the role of wearable sensors, big data and cloud computing as enabling technologies for WIoT.

Keywords Wearable internet of things · Wearable sensors · Personalized healthcare · Smart healthcare · Pervasive healthcare

1 Introduction

Recent past has seen a dramatic rise in the incidence of chronic, life-threatening diseases. Moreover, the cost of healthcare rests on an ever-rising curve. Thus, there is an urgent need to transmute the healthcare providers' approach from hospital-centric to patient-centric. In order words, in the modern scenario, focusing health efforts on

S. Khan (✉) · M. Alam
Department of Computer Science, Jamia Millia Islamia, New Delhi, Delhi, India
e-mail: samiyashaukat@yahoo.com

M. Alam
e-mail: malam2@jmi.ac.in

R. Patgiri et al. (eds.), *Health Informatics: A Computational Perspective in Healthcare*, Studies in Computational Intelligence 932,
https://doi.org/10.1007/978-981-15-9735-0_3

personalized disease management and individual well being, make most sense. The motivation behind the use of technology in health is aimed at providing e-health and m-health services to individuals, targeting to improve the operational efficiency of the healthcare system. Smart phones and mobile-based service provisioning are some of the most path breaking technological advancements of this era. According to a study [1], 21.2% of mobile users in India owned a smart phone in 2014 and this percentage is expected to increase to 36.2% by 2022, projecting an approximate rise of 70%. The graphical illustration is shown in Fig. 1. It is important to note that values for years 2014–2018 are actual values while the same for 2019–2022 are projections. Moreover, with slashed data usage costs, the number of India-based Internet users is expected to witness a rise of 40% by 2023 [2].

These statistics set the ground for a mobile-based personalized healthcare model, in which smart phones can be used for sensing, connectivity and establishing interaction with the individual, making it a core driving technology for mHealth [3]. With that said, mobile devices come with basic sensing facilities like motion tracking and activity recording. It is not possible for a standalone smart phone to capture the finer details and parametric assessment of an individual's health. It is for this reason that wearable devices have to be integrated with this model for expanding the sensing capabilities of a smart phone.

The wearable technology segment has grown immensely in the recent past recording a 5.3% increase in revenues for the U.S. market in 2018 [4]. Figure 2 shows a graphical illustration of consumer revenue generated for year 2014 and 2015, with value projections for the years ranging between 2016 and 2019. Moreover, the user penetration of this technological segment for the American market stood at 11.8%

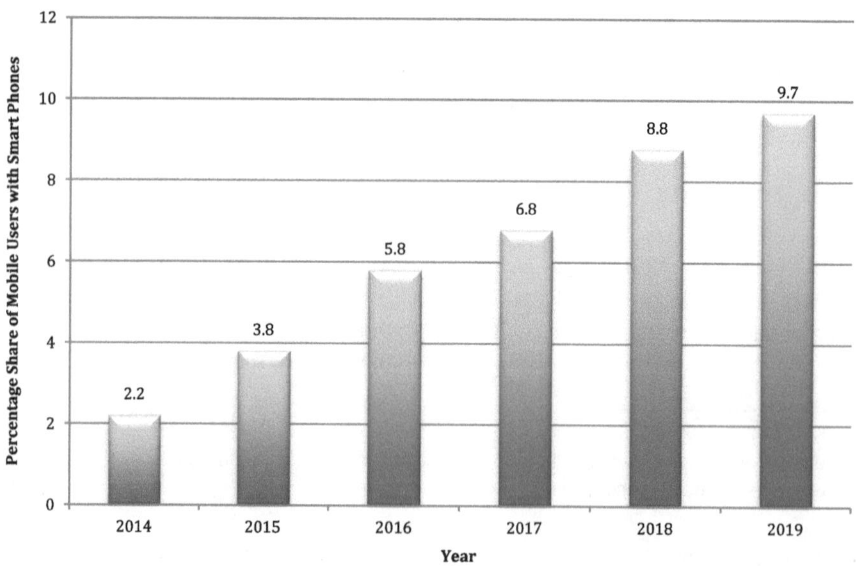

Fig. 1 Smart phone users' share in India [2]

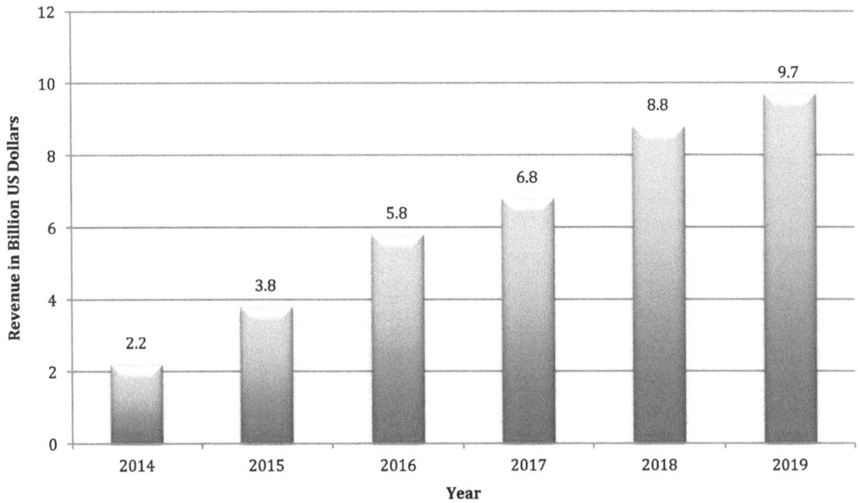

Fig. 2 Revenue analysis of consumer wearable in US [4]

[4]. As reported by Quid [4], majority of the people who buy wearable products use it for health, fitness and clinical reasons. Evidently, this market is expected to grow in the coming years for the obvious cause that a consumer can buy multiple wearable products and their applications are not limited to just fitness and health. Wearable technology is increasingly being purchased because of other reasons as well, such as improved connectivity and innovative value.

Wearable devices are capable of serving multiple functions, which include (1) body data collection (2) basic preprocessing (3) transient data storage, and (4) data transfer to server or mobile phone. The unique selling point of this technology is 'wearability', which allows collection of explicit data values on the basis of application-specific requirements. Fundamental advantages of using this technology include automatic diagnostic monitoring and allowance of timely interventions. On the hindsight, this technology is also confronted with significant challenges such as short communication bandwidth, limited battery life and restricted computing ability.

Internet of Things provides a robust technological framework by facilitating data collection from wearable sensors and mobile devices, and backing up the computing and storage capabilities by integrated use of state of the art technologies like cloud computing [69] and big data [70]. The rest of the chapter is organized in the following manner: Sect. 2 introduces the concept of Wearable Internet of Things (WIoT) and covers background concepts related to the same. There are a plethora of WIoT applications. However, this chapter limits its scope to personalized healthcare and Sect. 3 covers this facet in detail. Finally, Sect. 4 summarizes the challenges and future research prospects in the field with concluding remarks synopsized in Sect. 5.

2 Concept of Wearable Internet of Things

The ubiquitous nature of Internet connectivity has paved way for a new era in technology, that of Internet of Things. Simplistically, Internet of Things (IoT) can be described as a technology that allows Internet-backed connectivity between 'things' to allow data processing, analytics and visualization for development of domain-specific intelligent solutions [5]. Therefore, Internet of Things, essentially, uses technologies such as big data and cloud computing to empower its base framework. The past few decades have seen a swift transition from Internet to Internet-based services like social networks [6] and wearable web [7].

Traditionally, the concept of IoT is an extension of Internet to the real world and its entities. Therefore, its early versions depended on RFID technologies [8, 9] for transforming 'things' into sensing devices. Heterogeneous sensors such as accelerometers and gyroscopes succeeded this technology. However, the use of IoT in healthcare was well established only after the development of wearable devices [10]. Thus, WIoT is majorly used in healthcare for improving diagnostics, allowing early interventions and enabling execution of remote surgeries [11–14].

The emergence and growing popularity of wearable devices has led to the creation of a new segment in IoT, widely referred to as WIoT. In this context, wearable devices form an intrinsic fiber for the intelligent fabric of IoT, which connects numerous near-body and on-body sensors with Internet and each other. Another significant facet of WIoT framework is connecting the end-points to medical infrastructure like physicians and hospitals so that longitudinal assessment of patient conditions can be performed irrespective of their location.

Collected data needs be pushed to the concerned healthcare provider and timely intervention or management of emergencies can be performed. Therefore, Wearable Internet of Things is an infrastructure that enables this interconnectivity and facilitates examining of human factors like behavior, wellness and health, thereby contributing in making interventions for enhanced quality of life [15].

Data lifecycle consists of standard phases namely collection, storage, processing and visualization [16]. In view of this, Qi et al. [17] proposed an IoT-based architecture for personalized healthcare systems. Figure 3 illustrates the functional components of WIoT, which is inspired by the same proposed by Qi et al. [17]. However, the below-mentioned architecture focuses its attention on wearable devices and their integrated use with IoT for healthcare. The architecture divides WIoT into four functional components namely sensing, network, processing and applications. A detailed description of these functional components is provided below.

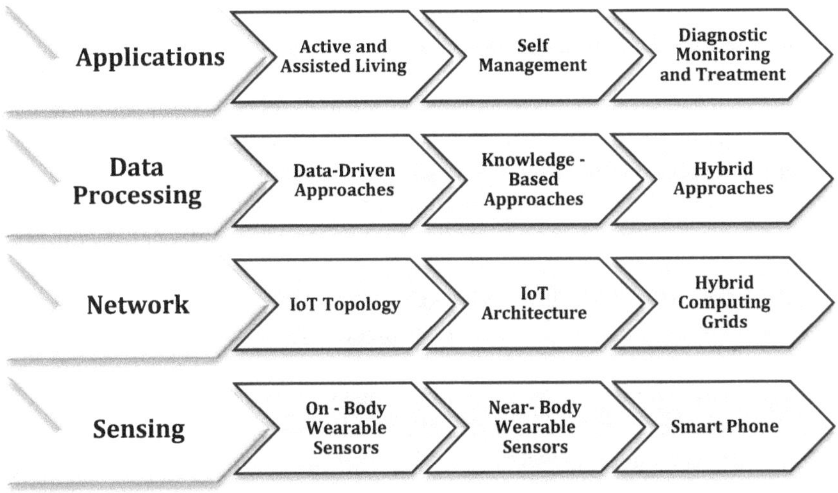

Fig. 3 Components of WIoT architecture

2.1 *Sensing*

The purpose of sensing layer is to efficiently acquire medical and personal information of an individual using sensing technologies. Qi et al. [17] provided a classification of available sensors. These include both near-body and on-body sensors. Details of the classification scheme are provided in Table 1. Available sensors are capable

Table 1 Classification of sensors

Category	Sensors	Measurements taken
Inertial sensors	Magnetic field sensor [18]	Higher spatial resolution's location
	Pressure sensor [19]	Altitude of the object
	Gyroscope [20]	Angular rotational velocity
	Accelerometer [21]	Measures linear acceleration
Physiological sensors	Galvanic skin response (GSR) [22]	Temperature of skin surface
	Electrooculography [23]	Movement of eye
	Spirometer [24]	Lung parameters like volume, expiration and flow rate.
	Electrocardiogram (ECG) [13]	Heart activity
	Blood pressure cuff [25]	Blood pressure
Image sensors	SenseCam [26]	Pictures of daily living activities
Location sensors	GPS [27]	Coordinates of outdoor location

of capturing physiological information like heart activity, eye movement and blood pressure. Besides this, inertial sensors, location sensors and image sensors may be used for tracking activity.

While near-body sensors may be helpful in gathering additional parameters for analysis, wearable body area sensors form the core component of WIoT. These sensors are responsible for capturing data from the body directly through contact or with the help of peripheral sensors for capturing behavioral patterns. Finally, these sensors preprocess data and prepare it for on-board analysis or offshore decision making. Typically, the design of a wearable device is application-dependent. However, most wearable devices can be expected to come packaged with communication capabilities, on-board power management and embedded computing device with limited storage support.

Lately, many commercial products have come into existence. Peripheral wearable sensors that can be worn on the wrist or arm like BodyMedia armband [28], are dedicated fitness monitoring wearable devices that work on minimum hardware and computing abilities to provide real time activity data of the individual. Smart watches [29] are also fitness and activity monitors, but they are generally capable of higher functionality and perform many other functions related to the smart phone as well.

Novelty in this domain largely focuses on the body-sensor interface for different kinds of parametric data collection. Some examples of such wearable sensors include Bio-Patch [30], ring sensor [31] and ECG monitor [32]. Recently, the concept of smart textiles and smart clothing have also gathered immense research attention, bringing forth the idea of embedding sensors in the textile or fabric used for creation of clothing to allow unobtrusive monitoring. These sensor fabrics are known to be extremely effective in monitoring response of human autonomous nervous system [33].

These sensors may be used in conjunction with ambient sensors such as environment monitoring sensors [34, 35] and indoor localization sensors [36, 37] for a comprehensive analysis of individual's intrinsic and extrinsic health. Moreover, some studies [38–41] suggest that smart phone applications' data can be used for human behavior monitoring, making smart phone, another source of data. The challenge in this domain is to develop non-invasive and cost-effective sensors for automatic data acquisition in uncontrolled surroundings like IoT-based systems and researches [42–44] are being performed in this direction.

2.2 *Network*

Sensing devices cannot function and serve their purpose in a standalone manner because of their restricted computing and storage capabilities. Moreover, limitations with communication bandwidth and power management also make them insufficient devices when alone. All the sensing devices need to be connected to the IoT infrastructure for data aggregation, storage and transmission for further analysis.

Firstly, all the sensing devices need to be configured and deployed using a standard or hybrid topology. At this level, transferring of mobile and static sensing devices to hybrid computing grids is an existing research challenge [17]. Several IoT infrastructures such as 6LoWPAN [45] have been proposed for efficient data transfer in view of the scalability and mobility issues that arise with the use of IoT systems.

Therefore, challenges at the network layer include interoperability, energy efficiency, QoS requirements and network management of heterogeneous components. With that said, one of the core issues that need to be tackled at this level for personalized healthcare applications is security and privacy of user data. It has been proposed that Mobile Cloud Computing (MCC) paradigm can be used [15] for management of power and performance issues associated with WIoT as MCC allows cloud-based storage and analysis of data and inherently tackles the issues associated with mobility and flexibility requirements of such applications.

2.3 Data Processing

The medical data generated by wearable sensors and smart phones is expected to be huge. Moreover, deriving knowledge from available data is just as crucial as acquisition of data. Applications can only be developed for patient benefit after acquired data is put through intelligent algorithms to process it and facilitate action-based decisions. Early works in this domain focus on development of algorithms and computational methodologies for processing of disease-specific datasets.

Research on generalized methods for processing of medical and health data caught the attention of scientists much later with possible use of intelligent algorithms for anomaly detection, pattern recognition and decision support being investigated in later works [46]. Qi et al. [17] classifies the data processing approaches used for healthcare systems into three categories namely data-driven, knowledge-based and hybrid approaches. While data-driven methods include supervised, unsupervised and semi-supervised approaches, knowledge-based approaches rely on semantic reasoning and modeling [17]. Depending upon the requirements of the application, a combination of two or more approaches belonging to data-driven or knowledge-based classes may be used. These methods are referred to as hybrid approaches.

Technologies such as cloud computing and big data analytics can play an instrumental role in data management and processing using machine learning and advanced data mining techniques. In line with this, Cloud-based body area sensors or CaBAS has emerged as a growing research area that integrates wearable sensors with the MCC paradigm to manage scalability issues associated with provisioning of data-driven pervasive healthcare solutions [15]. Advantages of using this paradigm include improved energy efficiency, creation of annotated data logs, support for event-based processing, development of individual-centric databases and advanced visualization to support self-management at the patient level and facilitate decision making at the healthcare provider's level.

2.4 Applications

The application layer of the WIoT architecture focuses on provisioning of high quality services to healthcare providers as well as individuals. The user interfaces need to be user-friendly in view of the fact that these solutions may or may not be used by technologically aware individuals. Personalized healthcare finds its best use cases in the elderly who are characteristically not accustomed to using complicated technological interfaces. An example of such interventions include monitoring of tremors in patients suffering from Parkinson's disease using the Smart watch's motion sensor [47].

Conventionally, application was not considered as an independent layer of the IoT architecture for healthcare and was typically integrated with the processing layer. However, with the widening of the application domain for IoT in healthcare and several applications like assistive living and self-management coming into existence, isolating this layer for the sake of application-level novelty became inevitable. The applications of IoT in healthcare [59] are summarized in Table 2. Challenges specific to this layer of the WIoT infrastructure include creation of usable applications that are modeled appropriately to abstract details that are irrelevant and probably not understandable for patients and summarizing details appropriately for healthcare providers to facilitate quick decision making at their end.

Table 2 Healthcare applications of IoT

Category	Applications
Pervasive monitoring	Monitoring of patient condition and response to treatment in real time irrespective of patient or clinician's location
Healthcare management	Management of health records with secure sharing of records between different entities of the healthcare system
	Staff management
	Quality assessment in terms of hospital infrastructure and patient outcome and satisfaction
	Optimizing resource utilization by managing usage of medication and evaluation the procedures and diagnostics performed
Management of chronic patients	Risk Assessment
	Tracking, monitoring and quantification of patient's health
Medical research	Monitoring of performance and efficiency of clinical trials
	Comparing the effects of treatment and quantifying the patient's functional recovery
	Finding new therapeutics

3 Enabling Personalized Healthcare with WIoT

Although, research efforts are far from mature when it comes to application of technologies for development of healthcare-specific applications, the number of applications and possibility of innovation in this domain lies in the infinite space of reality. It would not be wrong to state that we are living in the age of individuality, with all existing systems from e-commerce to daily living solutions turning to personalization for usage and business benefits. Healthcare is not an exception to this unsaid rule.

As shown in Fig. 4, applications of WIoT in personalized healthcare can broadly be divided into five categories namely physical activity monitoring, self-management and monitoring, clinical decision support systems for automated diagnosis and treatment, emergency health services and assisted living solutions for elderly and differently abled. Most wearable devices available today can be connected to the smart phone for monitoring physical activity parameters related to motion, breathing and heart activity. Some of the research projects that focus on this domain include Mobile Sensing Platform [48], Wireless Sensor Data Mining [49] and mHealthDroid [50].

Fig. 4 Classification of personalized healthcare applications

Such applications are specifically useful for patients or individuals suffering from conditions that require physical activity monitoring. One such example is a wearable device and message-based prompting service [60] for monitoring physical activity in individuals who are obese or expected to manifest such a problem. Moreover, integrated system for gymnasiums that monitor physical activity of people who are working out and sets an alarm on detection of a problem also exist [63]. Future research efforts required for evolving physical monitoring devices needs to be centered on clinical integration, privacy, measurement and adherence [61] for it to be widely adopted for clinical management.

Self-management and monitoring applications typically concentrate on telemonitoring and aim to improve the individual's quality of life by providing a seamless interface between the caregivers, physicians and individuals. The challenging aspect of these systems is to design solutions that can satisfy the user-specific needs because the success or failure of a therapy largely depends on individual's perception and feedback. Such systems include MOKUS [51] that is designed for arthritis patients' self-management and an in-home patient monitoring system [68] for at-home monitoring of patient health.

Clinical decision support systems typically require individual's health data that can be automatically analyzed for prediction of diseases and monitoring the response of the patient to provided treatment. This concept aids treatment planning and facilitates personalized medicine, also bringing down the costs and improving the overall accuracy of the healthcare process. METEOR [52] is a generic infrastructure that captures patient information and aids treatment planning and response monitoring. Besides this, disease-specific solutions like PredictAD [53] also exist. This solution specifically works for the prediction and management of Alzheimer's disease.

Personalized solutions can track individual information to capture movement data and vital parameter measurements for prediction of emergencies. On the onset of such a scenario, automated action from the healthcare providers' end can be initiated. Although, such solutions can be of benefit to all patients suffering from chronic disorders, they are specifically relevant for the elderly population. Emergency Monitoring and Prevention (EMERGE) [54] is a solution that focuses on this aspect of personalized healthcare. Another solution in this category is infant health monitoring system for emergency handling [67]. IoT-based ambulance emergency solutions have also been proposed [71].

In continuation to the concept of detection of emergencies and their prevention, individual health data tracking can also be used for development of assisted living solutions for the elderly and differently abled. Moreover, such solutions can also be expanded to serve patients suffering from chronic and life-threatening diseases so that continuous monitoring can be performed and timely interventions can be made. SMART [55] and PIA [56] are two projects that are working on these facets.

While SMART focuses on care for chronic patients, PIA is a dedicated service for the elderly. Another implemented solution in this domain is AlarmNet [62], which is a monitoring and assisted living solution for residential communities. It provides pervasive healthcare that is adaptable to the varying needs to individuals living in these communities.

In addition to the above mentioned, several applications of WIoT-based personalized healthcare can also be extended to monitoring, management and treatment of emotional issues in individuals. Besides this, hospital and rehabilitation centers' processes [64] can be modeled for development of patient-centric treatment and monitoring applications for use in these domains. The applications of WIoT in personalized healthcare are summarized in Table 3.

The recent advances in genomics [57] have driven research in the field of personalized medicine with higher zeal and momentum. This is expected to drive a paradigm shift from hospital-centric approach to optimized healthcare services that focus on the treatment and well being of individual subjects. Personalized healthcare is sure to revolutionize this industry and offers innumerable benefits to all entities of the system. However, it also suffers from potential shortcomings, ranging from scientific hurdles to legal and socio-economic challenges that need to be overcome before a transitional shift can be made in one of the most critical sectors of the society.

4 Challenges and Future Prospects

There is a rising need for sustainable healthcare for all sections of the society and personalization of treatment and management. In order to achieve the required efficacy, a solid infrastructural foundation needs to be laid for large-scale deployment of wearable sensors and their interaction with conventional medical facilities. The challenges and directions in the integrative use of WIoT for personalized healthcare exist both at the clinical as well as operational levels.

The objective of using technological interventions in the healthcare industry is to allow interaction between patients and healthcare providers beyond the walls of the clinic or hospital. Moreover, there is an ever-insistent demand of healthcare providers from individuals to remain proactive about their medical conditions and overall health. The WIoT infrastructure allows inter-entity communication, thereby allowing immediate feedback on systems, micro-management of patient condition and off-location treatment.

With respect to this facet of WIoT, the level of information to be shared between the patient and healthcare provider can be precise or detailed. For example, an application may just suggest physical activity of 30 min to a patient while another application may further fine-grain the information to the type of exercise, along with the details on how to perform them. Similarly, on the clinician's level, the amount of information shared may be a detailed case report or summary. Therefore, deciding on application-specific guidelines and standards is a daunting task because the patient may not be well versed with clinical terms to understand the details and abstraction may be needed. Moreover, the clinician must also just receive the information that is required to make an intervention or suggest an appropriate treatment.

Personalization of treatment is one of the key benefits of WIoT, which is particularly relevant in consideration of the fact that every disease, disorder or syndrome manifests different symptoms in different individuals. Moreover, the intensity of

Table 3 Applications of WIoT in Personalized Healthcare

Category	Application	Functionality
Physical activity monitoring	MSP [48]	For this application, the wearable is placed on the waist and is connected to the smart phone for activity monitoring
	WSDN [49]	This platform detects human activity using the Android phone carried by the individual and uses supervised learning for detection of the type of activity being performed
	mHealthDroid [50]	This solution connects multiple smart devices together for capturing ambulation and biomedical signals, which are further processed to give alerts and measure parameters like trunk endurance
	SMS-based Notification for Management of Obesity [60]	This application uses SMS-based prompting with Fitbit One for monitoring of physical activity in obese adults
	Sportsman Monitoring System [63]	This application monitors vital parameters of a person who is performing workout and sets the alarm in case any abnormal physiological parameter measurement is detected
Self-management and monitoring	MOKUS [51]	Self-disease management for patients suffering from arthritis
	In-Home Health Monitoring System [68]	This solution monitors vital parameters to assess the possibility of deterioration in patients at home
Emergency health services	EMERGE [54]	This application performs emergency monitoring and prevention and specifically targets the elderly population
	Infant Health Condition Check [67]	This is a proposed design that measures biometric information of an infant and can be used assess the possibility and cope with an emergency

(continued)

Table 3 (continued)

Category	Application	Functionality
Clinical decision support systems	METEOR [52]	Generic application centered on planning of treatment and monitoring of response
	PredictAD [53]	This solution specifically works for prediction and management of Alzheimer's disease
Assisted living for elderly and differently abled	SMART [55]	This solution is a service for patients suffering from disorders, which include stroke, chronic pain and heart failure
	PIA [56]	This project is an initiative for the elderly who live independently and follows the simple approach that allows elderly people to watch instructional videos uploaded by caregivers for efficient management
	AlarmNet [62]	It is an assisted adaptive solution for residential communities
Miscellaneous	Ubiquitous rehabilitation center [64]	Solution for monitoring of rehabilitation machines
	Etiobe [65]	Application for management of obesity in children
	SALSA [66]	Architecture for facilitating response to individual and clinician-specific demands

these symptoms shall also vary significantly. This is specifically the case with chronic disorders where doctors face challenges in creating individual treatment plans, as the response of the patient to any prescribed treatment cannot be predicted. Furthermore, the success of a treatment plan depends on the adherence of the plan, which needs to be monitored. In view of these, future research directions in this area include healthcare pattern identification, identification of anomalies and emergency management.

Other issues related with the use of wearable devices include standardization. There are some FDA guidelines that deal with wearable devices used for medical purposes [58]. Since, these devices work on multi-range communication protocols, their safety for human use needs to be established before they can be put to large-scale practice, which requires extensive clinical trials.

Finally, wearable devices may or may not be easy to maintain. On the hardware level, these devices suffer from battery issues. On the software level, one of the biggest challenges faced by designers of wearable devices is providing usable solutions that can present information in an abstractive form with the help of interactive interfaces. Besides this, these solutions must contribute to improving the activity levels of individuals. Furthermore, health data is private and confidential and ensuring safety and privacy and following the legislative guidelines set by different jurisdictions can be an arduous task.

5 Conclusion

The synergistic use of Internet of Things and wearable technology has led to the development of a new technological paradigm, Wearable Internet of Things or WIoT. This chapter discusses the different aspects of WIoT. The functional components of the WIoT architecture include wearable sensors and mobile devices for sensing, IoT infrastructure for connectivity and cloud-based big data support for data processing. All of these components collectively and progressively contribute to applications like personalized healthcare and assistive living.

This chapter particularly focuses on the use of WIoT for personalization of healthcare services and evidently, the use of this technology can be particularly beneficial for elderly and individuals who are already suffering from a chronic disease. WIoT is capable of revolutionizing healthcare sector by allowing early diagnosis and effective treatment with efficient patient monitoring possible even after the patient has left the hospital. However, in order to achieve success, some inherent challenges like incorporation of healthcare process flows and understanding of standards and requirements need to be tackled.

References

1. Smartphone penetration in India 2014–2022| *Statista.* (2020). Retrieved 16 April 2020, from https://www.statista.com/statistics/257048/smartphone-user-penetration-in-india/.
2. McKinsey. (2020). *Internet users in India to rise by 40%, smartphones to double by 2023.* Retrieved 16 April 2020, from https://economictimes.indiatimes.com/tech/internet/internet-users-in-india-to-rise-by-40-smartphones-to-double-by-2023-mckinsey/articleshow/69040395.cms?from=mdr.
3. Kay, M., Santos, J., & Takane, M. (2011). mHealth: New horizons for health through mobile technologies. *World Health Organization, 64*(7), 66–71.
4. Gaille, B. (2020). 29 *Wearable technology industry statistics, trends & analysis.* Retrieved 16 April 2020, from https://brandongaille.com/29-wearable-technology-industry-statistics-trends-analysis/.
5. Atzori, L., Iera, A., & Morabito, G. (2017). Understanding the Internet of Things: definition, potentials, and societal role of a fast evolving paradigm. *Ad Hoc Networks, 56,* 122–140.
6. Mislove, A., Marcon, M., Gummadi, K. P., Druschel, P., & Bhattacharjee, B. (2007, October). Measurement and analysis of online social networks. In *Proceedings of the 7th ACM SIGCOMM conference on Internet measurement* (pp. 29–42).

7. Dai, Y., Wang, X., Li, X., & Zhang, P. (2015, May). Reputation-driven multimodal emotion recognition in wearable biosensor network. In *2015 IEEE International Instrumentation and Measurement Technology Conference (I2MTC) Proceedings* (pp. 1747–1752). IEEE.
8. Acampora, G., Cook, D. J., Rashidi, P., & Vasilakos, A. V. (2013). A survey on ambient intelligence in healthcare. *Proceedings of the IEEE, 101*(12), 2470–2494.
9. Naranjo-Hernandez, D., Roa, L. M., Reina-Tosina, J., & Estudillo-Valderrama, M. A. (2012). SoM: A smart sensor for human activity monitoring and assisted healthy ageing. *IEEE Transactions on Biomedical Engineering, 59*(11), 3177–3184.
10. Spanakis, E. G., Kafetzopoulos, D., Yang, P., Marias, K., Deng, Z., Tsiknakis, M., et al. (2014, November). MyHealthAvatar: Personalized and empowerment health services through Internet of Things technologies. In *2014 4th International Conference on Wireless Mobile Communication and Healthcare-Transforming Healthcare Through Innovations in Mobile and Wireless Technologies (MOBIHEALTH)* (pp. 331–334). IEEE.
11. Kau, L. J., & Chen, C. S. (2014). A smart phone-based pocket fall accident detection, positioning, and rescue system. *IEEE Journal of Biomedical and Health Informatics, 19*(1), 44–56.
12. Ermes, M., Pärkkä, J., Mäntyjärvi, J., & Korhonen, I. (2008). Detection of daily activities and sports with wearable sensors in controlled and uncontrolled conditions. *IEEE Transactions on Information Technology in Biomedicine, 12*(1), 20–26.
13. Pawar, T., Anantakrishnan, N. S., Chaudhuri, S., & Duttagupta, S. P. (2008). Impact of ambulation in wearable-ECG. *Annals of Biomedical Engineering, 36*(9), 1547–1557.
14. Riaño, D., Real, F., López-Vallverdú, J. A., Campana, F., Ercolani, S., Mecocci, P., et al. (2012). An ontology-based personalization of health-care knowledge to support clinical decisions for chronically ill patients. *Journal of Biomedical Informatics, 45*(3), 429–446.
15. Hiremath, S., Yang, G., & Mankodiya, K. (2014, November). Wearable Internet of Things: Concept, architectural components and promises for person-centered healthcare. In *2014 4th International Conference on Wireless Mobile Communication and Healthcare-Transforming Healthcare Through Innovations in Mobile and Wireless Technologies (MOBIHEALTH)* (pp. 304–307). IEEE.
16. Khan, S., Shakil, K. A., & Alam, M. (2017). Big data computing using cloud-based technologies: Challenges and future perspectives. In *Networks of the Future* (pp. 393–414). Chapman and Hall/CRC.
17. Qi, J., Yang, P., Min, G., Amft, O., Dong, F., & Xu, L. (2017). Advanced internet of things for personalised healthcare systems: A survey. *Pervasive and Mobile Computing, 41,* 132–149.
18. Shoaib, M., Bosch, S., Incel, O. D., Scholten, H., & Havinga, P. J. (2015). A survey of online activity recognition using mobile phones. *Sensors, 15*(1), 2059–2085.
19. Moncada-Torres, A., Leuenberger, K., Gonzenbach, R., Luft, A., & Gassert, R. (2014). Activity classification based on inertial and barometric pressure sensors at different anatomical locations. *Physiological Measurement, 35*(7), 1245.
20. Dejnabadi, H., Jolles, B. M., & Aminian, K. (2005). A new approach to accurate measurement of uniaxial joint angles based on a combination of accelerometers and gyroscopes. *IEEE Transactions on Biomedical Engineering, 52*(8), 1478–1484.
21. Bouten, C. V., Koekkoek, K. T., Verduin, M., Kodde, R., & Janssen, J. D. (1997). A triaxial accelerometer and portable data processing unit for the assessment of daily physical activity. *IEEE Transactions on Biomedical Engineering, 44*(3), 136–147.
22. Sun, F. T., Kuo, C., Cheng, H. T., Buthpitiya, S., Collins, P., & Griss, M. (2010, October). Activity-aware mental stress detection using physiological sensors. In *International conference on Mobile computing, applications, and services* (pp. 282–301). Berlin, Heidelberg: Springer.
23. Bulling, A., Ward, J. A., & Gellersen, H. (2012). Multimodal recognition of reading activity in transit using body-worn sensors. *ACM Transactions on Applied Perception (TAP), 9*(1), 1–21.
24. Wensley, D., & Silverman, M. (2004). Peak flow monitoring for guided self-management in childhood asthma: A randomized controlled trial. *American Journal of Respiratory and Critical Care Medicine, 170*(6), 606–612.

25. Davies, R. J., Galway, L. B., Nugent, C. D., Jamison, C. H., Gawley, R. E., McCullagh, P. J., et al. (2011, May). A platform for self-management supported by assistive, rehabilitation and telecare technologies. In *2011 5th International Conference on Pervasive Computing Technologies for Healthcare (PervasiveHealth) and Workshops* (pp. 458–460). IEEE.
26. Berry, E., Kapur, N., Williams, L., Hodges, S., Watson, P., Smyth, G., et al. (2007). The use of a wearable camera, SenseCam, as a pictorial diary to improve autobiographical memory in a patient with limbic encephalitis: A preliminary report. *Neuropsychological Rehabilitation, 17*(4–5), 582–601.
27. Liao, L., Fox, D., & Kautz, H. (2007). Hierarchical conditional random fields for GPS-based activity recognition. In *Robotics Research* (pp. 487–506). Berlin, Heidelberg: Springer.
28. Armbands Archives » BodyMedia.com | fitness—weight loss—bodybuilding supplement reviews|. (2020). Retrieved 16 April 2020, from https://bodymedia.com/category/armbands/.
29. Reeder, B., & David, A. (2016). Health at hand: A systematic review of smart watch uses for health and wellness. *Journal of Biomedical Informatics, 63,* 269–276.
30. Yang, G., Xie, L., Mäntysalo, M., Zhou, X., Pang, Z., Da Xu, L., et al. (2014). A health-IoT platform based on the integration of intelligent packaging, unobtrusive bio-sensor, and intelligent medicine box. *IEEE Transactions on Industrial Informatics, 10*(4), 2180–2191.
31. Asada, H. H., Shaltis, P., Reisner, A., Rhee, S., & Hutchinson, R. C. (2003). Mobile monitoring with wearable photoplethysmographic biosensors. *IEEE Engineering in Medicine and Biology Magazine, 22*(3), 28–40.
32. Mankodiya, K., Hassan, Y. A., Vogt, S., Gehring, H., & Hofmann, U. G. (2010, September). Wearable ECG module for long-term recordings using a smartphone processor. In *Proceedings of the 5th International Workshop on Ubiquitous Health and Wellness, Copenhagen, Denmark* (Vol. 2629).
33. Seoane, F., Ferreira, J., Alvarez, L., Buendia, R., Ayllón, D., Llerena, C., et al. (2013). Sensorized garments and textrode-enabled measurement instrumentation for ambulatory assessment of the autonomic nervous system response in the ATREC project. *Sensors, 13*(7), 8997–9015.
34. Doherty, A. R., Caprani, N., Conaire, C. Ó., Kalnikaite, V., Gurrin, C., Smeaton, A. F., et al. (2011). Passively recognising human activities through lifelogging. *Computers in Human Behavior, 27*(5), 1948–1958.
35. Sugimoto, C., & Kohno, R. (2011, October). Wireless sensing system for healthcare monitoring thermal physiological state and recognizing behavior. In *2011 International Conference on Broadband and Wireless Computing, Communication and Applications* (pp. 285–291). IEEE.
36. Sixsmith, A., & Johnson, N. (2004). A smart sensor to detect the falls of the elderly. *IEEE Pervasive Computing, 3*(2), 42–47.
37. Lee, H. J., Lee, S. H., Ha, K. S., Jang, H. C., Chung, W. Y., Kim, J. Y., et al. (2009). Ubiquitous healthcare service using Zigbee and mobile phone for elderly patients. *International Journal of Medical Informatics, 78*(3), 193–198.
38. Penninx, B. W., Rejeski, W. J., Pandya, J., Miller, M. E., Di Bari, M., Applegate, W. B., et al. (2002). Exercise and depressive symptoms: a comparison of aerobic and resistance exercise effects on emotional and physical function in older persons with high and low depressive symptomatology. *The Journals of Gerontology Series B: Psychological Sciences and Social Sciences, 57*(2), P124–P132.
39. Salovey, P., Rothman, A. J., Detweiler, J. B., & Steward, W. T. (2000). Emotional states and physical health. *American Psychologist, 55*(1), 110.
40. Oh, K., Park, H. S., & Cho, S. B. (2010, October). A mobile context sharing system using activity and emotion recognition with Bayesian networks. In *2010 7th International Conference on Ubiquitous Intelligence & Computing and 7th International Conference on Autonomic & Trusted Computing* (pp. 244–249). IEEE.
41. Steptoe, A. S., & Butler, N. (1996). Sports participation and emotional wellbeing in adolescents. *The Lancet, 347*(9018), 1789–1792.
42. Bao, L., & Intille, S. S. (2004, April). Activity recognition from user-annotated acceleration data. In *International conference on pervasive computing* (pp. 1–17). Berlin, Heidelberg: Springer.

43. Atallah, L., Lo, B., King, R., & Yang, G. Z. (2011). Sensor positioning for activity recognition using wearable accelerometers. *IEEE Transactions on Biomedical Circuits and Systems, 5*(4), 320–329.
44. Longstaff, B., Reddy, S., & Estrin, D. (2010, March). Improving activity classification for health applications on mobile devices using active and semi-supervised learning. In *2010 4th International Conference on Pervasive Computing Technologies for Healthcare* (pp. 1–7). IEEE.
45. Imadali, S., Karanasiou, A., Petrescu, A., Sifniadis, I., Vèque, V., & Angelidis, P. (2012, October). eHealth service support in IPv6 vehicular networks. In *2012 IEEE 8th International Conference on Wireless and Mobile Computing, Networking and Communications (WiMob)* (pp. 579–585). IEEE.
46. Islam, S. R., Kwak, D., Kabir, M. H., Hossain, M., & Kwak, K. S. (2015). The internet of things for health care: a comprehensive survey. *IEEE Access, 3,* 678–708.
47. Sharma, V., Mankodiya, K., De La Torre, F., Zhang, A., Ryan, N., Ton, T. G., et al. (2014, June). SPARK: personalized parkinson disease interventions through synergy between a smartphone and a smartwatch. In *International Conference of Design, User Experience, and Usability* (pp. 103–114). Cham: Springer.
48. Choudhury, T., Borriello, G., Consolvo, S., Haehnel, D., Harrison, B., Hemingway, B., et al. (2008). The mobile sensing platform: An embedded activity recognition system. *IEEE Pervasive Computing, 7*(2), 32–41.
49. Kwapisz, J. R., Weiss, G. M., & Moore, S. A. (2011). Activity recognition using cell phone accelerometers. *ACM SIGKDD Explorations Newsletter, 12*(2), 74–82.
50. Banos, O., Garcia, R., Holgado-Terriza, J. A., Damas, M., Pomares, H., Rojas, I., et al. (2014, December). mHealthDroid: A novel framework for agile development of mobile health applications. In *International workshop on ambient assisted living* (pp. 91–98). Cham: Springer.
51. Chen, L., Kapoor, S., & Bhatia, R. (2016). *Emerging trends and advanced technologies for computational intelligence*. Springer.
52. Puppala, M., He, T., Chen, S., Ogunti, R., Yu, X., Li, F., et al. (2015). METEOR: an enterprise health informatics environment to support evidence-based medicine. *IEEE Transactions on Biomedical Engineering, 62*(12), 2776–2786.
53. Mattila, J., Koikkalainen, J., Virkki, A., van Gils, M., Lötjönen, J., & Initiative, Alzheimer's Disease Neuroimaging. (2011). Design and application of a generic clinical decision support system for multiscale data. *IEEE Transactions on Biomedical Engineering, 59*(1), 234–240.
54. Storf, H., Becker, M., & Riedl, M. (2009, April). Rule-based activity recognition framework: Challenges, technique and learning. In *2009 3rd International Conference on Pervasive Computing Technologies for Healthcare* (pp. 1–7). IEEE.
55. Huang, Y., Zheng, H., Nugent, C., McCullagh, P., Black, N., Hawley, M., & Mountain, G. (2011, September). Knowledge discovery from lifestyle profiles to support self-management of Chronic Heart Failure. In *2011 Computing in Cardiology* (pp. 397–400). IEEE.
56. Rafferty, J., Nugent, C., Chen, L., Qi, J., Dutton, R., Zirk, A., et al. (2014, August). NFC based provisioning of instructional videos to assist with instrumental activities of daily living. In *2014 36th Annual International Conference of the IEEE Engineering in Medicine and Biology Society* (pp. 4131–4134). IEEE.
57. McClaren, B. J., King, E. A., Crellin, E., Gaff, C., Metcalfe, S. A., & Nisselle, A. (2020). Development of an Evidence-Based, Theory-Informed National Survey of Physician Preparedness for Genomic Medicine and Preferences for Genomics Continuing Education. *Frontiers in Genetics, 11,* 59.
58. Mahn, T. G. (2013). Wireless Medical Technologies: Navigating Government Regulation in New Medical Age". A report on medical device regulation.
59. The Role of IoT in Healthcare: Applications & Implementation. (2020). Retrieved 20 April 2020, from https://www.finoit.com/blog/the-role-of-iot-in-healthcare-space/.
60. Wang, J. B., Cadmus-Bertram, L. A., Natarajan, L., White, M. M., Madanat, H., Nichols, J. F., et al. (2015). Wearable sensor/device (Fitbit One) and SMS text-messaging prompts to increase physical activity in overweight and obese adults: a randomized controlled trial. *Telemedicine and e-Health, 21*(10), 782–792.

61. Chiauzzi, E., Rodarte, C., & DasMahapatra, P. (2015). Patient-centered activity monitoring in the self-management of chronic health conditions. *BMC Medicine, 13*(1), 77.
62. Wood, A. D., Stankovic, J. A., Virone, G., Selavo, L., He, Z., Cao, Q., et al. (2008). Context-aware wireless sensor networks for assisted living and residential monitoring. *IEEE Network, 22*(4), 26–33.
63. Castillejo, P., Martínez, J. F., López, L., & Rubio, G. (2013). An internet of things approach for managing smart services provided by wearable devices. *International Journal of Distributed Sensor Networks, 9*(2), 190813.
64. Jarochowski, B. P., Shin, S., Ryu, D., & Kim, H. (2007, November). Ubiquitous rehabilitation center: An implementation of a wireless sensor network based rehabilitation management system. In *2007 International Conference on Convergence Information Technology (ICCIT 2007)* (pp. 2349–2358). IEEE.
65. Baños, R. M., Cebolla, A., Botella, C., García-Palacios, A., Oliver, E., Zaragoza, I., et al. (2011). Improving childhood obesity treatment using new technologies: the ETIOBE system. *Clinical practice and epidemiology in mental health: CP & EMH, 7,* 62.
66. Rodríguez, M. D., & Favela, J. (2012). Assessing the SALSA architecture for developing agent-based ambient computing applications. *Science of Computer Programming, 77*(1), 46–65.
67. Kim, S., & Ko, D. S. (2015, November). Design of Infant Health Condition Check Solution Based on a Wearable Device with Attitude Heading Reference System. In *2015 8th International Conference on Bio-Science and Bio-Technology (BSBT)* (pp. 1–3). IEEE.
68. Anzanpour, A., Rahmani, A. M., Liljeberg, P., & Tenhunen, H. (2015, December). Internet of things enabled in-home health monitoring system using early warning score. In *Proceedings of the 5th EAI International Conference on Wireless Mobile Communication and Healthcare* (pp. 174–177).
69. Khan, S., Ali, S. A., Hasan, N., Shakil, K. A., & Alam, M. (2019). Big Data Scientific Workflows in the Cloud: Challenges and Future Prospects. In *Cloud Computing for Geospatial Big Data Analytics* (pp. 1–28). Cham: Springer.
70. Khan, S., Shakil, K. A., & Alam, M. (2018). Cloud-based big data analytics—a survey of current research and future directions. In *Big Data Analytics* (pp. 595–604). Singapore: Springer.
71. Wani, M. M., Khan, S. & Alam, M. (2020). IoT—Based *Traffic management system for ambulances.*

Principal Component Analysis, Quantifying, and Filtering of Poincaré Plots for time series typal for E-health

Gennady Chuiko, Olga Dvornik, Yevhen Darnapuk, and Yaroslav Krainyk

Abstract This study deals with Poincaré Plots, which go a handy tool for visualizing and probing signals and records in medicine and E-health. The Poincaré Plot is a kind of recurrence graph as well as a scatter chart. It is also an embedding of a time series into 2D-space. We revised here the time-tested "ellipse fitting technique," a popular method of the quantifying of Poincaré Plots, within more general Principal Components Analysis. The "ellipse fitting" turned out a simplified option of the Principal Components Analysis. We have framed the central approximation of the "ellipse fitting" and given the numeric gage of its reality. We have offered a new way of filtering the signal within Principal Components Analysis. At last, we have tested the abilities of both theories in case studies. The typal series for E-health were in use: a short series of ambulatory blood pressure tests and a more extended one for self-monitoring of blood glucose. The accuracy of the numeric descriptors of Poincaré Plots is almost the same with both theories. Still, the "ellipse fitting" may give a notable fault for the direction of the first Principal Component. Filtered Poincaré Plots keep the shapes of its originals, the descriptors' values, and the fractal scaling law. However, the fractal dimension is a bit drop after the filtering.

Keywords Poincaré Plots · E-health · Quantifying · Filtering · Fractal nature

1 Introduction

Poincaré Plots (PPs) have got their title in honor of Henri Poincaré, though he never was a maker or user of those. This famed French scholar has framed a general recurrence lemma valid for many dynamical systems with finite energy. Still, the bond between PPs and this theorem is close enough.

The recurrence theorem states [1, 2]: "If the system has fixed total energy that restricts its dynamics to bounded subsets of its phase space, the system will eventually

G. Chuiko (✉) · O. Dvornik · Y. Darnapuk · Y. Krainyk
Petro Mohyla Black Sea National University, 68 Desantnikov St., 10, Mykolayiv 54003, Ukraine
e-mail: genchuiko@gmail.com

R. Patgiri et al. (eds.), *Health Informatics: A Computational Perspective in Healthcare*, Studies in Computational Intelligence 932,
https://doi.org/10.1007/978-981-15-9735-0_4

return as closely as you like to any given initial state". By the way, C. Carathéodory has proved this assertion many years later [3].

Let us consider a system described in this theorem. Let us say we know its states in a finite set of discrete times. The recurrence graph (RP) is an image of a square matrix of the system states similarity. The matrix terms are equal to 1 for those pairs of states that match repeating states. Those should be close to each other. That is two close points in the phase space of the system presents these states. Otherwise, the matrix elements are equal to zero. Thus, a point on RP fits a nonzero term of this similarity matrix. An excellent historical review of RP states the study and use of this visualization tool got intense only in the last three decades [4].

The point is that PP is a kind of recurrence plot [5]. Let reckon that any two successive terms of the time series (or several such as an option) match system's fairly close states. It sounds quite well if the sampling rate satisfies another well-known theorem. Here we have in mind the Nyquist-Shannon counting theorem. Then such a pair of successive states set a point in both RP and PP. One can specify terms of the series on the axes of PP instead of their indexes as in RP.

Imagine a time series of arbitrary provenance: $\{S_n\}_1^N = S_1, S_2, \ldots, S_n, \ldots, S_N$. Now consider all pairs of successive terms of the series: $(S_1, S_2), (S_2, S_3), \ldots,$ $(S_n, S_{n+1}), \ldots, (S_{N-1}, S_N)$. If each of the set's pair is a point on a two-dimensional graph, then one has got PP for this series. Such a plot is also termed as a return map, scatter plot, and Lorenz plot [5, 6].

Thus, any PP is a scatter plot. Scatter plots are the recognized champions in the field of scientific visualization [7, 8]. The statistics pointed out then more than 70% of all charts in scientific papers are namely scattered plots [7].

The PP analysis was used as a visual means at first. Earlier papers, which had used PPs to the heart variability study, were and stayed as examples of this approach [9–13]. Modern papers often use the same path, but more subtle methods as in [14]. A quantifying of PP was designed quite early [15–17]. Numerical descriptors (SD1 and SD2) proposed by the authors of [15, 16] are still in use. Both were introduced, pushing away from the approximately elliptical shape of a typical PP. This method was called the "ellipse fitting technique (EFT)." It had banked criticism and got some upgrade, but its regular basis kept unchanged [18–21].

Short-term variability in heart rate is associated with SD1, the minor axis of the fitting ellipse. Whereas long-term variability links with SD2, the longer one, and their ratio (SD1/SD2) is serving as the measure of series' randomness [18–21].

The "line-of-identity" plays a significant role in this framework. That is the bisectrix of the projective plane. The points, which are satisfying the condition $x_n = x_{n+1}$, belong to this line. The main assuming of the EFT theory is that one of the "fitting ellipse" axes ever coincides with this line.

Though it is worthy to point out that typal PP has an elliptic shape, but it is not mandatory rules. For instance, other forms, such as "comet shape," frequently can be met within the heart rate variability studies [5, 6].

The spread of the "ellipse fitting" method to other biomedical signals is performed virtually automatically [22]. The authors [21] warn as for possible misinterpreting above mentioned descriptors beyond the studies of heart rate variability. It especially touches the "short-time" or "long-time" definitions.

If one, knowing with Principal Components Analysis, is studying the "ellipse fitting technique," it can seem as if already known. The mathematical intuition hints that one deals with a simplified version of the known and powerful math tool. We mean here Principal Components Analysis (PCA) as the fundamental theory [23].

So, we aim to reformulate here the quantifying of PPs in the framework of PCA. Firstly, because it never was be done earlier. Secondly, we hope to understand the quantifying and processing of PP better. The comparison of EFT and PCA forecasting is also the object of our work. To achieve it, we will be using well-verified data.

2 Theory: Quantifying and Processing of a Poincaré Plots for biomedical series

2.1 *Embedding and Data Matrix*

Consider the series $\{S_n\}_1^N = S_1, S_2, \ldots, S_n, \ldots, S_N$ again. Let the series is centered regarding its mean value and this condition if fulfilled here and bellow. It is not a mandatory condition if one intends to build the PP for the visual ratings. Still, the descriptors (SD1, SD2) are computing as the square roots of empirical variances along the "ellipse axes" just for centered data [16, 18, 20].

One can consider this series as either N points (members) in a 1D-space or as one point in an ND-space. Then, is it possible to embed this series in spaces with intermediate sizes from 1 to N?

Let select $1 \le k \le N$and divide the series into the $N - k + 1$ lagged vectors with the same length k : $(S_1, S_2, \ldots, S_k)$, $(S_2, S_3, \ldots, S_k + 1)$, …, $(S_{N-k+1}, S_{N-k+2}, \ldots, S_N)$ [25, 26]. We can consider each of the lagged vectors as a point in kD-space. This set of points is the embedding of the series into *kD* space. The lagged vectors form rows of rectangle matrix with $N - k + 1$ rows and k columns:

$$\mathbf{D}_k = \begin{vmatrix} S_1 & S_2 & \ldots & S_k \\ S_2 & S_3 & \ldots & S_{k+1} \\ \ldots & \ldots & \ldots & \ldots \\ S_{N-k+1} & S_{N-k+2} & \ldots & S_N \end{vmatrix} \quad (1)$$

Authors of [23] term the array (1) as a "data matrix," while in [25, 26], the same subject entitled as a "trajectory matrix". The one-column data matrix corresponds to the trivial embedding in 1D-space, which is mentioned above, whereas the one-row data matrix describes the one point into ND-space.

The usability defines the parameter k ("the window length" [25, 26]). Usually $k = 2$, and PP is 2D-plot, although there are suggestions as for the 3D-plots ($k = 3$) [18, 19, 27]. The data matrix for the usual PP has two lagged vector-columns:

$$\mathbf{D}_2 = \begin{vmatrix} S_1 & S_2 \\ S_2 & S_3 \\ \dots & \dots \\ S_N - 1 & S_N \end{vmatrix} \quad (2)$$

Thus, the data matrix (2) presents conventional PP or the embedding of the time series into 2D-space (a plane of projection). Each row of the data matrix gives a point of PP. This data matrix has Hankel type, and the rank equal to 2 reflecting the dimensionality of the projective plane [23, 25].

The same scaling of column vectors is the second essential requirement for PCA [23]. It is provided by itself since the lagged vector-columns of matrices (1, 2) belong to the same series.

2.2 Principal Components on the Projective Plane

PCA is a potent method for the study of data patterns [28]. There are four ways to determine the main task of the PCA [23]. Let single out only one of them; it seems the fittest for our aims. Note that the vector columns of the data matrix (2) are well correlated. They are lagged each other but represent the same series.

Let find such an orthogonal basis, in which the covariance matrix for the data matrix (2) is diagonal. Vector-columns of transformed data matrix has to zero correlation within this basis. This basis consists of Principal Components [23].

Besides, PCA warrants three sequelae.

- First, the sum of squared distances from data points to their orthogonal projections on the plane is minimal.
- Second, the amount of empirical variances along the Principal Components is maximal.
- Third, the mean point-to-point squared distance between the orthogonal projections of data points on the plane is maximal [23].

Let us consider centered on the mean values, computed for each column, vector-columns of the data matrix D_2. Let a and b are such vector-columns and $D_{2,c}$ is the centered data matrix. Thus, the problem of Principal Components search match the task of diagonalization sich a covariance matrix [23, 27]:

$$\mathbf{Cov}_2 = \left(\frac{1}{N-1}\right)\mathbf{D}_{2,c}^T\mathbf{D}_{2,c} = \left(\frac{1}{N-1}\right)\begin{pmatrix} \mathbf{a}^2 & \mathbf{(a,b)} \\ \mathbf{(a,b)} & \mathbf{b}^2 \end{pmatrix} \quad (3)$$

where the upper index "T" means "transposed" and **(a,b)** is the scalar product of centered vector-columns.

The covariance matrix (3) is the symmetric and two-dimensional square one in this case. Its diagonalization procedure is well-known [28]. The eigenvalues of the covariance matrix are variances along the PCs, and the eigenvectors give the directions of both PCs.

Another way of solving is the singular value decomposition (SVD) for the centered data matrix [23]. This way is to prefer from the computing point of view, mostly for "long windows" ($k > 2$) [25, 26]. The singular values are the standard deviations along the PCs, and the right singular vectors show their directions.

The diagonalization of the covariance matrix (3) is possible by the rotation of the coordinate system with the Givens' matrix [29]:

$$G = \begin{pmatrix} \cos(\theta) & -\sin(\theta) \\ \sin(\theta) & \cos(\theta) \end{pmatrix} \tag{4}$$

This orthogonal matrix transforms the covariance matrix to the diagonal one in such a sense:

$$\mathbf{G}^{-1} \cdot \mathbf{Cov}_2 \cdot \mathbf{G} = \begin{pmatrix} \lambda_1 & 0 \\ 0 & \lambda_2 \end{pmatrix} \tag{5}$$

Here λ_1, λ_2 are eigenvalues of the covariance matrix in descending order. They upright define standard descriptors:

$$\left.\begin{matrix} \sqrt{\lambda_1} = \mathrm{SD2} \\ \sqrt{\lambda_2} = \mathrm{SD1} \end{matrix}\right\} \tag{6}$$

One can link the angle of rotation ($0 \le \theta \le \pi$) with terms of the covariance matrix (3) and, thus, with both vector-columns of the data matrix [29]:

$$\theta = \frac{1}{2} \arctan\left(\frac{2(\mathbf{a}, \mathbf{b})}{\mathbf{a}^2 - \mathbf{b}^2}\right) \tag{7}$$

The sign of the arctangent argument sets whether $0 \le \theta \le \frac{\pi}{4}$ or $\frac{\pi}{4} \le \theta \le \frac{\pi}{2}$ [29]. The rotation of the coordinate system with the angle (7) provides not only the diagonal shape of the covariance matrix. It also decorrelates the columns in the rotated data matrix. Besides, the rotation to the PCs also ensures another three results enlisted above in this section.

A strict inequality being fulfilled frequently for typal PP, though its check is a wish for each data matrix:

$$p = \left|\frac{2(\mathbf{a}, \mathbf{b})}{\mathbf{a}^2 - \mathbf{b}^2}\right| >> 1 \tag{8}$$

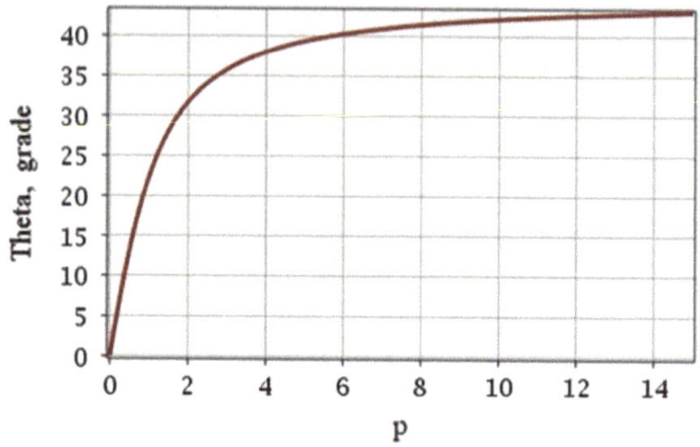

Fig. 1 The rotation angle (θ) depends on the dimensionless parameter (p). The central assumption within the "fitting ellipse technique" ($\theta \approx 45°$) sounds more or less reasonable only if this parameter is large enough: $p \geq 7$

Figure 1 shows the dependence of the coordinates rotation angle on the dimensionless parameter p (see Eq. (8))

Only if the condition (8) is actual, then we have $\theta = \frac{\pi}{4}$. Only if so, the direction of the first Principal Component virtually coincides with the "line of identity" on the projective plane. Otherwise, the longer "ellipse axis" and the "line of identity" can be diversely directed (see Fig. 1).

So, the gauge (8) is implicit, but the mandatory treat of the EFT. As better fulfills the condition (8) so exacter are the approximations of the "ellipse fitting". That has to touch as the descriptors ($SD1$, $SD2$) as well as the terms of the rotation matrix (4).

One could also use the singular vector decomposition of the data matrix D_2 (Eq. 2) [23]. Then descriptors are equal to singular values, while the right singular vector gives the rotation matrix (7).

If one is using EFT, he/she has to hope the data matrix that had rotated to the "line of identity" being have the weakly correlated columns. If so, then the gauge (8) is fulfilled, and the descriptors are equal to the standard deviations for each column of the rotated data matrix [30].

2.3 Decomposition and Filtering of the Poincaré Plots

A few papers were devoted to the decomposition and filtering of PPs [30–33]. The last three of them have used the singular decomposition (SVD) of the data matrix. Such disintegration is possible also for the data matrix of a PP. This matrix with the rank equal to 2 decomposes in the linear combination of two arrays with the same one ranks. To do that, one has to know singular values and singular vectors of the data matrix [31–33].

The algorithm of such filtering comprises four stages:

- SVD of data matrix (2) with the finding of its singular vectors and values;
- Decomposition of the two-rank matrix (2) in the sum of two one-rank matrices;
- Antidiagonal averaging (hankelization) of both one-rank matrices [25];

- Downsampling ("lazy wavelet transforming" [34]) of both parts of the restored series.

The results of the filtering are the same as if to apply a digital filter with the finite impulse response [32]. Thus, one can separate the low-frequency part of the signal from the high-frequency one. The low-frequency (LF) component of the series is bound with the higher singular value of the data matrix. The minor singular value sets the high-frequency (HF) part [35].

One can likely consider the HF part as additive noise, especially if the singular values are sharply different. So, the filtering should be handy for denoising of the signal [35].

The authors would like to suggest here another way of filtering bound with PCs and PCA. Admit, the condition (8) fulfills, and hence the rotation angle (7) is close to 45°. Then the rotation matrix (4) has the simple shape:

$$\mathbf{G}_{45} = \sqrt{2}\begin{pmatrix} \frac{1}{2} & -\frac{1}{2} \\ \frac{1}{2} & \frac{1}{2} \end{pmatrix} \tag{9}$$

Consider the transforming of the data matrix (2) with the rotation matrix (9) to new axes. These axes coincide with the "line of identity" and the normal line to it. The data matrix gets such a unique shape:

$$\mathbf{D}_{2,\text{new}} = \sqrt{2}\begin{pmatrix} \frac{S_1+S_2}{2} & \frac{S_2-S_1}{2} \\ \frac{S_2+S_3}{2} & \frac{S_3-S_2}{2} \\ \cdots & \cdots \\ \frac{S_{N-1}+S_N}{2} & \frac{S_N-S_{N-1}}{2} \end{pmatrix} \tag{10}$$

The rows of the rotation matrix (9) are proportional to the Haar digital filters with scaling factor $\sqrt{2}$. One can see there two Haar digital filters: 1) the high-pass band (the first row), or the HF-filter; 2) the low-pass band (the second row), or the LF-filter [36, 37].

Columns of the matrix (10) present Haar's wavelet coefficients for the starting series if one does not pay attention to the above scaling factor. The first column is proportional to the so-called approximation coefficients, associated with the LF-filter. The second column is related to HF-filter and shows the so-called detalization factors.

Therefore, the rotation (9) to the "line of identity," which is a mandatory action in EFT, simultaneously provides the decomposition for the initial data. If discard the scaling factor in front of (10), and to do downsampling for both columns, then it will be the filtering. The results will be the same as the filtering of the original series with Haar's wavelets. Thus, the columns of the matrix (10) comprise both LF- and HF-parts of the initial signal, and both are nearly statistically independent.

So, we can recommend two identical, as regards the result, ways of PPs filtering:

- Twofold downsampling (lazy wavelet transforming) of the data matrix (10) and then considering of columns for the downsampled array as LF and HF parts of PP respectively;
- The transforming of original series by Haar's wavelet and then constructing the data matrix of filtered PP from the LF and HF parts as columns, which both have to be multiplying on the scaling factor $\sqrt{2}$.

Both algorithms are markedly simpler than one suggested in [31–33] and described at the start of this section.

Note the condition (8), if fulfilled, ensures the virtually zero correlation for the columns of the matrix (10). It is essential, because descriptors within EFT are the standard deviations of columns of the matrix (10), without downsampling but with the account of the scaling factor [30]. It means they should be mostly close enough to the exact values (6) from PCA. Despite the rotation angle (7) can notably differ from 45°. We will be considering such an example below.

However, the question arises. What if the column correlation coefficient for matrix (10) is unacceptably high? Then one has to use for filtering the rotation matrix (4), with the real rotation angle (6) instead of (9). Of course, one can not connect already such a filtration with Haar's wavelets. Still, the product of the data matrix (2) on the rotation matrix (2) contains two strictly independent columns corresponding to the LF and HF parts of the signal.

One can assert, based on the previous discussion, descriptors are measures of scattering for the LF and HF parts of the initial signal. The ranges of LF and HF bands, sure, dependent on the sampling rate.

2.4 Fractal Dimension of Poincaré Plots as a quantity measure

Poincaré Plots in medicine have historically begun from heart rate studies. The scaling law for cardio intervals was mentioned in the thesis by Makikallo [17]. Later, the fractal properties of heart rate *R–R* intervals have been discussed in many papers. The reader can turn, for instance, to [38–43]. Higuchi's fractal dimension for cardio intervals can vary, for example, due to the physiological activity of the patient [41]. That can depend on his/her diagnosis [38, 40].

At first, fractal properties were tied just with a series of cardio intervals [17, 38–42]. Methods, which had used in these works, are reviewed in [39]. Poincaré Plot is among these tools, but only due to its descriptors. The fractal nature has been associated with primary heart rate intervals series, but not with PPs themself.

On the contrary, we believe that fractal nature is inherent in other medical signals, and their PP should reflect that [43, 44]. The scaling law establishes the fractal nature of a geometric object as a PP [45, 46]. The "Box Counting Method" [46] turned out to be a convenient tool for studying the fractal dimension of PP [43, 44]. Moreover, this method is easily programmed [46].

Consider typical PP as a set (a "cloud") of points on the projective plane. Points group around the direction of first Principal Component, or around "line of identity," if they coincide. Let us frame the query. How many are flat "boxes" needed for a complete covering of the point's cloud? This number depends on the linear size of the "box" (let this size is denoted as a), that is $N(a)$. Under the condition, that every box covers although one point, one can get such a scaling law [45]:

$$N(a) \sim a^{-d} \tag{11}$$

Here d is the fractal dimension, which is also known as the Minkowski-Bouligand dimension or Kolmogorov dimension [45]. The scaling law (11) looks a straight line in the double-logarithmic coordinates [45].

This dimensionless parameter (d) we suggest using as the quantity index for PP of the medical signals [43, 44]. Let the scaling law is right in some range of scales. Then the Poincaré Plot has a fractal nature (is self-similar) on the same sizes. It means the fragment or the part of PP is statistically similar to the whole one.

Why is it important? If PP is self-similar, then its LF part, which is the filtered PP, keeps all main traits of the whole one. It means keeping of descriptors, fractal dimension, mean value, and shape of PP. Meantime, the number of points and orientation of PP will change.

3 Case Studies

3.1 Short Series: Ambulatory Blood Pressure Monitoring

Ambulatory blood pressure monitoring (that also called a 24-hour test) gives a relatively short series. It is a standard and widespread trial for the diagnosis of hypertension [44, 47, 48]. A breach of the criterion (8) could be most likely for similar short tests. Besides, there is still exists some prejudice regarding the application of PP to short time series. The authors would like to break up this wrong idea.

Figure 2 shows three PPs for heart rate, systolic, and diastolic pressures for data [44, 48]. Note the shape of the plots. They only roughly resemble ellipses, while the graph for heart rate does not look alike, even remotely.

Table 1 presents some quantitative parameters of these PPs in comparison.

The criterion (8) is fulfilled not quite well for heart rate series, as we have expected. The direction of first Principal Component notably differs from the "line of identity" for this series. Surprisingly, that fact does not affect the accuracy of the determination of descriptors. Ellipse fitting technique (EFT) and Principal Component Analysis (PCA) yield very close results. Even in the worse case from these three.

Note that determination coefficients (R squared) are close enough to one in last column of Table 2. It means the scaling law (11) is well satisfied. Thus, the PPs on

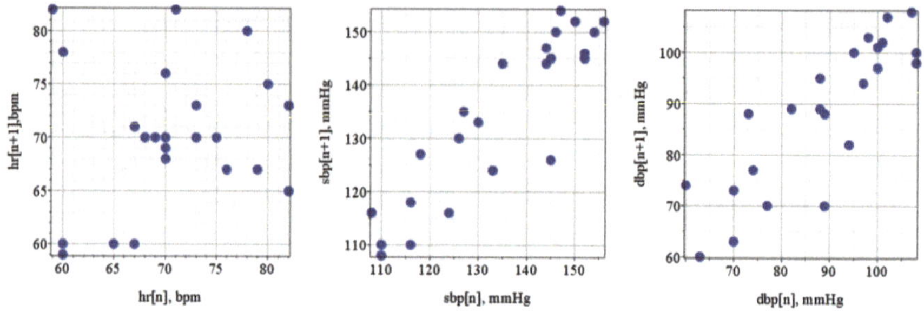

Fig. 2 Poincaré Plots for data [44, 48]. HR—heart rate (in bpm, beats per minute); SBP, DBP—systolic, and diastolic blood pressures (in mmHg)

Table 1 Parameters of Poincaré Plots

Parameters	Heart rate series	Systolic pressure	Diastolic pressure
p, (exp. (8))	4.4	45.2	47.7
θ,degree	38.6	44.4	44.4
SD1 (ETF)	6.33	4.90	5.66
SD1 (PCA)	6.32	4.90	5.66
SD2 (ETF)	7.36	21.59	19.71
SD2 (PCA)	7.37	21.59	19.71

Table 2 Fractal dimensions Hurst exponent and adjusted determination coefficients (*R* squared) [23]

	d, fractal dimensions (Mean ± Std)	HE, Hurst exponent	*R* squared
Heart rate	0.72 ± 0.09	0.28	0.91
Systolic pressure	0.69 ± 0.07	0.31	0.94
Diastolic pressure	0.79 ± 0.08	0.21	0.94

Fig. 2 are fractals. As a result, one can filter both PPs and series in the sense of Sect. 2.3, keeping the shape, the mean values, descriptors, and fractal dimension.

Though, the twofold downsampling of PPs with such a minor number of points is a bit risky. That is why authors [44] omit it. However, the sensible separation of such a short series on the independent (LF and HF) parts, in accord with the algorithm of Sect. 2.3, looks as hopeful at least.

3.2 More Extended Series: Self-monitoring of Blood Glycemia

Control of glycemic levels in the blood is one of the fields where the PPs are applying with success [49–51]. Self-monitoring of blood glucose series had 528 samples length [51]. It is a middle-length series, compared with other medical signals, for instance, with electromyograms [43].

Note the points in Fig. 3 (left graph) group themselves around the "line of identity," and the shape of PP is much closer to an ellipse than in Fig. 2. The matter is that the parameter (8) is now about 930, and the rotation angle (7) is equal to 44.969°. The excellent agreement between descriptors computed by PCA and EFT methods does not be already surprised, as it was for the shorter series above.

The filtering of data [51] has performed in the way described in section 2.3 (Haar's wavelets). Figure 4 shows that the LF part of the signal well fits the experimental results, while HF one looks like ordinary noise. LF part of series had trend and seasonality, whereas the HF one had considered as noise [51].

The filtered PP was the scatter plot of the HF part of the series as a function LF one. This graph has twice lesser points than the PP in the Fig. 2, though well keep the shape and descriptors. The divergence in descriptors does not exceed one percent. Moreover, the filtered PP shows the fractal nature in the same range of scales (from 5 to 50 mg/dl). Though, the fractal dimension of the filtered plot turned out a few percent lower: 1.27 ± 0.03 versus 1.39 ± 0.03. These decreases are relatively small but those exist.

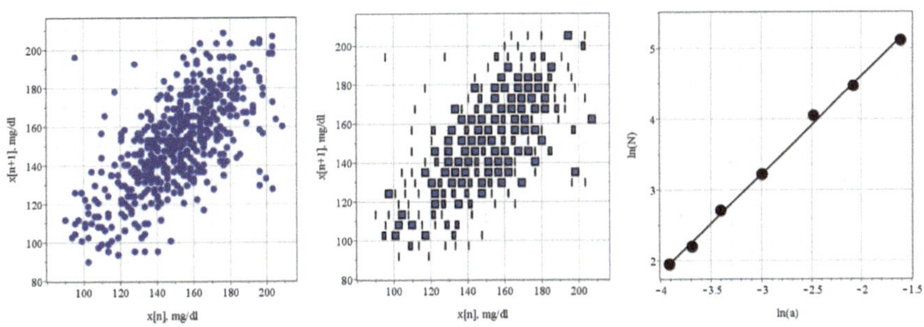

Fig. 3 The left graph shows the Poincaré Plot for data [51], the middle graph is the example of PP covered by "boxes" with linear size 12 mg/dl, the right graph shows the dependence of boxes number on its linear dimensions in double-logarithmic scale

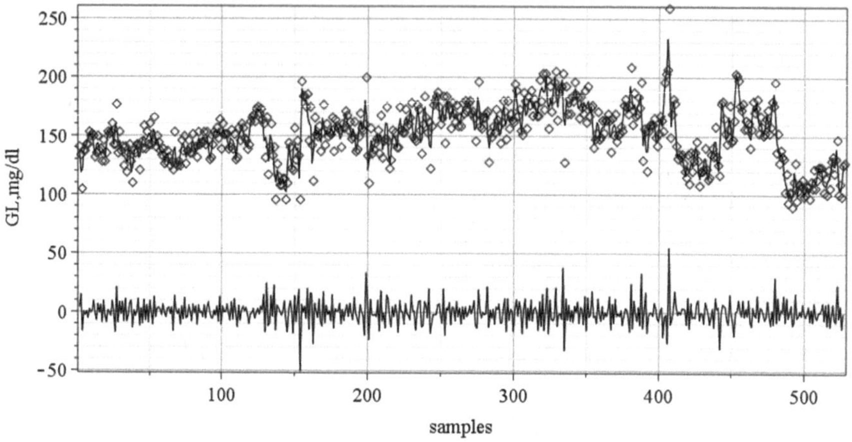

Fig. 4 The LF-part of the series as the upper curve, HF-part as the lower curve, on the background of experimental results (points)

4 Summary

The reader could convince, the time-tested "ellipse fitting technique" (EFT) turned out a simplified version of Principal Components Analysis (PCA).

The cardinal simplification of EFT is to consider the "line of identity" as universal first Principal Component for any Poincaré Plot (PP). However, this assumption may be incorrect, especially for the short time series. We have offered above the numeric criterion, estimating the veracity of this approximation.

Wonderly, but numeric descriptors for PPs in EFT are almost the same as in PCA. Meantime, they have even different definitions within both theories. Descriptors are equal to standard deviations for the columns of the data matrix after its rotation to the "line of identity" within EFT. That is strictly on the angle of 45°.

Descriptors are equal either to singular values of the initial data matrix or to square roots of eigenvalues of its two-dimensional covariance matrix in the framework of PCA. Besides, the structure of the series sets the angle of rotation in the direction of the first Principal Component. It is not universal, and maybe not equal to 45°. The rotation matrix is equal to the matrix of the right singular vectors of the data matrix within PCA.

Many biomedical signals show the fractal properties. That has to reflect on their PPs. Thus, the fractal dimension of PPs and range, in which the scaling law fulfills, could be quantitative indicators of them. Both studied series, short ambulatory blood pressure monitoring as well as more long self-monitoring of the blood glycemic level, confirm the fractal nature of their PPs. Fractal dimensions naturally are individual for both.

Fractal properties allow the filtering of the series as well as the matching PP. It means finding and separating the low-frequency components (LF) from high-frequency (HF). These two parts are decorrelated and, thus, statistically independent. The LF part keeps the mean of series; its standard deviation is equal to SD2. The standard deviation of the HF part is equal to SD1, and it reflects random and noise holding in the time series. The scatter plot of the HF part versus HF one is the filtered PP. That has twice fewer graph points than its prototype. It is the result of the twofold downsampling. Now each term of series figures in the filtered PP only once.

Filtered PP keeps the shape and descriptors of its original. It detects the fractal properties in the same range of scales. However, the fractal dimension of filtered PP is a bit lesser than it has its origin. It sounds likely this difference decreases with the length of the series.

Conflict of Interest Statement No part of this investigation has a conflict of interest.

References

1. Poincaré Recurrence Theorem (1890–1897), 2001, http://www.math.umd.edu/~lvrmr/History/Recurrence.html. Last accessed 25 Feb 2020.
2. Nadkarni, M. G. (2013). The Poincaré recurrence lemma. In *Basic ergodic theory. Texts and readings in mathematics* (Vol. 6, pp. 1–12). Gurgaon: Hindustan Book Agency (2013). https://doi.org/10.1007/978-93-86279-53-8_1.
3. Carathéodory, C.: Über den Wiederkehrsatz von Poincaré., Sitzungsber. Preuß. Akad. d Wiss. Berlin, math-phys. Kl. 1919, pp. 580–584 (1919) (in German).
4. Marwan, N. (2008). A historical review of recurrence plots. *The European Physical Journal Special Topics*, *164*, 3–12. https://doi.org/10.1140/epjst/e2008-00829-1.
5. Yang, A. C.-C. (2006). Poincaré Plots: a mini-review, Physionet.Org. (2006) 16. https://archive.physionet.org/events/hrv-2006/yang.pdf. Last accessed February 25, 2020.
6. BTL corp., Poincaré Graph Complete ECG record in one sight Constructing a Poincaré graph, BTL (2014).https://files.btlnet.com/product-document/9792e3d5-3dbf-45d8-9e84-5c964a6a8602/BTL-Cardiopoint_WP_Poincare-graph_EN400_9792e3d5-3dbf-45d8-9e84-5c964a6a8602_original.pdf. Last accessed February 25, 2020.
7. Kopf, D. (2018) A brief history of the scatter plot—data visualization's greatest invention, March 31, 2018. https://qz.com/1235712/the-origins-of-the-scatter-plot-data-visualizations-greatest-invention. Last accessed February 25, 2020.
8. Friendly, M., & Denis, D. (2005). The early origins and development of the scatterplot. *Journal of the History of the Behavioral Sciences*, *41*, 103–130. https://doi.org/10.1002/jhbs.20078.
9. Schechtman, V. L., Raetz, S., Harper, R. K., Garfinkel, A., Wilson, A. J., Southall, D. P., et al. (1992). Dynamic analysis of cardiac R-R intervals in normal infants and in infants who subsequently succumbed to the sudden infant death syndrome. *Pediatric Research*, *31*, 606–612. https://doi.org/10.1203/00006450-199206000-00014.
10. Woo, M. A., Stevenson, W. G., Moser, D. K., Trelease, R. B., & Harper, R. M. (1992). Patterns of beat-to-beat heart rate variability in advanced heart failure. *American Heart Journal*, *123*(3), 704–710. https://doi.org/10.1016/0002-8703(92)90510-3V.
11. Schechtman, L., Harper, R. K., & Harper, R. M. (1993). Development of heart rate dynamics during sleep-waking states in normal infants. *Pediatric Research*, *34*, 618–623.
12. Woo, M. A., Stevenson, W. G., Moser, D. K., & Middlekauff, H. R. (1994). Complex heart rate variability, and serum norepinephrine levels in patients with advanced heart failure. *Journal of the American College of Cardiology*, *23*, 565–569. https://doi.org/10.1016/0735-1097(94)90737-4.

13. Brouwer, J., van Veldhuisen, D. J., Man in 't Veld, A. J., Haaksma, J., Dijk, W. A., Visser, K. R., Boomsma, F., et al. (1996). Prognostic value of heart rate variability during long-term follow-up in patients with mild to moderate heart failure. The Dutch Ibopamine Multicenter Trial Study Group. Journal of the American College of Cardiology, 28, 1183–1190 (1996). https://doi.org/10.1016/s0735-1097(96)00279-3.
14. Henriques, T. S., Mariani, S., Burykin, A., Rodrigues, F., Silva, T. F., & Goldberger, A. L. (2016). Multiscale Poincaré plots for visualizing the structure of heartbeat time series. *BMC Medical Informatics and Decision Making*, *16*, 1–7. https://doi.org/10.1186/s12911-016-0252-0.
15. Marciano, F., Migaux, M. L., Acanfora, D., Furgi, G., & Rengo, F. (1994). Quantification of Poincaré' maps for the evaluation of heart rate variability. *Computers in Cardiology, 1994*, 577–580. https://doi.org/10.1109/CIC.1994.470126.
16. Tulppo, M. P., Mäkikallio, T. H., Takala, T. E., Seppanen, T., & Huikuri, H. V. (1996). Quantitative beat-to-beat analysis of heart rate dynamics during exercise. *Heart and Circulatory Physiology*, *271*, H244–H253. https://doi.org/10.1152/ajpheart.1996.271.1.H244.
17. Mäkikallio, T. H. (1998). *Analysis of heart rate dynamics by methods derived from nonlinear mathematics: clinical applicability and prognostic significance*. Oulu University, Finland. http://jultika.oulu.fi/files/isbn9514250133.pdf.
18. Brennan, M., Palaniswami, M., & Kamen, P. (2001) New insight into the relationship between Poincaré Plot geometry and linear measures of heart variability. In Proceedings of 23rd Annual Conference on IEEE/EMBS, pp. 1–4, Istanbul, TURKEY, October 25-28, 2001. https://apps.dtic.mil/dtic/tr/fulltext/u2/a411633.pdf.
19. Brennan, M., Palaniswami, M., & Kamen., P. W. (2001). Do existing measures of Poincar plot geometry reflect nonlinear features of heart rate variability?. *IEEE Transactions on Biomedical Engineering, 48*(11), 342–347 (2001). https://doi.org/10.1109/10.959330.
20. Karmakar, C., Khandoker, A. H., & Palaniswami, M. (2009). Complex correlation measure: A novel descriptor for Poincaré plot. *BioMedical Engineering OnLine*, *8*(17), 1–12. https://doi.org/10.1186/1475-925X-8-17.
21. Fishman, M., Jacono, F. J., Park, S., Jamasebi, R., Thungtong, A., Loparo, K. A., et al. (2012). A method for analyzing temporal patterns of variability of a time series from Poincaré plots. *Journal of Applied Physiology*, *113*, 297–306. https://doi.org/10.1152/japplphysiol.01377.2010.
22. Kitlas-Golinska, A. (2013). Poincaré Plots in analysis of selected biomedical signals. *Studies in Logic, Grammar and Rhetoric, 35*, 117–127 (2013). https://doi.org/10.2478/slgr-2013-0031.
23. Gorban, A. N., & Zinovyev, A. Y. (2010). Principal graphs, and manifolds. In: E. S. Olivas, J. D., Guerra, M. Martinez-Sober, J. R Magdalena-Benedito, & A. J Serrano López (Eds.), *Handbook of research on machine learning applications and trends: Algorithms, methods and techniques* (2010), 28–59. https://doi.org/10.4018/978-1-60566-766-9.
24. Rutkove, S. (2016). Examples of Electromyograms. Physionet, 2016, https://physionet.org/physiobank/database/emgdb/. Last accessed February 25, 2020.
25. Golyandina, N., Nekrutkin, V., & Zhigiljavsky, A. A. (2001). *Analysis of time series structure: SSA and related techniques*. https://doi.org/10.1201/9780367801687.
26. Korobeynikov, A. (2010). Computation- and space-efficient implementation of SSA. *Statistics and Its Interface*, *3*, 357–368. https://doi.org/10.4310/SII.2010.v3.n3.a9.
27. Chuiko, G., Dvornik, O., Darnapuk, Y., Yaremchuk, O., Krainyk, Y., & Puzyrov, S. (2019). Computer processing of ambulatory blood pressure monitoring as multivariate data. In: *Proceedings of 2019 IEEE XVth International Conference on the Perspective Technologies and Methods in MEMS Design (MEMSTECH)* (2019). https://doi.org/10.1109/MEMSTECH.2019.8817375.
28. Smith, L. I. (2020). *A tutorial on principal components analysis*, pp. 1–26 (2002). http://www.iro.umontreal.ca/~pift6080/H09/documents/papers/pca_tutorial.pdf. Last accessed February 21, 2020.
29. Layton, W., & Sussman, M. (2020). *Numerical linear algebra*. University of Pittsburgh Pittsburgh, pp. 1–307 (2014).https://people.sc.fsu.edu/~jburkardt/classes/nla_2015/numerical_linear_algebra.pdf. Last accessed February 21, 2020.

30. Piskorski, J., & Guzik, P. (2005). Filtering Poincaré plots. *Computational Methods in Science and Technology, 11*, 39–48 (2005). https://doi.org/10.12921/cmst.2005.11.01.39-48.
31. Hansen, P. C. (1998). FIR filter representations of reduced-rank noise reduction. *IEEE Transactions on Signal Processing*, *46*, 1737–1741. https://doi.org/10.1109/78.678511.
32. Figueiredo, N., Georgieva, P., Lang, E. W., Santos, I. M., Teixeira, A. R., & Tomé, A. M. (2013). SSA of biomedical signals: A linear invariant systems approach. *Statistics and Its Interface*, *3*, 345–355. https://doi.org/10.4310/sii.2010.v3.n3.a8.
33. Harris, T. J., & Yuan, H. (2010). Filtering and frequency interpretations of Singular Spectrum Analysis. *Physics D Nonlinear Phenomena*, *239*, 1958–1967. https://doi.org/10.1016/j.physd.2010.07.005.
34. Patel, K., Rora, K. K., Singh, K., & Verma, S. (2013). Lazy wavelet transform based steganography in video. In *2013 International Conference on Communication Systems and Network Technologies*, Gwalior, pp. 497–500 (2013). https://doi.org/10.1109/CSNT.2013.109.
35. Starovoitov, V. V. (2017). Singular value decomposition in digital image analysis. *Informatics, 2*, 70–83 (2017). https://inf.grid.by/jour/article/viewFile/213/215. Last accessed March 1, 2020 (in Russian).
36. Haar, A. (1910). Zur Theorie der orthogonalen Funktionensysteme - Erste Mitteilung. *Mathematische Annalen*, *69*, 331–371. https://doi.org/10.1007/BF01456326. (in German).
37. Dastourian, B., Dastourian, E., Dastourian, S., & Mahnaie, O. (2014). Discrete wavelet transforms of Haar's wavelet. In *International Journal of Science and Technological Research, 3*(9), 247–251 (2014). http://www.ijstr.org/final-print/sep2014/Discrete-Wavelet-Transforms-Of-Haars-Wavelet-.pdf. Last accessed March 1, 2020.
38. Huikuri, H. V., Mäkikallio, T. H., Peng, C. K., Goldberger, A. L., Hintze, U., & Møller, M. (2000). Fractal correlation properties of R-R interval dynamics and mortality in patients with depressed left ventricular function after an acute myocardial infarction. *Circulation*, *101*, 47–53. https://doi.org/10.1161/01.CIR.101.1.47.
39. Voss, A., Schulz, S., Schroeder, R., Baumert, M., & Caminal, P. (2009). Methods derived from nonlinear dynamics for analyzing heart rate variability. *Philosophical Transactions of The Royal Society A Mathematical Physical and Engineering Sciences, 367*(1887), 277–296 (2009). 1https://doi.org/10.1098/rsta.2008.0232.
40. de Carvalho, T. D., Pastre, C. M., de Godoy, M. F., Fereira, C., Pitta, F. O., de Abreu, L. C., et al. (2011). Fractal correlation property of heart rate variability in chronic obstructive pulmonary disease. *International Journal of COPD*, *6*, 23–28. https://doi.org/10.2147/COPD.S15099.
41. Gomes, R. L., Vanderlei, L. C. M., Garner, D. M., Vanderlei, F. M., & Valenti, V. E. (2017). Higuchi fractal analysis of heart rate variability is sensitive during recovery from exercise in physically active men. *Med Express*, *4*, 1–8. https://doi.org/10.5935/medicalexpress.2017.02.03.
42. Antônio, A .M. S., Cardoso, M. A., Carlos de Abreu, L., Raimundo, R. D., Fontes, A. M. G. G., Garcia da Silva, A., et al. (2014). Fractal dynamics of heart rate variability: A study in healthy subjects. *Journal of Cardiovascular Disease, 2*(3), 138–142 (2014). http://researchpub.org/journal/jcvd/number/vol2-no3/vol2-no3-3.pdf. Last accessed February 26, 2020.
43. Chuiko, G .P., Dvornik, O. V., & Darnapuk, Y. S. (2018). Shape evolutions of Poincaré plots for electromyograms in data acquisition dynamics. In *Proceedings of the 2018 IEEE 2nd International Conference on Data Stream Mining and Processing* (SMP 2018), p. 119–122 (2018). https://doi.org/10.1109/DSMP.2018.8478516.
44. Chuiko, G., Dvornik, O., Yaremchuk, O., & Darnapuk, Y. (2019). Ambulatory blood pressure monitoring: Modeling and data mining. CEUR Workshop Proceedings, M. Jeusfeld c/o Redaktion Sun SITE, Informatik V, RWTH Aachen (Aachen, Germany), 2516, pp. 85–95, (2019). http://ceur-ws.org/Vol-2516/paper6.pdf. Last accessed March 3, 2020
45. Mandelbrot, B. (1967). How long is the coast of Britain? Statistical self-similarity and fractional dimension. *Science, 156*, 636–638 (1967). https://doi.org/10.1126/science.156.3775.636
46. Bourke, P. (2014). *Box counting fractal dimension of volumetric data.* http://paulbourke.net/fractals/cubecount. Last accessed February 29, 2020.

47. O'Brien, E., Parati, G., Stergiou, G., Asmar, R., Beilin, L.. Bilo, G., Clement, D., et al. (2013). European Society of hypertension position paper on ambulatory blood pressure monitoring, *Journal of Hypertension, 31*(9), 1731–1768 (2013). https://doi.org/10.1097/HJH.0b013e328363e964.
48. Ambulatory Blood Pressure Report, 29-Jun-2005, QRS ®., ML 402. http://qrsdiagnostic.com/sites/default/files/Blood%20Pressure/ML402%20ABPM%20Sample%20Report.pdf.
49. Albisser, A. M., Alejandro, R., Meneghini, L. F., & Ricordi, C. (2005). How good is your glucose control? *Diabetes Technology & Therapeutics, 7*, 863–875 (2005). https://doi.org/10.1089/dia.2005.7.863.
50. Crenier, L. (2014). Poincaré plot quantification for assessing glucose variability from continuous glucose monitoring systems and a new risk marker for hypoglycemia: application to type 1 diabetes patients switching to continuous subcutaneous insulin infusion. *Diabetes Technology & Therapeutics*, *16*, 247–254. https://doi.org/10.1089/dia.2013.0241.
51. Chuiko, G. P., Dvornik, O. V., & Darnapuk, Ye. S. (2019). Combined processing of blood glucose self-monitoring. *Medical Informatics & Engineering, 3*, 59–68. https://doi.org/10.11603/mie.1996-1960.2019.3.10433.

Medical Image Generation Using Generative Adversarial Networks: A Review

Nripendra Kumar Singh and Khalid Raza

Abstract Generative adversarial networks (GANs) are unsupervised deep learning approach in the computer vision community which has gained significant attention from the last few years in identifying the internal structure of multimodal medical imaging data. The adversarial network simultaneously generates realistic medical images and corresponding annotations, which proven to be useful in many cases such as image augmentation, image registration, medical image generation, image reconstruction, and image-to-image translation. These properties bring the attention of the researcher in the field of medical image analysis and we are witness of rapid adaption in many novel and traditional applications. This chapter provides state-of-the-art progress in GANs based clinical application in medical image generation and cross-modality synthesis. The various framework of GANs which gained popularity in the interpretation of medical images, such as deep convolutional GAN (DCGAN), Laplacian GAN (LAPGAN), pix2pix, CycleGAN, and unsupervised image-to-image translation model (UNIT),continue to improve their performance by incorporating additional hybrid architecture, has been discussed. Further, some of the recent applications of these frameworks for image reconstruction, and synthesis, and future research directions in the area have been covered.

Keywords Unsupervised deep learning · Image processing · Medical image translation

1 Introduction

Medical imaging plays a pivotal role in capturing high-quality images of almost all the visceral organs like the brain, heart, lungs, kidneys, bones, soft tissues, etc. For image acquisition, there is a plethora of techniques used by a variety of imaging

N. K. Singh · K. Raza (✉)
Department of Computer Science, Jamia Millia Islamia, New Delhi 110025, India
e-mail: kraza@jmi.ac.in

R. Patgiri et al. (eds.), *Health Informatics: A Computational Perspective in Healthcare*, Studies in Computational Intelligence 932,
https://doi.org/10.1007/978-981-15-9735-0_5

modalities including ultrasonography, computed tomography (CT), positron emission tomography (PET), and magnetic resonance imaging (MRI). However, the basic principles behind every modality are different for image acquisition, data processing, and complexity [1]. For example, images from CT, PET, and MR images differ from each other in terms of complexity and dimensionality to incorporate modality-specific information which ultimately assists in better diagnosis. However, these diversities create a major constrain when it comes to cross-modality image synthesis. For instance, hybrid imaging involves simultaneous imaging from two modalities like MRI/PET, CT/PET imaging. The extraction of information of one modality from the hybrid images is usually a tough exercise.

For automated analysis of the medical image, it needs to meet certain criteria like high-quality images, preserved low and high-level features, etc. A framework that performs translation of images from one modality to the other can be very promising by eliminating the need for multimodality scanning of the patient and help reduce time and expenditure. Generative adversarial network (GAN) is one such unsupervised framework that has carried out cross-modality image synthesis with significant accuracy and reliability [2].

This chapter is organized in the four sections and a discussion at the end. The first section is an introduction, the second section describes a brief background of GAN and its variant widely used the reconstruction and cross-modality translation. In the third section, we elaborate on some powerful variants of the GAN framework which got popularity in the medical image generation with desired output image resolution and cross-modality image-to-image translation. The fourth section contributes application of GAN in the medical image reconstruction and synthesis of different modality.

2 Generative Adversarial Network

The generative adversarial networks (GAN), introduced by Ian J. Goodfellow and collaborators in 2014 [3], is one of the recently developed approachesto 'generative model' using a flexible unsupervised deep learning architecture [2]. Generative model is an important task carried out using unsupervised learning to automatically generate and learn the patterns in input data so that the model can be utilized for generating new examples (output) that could have been drawn using the original dataset. The ability of GAN to generate new content makes it more popular and useful in real-life image generation.

Vanilla GAN

Vanilla GAN is the initial variant for the synthesis of artificial images proposed by Goodfellow and colleagues [3]. The building block of this network, shown in Fig. 1, is generative (G) and discriminative (D) models which use fully connected layers of the neural network and due to this, it has limited performance. It performs generative approach for generating samples directly taking input z from noise distribution $p(z)$,

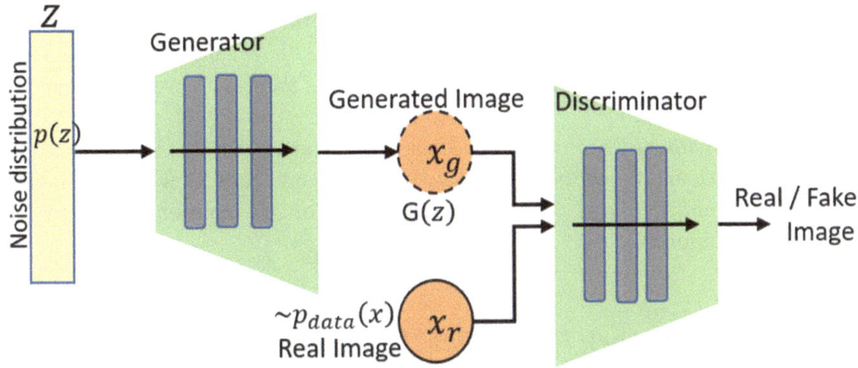

Fig. 1 Typical structure of vanilla GAN

without any conditional information. The output of the generator is $x_g \sim G(z)$ and at the same time, instance of the real distribution $x_r \sim p_{\text{data}}(x)$ input to the discriminator model D, which produces single value output indicating the probability of generated sample is real or fake. In the case of the real image, the generator gets a reward in terms of positive gradient learning from discriminator and punishes the generator when the sample (image) is not close to real. However, the objective of D's is like a binary classifier to distinguish pair of real or fake samples, while generator G is trained much to generate a variety of realistic samples to confuse the discriminator model. The objective of competing models $G\&D$ shown in the following mathematical representation [3],

$$\min_G \max_D V(D, G) = E_{x_r \sim p_{\text{data}(x)}}\left[\log D(x_r)\right] + E_{x_g \sim p_z(z)}\left[1 - \log D(G(z))\right] \quad (1)$$

The challenges in GANs optimization are as follows:

(i) *Mode collapse*: A complete mode collapse is not arising commonly but happens partially, which is the most difficult and unreliable problem to solve in GAN. As the name suggests, it is a situation when the generator continually produces a similar image and discriminator unable to consider the difference in generated samples, and in this way, generator easily fools the discriminator. It restricts the learning of the generator and focuses on a limited set of images instead of producing verities of images. The problem of collapse might be arising in inter-class or intra-class mode collapse.

(ii) *Vanishing gradients*: When discriminator becomes too strong, then in that situation, discriminator does not provide enough corresponding gradients as feedback to the generator (when gradient loss function $(1 - \log D(G(z)) \approx 0$, and learning of the generator stopped) and finally, generator is unable to produce a competitive sample. Another condition is that when D's become too weak, then loss represents nothing to the generator.

(iii) *Problem with counting*: Early GANs framework was unable to distinguish several objects at particular location in generated image, and sometimes, GAN produce more or lesser number of nose holes, eye's and ear's even fails to place the right location.

(iv) *Problem with perspective*: Sometimes, GANs are unable to understand the perspective and failed to differentiate front view and back view objects, hence GANs could not work well at the conversion of 3D representation into 2D representation [4].

3 GANs Framework for Medical Image Translation

In the initial setup, GAN was used as fully connected layers and no restrictions on data generation but, later on, it was replaced by fully convolutional down-sampling/up-sampling layers and conditional images constraints to get images with desired properties. Many different variants of the GAN framework were proposed to meet the desired output, which are Deep Convolutional generative adversarial networks (DCGAN), Laplacian generative adversarial networks (LAPGAN), pix2pix, CycleGAN, UNIT, CatGAN, BiGAN, InfoGAN, VAEGAN, StyleGAN, and more. However, our main objective of this paper is to discuss GAN for image generation framework especially those which are popular among computer vision scientists for medical image-to-image translation. In this paper, we discuss DCGAN, LAPGAN, pix2pix, CycleGAN, and UNIT framework.

3.1 DCGAN

Deep convolutional generative adversarial networks (DCGAN) [5] produce better and stable training results when a fully connected layer is replaced by a fully convolutional layer. The architecture of the generator in DCGAN is illustrated in Fig. 2a. In the core of the framework, pooling layers replaced with fractional-stride convolutions that allowed it to learn from random input noise vector by own spatial up-sampling to generate an image from it. There are two important changes adopted to modify the architecture of CNN are Batch Normalization (BatchNorm) and LeakyReLU-activation. BatchNorm [6] for regulating the poor initialization to prevent the deep generator from mode collapse which is a major drawback in the early GAN framework. LeakyReLU [7] activation introduced at the place of maxout activation(present in the vanilla GAN) all layers of a discriminator which improve higher-resolution image output.

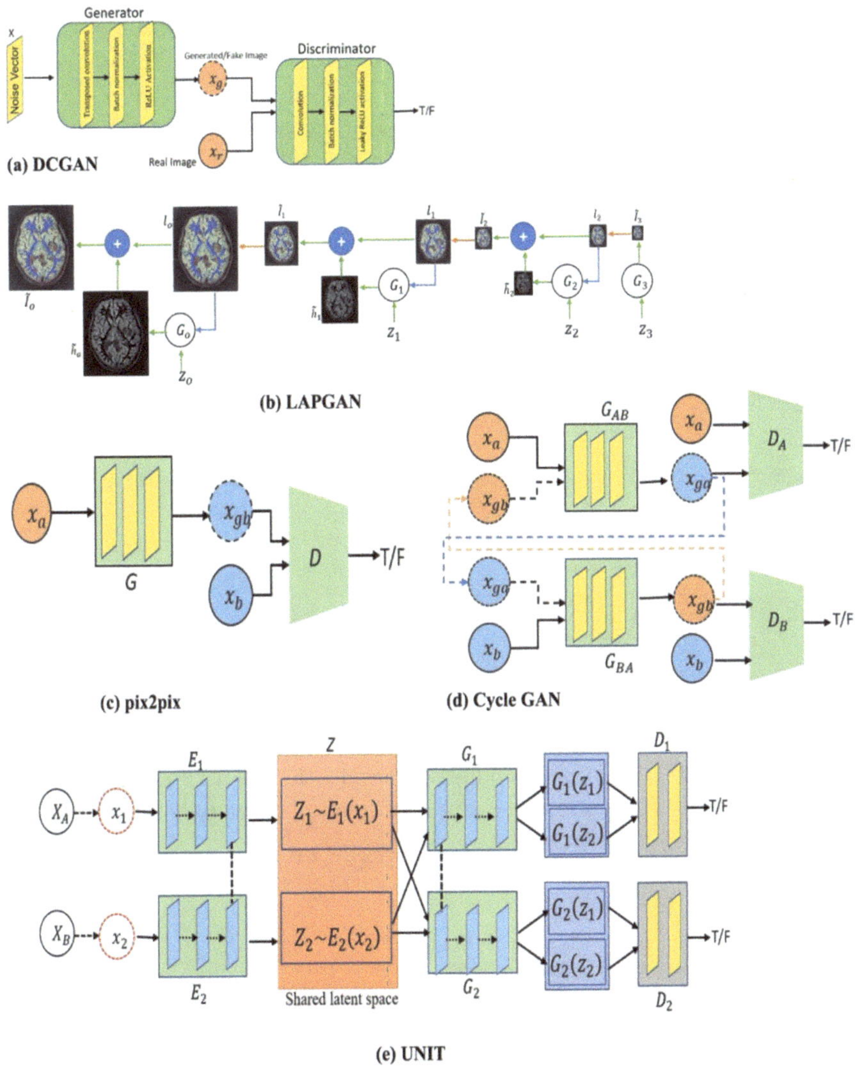

Fig. 2 A schematic representation of a variant of GANs framework for image synthesis. **a** Represent architecture of DCGAN, where generator consists convolutional neural network followed by ReLU activation while discriminator uses another neural network followed by Leaky ReLU activation **b** Shows sampling procedure of LAPGAN **c** shows pix2pix framework takes input x_a and x_b as aligned training sample **d** shows the architecture of CycleGAN which takes input x_a and x_b as unaligned training sample **e** represents the architecture of the UNIT framework that contains two autoencoders with shared-latent space

3.2 LAPGAN

It is very difficult to generate a high-resolution image directly from the noise vector. To solve this problem, Denton et al. [8] proposed Laplacian generative adversarial networks (LAPGAN) (Fig. 2b) is a stack of conditional GAN model with Laplacian pyramid representation, each of layers adds higher frequency into a generated image. The merit of this model is successive sampling procedure used to get full resolution image, for the training, a set of generative models $\{G_0, G_1, \ldots G_k\}$ at each level k of the Laplacian Pyramid L(I) to captures the distribution coefficients h_k for given input images I, h_k is calculated by difference of adjacent levels in Gaussian Pyramid $G_k(I)$ and up-sampled value $U(I)$, i.e.,

$$h_k = L_k(I) = G_k(I) - U(G_{k+1}(I)) = I_k - U(I_{k+1}) \tag{2}$$

At the end of the level, it simply represents a low-frequency residual which is $h_k = I_k$.

Following equation is used for sampling procedure with initializing $\tilde{I}_{k=1} = 0$,

$$\tilde{I}_k = U\left(\tilde{I}_{k=1}\right) + \tilde{h}_k = U\left(\tilde{I}_{k=1}\right) + G_k\left(Z_k, U\left(\tilde{I}_{k=1}\right)\right) \tag{3}$$

Figure 2b illustrates the sampling procedure for LAPGAN model. Suppose we need to sample a 64×64 image, for the number of layers $K = 3$ required four generator models. Sampling started with a noise z_3 and generative model G_3 to generate $\tilde{I}_3$, which is up-sampled to the next level l_2 for the generative model G_2. This process is repeated across successive levels to get the final full resolution image I_o.

3.3 Pix2pix

The pix2pix is a supervised image-to-image translation model proposed by Isola et al. [9] as depicted in Fig. 2c. It has received a multi-domain user acceptance in the computer vision community for image synthesis, whose merit is to combine the loss of conditional GAN (CGAN) [10] with $L1$ regularizer loss, so that network not only learns the mapping from the input image to output image but also learn the loss function to generate the image as close to ground truth. The loss of CGAN is expressed as:

$$L_{\text{CGAN}}(G, D) = E_{x,y}\left[\log D(x, y)\right] + E_{x,z}\left[\log(1 - D(x, G(x, z)))\right] \tag{4}$$

where $z \sim p(z)$ is random noise. The $L1$ regularization loss can be computed as,

$$L_{L1}(G) = E_{x,y\sim P\text{data}(x,y),z\sim P(z)}\left[||y - G(x, z)||_1\right] \tag{5}$$

The final objective function can be obtained by combining the above two equations as:

$$G^*, D^* = \arg\min_{G}\max_{D} L_{\text{CGAN}}(G, D) + \lambda L_{L1}(G) \tag{6}$$

where λ is a hyper-parameter coefficient introduced to balance the losses. Isola et al. propose two choices for training the pix2pix model [9], first for generator architecture based on U-Net [11] have an encoder/decoder with skip connections (concatenate all channels between two layers), so it allows until a bottleneck layer to gather low-level information like the location of edges. The second scheme for discriminator architecture is PatchGAN [12] which tries to classify $N \times N$ patches of images instead of the whole image.

3.4 CycleGAN

The cyclic adversarial generative network (CycleGAN) is proposed to perform higher-resolution image-to-image translation using unpaired data [13]. Figure 2d illustrates the architecture of CycleGAN, which preserves the history of input training image after the cycle of transformation and adding reconstruction loss. It consists of two generators,G_{AB}: transfer an image of the domain from A to B and another generator G_{BA}: doing the opposite transformation of G_{AB}. This cyclefacilitates dual learning to the model. Also, the model consists of two discriminators, namely $D_A a$ and D_B that decide the domain of an image. The adversarial loss function for G_{AB} and D_B pair is expressed as,

$$L_{\text{GAN}}(G_{AB}, D_B) = E_{b\sim P_B(b)}\big[\log D_B(b)\big] + E_{a\sim P_A(a)}\big[1 - \log(D_B(G_{AB}(a)))\big] \tag{7}$$

And similarly, the adversarial loss for another pair G_{BA} and D_A is represented as $L_{\text{GAN}}(G_{BA}, D_A)$. Another loss is a cyclic-consistency loss to minimize the reconstruction error when an image in one domain translates to another domain and reverses back to the original domain. The cyclic-consistency loss is represented by the equation,

$$L_{\text{cyc}}(G_{AB}, G_{BA}) = E_{a\sim P_A(a)}[a - G_{BA}(G_{AB}(a))||_1] + E_{b\sim P_B(b)}[b - G_{AB}(G_{BA}(b))||_1] \tag{8}$$

After combining the above two Eqs. (7) and (8) to obtain overall loss of the model, it would be,

$$L(G_{AB}, G_{BA}, D_A, D_B) = L_{\text{GAN}}(G_{AB}, D_B) + L_{\text{GAN}}(G_{BA}, D_A) + L_{\text{cyc}}(G_{AB}, G_{BA}) \tag{9}$$

The objective function of the CycleGAN can be represented by the following expression,

$$G_{AB}^{*}, G_{BA}^{*} = \arg \min_{G_{AB}, G_{BA}} \max_{D_A, D_B} L(G_{AB}, G_{BA}, D_A, D_B) \tag{10}$$

Even CycleGAN generates high-quality cross-domain medical images, pix2pix outperforms CycleGAN with a significant margin. Although, both CycleGAN and pix2pix are unable to construct reverse geometric transformation (for example, Zebra ↔ Horse). Visit CycleGAN project website (https://junyanz.github.io/CycleGAN/) for more examples and readings.

3.5 UNIT

An unsupervised image-to-image translation model (UNIT) was proposed by Liu and collaborators in 2017 [14]. The model is hybrid in terms of the sharing of the weight of VAE (variational autoencoder) to coupled GAN (CGAN) [15]. Assumed that x_1 and x_2 be the same input image of different domains X_A and X_B, then the encoders E_1 and E_2 share the same latent space, i.e., $E_1(X_A) = E_2(X_B)$. The UNIT framework is depicted in Fig. 2e.

UNIT framework implements the shared-latent space assumption using weight sharing between last few layers of autoencoders and first few layers of generators. Due to shared-latent space, the objective function of UNIT is a combination of GAN and VAE objective function which implies the cycle-consistency constraints [16, 17]. Therefore, the result of processing stream is called cycle-reconstruction stream represented by the following mathematical equation,

$$\min_{E_1, E_2, G_1, G_2} \max_{D_1, D_2} L_{\mathrm{VAE}_1}(E_1, G_1) + L_{\mathrm{GAN}_1}(E_1, G_1, D_1) + L_{CC_1}(E_1, G_1, E_2, D_2)$$

$$L_{\mathrm{VAE}_2}(E_2, G_2) + L_{\mathrm{GAN}_2}(E_2, G_2, D_2) + L_{CC_2}(E_2, G_2, E_1, D_1) \tag{11}$$

where L_{VAE} represents objective for minimizing variational upper bond, L_{GAN} is theobjective function of GAN, and L_{CC} is the objective function like VAE's to model the cycle-consistency constraint. Although, the UNIT framework performs superior to the CGANon MNIST datasets [15], and there is no comparison available with another unsupervised model such as CycleGAN [13].

4 Applications of GANs in Medical Imaging

Medical imaging exploits GAN in two different ways, which are generative and discriminative aspects. Generative aspects deal with the generation of new images

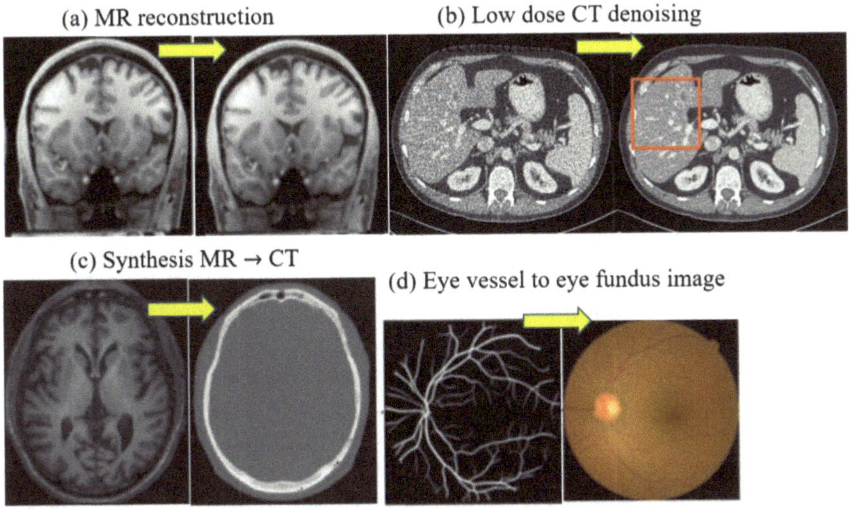

Fig. 3 Application of GAN in medical image synthesis. All the figures are adapted from corresponding articles. **a** shows MR reconstruction from given reference image [18] **b** Low dose CT denoising [19] **c** shows input brain MRI used to generated equivalent CT image close to ground truth [20] **d** generation of synthetic eye fundus image from corresponding synthetic eye vessels [21]

using underlying structural information present in the training data. On the contrary, descriptive aspects of GAN learns structural feature from the natural or original images and rule out the anomalies present in the abnormal generated image. Most of the literature reviewed in this section has applied conditional GAN methods for image-to-image translation that suffers in certain forms such as under sampling, noise in the output image, and low spatial resolution. Figure 3 shows the example of GANs application for the generative and discriminative aspect of medical image generation.

4.1 Reconstruction

The medical image reconstruction is an essential step to obtain high-quality images for diagnosis with minimal patient discomfort, but the quality of such images limited by noise and artifact due to clinical constraints like the concentration of contrast media, amount of radiation administered to a patient in undergoing contrast MRI and PET, respectively, during the acquisition of images. Therefore, the objective to get reduced noise and another factor, analytical and iterative methods of reconstruction paradigm shifted to data-driven-based machine learning methods [22].

During literature survey, we have observed that pix2pix and CycleGAN framework is frequently used in magnetic resonance imaging (MRI) reconstruction [18], [23–26], low dose CT denoising [19], [27], [28], optimization of the pre-trained network for sharpness detection and highlighting low contrast region in CT image [29], and synthesizing full dose equivalent PET from low dose concentration using skip connection introduced in the generator of conditional GAN(cGAN). Similarly, Liao et al. [30] explore sparse view CBCT reconstruction for artifact reduction. They propose feature pyramid networks for the specialized discriminator and compute modulated focus map to reconstruct the output while preserving anatomical structure. Besides the reconstruction from lower sampling, it must ensure the domain data accuracy. MR reconstruction also imposes under-sample k-space data in the frequency domain [19, 31, 32]. In image reconstruction, different types of losses have been used to distinguish local image structures, such as cycle-consistency and identity loss together [33] in the denoising of cardiac CT. Wolterinket al. proposed low dose CT denoising after removing some domain loss but the final result compromised with local image structure [28]. Reconstruction in MR is an exceptional case as it has a very much characterized forward and backward formula, for example, Fourier transformation. We summarized some studies related to medical image reconstruction in Table 1, and various losses to improve reconstruction accuracy described in Table 5.

4.2 Medical Image Synthesis

GANs framework provides a collective solution for augmenting training samples with sound results compared to traditional transformation, thus it is widely accepted for medical image synthesis and successfully overcomes the problem lacking in the volume of diagnostic imaging dataset of the positive or negative instance of each pathology. Another problem is lacking expertise in the annotation of diagnostic images which might be a big hurdle in the selection of supervised methods. Although, the multiple numbers of healthcare organization across the world and collaborative effort to build an open-access dataset of different modalities and pathology have been done, for example, The Cancer Imaging Archive (TCIA), National Biomedical Imaging Archive (NBIA), Radiologist Society of North America (RSNA), and Biobank. Researchers can access these image datasets with certain constraints.

Unconditional Synthesis: Unconditional synthesis simply generates an image from the latent space of a real sample before any conditional information. Commonly, GAN models, DCGAN, PGGAN, and LAPGAN are adopted in medical image synthesis due to exceptional training stability. Where DCGAN generates limited output image quality, that could be up to 256 × 256 image size. However, DCGAN has been used to generate high-quality image samples of lungs nodule and liver lesion which easily deceive radiologists [41, 42]. Other methods used for generating higher-resolution images are the iterative method, sharing weights among generators, but the hierarchical method may not do the same. Progressive growing generative adversarial networks (PGGAN) performs the progressive growing techniques to get the desired realistic image. For example, Beers et al. can produce a synthetic image of MRI and

Table 1 Summary of contributions in the medical image reconstruction over different modalities,

Modalities	Methods	Losses	Remarks	References
MRI	Pix2pix	L1, 2	3D super-resolution from single low-resolution input image using multi-level densely connected super-resolution network (mDCSRN)	[18]
MRI	Pix2pix	L1, 2, 7, 9	Inpainting	[22]
MRI	Pix2pix	L1, 2	Super-resolution	[23]
MRI	Pix2pix	L1, 2	Under-sampled K-space reconstruction for accelerated MRI scan	[24]
MRI	Pix2pix	L1, 2	Under-sampled K-space	[25]
MRI	Pix2pix	L1, 2,7	Two-stage	[26]
MRI	Pix2pix	L1, 2, 11	Under-sampled K-space	[31]
MRI	Pix2pix	L1, 2, 11	Reconstruction into high-quality image under sampled K-space	[32]
MRI	Pix2pix	L1, 2, 7, 11	Under-sampled K-space	[19]
MRI	Pix2pix	L1, 2	Motion correction	[34]
MRI	Pix2pix	L1, 2, 7, 10	Directly in complex-valued k-space data	[35]
MRI	Pix2pix	L1, 2, 7, 9	Motion correction	[36]
PET	cGAN	L1, 2	3D high-resolution image synthesizes equivalent to full dose PET image	[29]
CT	Pix2pix	L1, 7	3D denoising, transfer from 2D	[19]
CT	Pix2pix	L1, 2, 5	Denoising	[27]
CT	Pix2pix	L1, 2	3D denoising	[28]
CT	Pix2pix	L1, 2, 7	Sparse view CT reconstruction	[30]
CT	Pix2pix	L1, 2, 8	3D denoising	[37]
CT	SGAN	L1, 2, 7	Denoising, contrast enhance	[38]
CT	CycleGAN	L1, 2, 10	Super-resolution, denoising	[39]
CT	CycleGAN	L1, 3, 12	Denoising CT	[33]
CT	Pix2pix	L1, 2, 7	Denoising using the adjacent slice	[40]

The method for basic training network architecture, or with some modification with losses incurred (more description about losses described in Table 5) and the last column discuss remark for each contribution

retinal fundus of size up to 1024 × 1024 using the PGGAN model which is unprecedented for the previous model [43]. The summary of articles related to unconditional synthesis is presented in Table 2.

Conditional Synthesis: Availability of right samples of medical imaging data is going to be a challenge especially when pathologies are involved. They raise two factors, like scarcity of the number of cases and large variation in anatomical location, appearance, and scale. Therefore, it is useful to synthesize artificially generated medical images in uncommon conditions by constraints on locations, segmentation

Table 2 Summarize articles of unconditional synthesis of medical images

Modalities	Methods	Remark	References
CT	PGGAN	Segmentation mapping using joint learning in augmenting brain image	[44]
CT	DCGAN	Synthesizing liver lesion of each class using DCGAN, then classifying different class of lesion	[42]
CT	DCGAN	Generate realistic lung nodule separately benign and malignant nodules	[41]
MRI	Semi-Coupled GAN	Two-stage semi-supervised methods for detection of missing features from cardiac MR image	[45]
MRI	LAPGAN	Generating synthetic brain MR image slices	[46]
MRI	DCGAN*	Semi-supervised achieve better than fully supervised learning with labelled and unlabelled 3D image segmentation	[47]
MRI	DCGAN	Manifold learning for image synthesis and denoising	[48]
MRI	PGGAN	Generating high-resolution Multimodal MR image of glioma and retinal fundus using progressive training,	[43]
X-ray	DCGAN	Artificial chest X-ray augmentation and pathology classification	[49]
X-ray	DCGAN	Semi-supervised learning for abnormal cardiac classification	[50]
Retinal	DCGAN	Vessel segmentation in the retinal fundus image	[51]
Dermo	LAPGAN	Generating high-resolution skin lesion image	[52]

maps or text, etc. Jin et al. [53] augmented the lung CT data set with artificially synthesize nodules touching the lung border to improve pathological lung segmentation of CT. An adversarial auto encoder for a conditional segmentation map has been used to generate a retinal color image from a synthetic vessel tree which is at two-stage process [21]. Moreover, generating brain MR by conditioned segmentation map used conditional GAN to learn automatic augmentation as well training samples for brain tumor segmentation [54], and trained CycleGAN network to correct geometric distortion in diffusion MR [55]. Some contributions to conditional synthesis are summarized in Table 3.

Cross-Modality Synthesis: Cross-modality synthesis, for example, creating CT equivalent image dependents on MR images is esteemed to be helpful for different reasons. Consider a case study, when two or more imaging modalities say CT and MR require providing supplementary information in diagnostic planning, in this case, the separate acquisition is required for the complete diagnosis, which increases the cost and time in the acquisition. So, cross-modality synthesis provides artificially generated samples of target modality from available modality with preserving

Table 3 Summarize articles of conditional image synthesis of different modalities

Modalities	Methods	Conditional information	References
CT	Pix2pix	VOI with a removed central region	[53]
MRI	CycleGAN	MR	[55]
MRI	Cascade cGAN	Segmentation map	[56]
MRI	Pix2pix	Segmentation map	[57]
MRI	cGAN	Segmentation map	[54]
Ultrasound	Cascade cGAN	Segmentation map	[58]
Retinal	cGAN	Vessel map	[59]
Retinal	VAE + cGAN	Vessel map	[21]
Retinal	cGAN	Vessel map	[60]
X-ray	Pix2pix	Segmentation map	[61]

Representing modification in the given method either in network architecture or induced losses

anatomical structure or features, without separate medical image acquisition. Most of the methods are used in this section are similar to previous sections such as the CycleGAN-based method used where registration of images is more challenging. The pix2pix-based method is another well-accepted model used where imaging data registration ensures the data fidelity. Articles related to cross-modality synthesis summarized in Table 4. Summary of various losses used in the literature cited and losses introduced in different variants of GANs framework to get the desired output result is shown in Tables 4 and 5.

5 Conclusion and Future Research Directions

GANs framework has achieved great success in the field of medical image generation and image-to-image translation. We have discussed the weightiness of a significant rise in the study of medical imaging during the past 2–3 years. A detailed literature survey of GANs in medical imaging reported that about 46% of these articles are related to cross-modality image synthesis [76]. A large section of research has focussed on the application of GANs in medical image synthesis of MRI imaging. The probable reason for the synthesis of MRI images is that it takes longer scan time for multiple sequence acquisition. Conversely, GAN effectively generates the next sequence from the acquired one, which saves time slots for another patient. The second reason may be the large number of MRI data set available in the public domain allowing researchers to have a surplus sample size for better model training. Further, a large fraction of studies conducted in the area of reconstruction and segmentation applications are due to better adversarial training and regulation on the generator's output of the GAN model for image-to-image translation framework. Although, conditional generation provides flexibility over augmentation and high resolution

Table 4 Summary of articles for cross-modality synthesis among different modality

Modality	Methods	Losses	Remark	References
MR ↔ CT	Cascade GAN	L1, 2, 4	Context-aware network for the multi-subject synthesis	[20]
MR ↔ CT	CycleGAN	L1, 3	Unpaired training in synthesizing the cardiac image	[62]
MR ↔ CT	Cycle GAN	L1, 3	Training of unpaired 2D images to synthesis cross imaging modality	[63]
MR ↔ CT	cGAN	L1, 2	Brain cancer analyzed to generate synCT	[64]
MR ↔ CT	CycleGAN*	L1, 3, 6	Generic synthesis of unpaired 3D cardiovascular data	[65]
MR ↔ CT	CycleGAN*	L1, 3, 4	Unpaired training to synthesize musculoskeletal image	[66]
MR ↔ CT	Pix2pix	L1, 2	Paired training of 2D image to analyse prostate cancer for the complete pelvic region	[67]
MR ↔ CT	CycleGAN	L1, 3, 6	Two-stage training and synthesis for abdominal image	[32]
MR ↔ CT	3D U-Net	–	3D patch-based network for pelvic bone synCT generation	[68]
CT ↔ MR	CycleGAN*	L1, 2, 3, 6, 7	A two-step process to synthesis synMR in lung tumor segmentation	[69]
CT ↔ MR	CycleGAN	L1, 2	Both paired and unpaired training for brain tumour	[70]
CT ↔ PET	FCN + cGAN	L1, 2	Synthesize paired training for liver lesion detection	[71]
PET ↔ CT	cGAN	L1, 2, 7, 9	Paired training for motion artifact and PET denoising	[72]
MR ↔ PET	Cascade cGAN	L1, 2	Brain anatomical feature from the sketch-refinement process used in the synthesis	[73]
MR ↔ PET	3D Cycle GAN	L1, 2, 3	Two stages paired training for Alzheimer's disease diagnosis	[74]
PET ↔ MR	Pix2pix	L1, 2	Paired templet-based training for brain imaging data	[75]

The arrow → represents one-way synthesis, and a dual arrow represents two-way synthesis, * represents modification in the given method either in network architecture or induced losses

Table 5 Summary of various losses used in the literature cited and introduced in different variants of the pix2pix framework to get the desired output result

Abbreviation	Losses	Remark
*L*1	$L_{adversarial}$	Discriminators introduced adversarial loss to maximize the probability of real or fake images
*L*2	L_{image}	Element-wise loss in the structural similarity between real or fake in the image domain when aligned training is provided
*L*3	L_{cycle}	Loss during cycle transformation to ensure self-similarity when unaligned training is provided
*L*4	$L_{gradient}$	Loss in the gradient domain to focus on edges
*L*5	L_{sharp}	Element-wise loss in which low contrast region computed to be image sharpness using a pre-trained network
*L*6	L_{shape}	Shape loss is also to be segment loss in the reconstruction of the specified region
*L*7	$L_{perceptual}$	Element-wise loss to get a visual perception in a feature domain
*L*8	$L_{structure}$	Structural loss is the patch-wise loss to get a human visual perception in the image domain
*L*9	$L_{style\text{-}content}$	Style-content loss resembles style and content, where style is a correlation of low-level features
*L*10	$L_{self\text{-}reg}$	Element-wise loss in identifying among similar structure or in denoising in the image domain
*L*11	$L_{frequency}$	Data fidelity loss in the frequency domain (K-space) especially in MRI reconstructions
*L*12	$L_{regulation}$	Regulation loss in the generation of image contrast while keeping the balance across the row and column

for training data. Some studies have synthesized chest X-rays for the classification of cardiac abnormalities and pathology [49, 50]. However, a very limited number of studies have been reported for the detection and registration of medical images.

Despite the diverse use of GANs, it has faced many challenges on the way for the adaptation of generated medical images directly into clinical diagnosis and decision making. Most of the work for image translation and reconstruction uses traditional methods of the metric system for quantitative evaluation of proposed methods. Especially, when GAN incorporate additional loss, there arises difficulty in the optimization of the visual standard of an image in the absence of a dedicated reference metric. Recently, Armanious et al. have proposed MedGAN adopted perceptual study along with subjective measure, conducted by the domain expert (experienced radiologist) for an extensive evaluation of GAN generated image, but the downside is that it bears high-cost, time-consuming and difficult to generalize [72]. So, it is required to explore the validity of the metrics. Another big challenge is the absence of data fidelity loss in case of unpaired training. Therefore, it is unable to retain the information of the minor abnormality region during the cross-domain image-to-image translation process. Due to these problems, Cohen et al. suggested that the GANs generated image should not be straightaway used in clinical practice [77]. Cohen et al. further experimented to confirm that unpaired training of CycleGAN subjected to bias in generated data from the target domain [77]. In a similar study of Mirsky et al. proven the possibility of intervening 3D medical imaging and bias only exists when the model was trained with normal standard data and tested with abnormal data [78].

Finally, we conclude that, even though there are many promising outcomes announced, the appropriation of GANs in clinical imaging is still in its early stages and further research in the area is needed to achieve a level of advancements essential for reliable application of GANs based imaging techniques in the clinical setup.

References

1. Wani, N. & Raza, K. (2018). Multiple Kernel Learning Approach for Medical Image Analysis. In: Dey N, Ashour A, Shi F, Balas E (eds), Soft Computing Based Medical Image Analysis, Elsevier, 31-47. https://doi.org/10.1016/B978-0-12-813087-2.00002-6.
2. Raza, K., & Singh, N. K. (2018). *A tour of unsupervised deep learning for medical image analysis* (pp. 1–29), 2018, [Online]. Available: http://arxiv.org/abs/1812.07715.
3. Goodfellow, I. J., et al. (2014). Generative adversarial nets. In *Advances in neural information processing systems.*
4. Yadav, A., Shah, S., Xu, Z., Jacobs, D., & Goldstein, T. (2018). Stabilizing adversarial nets with prediction methods. In *6th International Conference on Learning Representations, ICLR 2018 - Conference Track Proceedings.*
5. Radford, A., Metz, L., & Chintala, S. (2016). Unsupervised representation learning with deep convolutional generative adversarial networks. In *4th International; Conference on Learning Representations ICLR 2016—Conference Track Proceedings* (pp. 1–16).
6. Ioffe, S., & Szegedy, C. (2015). Batch normalization: Accelerating deep network training by reducing internal covariate shift. In *32nd International Conference on Machine Learning, ICML 2015.*
7. Maas, A. L., Hannun, A. Y., & Ng, A. Y. (2013). Rectifier nonlinearities improve neural network acoustic models. In *ICML Workshop on Deep Learning for Audio, Speech and Language Processing.*
8. Denton, E., Chintala, S., Szlam, A., & Fergus, R. (2015). Deep generative image models using a laplacian pyramid of adversarial networks. In *Advances in neural information processing systems.*
9. Isola, P., Zhu, J. Y., Zhou, T., & Efros, A. A. (2017). Image-to-image translation with conditional adversarial networks. In *Proceedings–30th IEEE Conference on Computer Visualization Pattern Recognition, CVPR 2017*, vol. 2017-January, pp. 5967–5976. https://doi.org/10.1109/cvpr.2017.632.
10. Mirza, M., & Osindero, S. (2017). *Conditional generative adversarial nets* (pp. 1–7), [Online]. Available: http://arxiv.org/abs/1411.1784.
11. Ronneberger, O., Fischer, P., & Brox, T. (2015) U-net: Convolutional networks for biomedical image segmentation. In *Lecture notes in computer science (including subseries lecture notes in artificial intelligence and lecture notes in bioinformatics).* https://doi.org/10.1007/978-3-319-24574-4_28.
12. Li C., & Wand, M. (2016). Precomputed real-time texture synthesis with markovian generative adversarial networks. In *Lecture notes in computer science (including subseries lecture notes in artificial intelligence and lecture notes in bioinformatics).* https://doi.org/10.1007/978-3-319-46487-9_43.

13. Zhu, J. Y., Park, T., Isola, P., & Efros, A. A. (2017). Unpaired image-to-image translation using cycle-consistent adversarial networks. In *Proceedings of the IEEE International Conference on Computer* Vision, vol. 2017-October, pp. 2242–2251. https://doi.org/10.1109/iccv.2017.244.
14. Liu, M. Y., Breuel, T., & Kautz, J. (2017). Unsupervised image-to-image translation networks. In *Advances in neural information processing systems.*
15. Liu, M. Y., & Tuzel, O. (2016). Coupled generative adversarial networks. *Advances in neural information processing systems*, no. Nips, (pp. 469–477).
16. Kim, T., Cha, M., Kim, J., Lee, J. K., & Kim, J. (2017). Learning to discover cross-domain relations with generative adversarial networks. In *34th International Conference* on *Machine Learning* (*ICML 2017*) (vol. 4, pp. 2941–2949).
17. Yi, Z., Zhang, H., Tan, P., & Gong, M. (2017). DualGAN: Unsupervised dual learning for image-to-image translation. In *Proceedings of the IEEE International Conference on Computer Vision.* https://doi.org/10.1109/iccv.2017.310.
18. Chen, Y., Shi, F., Christodoulou, A. G., Xie, Y., Zhou, Z., & Li, D. (2018). Efficient and accurate MRI super-resolution using a generative adversarial network and 3D multi-level densely connected network. In *Lecture notes in computer science (including subseries lecture notes in artificial intelligence and lecture notes in bioinformatics)*, 2018. https://doi.org/10.1007/978-3-030-00928-1_11.
19. Shan, H., et al. (2018). 3-D convolutional encoder-decoder network for low-dose CT via transfer learning from a 2-D trained network. *IEEE Transactions on Medical Imaging, 37,* 0001. https://doi.org/10.1109/TMI.2018.2832217.
20. Nie, D., et al. (2017). Medical image synthesis with context-aware generative adversarial networks. In *Lecture notes in computer science (including subseries lecture notes in artificial intelligence and lecture notes in bioinformatics)*, 2017. https://doi.org/10.1007/978-3-319-66179-7_48.
21. Costa, P., et al. (2018). End-to-end adversarial retinal image synthesis. *IEEE Transactions on Medical Imaging, 37*(3), 0001. https://doi.org/10.1109/TMI.2017.2759102.
22. Armanious, K., Mecky, Y., Gatidis, S., & Yang, B. (2019). Adversarial inpainting of medical image modalities. In *ICASSP, IEEE international conference on acoustics, speech and signal processing—proceedings*, 2019. https://doi.org/10.1109/icassp.2019.8682677.
23. Kim, K. H., Do, W. J., & Park, S. H. (2018). Improving resolution of MR images with an adversarial network incorporating images with different contrast. *Medical Physics, 47,* 0001. https://doi.org/10.1002/mp.12945.
24. Shitrit, O., & Riklin Raviv, T. (2017). Accelerated magnetic resonance imaging by adversarial neural network. In *Lecture notes in computer science (including subseries lecture notes in artificial intelligence and lecture notes in bioinformatics).* https://doi.org/10.1007/978-3-319-67558-9_4.
25. Ran, M., et al. (2019). Denoising of 3D magnetic resonance images using a residual encoder–decoder Wasserstein generative adversarial network. *Medical Image Analysis, 55,* 0001. https://doi.org/10.1016/j.media.2019.05.001.
26. Seitzer, M., et al. (2018). Adversarial and perceptual refinement for compressed sensing MRI reconstruction. In *Lecture notes in computer science (including subseries lecture notes in artificial intelligence and lecture notes in bioinformatics).* https://doi.org/10.1007/978-3-030-00928-1_27.
27. Yi, X., & Babyn, P. (2018). Sharpness-aware low-dose ct denoising using conditional generative adversarial network. *Journal of Digital Imaging, 55,* 0001. https://doi.org/10.1007/s10278-018-0056-0.
28. Wolterink, J. M., Leiner, T., Viergever, M. A., & Išgum, I. (2017). Generative adversarial networks for noise reduction in low-dose CT. *IEEE Transactions on Medical Imaging, 36,* 0001. https://doi.org/10.1109/TMI.2017.2708987.
29. Wang, Y., et al. (2018). 3D conditional generative adversarial networks for high-quality PET image estimation at low dose. *Neuroimage, 174,* 0001. https://doi.org/10.1016/j.neuroimage.2018.03.045.

30. Liao, H., Huo, Z., Sehnert, W. J., Zhou, S. K., & Luo, J. (2018). Adversarial sparse-view CBCT artifact reduction. In *Lecture notes in computer science (including subseries lecture notes in artificial intelligence and lecture notes in bioinformatics)*.
31. Quan, T. M., Nguyen-Duc, T., & Jeong, W. K. (2018). Compressed sensing mri reconstruction using a generative adversarial network with a cyclic Loss. In *IEEE* Transactions *on Medical Imaging*.
32. Mardani, M., et al. (2019). Deep generative adversarial neural networks for compressive sensing MRI. *IEEE Transactions on Medical Imaging, 38,* 0001. https://doi.org/10.1109/TMI.2018.2858752.
33. Kang, E., Koo, H. J., Yang, D. H., Seo, J. B., & Ye, J. C. (2019). Cycle-consistent adversarial denoising network for multiphase coronary CT angiography. *Med Phys*.
34. Oksuz, I. et al. (2018) Cardiac mr motion artefact correction from k-space using deep learning-based reconstruction. In *Lecture notes in computer science (including subseries lecture notes in artificial intelligence and lecture notes in bioinformatics)*.
35. Zhang, P., Wang, F., Xu, W., & Li, Y. (2018) Multi-channel generative adversarial network for parallel magnetic resonance image reconstruction in k-space. In *Lecture notes in computer science (including subseries lecture notes in artificial intelligence and lecture notes in bioinformatics)*. https://doi.org/10.1007/978-3-030-00928-1_21.
36. Armanious, K., Gatidis, S., Nikolaou, K., Yang, B., & Kustner, T. (2019). Retrospective correction of rigid and non-rigid mr motion artifacts using gans. In *Proceedings—International Symposium on Biomedical Imaging*, 2019. https://doi.org/10.1109/isbi.2019.8759509.
37. You, C., et al. (2018). Structurally-sensitive multi-scale deep neural network for low-dose CT denoising. *IEEE Access, 6,* 0001. https://doi.org/10.1109/ACCESS.2018.2858196.
38. Tang, T. et al. (2018). CT image enhancement using stacked generative adversarial networks and transfer learning for lesion segmentation improvement. In *Lecture notes in computer science (including subseries lecture notes in artificial intelligence and lecture notes in bioinformatics)*. https://doi.org/10.1007/978-3-030-00919-9_6.
39. You, C., et al. (2018) CT Super-resolution GAN constrained by the identical, residual, and cycle learning ensemble(GAN-CIRCLE). *IEEE Transactions on Computational Imaging*.
40. Liu, Z., Bicer, T., Kettimuthu, R., Gursoy, D., De Carlo, F., & Foster, I. (2020). TomoGAN: low-dose synchrotron x-ray tomography with generative adversarial networks: Discussion. *Journal of the Optical Society of America A. Optics and Image Science, 37,* 442. https://doi.org/10.1364/josaa.375595.
41. Chuquicusma, M. J. M., Hussein, S., Burt, J., & Bagci, U. (2018). How to fool radiologists with generative adversarial networks? A visual turing test for lung cancer diagnosis. In *Proceedings—International Symposium on Biomedical Imaging*.
42. Frid-Adar, M., Diamant, I., Klang, E., Amitai, M., Goldberger, J., & Greenspan, H. (2018). GAN-based synthetic medical image augmentation for increased CNN performance in liver lesion classification. *Neurocomputing, 321,* 321–331. https://doi.org/10.1016/j.neucom.2018.09.013.
43. Beers, A., et al. (2018). *High-resolution medical image synthesis using progressively grown generative adversarial networks*, 2018, [Online]. Available: http://arxiv.org/abs/1805.03144.
44. Bowles, C., et al. (2018). *GAN augmentation: augmenting training data using generative adversarial networks*, 2018, [Online]. Available: http://arxiv.org/abs/1810.10863.
45. Zhang, L., Gooya, A., & Frangi, A. F. (2017). Semi-supervised assessment of incomplete LV coverage in cardiac MRI using generative adversarial nets. In *Lecture notes in computer science (including subseries lecture notes in artificial intelligence and lecture notes in bioinformatics)*, https://doi.org/10.1007/978-3-319-68127-6_7.
46. Calimeri, F., Marzullo, A., Stamile, C., & Terracina, G. (2017). Biomedical data augmentation using generative adversarial neural networks. *Lecture Notes in Computer Science (including* subseries *Lecture Notes in Artificial Intelligence and Lecture Notes in Bioinformatics*), vol. 10614, LNCS, no. 690974, pp. 626–634, https://doi.org/10.1007/978-3-319-68612-7_71.
47. Mondal, A. K., Dolz, J., & Desrosiers, C. (2018). Few-shot 3D multi-modal medical image segmentation using generative adversarial learning (pp. 1–10), 2018, [Online]. Available: http://arxiv.org/abs/1810.12241.

48. Plassard, A. J., Davis, L. T., Newton, A. T., Resnick, S. M., Landman, B. A., & Bermudez, C. (2018). *Learning implicit brain MRI manifolds with deep learning* (p. 56).
49. Salehinejad, H., Valaee, S., Dowdell, T., Colak, E., & Barfett, J. (2018). Generalization of deep neural networks for chest pathology classification in x-rays using generative adversarial networks. In *ICASSP, IEEE International Conference on Acoustics, Speech and Signal Processing—Proceedings*, (vol. 2018-April, pp. 990–994).
50. Madani, A., Moradi, M., Karargyris, A., & Syeda-mahmood, T. (2018). *Semi-supervised learning with generative adversarial networks for chest x-ray classification with ability of data domain adaptation.* no. Isbi, pp. 1038–1042.
51. Lahiri, A., Jain, V., Mondal, A., Biswas, P. K., & Member, S. *Retinal vessel segmentation under extreme low annotation : a generative adversarial network approach* (pp. 1–9).
52. Baur, C., & Navab, N. *MelanoGANs : High resolution skin lesion synthesis with GANs.*
53. Jin, D., Xu, Z., Tang, Y., Harrison, A. P., & Mollura, D. J. (2018). CT-realistic lung nodule simulation from 3D conditional generative adversarial networks for robust lung segmentation. In *Lecture notes in computer science (including subseries lecture notes in artificial intelligence and lecture notes in bioinformatics).* https://doi.org/10.1007/978-3-030-00934-2_81.
54. Mok, T. C. W., & Chung, A. C. S. (2019). Learning data augmentation for brain tumor segmentation with coarse-to-fine generative adversarial networks. In *Lecture notes in computer science (including subseries lecture notes in artificial intelligence and lecture notes in bioinformatics).* https://doi.org/10.1007/978-3-030-11723-8_7.
55. Gu, X., Knutsson, H., Nilsson, M., & Eklund, A. (2019). Generating diffusion MRI scalar maps from T1 weighted images using generative adversarial networks. In *Lecture notes in computer science (including subseries lecture notes in artificial intelligence and lecture notes in bioinformatics).* https://doi.org/10.1007/978-3-030-20205-7_40.
56. Lau, F., Hendriks, T., Lieman-sifry, J., & Sall, S. (2017). ScarGAN: chained generative adversarial networks to simulate pathological tissue on cardiovascular MR scans. In *Deep learning in* medical *image analysis and multimodal learning for clinical decision support.* https://doi.org/10.1007/978-3-319-67558-9.
57. Shin H. C., et al. (2018). Medical image synthesis for data augmentation and anonymization using generative adversarial networks. In *Lecture notes in computer science (including subseries lecture notes in artificial intelligence and lecture notes in bioinformatics).*
58. Tom, F., & Sheet, D. (2018). Simulating patho-realistic ultrasound images using deep generative networks with adversarial learning. In *Proceedings–International Symposium on Biomedical Imaging*, 2018. https://doi.org/10.1109/isbi.2018.8363780.
59. Zhao, H., Li, H., Maurer-Stroh, S., & Cheng, L. (2018). Synthesizing retinal and neuronal images with generative adversarial nets. *Medical Image Analysis, 49,* 14–26. https://doi.org/10.1016/j.media.2018.07.001.
60. Iqbal, T., & Ali, H. (2018). Generative adversarial network for medical images (MI-GAN). *Journal of Medical Systems, 49,* 14–26. https://doi.org/10.1007/s10916-018-1072-9.
61. Mahapatra, D., Bozorgtabar, B., Thiran, J. P., & Reyes, M. (2018). Efficient active learning for image classification and segmentation using a sample selection and conditional generative adversarial network. In *Lecture notes in computer science (including subseries lecture notes in artificial intelligence and lecture notes in bioinformatics).*
62. Chartsias, A., Joyce, T., Dharmakumar, R., & Tsaftaris, S. A. (2017) Adversarial image synthesis for unpaired multi-modal cardiac data. In *Lecture notes in computer science (including subseries lecture notes in artificial intelligence and lecture notes in bioinformatics).*
63. Wolterink, J. M., Dinkla, A. M., Savenije, M. H. F., Seevinck, P. R., van den Berg, C. A. T., & Išgum, I. (2017). Deep MR to CT synthesis using unpaired data. In *Lecture notes in computer science (including subseries lecture notes in artificial intelligence and lecture notes in bioinformatics).* https://doi.org/10.1007/978-3-319-68127-6_2.
64. Emami, H., Dong, M., Nejad-Davarani, S. P., & Glide-Hurst, C. K. (2018). Generating synthetic CTs from magnetic resonance images using generative adversarial networks. *Medical Physics.*
65. Zhang, Z., Yang, L., & Zheng, Y. (2018). Translating and segmenting multimodal medical volumes with cycle- and shape-consistency generative adversarial network. In *Proceedings of the IEEE Computer Society Conference on Computer Vision and Pattern Recognition.*

66. Hiasa, Y., et al. (2018). Cross-modality image synthesis from unpaired data using cyclegan: Effects of gradient consistency loss and training data size. In *Lecture notes in computer science (including subseries lecture notes in artificial intelligence and lecture notes in bioinformatics)*. https://doi.org/10.1007/978-3-030-00536-8_4.
67. Maspero, M., et al. (2018). Dose evaluation of fast synthetic-CT generation using a generative adversarial network for general pelvis MR-only radiotherapy. *Physics in Medicine & Biology, 63,* 185001. https://doi.org/10.1088/1361-6560/aada6d.
68. Florkow M. C., et al. (2020) Deep learning–based MR-to-CT synthesis: The influence of varying gradient echo–based MR images as input channels. *Magnetic Resonance in Medicine.*
69. Jiang, J., et al. (2018). Tumor-aware, adversarial domain adaptation from CT to MRI for lung cancer segmentation. In *Lecture notes in computer science (including subseries lecture notes in artificial intelligence and lecture notes in bioinformatics).*
70. Bin Jin, C., et al. (2019) Deep CT to MR synthesis using paired and unpaired data. In *Sensors.* Switzerland.
71. Ben-Cohen, A., et al. (2019). Cross-modality synthesis from CT to PET using FCN and GAN networks for improved automated lesion detection. *Engineering Applications of Artificial Intelligence, 78,* 186–194. https://doi.org/10.1016/j.engappai.2018.11.013.
72. Armanious, K., et al. (2020). MedGAN: Medical image translation using GANs. *Computerized Medical Imaging and Graphics.*
73. Wei, W., et al. (2018) Learning myelin content in multiple sclerosis from multimodal MRI through adversarial training. In *Lecture notes in computer science (including subseries lecture notes in artificial intelligence and lecture notes in bioinformatics).* https://doi.org/10.1007/978-3-030-00931-1_59.
74. Pan, Y., Liu, M., Lian, C., Zhou, T., Xia, T., & Shen, D. (2018). Synthesizing missing PET from MRI with cycle-consistent generative adversarial networks for Alzheimer's disease diagnosis. In *Lecture notes in computer science (including subseries lecture notes in artificial intelligence and lecture notes in bioinformatics).* https://doi.org/10.1007/978-3-030-00931-1_52.
75. Choi, H., & Lee, D. S. (2018). Generation of structural MR images from amyloid PET: Application to MR-less quantification. *Journal of Nuclear Medicine, 59,* 0001. https://doi.org/10.2967/jnumed.117.199414.
76. Yi, X., Walia, E., & Babyn, P. (2019). Generative adversarial network in medical imaging: A review. *Medical Image Analysis, 58.* https://doi.org/10.1016/j.media.2019.101552.
77. Cohen, J. P., Luck, M., & Honari, S. (2018). Distribution matching losses can hallucinate features in medical image translation. In *Lecture notes in computer science (including subseries lecture notes in artificial intelligence and lecture notes in bioinformatics).* https://doi.org/10.1007/978-3-030-00928-1_60.
78. Mirsky, Y., Mahler, T., Shelef, I., & Elovici, Y. (2019) CT-GAN: Malicious tampering of 3D medical imagery using deep learning. In *Proceedings of the 28th USENIX Security Symposium.*

Comparative Analysis of Various Deep Learning Algorithms for Diabetic Retinopathy Images

Neha Mule, Anuradha Thakare, and Archana Kadam

Abstract Diabetic retinopathy is a disorder in which neurons and blood vessels of the retina rupture due to diabetes mellitus. The 33% of patients suffering from diabetes have signs of diabetic retinopathy. Diabetic retinopathy leads to blurred vision and blindness, if not cured at early stage. Deep learning is a technique which makes the computer to learn filter inputs through the layers and predicts or classifies the data. Medical imaging is a technique which shows interior structure of a body. In this research, we used diabetic retinopathy dataset from kaggle. The deep convolutional neural networks classify the input image set. For the experimentation, the Dense Net, ResNet 50, and VGG16 architectures are preferred along with the implementation of image processing techniques like resizing, cropping, Gaussian blur method, feature extraction, etc. The result represents that VGG16 performed better with 77.49% accuracy compared to DenseNet and ResNet 50 for the detection of diabetic retinopathy.

Keywords Diabetic retinopathy · Image processing methods · Convolutional neural network · ResNet 50 · Dense net and VGG 16

1 Introduction

Diabetic retinopathy is a disorder of diabetes, in which blood vessels presence in retina ruptures. New blood vessels which enter in retina bleeds, clouds the vision, and destroy the retina. The effect of diabetic retinopathy disease is represented in Fig. 1.

N. Mule · A. Thakare · A. Kadam (✉)
Pimpri- Chinchwad College of Engineering, Savitribai Phule Pune University, Pune, India
e-mail: archana.kadam@pccoepune.org

N. Mule
e-mail: neha.Mule@pccoepune.org

A. Thakare
e-mail: anuradha.thakare@pccoepune.org

R. Patgiri et al. (eds.), *Health Informatics: A Computational Perspective in Healthcare*,
Studies in Computational Intelligence 932,
https://doi.org/10.1007/978-981-15-9735-0_6

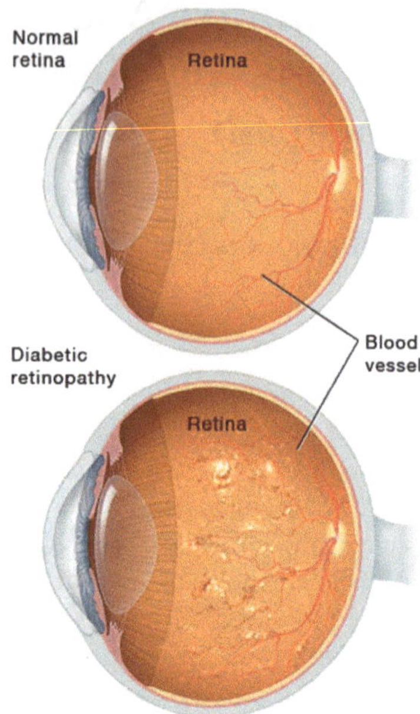

Fig. 1 Normal retina and infected retina [9]

In order to protect the eye from blurred vision, disease should be cured with proper treatment at mild stage. There is high risk of diabetic retinopathy disease, if person with diabetes have high blood pressure and smoking problem. Diabetic retinopathy is classified in two types [15]; No proliferative diabetic retinopathy (NPDR) and proliferative diabetic retinopathy (PDR).

No proliferative diabetic retinopathy is symptomless stage which shows cotton wool spots in the retina and can be easily cured. Detection of no proliferative DR is done by fundus photography. Non-proliferative diabetic retinopathy includes three types: Mild, moderate, and severe diabetic retinopathy. Mild diabetic retinopathy is a stage in which blood vessels ruptures called as micro aneurysms. In moderate diabetic retinopathy, blood vessels which give nourishment to retina are blocked. Severe diabetic retinopathy is a stage which is more complicated stage of NPDR. Proliferative diabetic retinopathy (PDR) is complicated stage which destroys vision. It generates new abnormal blood vessels in retina, which can burst the retina and bleeds. PDR can be cured by laser treatment in some cases. Figure 1 represents the stage where diabetic retinopathy disease blood vessels in retina ruptures, bleeds, and destroys due to presence of diabetes mellitus.

2 Related Work

Convolutional neural network [1] has shown great performance in image analysis. Block-based architecture is simple used to increase performance of CNN. Multiple feature extraction stages in CNN help to learn representations of data. CNN with approximate functions on the unit sphere with sobolev and Euclidean space is used for theoretical conclusions of neural network [2]. Spherical analysis with factorization filters is use to show the generated linear features. Deep MIL method [3], extraction of image patches fed to CNN to obtain probabilities, and combination of these extracted patches into DR map using global aggregation in single-scale framework. In multiple-scale framework, image transformation with multiple scales and DR map estimated.

Image augmentation transformations like, mirroring, inclining, brightness, contrast, sharpness and rotation with Ad boost algorithm used to form integrated model [4] using Inception V3, Resnet152, and Inception-Resnet-V2. Ensemble learning with algorithm used to decrease bias of integrated model. Data Augmentation methods like flipping and sampling are used to increase the prediction. An ensemble (Stacking) model formed by combining results from five CNN models [5] such as Xception, Inceptionv3, Dense169, Xception, ResNet 50, Dense121 to decrease variance and bias with was proposed. The results show that ensemble model performs better than traditional methods.

Image processing, augmentation techniques, and CNN model Siamese like Structure [6] accept left and right eye as inputs and transmits into a Siamese blocks. To gather features of binocular fund us images of and to predict each eye.

Used to compare correlation between images. First module includes feed forward neural network with deep neural network performance on unprocessed images. In second module, grayscale, feature extraction methods applied on images with (FNN) and (DNN) [7]. Third module includes CNN performance on grayscale-extracted images. By comparative analysis conclude that DNN performs better. Convolutional neural networks have the potential to be trained to identify the features of diabetic retinopathy in fundus images [8]. CNN able to learn the features required to classify the fundus images, accurately classifying the majority of proliferative cases and cases with no DR.

To reduce the rates of blindness caused by diabetic retinopathy retinal pathologies, blood vessels, macula, and optic disc should diagnosed at early stage to protect retinas from severe diabetic retinopathy disease [9].Optimization route with Gaussian blur methods [10] to visualize and extract meaningful information from the images filter by increasing activations neurons with Alex Net, VGGNet, and Google Net architectures. Neural network trained with large number of parameters, to calculate grading (presence of macular edema) of each image in the EyePACS-1 and Messidor-2 dataset [11]. Grade received from function compared with known grade from dataset and parameters changed according to comparison.

Supervised segmentation technique for blood vessels is infected by diabetic retinopathy [12] deep neural network train using processed global contrast normalization, 0-phase whitening with image augmentation transformations and gamma corrections.

An ensemble-based framework [13] is proposed by combining internal components of micro-aneurysm detectors with preprocessing methods like gray-scale imaging, extrapolation of missing part from images, and extractors which is useful for retinopathy grading. Messidor-2 reference standard [14] for trained diabetic retinopathy fundus images created 2 levels of diabetic retinopathy as vision threatening diabetic retinopathy and retinopathy with macular edema.

Data augmentation with preprocessing, scaling, and noise removal techniques applied on data which developed by EyePacs [15] initialization of weights, regulization on parameters in convolutional neural network to increase the accuracy.

3 Convolutional Neural Networks (CNN) and Architectures

Deep learning is a technique in which it makes computer learn filter inputs through layers to predict and classify the data. Convolutional neural network [11] has weights that learn from input and biases. Each neuron which is connected in network receives an input and performs a dot product and proceeds nonlinear fashion. It gives singular differentiable score function at the end called as sigmoid function. Function consists of scores which is output of various layers of neural network. To evaluate performance of CNN loss function is used. Convolutional layer performs complex computations. Kernels are convoluted into input matrix; number of filters which are used in input matrix determines depth of the output layer.

Activation layer applies the rectified linear unit (ReLU) function to increase nonlinearity, because usually, images are not linear to each other. Pooling layer is applied through every layer in 3D volume. Function of pooling layer is to reduce parameters and computation in convolutional neural network. Pooling layer performs on each feature map of convolutional neural network. Fully connected layer, there is transformation between pooled matrix into a single column and then it feed to network for classification. Using fully connected layers, features are combined together to create a model. At the end, we get sigmoid function to classify the output.

As shown in Fig. 2, at first, convolution layer performs computations on input. Sub-sampling layer is used to reduce the number of parameters and computations on

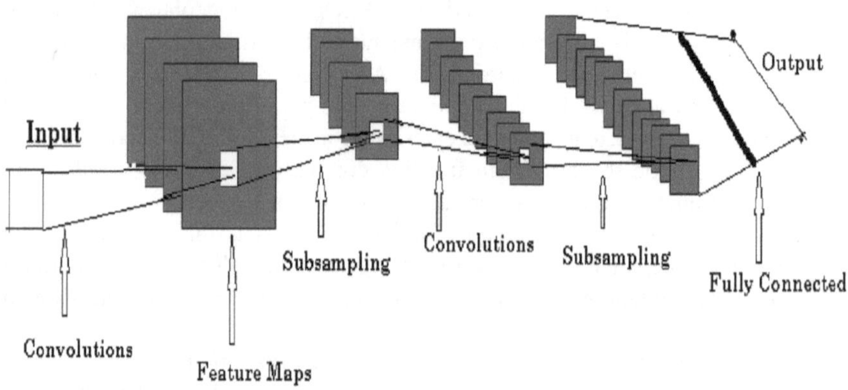

Fig. 2 Working of CNN

feature maps. At the end, features are combined to get the model, sigmoid function to classify the output using fully connected layer [8].

3.1 ResNet 50 Architecture

In ResNet, input with a state passed from one Res Net module to another module includes skip connections. Normally, stacking of convolution layers one after the other is done. Using skip connections of resnet, output of convolution block receives with better performance. Layers which contain nonlinearities, i.e., ReLU are skipped in Resnet model as shown in Figs. 3 and 4, respectively.

Fig. 3 ReLU function

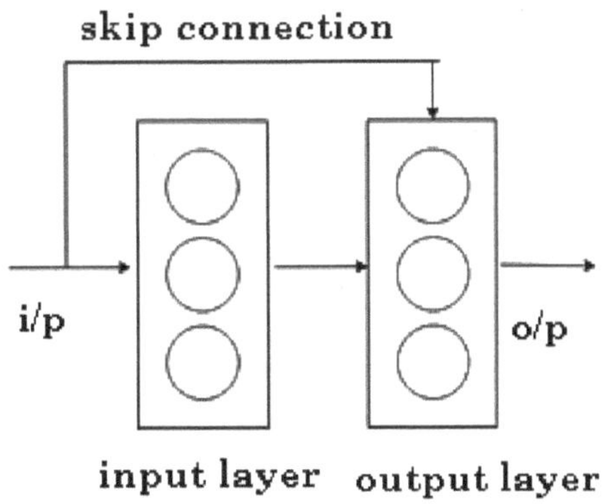

Fig. 4 ResNet model (skip connections)

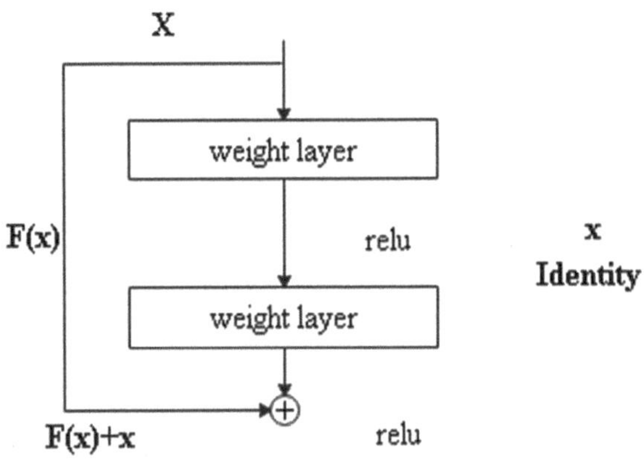

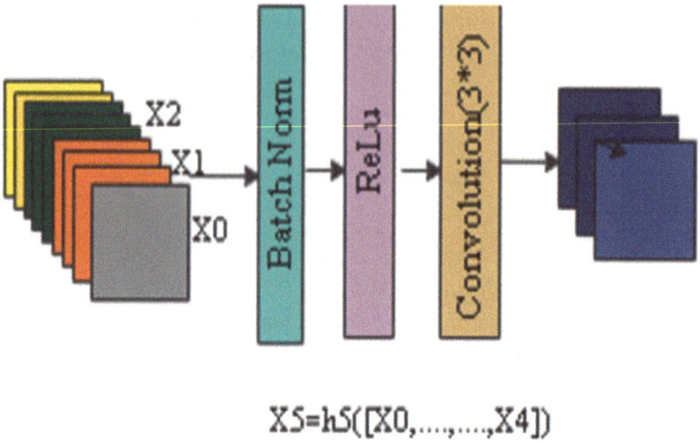

Fig. 5 Dense net model

3.2 Dense Net Architecture

As shown in Fig. 5, Dense Net architecture includes feed forward fashion way which connects every layer to every another layer. Each layer in dens net model receives feature maps from all preceding layers, due to feature maps densenet network becomes thin and compact, i.e., number of channels decreases and growth rate k of channels increases for each layer. Each layer in dense net receives collection of knowledge obtained from all preceding layers. Dense net architecture have higher computational and memory efficiency and also encourages reuse and propagation of features, reduces the number of parameters.

$L(L + 1)/2$ direct connections having a dense net, each layer receives feature maps as input from preceding layer, for all subsequent layers each layer's feature map used as input. Therefore, there is no requirement to relearn feature maps in dense net, each layer reads the state as an input from its preceding layer and writes to subsequent layer [1].

3.3 VGG 16 (Virtual Geometry Group) Architecture [10]

VGG16 is excellent vision model as compared to other models. It contains convolution layers of 3 × 3 filters and 1 stride and maxpool layer of 2 × 2 filter of stride 2 with same padding as shown in Fig. 6. Vgg 16 have 2 (fully connected layers) with softmax at the end in architecture. VGG16 has 16 layers that contain weights, and is a network with 138 million (approx) parameters.

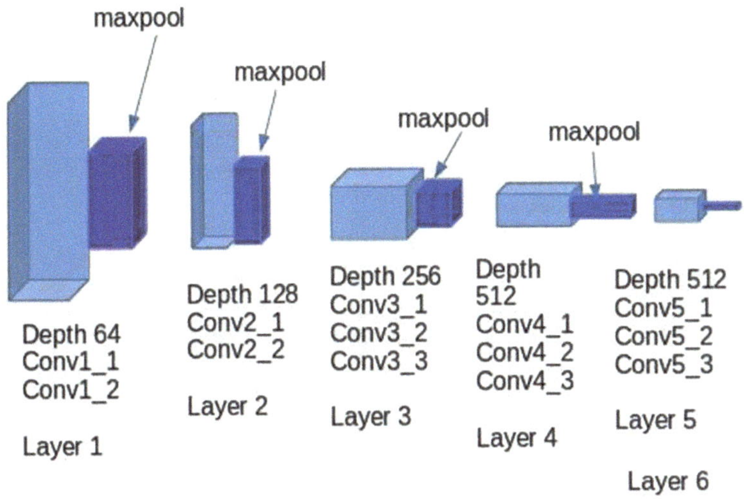

Fig. 6 VGG 16 architecture

4 Comparative Analysis of Deep Learning Algorithms for Detection of Diabetic Retinopathy

In proposed model, following image processing and data augmentation techniques are used [14].

(i) Reading an Image: To process the image, images are converted into arrays consist of pixel values. Depending on the RGB color scale, each image represents the pixel values.
(ii) Cropping: Cropping of images is very important to make images more clear and easy to understand. In cropping, unnecessary parts of images are cropped. If there are number of images, then cropping technique is difficult, important part of images can also be missed. If images are represented using arrays, then cropping of images will become easy. We cropped images from the dataset which contain black space.
(iii) Resizing: Deep learning architectures works good, if all the images are in same dimensions/(Pixel values). Dataset contains images which are of very large size, so these images are resized with same dimensions as (224, 224, 3).
(iv) Feature extraction method: Feature extraction is method of image processing which is related to dimensionality reduction. When there is big data to be processed, then features are reduced from the dataset. It will increase the accuracy and prediction.

Figure 7 represents system architecture of model developed. Input dataset of retinopathy images is divided in training and testing. After applying image processing techniques, input is given to convolution neural network techniques. ResNet50, DenseNetn and VGG16 applied on input dataset and finally output is analyzed.

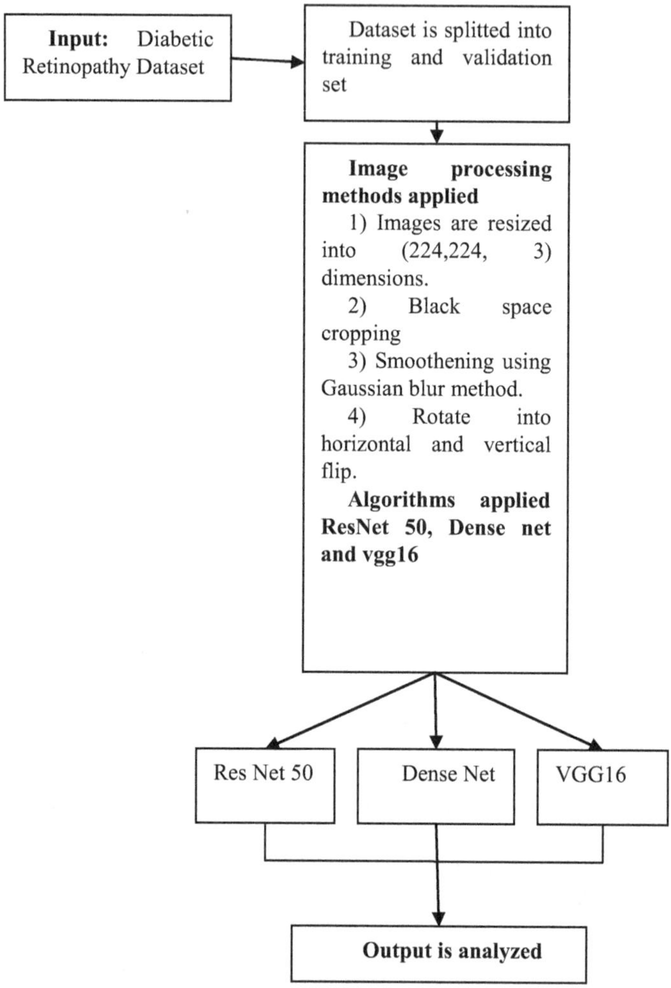

Fig. 7 System architecture

4.1 Dataset

The image dataset is taken from kaggle which includes 35,125 images with left and right eye retina images. The images are with dimensions 1024×1024. These images are resized and cropped using crop function, another file which is trainLabels.csv contains labels and levels of diabetic retinopathy. The images description is given in Table 1, with normal, mild, moderate, severe, and proliferative diabetic retinopathy, respectively.

Table 1 Dataset: distribution of DR

Diabetic retinopathy (DR) stages	Label	Number of images
Normal	0	25,810 images
Mild DR	1	2443 images
Moderate DR	2	5292 images
Severe DR	3	873 images
Proliferative DR	4	708 images

Table 2 Comparative analysis

Sr. No.	CNN architectures	Accuracy (%)
01	Res Net 50	73.82
02	Dense Net	73.10
03	VGG 16	77.49

4.2 Comparative Analysis and Evaluation

In this work, we compare different neural networks on diabetic retinopathy dataset which is used from kaggle. Dataset contains 35,126 images with left and right eye retina images. Images include mild, moderate, severe, proliferative and No DR images. Dataset is splitted into train and validation set using sklearn model. Some of images include black space which obstructs to identify the center and radius of the circle of the fund us image. These images are cropped, by applying threshold to the images and are resized into (224, 224, and 3) dimensions for further analysis. We used Gaussian blur technique for smoothening of images.

Using rotation technique, images are rotate into horizontal and vertical flip. We applied convolutional neural network with three models such as ResNet 50, Dense Net, and VGG 16, with 20 epochs for each. Result concludes that VGG16 gives better performance as compared to other models of neural networks. Table 2 shows VGG 16 gives better accuracy as compared to Dense net and Resnet 50.

5 Conclusion

Diabetic retinopathy is a disease which leads to blurred vision and blindness if it is not cured at early stage. In this paper, the comparative analysis of deep learning approaches for detection of diabetic retinopathy from input images is presented. The convolutional neural network with ResNet 50, DenseNet, and VGG 16 architectures is used to detect diabetic retinopathy. Image processing techniques made the images more understandable for the proposed work. All images from the dataset are represented as arrays to process the image with cropping, resizing, Gaussian blur, and feature extraction techniques. The result shows that the convolutional neural network with VGG16 performs better with accuracy 77.49% as compared to ResNet

50 and Dense Net. In further work, accuracy can be increased by applying more image processing methods.

References

1. Khan, A., et al. (2019). *A survey of the recent architectures of deep convolutional neural networks*. arXiv:1901.06032.
2. Fang, Z., Feng, H., Huang, S., & Zhoua, D.-H. Theory of deep convolutional neural networks II: Spherical analysis. *Neural Networks*.
3. Zhou, L., et al. (2017). Deep multiple instance learning for automatic detection of diabetic retinopathy in retinal images. *IET Image Process., 12*(4), 563–571.
4. Hong, Y. J., et al. (2019). An interpretable ensemble deep learning model for diabetic retinopathy disease classification. *IEEE Access*.
5. Qummar, S., Khan, F.G., Shah, S., Khan, A., Shamshirband, S., Rehman, Z. U., et al. A deep learning ensemble approach for diabetic retinopathy detection. *IEEE Access, 7*, 150530–150539.
6. Zeng, X., Chen, H., Luo, Y., & Ye, W. (2019). Automated diabetic retinopathy detection based on binocular siamese-like convolutional neural network. *IEEE Access, 7,* 30744–30753.
7. Dutta, S., Manideep, B., Basha, S., Caytiles, D., & Iyenagar, N. (2018). Classification of diabetic retinopathy images by using deep learning models. *International Journal of Grid and Distributed Computing, Springer, 11*(1), 89–106.
8. Pratt, H., Coenen, F., Broadbent, D. M., Harding, S. P., & Zheng, Y. (2016). Convolutional neural networks for diabetic retinopathy. *Procedia Computer Science, 90,* 200–205.
9. Utku, K., Omer, D., Jafar, A., & Bogdan, P. Diagnosing diabetic retinopathy by using a blood vessel extraction technique and a convolutional neural network. *Deep learning for medical decision support systems*, (pp. 53–72).
10. Feng, W., Liu, H., & Cheng, J. (2018). Visualizing deep neural network by alternately image blurring and deblurring. *Neural Networks.*
11. Gulshan, V., et al. (2016). Development and validation of a deep learning algorithm for detection of diabetic retinopathy in retinal fundus photographs. *JAMA, 316*(22), 2402–2410.
12. Liskowski, P., & Krawiec, K. (2016). Segmenting retinal blood vessels with deep neural networks. *IEEE Transactions on Medical Imaging, 35*(11), 2369–2380.
13. Antal, B., & Hajdu, A. (2012). An ensemble-based system for microaneurysm detection and diabetic retinopathy grading. *IEEE Transactions on Biomedical Engineering, 59*(6), 1720–1726.
14. Abràmoff, M. D., Lou, Y., Erginay, A., Clarida, W., Amelon, R., Folk, J. C., & Niemeijer, M. (2016). Improved automated detection of diabetic retinopathy on a publicly available dataset through integration of deep learning. *Investigative Ophthalmology & Visual Science, 57*(13), 5200–5206.
15. Ghosh, R., Ghosh, K., & Maitra, S. (2017). Automatic detection and classification of diabetic retinopathy stages using CNN. In: *4th International Conference on Signal Processing and Integrated Networks (SPIN)*, (pp. 550–554).

Software Design Specification and Analysis of Insulin Dose to Adaptive Carbohydrate Algorithm for Type 1 Diabetic Patients

Ishaya Gambo, Rhodes Massenon, Terungwa Simon Yange, Rhoda Ikono, Theresa Omodunbi, and Kolawole Babatope

Abstract Crucial in the development of a technological solution for managing insulin-dependent patients is an appropriate method of software engineering (SE) process. The SE process aims at providing supports for the design and implementation of a high-quality system by engaging patients and other healthcare professionals in knowing the exact specification for development. Primarily, insulin-dependent patients have a big challenge in determining the right dose of insulin to be injected according to measurements of glucose level and estimated carbohydrate from food intake. The result of this is often hypoglycaemia and hyperglycaemia, which may lead to coma and cause unfortunate death. The objective of this research work is to develop an adaptive model dedicated to the adjustment of insulin dose requirements in patients with type 1 diabetes. A mathematical model is formulated based on insulin sensitivity, basal insulin, bolus insulin, correction factor, carbohydrate counts, bolus on board equations and continuous blood glucose levels. We have evaluated the model by using root-mean-square error (RMSE) and mean absolute error (MAE) as parameters. The results showed the correct insulin dose values within the range of 4.76–0.18 IU for the fifty-two (52) patients with T1DM. Consequently, the developed model suggests a reduction in the incidence of hypoglycaemia, which can be used to predict the next insulin dose.

I. Gambo
Institute of Computer Science, University of Tartu, Tartu, Estonia

I. Gambo (✉) · R. Massenon · R. Ikono · T. Omodunbi
Department of Computer Science and Engineering, Obafemi Awolowo University, Ile-Ife, Nigeria
e-mail: ishaya.gambo@ut.ee

T. S. Yange
Department of Mathematics, Statistics and Computer Science, Federal University of Agriculture, Makurdi, Nigeria

K. Babatope
Department of Medicine, Faculty of Clinical Sciences, Obafemi Awolowo University, Ile-Ife, Nigeria

R. Patgiri et al. (eds.), *Health Informatics: A Computational Perspective in Healthcare*, Studies in Computational Intelligence 932,
https://doi.org/10.1007/978-981-15-9735-0_7

Keywords Type 1 diabetes · Insulin pump · Artificial pancreas · Carbohydrate counting · Algorithm · Design specification

1 Introduction

If the impact of technology is to be as successful as it can be, the healthcare domain needs to embrace its use effectively. In particular, the continuous application of technological solutions (processes and products) in the management of chronic diseases, like type 1 diabetes mellitus (T1DM), can improve the quality of healthcare delivery. Rather than the operational manual procedures of managing insulin-dependent diabetes patients, suitable technology can be developed to adapt to the procedures in reducing the incidence of hypoglycaemia.

Crucial in the development of the technological solution for managing insulin-dependent patients is an appropriate method of software engineering (SE) process. The SE process in this context aims at providing supports for engineering a solution of high quality by engaging patients and other healthcare professionals in knowing the exact specification for an improved solution to control diabetes mellitus. The SE process is of utmost importance to understand the treatment procedures and to achieve an adaptable solution.

For a long time, the control of diabetes mellitus has been experienced by numerous means. The prevalence is proliferating for several reasons: social factors, environmental factors, obesity and eating habits. These reasons contribute to an increase in the number of cases of diabetes. For all these reasons, diabetes mellitus represents a public health problem [1]. Scientists stated that a nutritional factor during childhood or adolescence causes the immune system to destroy pancreatic insulin-producing cells, mostly for patients with T1DM [2]. When the pancreatic production of insulin is reduced or absent, the blood glucose level can be higher than the hyperglycaemic limit [3]. To compensate for the loss of insulin production, the treatment of this disease, for the patient, requires a dose of insulin to be injected according to measurements of his glycemia and of specific characteristics, intervening in the regulation of meal, physical activity or stress.

The ideal treatment aims at optimal glycaemic control in order to reduce the risks of long-term complications of diabetes (retinopathy, nephropathy, neuropathy and probably macro-vascular complications) linked to hyperglycaemia, while minimizing the risk of complications in the short term: an acute term, especially the risk of hypoglycaemia [4]. The risk of hypoglycaemia, which can lead to confusion, loss of consciousness and even death, is the main barrier to reaching target blood sugar levels [5]. The automation of this treatment would avoid certain errors specific to this type of regulation, such as a sparse estimation of action of insulin by the patient. Despite progress in available treatment options such as insulin analogues, insulin pens or insulin pumps, almost 75% of patients do not reach blood sugar targets while facing an average of three episodes of hypoglycaemia every week [5, 6].

At this stage, the most significant treatment is to keep up blood glucose in the typical range to avoid or interrupt long-term diabetes complexities in T1DM [7]. Blood glucose monitoring and injection of insulin doses are not adequate to control the variability of blood glucose in patients with T1DM. Some scientists have investigated that the use of dietary management can play a vital role in food intake and can be associated with the management and control of blood glucose. Dietary management has been introduced as an educational recommendation tool since the 1920s, helping patients with diabetes to get knowledge of food nutrients [8]. The essential nutrient that can raise blood glucose is carbohydrate. This nutrient is seen as an essential supplement influencing postprandial glycaemia reaction. It is also one of the primary nutrients found in food and drinks. The goal of carbohydrate counting in managing type 1 diabetes is to match insulin dose to food intake in order to allow flexibility in food choices without compromising metabolic control and health outcomes [9]. If the action of insulin is not proportional to the number of carbohydrates ingested, the blood glucose level will increase [10]. However, it is crucial to get knowledge of the type of Carbohydrate, other nutrients in food intake, the size of the portion and the amount of these nutrients, and time of consumption.

From a practical standpoint, the results of the Diabetes Control and Complications Trial (DCCT) showed that by adjusting insulin based on meal size and content, using planning strategy meals (including carbohydrate counting, trading system, weighing and measuring food, and estimating portion size) in the intensive management group was associated with better glycemic control [11]. Patients with T1DM on intensive insulin therapy can adjust their mealtime insulin doses relative to food intake by using the concept of advanced counting [12]. By using this concept at each meal, the doses of insulin administered can be predicted to cover the amounts of carbohydrates present in these meals and keep the blood sugar level within normal limits [13, 14]. According to the American Diabetes Association (ADA) [15], current guidelines recommend that algorithms for calculating mealtime insulin should take into account the amount of carbohydrates in the meal to prevent chronic complications of diabetes such as hyperglycaemia.

Automating the adjustment of insulin dose would result in improved glycaemic control, as well as an improved quality of life by significantly reducing the burden on the patient [16]. The purpose of this research is to design a model dedicated to the dynamic adjustment (in real time) of the administration of insulin according to blood sugar levels in order to maintain them in the target values.

Our work is organized as follows: The second section provides reviews of the related works. After that, in Sect. 3, methodologies covered by this research and the insulin dose to carbohydrate determination protocol are discussed in light of the mathematical equations, the design specifications of our analysis. The fourth section reports on the system implementation that validates the accuracy of the model formulated. The empirical analysis is presented in the fifth section. Next is the results and discussion in the sixth section, followed by a conclusion and future work in the seventh section.

2 Related Prior Work

The treatment of T1DM is restrictive to numerous blood sugar measurements, frequent insulin injections and manual adjustment of insulin doses according to meals. The patient may, therefore, feel that the treatment is too demanding, which could lead to poor compliance: forgetting to inject insulin, poorly evaluated insulin dose, non-readjustment of insulin doses and unpredictable food intake [17]. However, a poor balance of diabetes leads to complications that shorten the lifespan of patients and multiply the cost of the disease [18]. Automation of treatment would respond to this problem [19]. In recent years, the availability of sensors for measuring glycemia (CGM) and actuators such as insulin pumps makes it possible to envisage the implementation of a closed-loop solution. The development of adjustment insulin models is a new research axis within artificial pancreas technology [20, 21]. Some scholars have advised and developed a model for carbohydrate counting to match insulin dose to the carbohydrate content of the meal [22].

Wilinska et al. [23] have investigated insulin lispro kinetics with bolus and continuous subcutaneous insulin infusion (CSII) modes of insulin delivery. They proposed eleven alternative models of insulin kinetics. These models were validated through assessing physiological feasibility of parameter estimates, posterior identifiability and distribution of residuals [23]. The results show that 67% of delivered insulin passed through the slow absorption channel, with the remaining 33% that passed through the fast channel.

Ellingsen et al. [24] structured a predictive model with insulin on board (IOB) to control glycaemia by controlling exogenous insulin. MPC contained a dynamic requirement and IOB. The results showed that half of the simulations led without IOB brought hypoglycaemic, compared to 10% with IOB. Accomplishing both adequacy and safety in blood glucose control, IOB imperative can abrogate forceful control moves (huge amount of insulin dose), limiting the complications of hypoglycaemia, accordingly.

Murphy et al. [25] evaluated closed-loop insulin delivery with an MPC algorithm during early and late gestation in pregnant women with T1DM. They adjusted the basal insulin infusion rate before each insulin delivery as a safety precaution, and prandial insulin boluses were calculated according to the women's insulin–carbohydrate ratio and capillary fingerstick glucose concentrations [25]. The results showed that 84 and 100% of plasma glucose reach in the normal target during the overnight in early and late pregnancy, respectively. On the one hand, 7% of hyperglycaemia events have been detected in early pregnancy during an overnight, and on the other hand, hypoglycaemia has been detected even in early and late pregnancy. Although it was performed in women with T1DM during pregnancy, the algorithm was not fully automated. They manually adjusted the insulin rate based on the values given by the CGM, which were fed to the MPC algorithm.

Percival et al. [26] developed a multi-parametric model predictive control (mpMPC) algorithm that is computationally effective, robust to insulin variations and involves minimal burden for the user. The algorithm was developed and tested using three different modelling scenarios: an unannounced meal, a measured meal and an announced meal. They mixed two models—Hovorka et al. and UVa/Padova model. The results showed that in the Hovorka model, unannounced meals were found in low postprandial blood glucose, but announced meals reduced peak blood glucose. On the other hand, 30% of unannounced meals were detected; 30% of announced meals have helped to avoid hypoglycaemia in the UVa/Padova model. MpMPC has been shown to reduce the number of hypoglycaemic events. However, the research should focus on limiting postprandial blood glucose.

Campos-Delgado et al. [27] developed a self-tuning insulin adjustment algorithm for type I diabetic patients based on multi-doses regime. They used types of insulin: rapid (Lispro) and slow (NPH). The model was simulated using MATLAB/Simulink. Two simulation cases were considered: patient with high doses and with small doses for both types of insulin, in case 1. BG level was below 70 mg/dl during long periods, and the algorithms were able to decrease the insulin infusions properly. In the other case, the doses were low, and the BG level initially reached a high value of ≈220 mg/dl. It was observed that the tuning algorithm did not converge to the same insulin doses.

Bishop et al. [28] assessed the accuracy of carbohydrate counting in adolescents with T1DM who used insulin: carbohydrate (I: C) ratios for at least one meal per day. The consequences showed that only 23% of adolescents estimated carbohydrates from day to day to less than 10 grams of the actual amount despite the determination of frequent meals. For evening meals, patients with T1DM with a correct estimation of grams of carbohydrates had the lowest A1C values ($7.69 \pm 0.82\%$, $P = 0.04$). Adolescents with T1DM are no longer accurately counted. Meanwhile, they generally overestimate or underestimate the grams of carbohydrates in a given meal. The study used to be cross-sectional and focused on a single measure of the accuracy of counting carbohydrates and A1C, which can both be exchanged over time due to several important factors that affect blood sugar control, such as exercise and dietary factors.

Lee et al. [29] designed a synthetic closed-loop pancreas using MPC and a sliding meal measurement estimator. They developed a new-meal-size-estimation technique to provide realistic insulin bolus quantities based entirely on a collection of food impulses. The results showed that the integrated synthetic pancreas system gave daily glucose levels of 138 and 132 mg/dl for children and adults, respectively, which is a significant improvement, compared to the MPC case only, which generated 159 and 145 mg/dl. They no longer estimated the exact size of carbohydrates from meal to meal.

Dias et al. [30] evaluated the influence of diet intervention on glycaemic control. They used various short-acting insulins based on the carbohydrate counting approach on clinical and metabolic manipulations in patients with T1DM. The result showed a considerable improvement in glycaemic control in patients with T1DM without any change of body weight, regardless of the increase in supplementing of daily insulin doses. They concluded that it was possible to effectively use the carbohydrate counting approach in addition to home self-monitoring. Significant difficulties are linked to the fact that blood glucose monitoring was no longer carried out before.

Thus, the blood glucose level can reach hypoglycaemia, even when taking a bolus of carbohydrates.

Bell et al. [31] showed the effectiveness of carbohydrate counting in T1DM through glycated haemoglobin (HbA1c) and the random-effects model. They recommended carbohydrates counting compared to alternative advice in adults with T1DM to adjust the insulin dose of food intake. Other authors, similarly, Finner et al. [32], have given the expertise in carbohydrate counting and insulin dose calculations in paediatric patients with T1DM, by assessing a questionnaire called PedCarbQuiz (PCQ) to them. The mean total PCQ score (%) was higher in the continuous subcutaneous insulin infusion group (CSII) than in the daily multiple insulin injection groups (MDI).

Rhyner et al. [33] implemented a cellphone-based system designed to guide people with T1DM for the duration of each carbohydrate estimation during the day. However, carbohydrate content is calculated by combining the volume of each food with the food statistics provided by the USDA nutrient database for standard reference. The results showed that MAE was 23.52 grams of carbohydrates for the participant estimated. In comparison, the corresponding value for the system was 9.54 grams of carbohydrates, which represented a significantly higher overall performance (p = 0.001). In the database of 86 meals consumed by patients of 156 in total, computerized machine segmentation was profitable at 75.4%, and 85.1% of individual food items were effectively recognized.

Fu et al. [12] examined and analysed the effectiveness of advanced carbohydrate counting in T1DM. They found out that carbohydrate counting significantly reduced the concentration of HbA1c in the adult group when it was no longer in the children group. They suggested that future research should focus on discovering the effect of carbohydrate counting on hypoglycaemia events, insulin doses and BMI, using remarkably random experiments. The influence of carbohydrate counting on these components is a new direction in future research.

Reiterer et al. [34] analysed the effect of carb counting errors on glycaemic outcomes during basal–bolus therapy in a simulation study. The authors used so-called Deviation Analyses and Adaptive Bolus Calculator (ABC) algorithm. The results showed that systematic estimation biases in the carbohydrate counting hardly affect the results. As observed by Reiterer et al. [34], the same biases are usually implicitly accounted for in the therapy settings if carbohydrate to insulin ratio (CIR) and insulin sensitivity factor (ISF) are well adjusted. However, random carb counting inaccuracies, on the other hand, do lead to an inevitable deterioration of glycaemic control. Though, ACC is relatively robust towards this type of inaccuracies. They suggested the use of computer vision to estimate the carb content in meals based on a picture.

Oviedo et al. [35] used machine learning techniques to minimize postprandial hypoglycaemia in T1DM. Multiple insulin injections and capillary blood glucose self-monitoring were used in developing the prediction system. The system generated a bolus reduction suggestion as to the scaled weighted sum of the predictions. The results indicated that more than 40% reduction in postprandial events fell below 54 mg/dL hypoglycaemia. This method is an excellent candidate to be integrated with multiple daily insulins (MDI) injections therapies based on self-monitoring blood glucose (SMBG). However, the approach is limited in the case of hypoglycaemia when the blood glucose goes high.

Reiterer and Freckmann [36] developed a common approach to determine bolus insulin requirements in T1DM known as advanced carbohydrate counting (ACC). They discussed implicit assumptions and limitations of ACC from an engineering perspective. As a limitation, ACC has only been discussed as part of standard basal–bolus therapy but is limited to hybrid closed-loop systems.

Ziegler et al. [37] evaluated the accuracy of bolus and basal rate delivery of various available insulin pumps. The results showed that the accuracy of insulin delivery using very low doses is limited in most insulin pumps. It can be adapted for CSII therapy in children adjusting boluses and basal rate more than MDI.

In summary, we observed that insulin dose could not be expelled from the body once it had been injected before or after meal intake. Consequently, insulin absorption and insulin sensitivity can affect blood glucose regulation. The advanced method must be intended to consider insulin to carbohydrate ratio, carbohydrate bolus insulin and past blood glucose levels in the development of new operations and adaptive systems.

In the next section, we described the process of building the new insulin dose adjustment model automatically while estimating the carbohydrate counting from food intake. This point will condition the mathematical model and the algorithmic process. In order to show that this model can be used as a computerized model, we implemented a prototype of this model and carried out tests based on data from type 1 patients.

3 Methodology

In this paper, both qualitative and quantitative approach in case study research [38, 39] were used. Patients with T1DM and medical doctors at the at CNHU-HKM Hospital in Benin republic were the respondents that provided data for the study. We had a one-on-one interview with these patients, medical doctors and other concerned healthcare professionals to understand the treatment procedures. Additionally, we inspected the case file of patients to extract relevant information for further analysis. Moreover, a mathematical model was formulated to establish the framework for estimating carbohydrate count and level in food. We used the insulin requirements, past blood glucose level and physical activity level in formulating the model.

3.1 Design Specification of the Adaptive Insulin Dose Model

We began by noting that the insulin input injected by the pump does not have an instantaneous effect on blood sugar. Therefore, a real-time system of insulin dose seems necessary to compute the insulin used to lower blood glucose levels and the remaining insulin dose when the peak time occurs. Likewise, during the absorption of a meal, the carbohydrates ingested have an action on blood sugar only when they leave the intestine at the level of the portal vein. There is an initial phase of digestion than the transport of glucose to the organs and the liver. A comparison of actual blood glucose level with the estimated target range before digestion and after digestion, therefore, seems to be considered. It then remains to compute a correction bolus insulin model to adjust the variations of insulin requirements to carbohydrate metabolism and blood glucose control.

The diagram of our design concept is illustrated in Fig. 1. We have considered three conditions to model the adjustment of insulin to carbohydrate dose, such as:

i. actual blood glucose level higher than estimated maximum blood glucose target;
ii. actual blood glucose level less than estimated maximum blood glucose target, and
iii. actual blood glucose level within the normal target. Each condition is set up at each moment fasting, pre-prandial and postprandial time. In the next paragraph, we have made some assumptions about the problem encounter by a patient with T1DM.

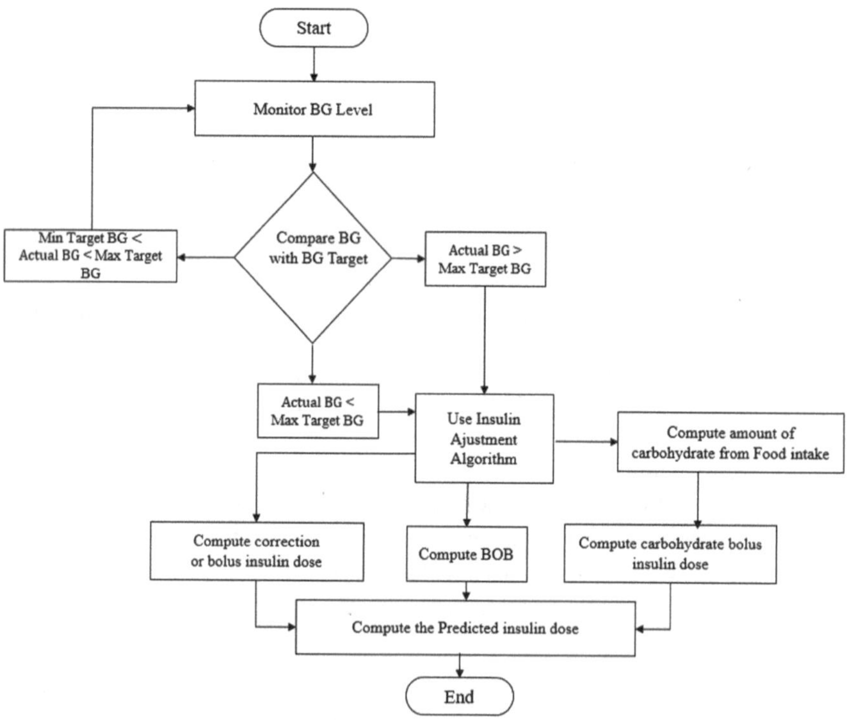

Fig. 1 Diagram of adaptive insulin dose to carbohydrate model

Assumptions: The adjustment of the insulin doses is made based on blood sugar measurement and the period considered:

- Measurement of blood glucose of postprandial time:
  i. it is less than 150 mg/l and more than 70 mg/l; the quantity of insulin injected is only the bolus suitable for the meal.
  ii. it is less than 70 mg/l; carbohydrates are ingested to raise the blood glucose, and the bolus adapted to the meal is made 15–30 min after the start of the meal, or at the end of the meal.
  iii. it is less than 70 mg/l; carbohydrates are ingested to raise the blood glucose, and the bolus adapted to the meal is made 15–30 min after the start of the meal, or at the end of the meal.
- Measurement of blood glucose to pre-prandial time:
  i. it is higher than 150 mg/l; a corrective bolus is effected.
  ii. it is less than 70 mg/l; carbohydrates are ingested.
  iii. it is less than 70 mg/l; carbohydrates are ingested.
- Measurement of blood glucose shortly after the meal:
  i. it is more significant than 150 mg/l; no action.
  ii. it is less than 70 mg/l; carbohydrates are ingested.

Furthermore, we used the UML tool to specify the design. In particular, Fig. 2 described the activity diagram for carbohydrate counting. The emphasis in Fig. 2 is on the treatment procedures that begins with food intake (the time and type). It ends with the computed net amount of carbohydrate intake. When the food type is entered into the system within a given time, the system checks if this food has a high glycaemic index in the prohibited food list prescribed by dietician. If the checking out is wrong, patients input the food serving size (cups or portions) and the amount of food nutrients (carbs, fibre or sugar) that have an impact on blood glucose, which contain carbohydrate using the nutritional fact panel of the food. The system computes the net amount of carbohydrate. It saves it into a database for determining the insulin dose required to cover this amount.

Additionally, Fig. 3 shows the activity diagram of the remaining insulin dose. The system will check if any type of insulin (basal, bolus or correction) dose has been registered or administered to the patient with T1DM. If yes, it will compute the difference timestamp and compare with the maximum duration time of insulin, which is 5 h. If the comparison shows that it is less than 5 h, it means that it remains some quantities of insulin dose working in the patient's body. So, the system will compute that remaining insulin dose and adjust the next insulin dose by subtracting or adding, which will not affect the next BG. In case of more or equals than 5 h, there is no remaining insulin dose.

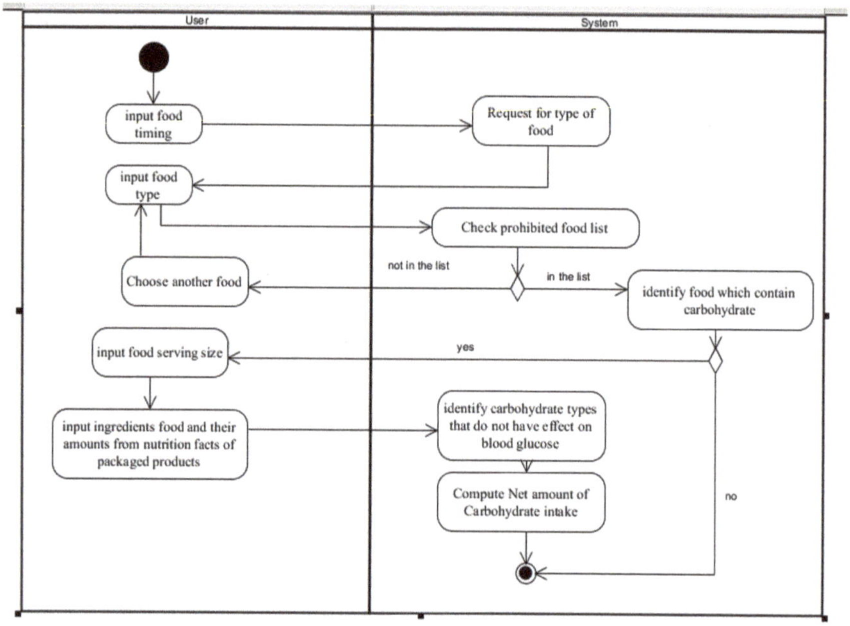

Fig. 2 Activity diagram of carbohydrate counting

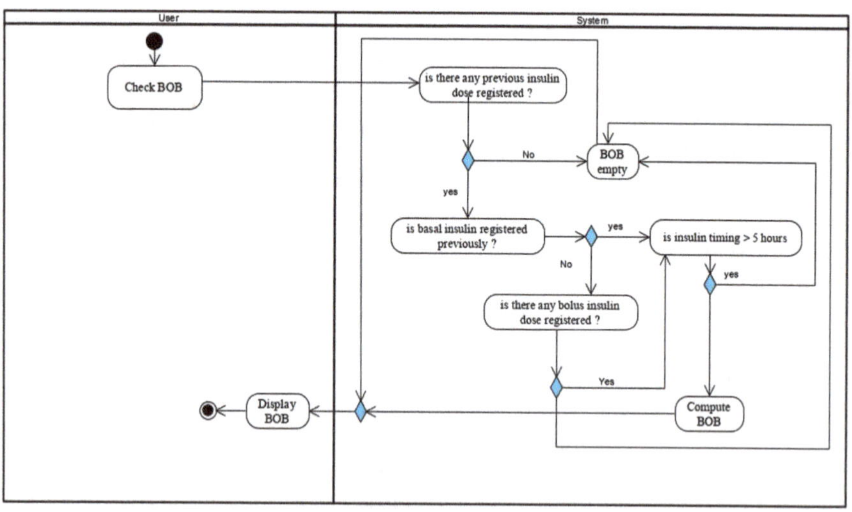

Fig. 3 Activity diagram of remaining insulin dose

3.2 Mathematical Model of Adaptive Insulin Dose to the Carbohydrate

The inputs considered for our model are noted U (unit/min) for insulin dose and grams (g) for the quantity of carbohydrates.

The correction insulin dose can be represented, as shown in Eq. (1).

$$I(t) = I_{\text{basal}} + \frac{t_1}{5} * I_{\text{actualbolus}} + \sum_{t=1}^{n} I_{\text{prevbolus}} * \left(1 - \frac{t_2}{5}\right) \tag{1}$$

The insulin dose to cover carbohydrate is as shown in Eq. (2)

$$\text{IC} = \frac{\text{Carb}}{\text{Carb}F} \tag{2}$$

So, to determine the adaptive insulin dose, we combine Eqs. (1) and (2) to get Eq. (3):

$$I(t) = I_{\text{basal}} + \frac{t_1}{5} * I_{\text{actualbolus}} + \sum_{t=1}^{n} I_{\text{prevbolus}} * \left(1 - \frac{t_2}{5}\right) + \frac{\text{Carb}}{\text{Carb}F} \tag{3}$$

3.3 Adaptive Insulin Dose to Carbohydrate Algorithms

The heart of this research lies within the computation of the right insulin dose from the remaining insulin dose; and the bolus insulin doses with time delay. Algorithm 1, 2, 3 and Table 1 show the process of computing the acting insulin dose, bolus insulin dose, insulin to carbohydrate and parameters, respectively.

Table 1 Parameters used in Eqs. (1)–(3) for the model

Parameters	Description	Units
$I_{\text{actualbolus}}$	Value of actual bolus insulin dose	U
$I_{\text{prevbolus}}$	Value of previous bolus insulin dose	U
I_{basal}	Value of basal insulin dose	U
$I\ (d, t)$	Value of basal insulin for date and moment	U
Carb$F$	Carb Factor	mmol/dl/IU
Carb	Net amount of carbohydrate	G
t_1	the time between the insulin dose injected and the prediction time	h

Algorithm: Remaining Insulin Dose Algorithm

Algorithm: Remaining Insulin Dose Algorithm
Constant:
Post-meal blood glucose target $G_1 = 70mg/dL$;
Pre-meal blood glucose target $G_2 = 150mg/dL$;

Input:
$G\ (d,\ t)$, $G\ (d\text{-}1.\ t)$, $G\ (d,\ t\text{-}1)$, $I_{basal}\ (d,\ t)$; $I_{basal}\ (d,\ t-1)$; $I_{basal}\ (d,\ t)$; $I_{basal}\ (d,\ t-1)$;
$I\ (d,\ t)$; $CorrF$, $CarbF$; $Carb$, IS;

Output:

The value of insulin dose in action, $I\ (d,\ t)$; action;

BEGIN
Calculate the remaining insulin dose from the previous insulin dose
for each $t \in [0.\ n]$ **do**
if (($t+1$ - $t_{prevbasal}$) <= 5 or ($t+1$ - $t_{prevbolus}$) <= 5 **then**
$I_{prevBOB} = (I_{basal}\ (d,\ t-1) + I_{bolus}\ (d,\ t-1)) * (1 - (t+1 - t_2) / 5)$
else
$I_{prevBOB} = 0\ U$
end if
end for
END

Algorithm 1: Remaining Insulin Dose
Algorithm: Bolus Insulin Dose Algorithm

```
BEGIN
 Calculate the bolus insulin dose
  if (t = fasting time or postprandial time) then
    if (G (d, t) > G1) then
         Ibolus = (G (d, t) - G1) / IS
  else
              if (G (d, t) >= G1) && (G (d, t) =< G2) then
                 if (previous_meal_register==true) then
                 Ibolus =0 U
                 else
                 Ibolus = IC (d, t)
                 endif
            else
           action=''Patient eat''
           Ibolus = IC (d, t)
       end if
   else if (t = pre-prandial time or prandial time) then
     if (G (d, t) > G2) then
          Ibolus = (G (d, t) - G1) / IS
     else
       if (previous_meal_register==true && time > 3hours)
then
          Ibolus = 0 U
       else
       action=''Patient eat''
          Ibolus = O U
      end if
    end if
  else
      Ibolus = 0 U
  end if
END
```

Algorithm 2: Bolus Insulin Dose
Algorithm: Net Amount of Carbohydrate Algorithm

Input:
Net Carbohydrate form Fiber *NCf;*
Net Carbohydrate from Sugar Alcohol *NCa;*
Amount of Dietary *ADF;*
Amount of Sugar Alcohol *SA;*
Serving size: ps

Output:

The value of carbohydrate form food intake,

```
BEGIN
  Output: Food contains fibre? "
  If (answer==yes) then
        NCf= TAC – ADF
  endif
  Output: "Food contains Sugar Alcohol?"
  If (answer==yes) then
        NCa = TAC – 50%*SA
                    endif
  Output: "Food contains Polydextrose?"
  If (answer==yes) then
        NCp = TAC – AP
  endif
  Output: "Serving size of food"
  Input: ps
  Compute NC = (NCa + NCf +NCp)* ps
  Output: "Amount of carbohydrate is" NC

END
```

Algorithm 3: Net Amount of Carbohydrate Algorithm
Algorithm: Insulin Dose to Carbohydrate Algorithm

BEGIN
Calculate the net amount of carbohydrate *Carb*

$$IC\ (d,\ t) = \frac{Carb * Carb_{BIO} * t * e^{(-t \backslash t_{max,G})}}{CarbF * t^2_{max,G}}$$

END

Algorithm 3: Net Amount of Carbohydrate Algorithm

4 Implementation and Evaluation

We have carried out the proposed model and built it into our prototype mobile application (PMA). Figure 4 indicates the screenshots of the mobile application. It allows the patient with T1DM to record all information about the meal intake. For meal intake records, fixed times were assigned for patients with T1DM to breakfast (08:00 AM), lunch (12:00 PM), dinner (8:00 PM) and bedtime (10:00 PM). All the information (food serving size, food name, amount of sugar-alcohol, amount of fibre, amount of polydextrose and food intake time) are saved in the system, and it helps to estimate the amount of carbohydrate. The amount of insulin to cover the carbohydrate is computed by the system. This amount is injected to the patient through the insulin pump before the patients start eating food. Furthermore, patients with T1DM can view the insulin report chart to avoid hypoglycaemia and hyperglycaemia, even in a coma.

Fifty-two (52) patients with T1DM partook in the testing and filled the questionnaire which was designed and administered. Collected data were also analysed and expressed as mean ± standard derivation (SD) as shown in Table 2. Patients were young with an age range of 8–21 years, body mass index (BMI) of 21.18 ± 2.64 kg/m^2 and duration of diabetes of 5.65 ± 2.13 years.

Furthermore, we conducted tests to assess the performance of the proposed model using T1DM dataset collected from CNHU-HKM. This dataset consists of 72 sets of facts recorded on sufferers with T1DM. Among the many criteria for comparing forecasting models, we pick the two most frequently used ones, specifically mean absolute error (MAE), root-mean-square error (RMSE) to consider the prediction performance. The MAE is the average error between the predicted output and the actual

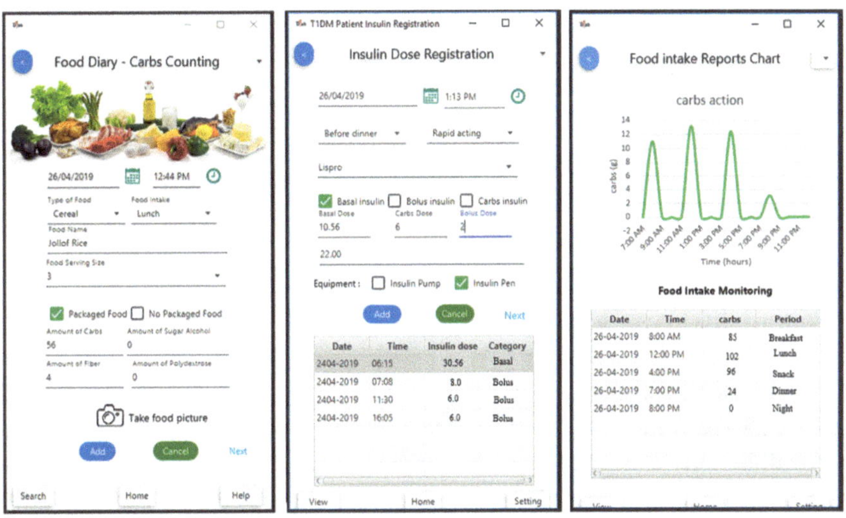

Fig. 4 Screenshots of the PMA

Table 2 Profile characteristics of fifty-two (52) patients with T1DM

S. No.	Characteristics of fifty-two (52) patients with T1DM	
1	Age (years) range	(8–21)
2	Sex: male and female	30 (58%) and 22 (42%)
3	Weight (kg): Range Mean ± SD	23.9–53.5 39.60 ± 12.97
4	Duration of T1DM (years)	5.65 ± 2.13
5	HbA1c (NGSP; %)	7.5 ± 1.01
6	Body Mass Index (kg/m^2) Range Mean ± SD	15.72–27.98 21.18 ± 2.64
7	Insulin dose (IU) Mean total daily insulin (IU/day) Insulin bolus Insulin basal	38.33 25.27 ± 11.64 16.75 ± 10.91

Legend: *SD* Standard derivation

input. RMSE measures the standard deviation of the differences in the predicted output ($\widehat{y}$) and the actual input (y) [40]. Lower estimation of RMSE indicates that the model performed in the most favourable way [40]. Both MAE and RMSE are defined in Eqs. (4) and (5), respectively [40–43].

$$\text{MAE} = \frac{1}{n}\sum_{i=1}^{n}|p_i - y_i| \tag{4}$$

$$\text{RMSE} = \sqrt{\frac{\sum_{i=1}^{n}\left(y_i - \widehat{y}_i\right)^2}{n}} \tag{5}$$

Here, p is the predicted blood glucose level, y is the actual blood glucose level, and n is the number of BG measurements taken.

5 Empirical Analysis

The study was conducted at CNHU-HKM Hospital that involved 52 patients with type 1 diabetes. A total of three (3) meals (breakfast, lunch and dinner) per patient of broad diversity was taken from the hospital's restaurant. The food items were weighed on a standard balance, and the exact amount of carbohydrate was calculated from the USDA nutrient database. Participants were asked to count the carbohydrate content of each meal independently by using the implemented application. A total of twenty (20) food categories were considered, such as: pasta, rice, potatoes, mashed potatoes, meat, green beans, meat, carrots, salad and fish. The data related to a meal (amount of carbohydrate per patient) can be seen in Fig. 5, 6, 7 and 8. Therefore, a total of 156 (52 × 3) meals data were used. All patients have a different amount of carbohydrate at each time (breakfast, lunch and dinner). According to Fig. 8, for example, patient N°23 and N°2 had the same amount of carbohydrate (360 grams) and amount of carbohydrate of patient N°48 and N°49 are under 100 grams. It means that some patients did not eat at some times in the same hours. A better illustration is shown in Fig. 9 between patient N°4 and N°11 who have the same amount of daily carbohydrate (200 grams), but different amount of carbohydrate at breakfast, lunch and dinner periods.

Insulin dosages were also recorded, including basal. Bolus insulin dose and correction bolus are computed. The distribution of these variables can be seen in Fig. 10, 11 and 12. The amount of bolus insulin infused in each patient, as obtained from the sum of pre-breakfast, pre-lunch and pre-dinner insulin doses, is shown in Fig. 10. The total daily dose (TDD) of insulin is calculated based on the correction factor, as shown in Fig. 13. The mean TDD was 38.33. 16.75 ± 10.91 for basal insulin and 25.27 ± 11.64 for bolus insulin. According to Fig. 7, patient N°25 has the most significant basal insulin dose (50 IU) and biggest daily insulin dose (80 IU); on the other hand, his bolus insulin dose in Fig. 10 is about 30 IU with 50 mg/dL/IU of the

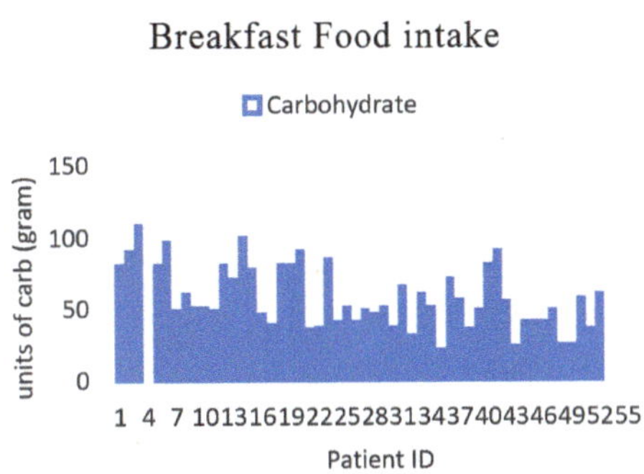

Fig. 5 Distribution of carbohydrate during breakfast of fifty-two (52) patients with T1DM

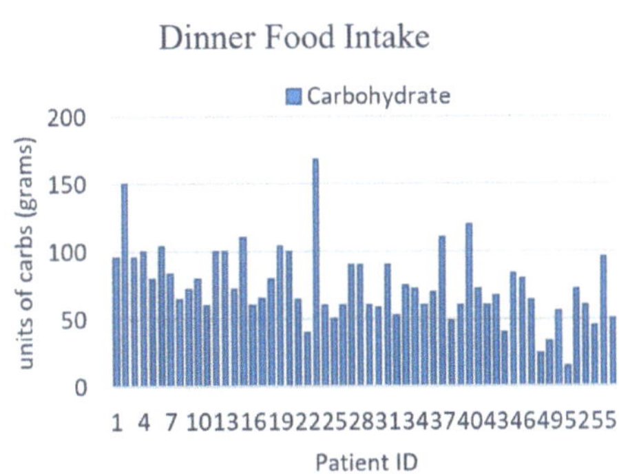

Fig. 6 Distribution of carbohydrate during dinner of fifty-two (52) patients with T1DM

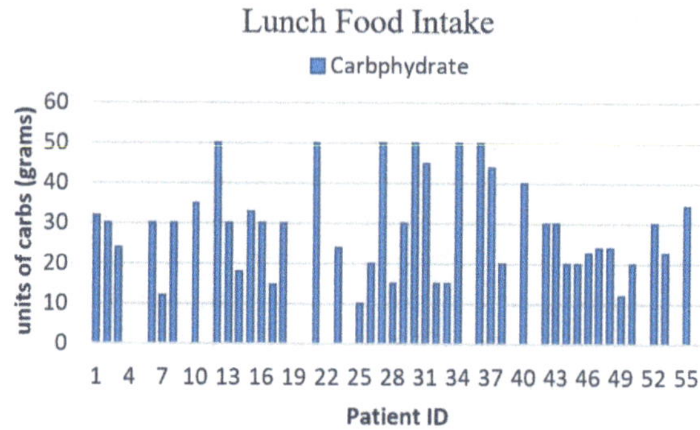

Fig. 7 Distribution of carbohydrate during lunch of fifty-two (52) patients with T1DM

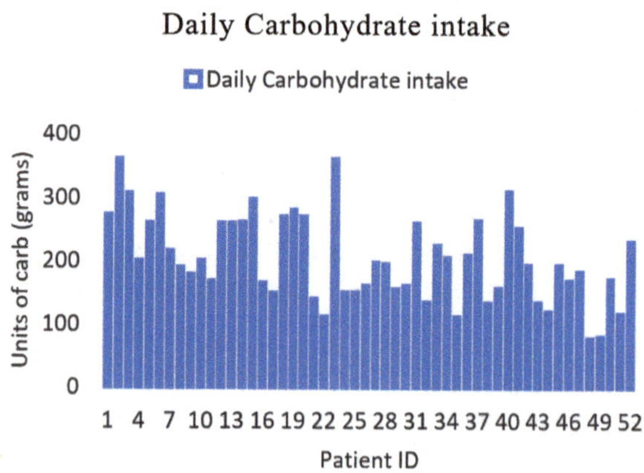

Fig. 8 Distribution of daily carbohydrate during breakfast of fifty-two (52) patients with T1DM

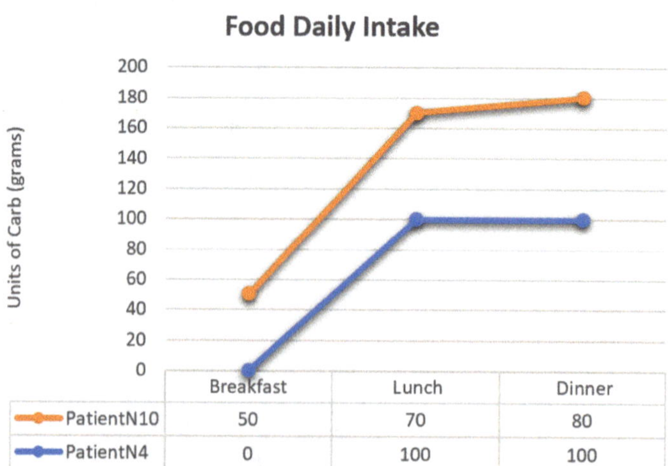

Fig. 9 Comparison of carbohydrate intake during a day between patient 4 and 10

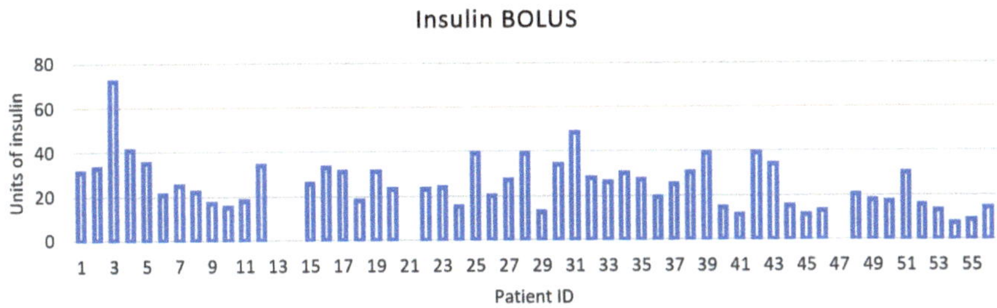

Fig. 10 Distribution of insulin bolus data of 52 patients with T1DM

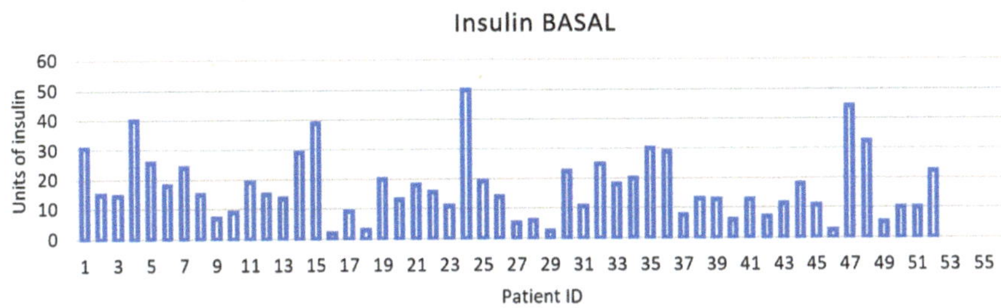

Fig. 11 Distribution of basal insulin data of 52 patients with T1DM

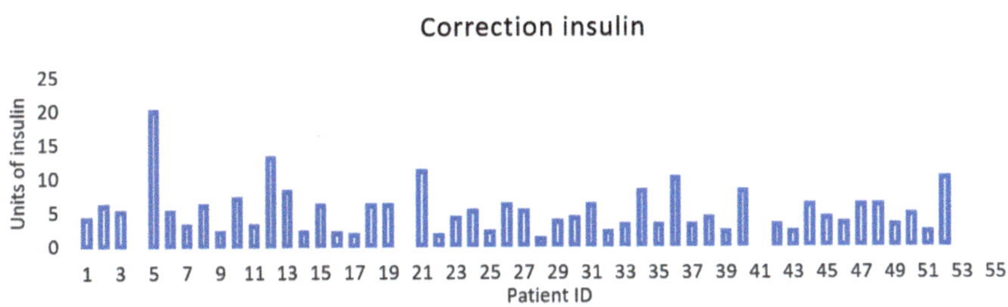

Fig. 12 Distribution of correction insulin data of 52 patients with T1DM

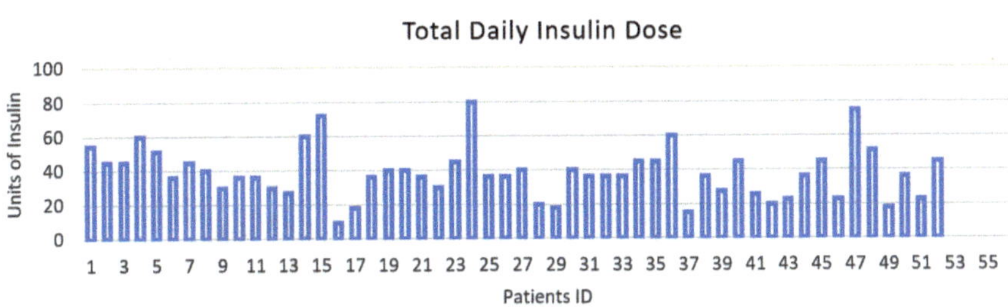

Fig. 13 Distribution of daily insulin dose data of 52 patients with T1DM

correction factor. It means that during the days, his blood glucose drops of 50 mg/dL with each unit of insulin taken.

Figures 14, 15, 16 and 17 show the poles variation in the number of patients relative to bolus insulin dose computed before each period breakfast, lunch, dinner and bedtime, respectively. Figure 14 showed that only one patient with T1DM had injected some quantity of bolus Insulin before breakfast, and 40 patients had injected bolus insulin doses before bedtime is shown in Fig. 17. It means that patients with a small amount of basal insulin dose have significant correction insulin in addition to basal insulin.

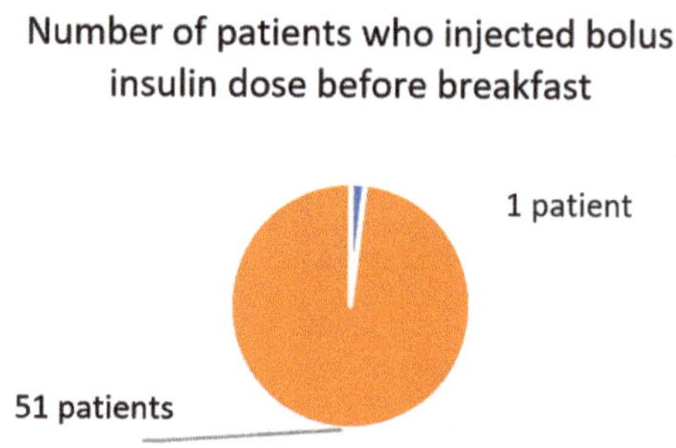

Fig. 14 Number of patients who injected bolus insulin before breakfast time

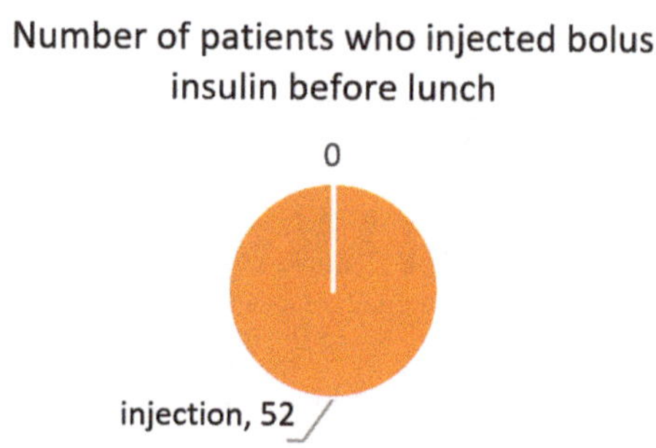

Fig. 15 Number of patients who injected bolus insulin before lunchtime

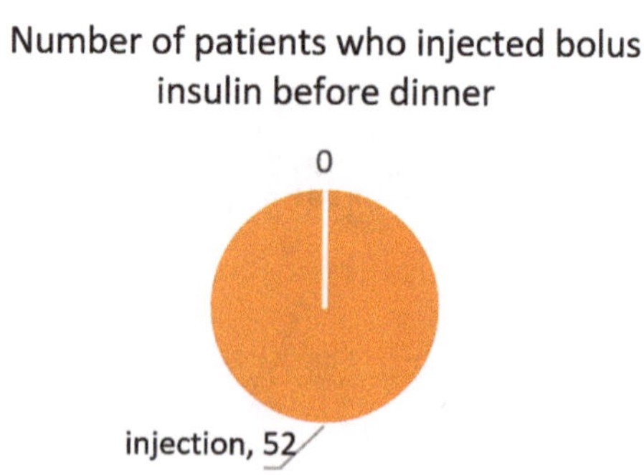

Fig. 16 Number of patients who injected bolus insulin before dinner time

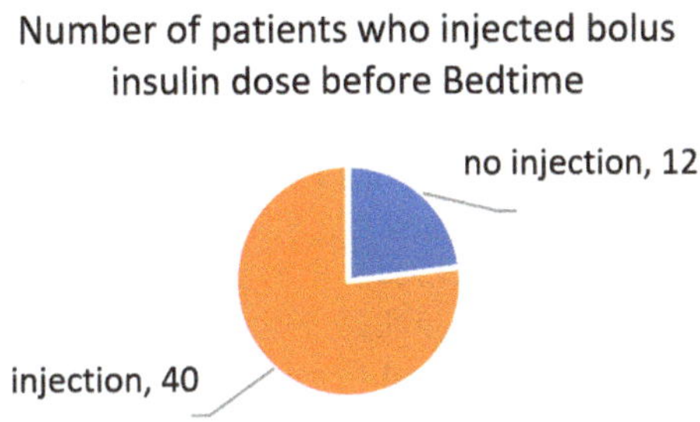

Fig. 17 Number of patients who injected bolus insulin before bedtime

6 Results and Discussion

We used RSME and MAE to evaluate the improvement achieved by applying the proposed correction. We applied the standard calculation of insulin dose and the corrected insulin model to predict BOB and correction insulin with various basal insulin profiles. Moreover, we also computed the average absolute error on all the 52 patients with T1DM.

Table 3 showed the results of carbohydrate intake by 52 patients with T1DM. As Table 3 reveals, twelve (12) patients have a null value, representing 23% of the

Table 3 Results of fifty-two (52) patients including the MAE and RMSE of carbohydrate counting

Patient	MAE [IU]	RMSE [IU]		Patient	MAE [IU]	RMSE [IU]		Patient	MAE [IU]	RMSE [IU]
1	1.59	10.23		19	0.00	0.00		37	3.30	43.56
2	1.50	9.00		20	0.00	0.00		38	1.00	4.00
3	1.20	5.76		21	3.95	62.67		39	0.00	0.00
4	0.00	0.00		22	0.00	0.00		40	2.00	16.00
5	0.00	0.00		23	1.20	5.76		41	0.00	0.00
6	2.37	22.56		24	0.00	0.00		42	1.50	9.00
7	0.60	1.44		25	0.50	1.00		43	1.50	9.00
8	1.50	9.00		26	1.00	4.00		44	1.00	4.00
9	0.00	0.00		27	2.50	25.00		45	1.00	4.00
10	1.75	12.25		28	0.75	2.25		46	1.12	5.06
11	0.00	0.00		29	1.50	9.00		47	1.2	5.76
12	4.50	8.10		30	2.50	25.00		48	1.19	5.75
13	2.61	27.45		31	2.25	20.25		49	0.60	1.44
14	0.90	3.24		32	0.75	2.25		50	1.00	4.00
15	1.65	10.89		33	0.75	2.25		51	0.00	0.00
16	1.50	9.00		34	2.50	25.00		52	2.37	22.46
17	0.73	2.16		35	0.00	0.00				
18	1.50	9.00		36	2.50	25.00				

patients. These 12 patients (N°4, N°5, N°9, N°11, N°19, N°20, N°22, N°24, N°35, N°39, N°41 and N°51) did not take any food containing carbohydrate nutrients compared to the remaining 40 patients. Among the 40 patients, patient N°21 had the highest error value of MAE and RSME as 3.95 IU and 62.67 IU, respectively. The high value indicates that the patient (N°21) also had the highest daily carbohydrate nutrient, as shown in Fig. 8. In all, the PMA detected 77% of patients having a high amount of carbohydrate nutrients in their food intake. Nevertheless, insulin dose is given to take care of the high glucose levels (carbohydrate contents) as reflected in the design specification (Fig. 1), Eq. (3) and algorithm (Sect. 3.3).

As Table 4 shows, patients with T1DM with relatively big remaining insulin doses proved the best concerning the improvement in the average absolute error.

Table 4 Results of fifty-two (52) patients including the MAE and RMSE of corrected insulin dose

Patient	MAE [IU]	RMSE [IU]		Patient	MAE [IU]	RMSE [IU]
1	0.48	0.18		27	1.39	1.29
2	0.84	0.46		28	2.42	2.11
3	1.070	0.71		29	2.27	1.39
4	0.48	0.26		30	0.80	0.39
5	1.36	1.68		31	1.09	0.66
6	2.03	2.29		32	0.74	0.32
7	0.75	0.44		33	0.95	0.52
8	0.91	0.55		34	0.76	0.37
9	1.64	1.28		35	0.60	0.23
10	1.13	0.71		36	0.54	0.25
11	0.90	0.49		37	4.37	4.37
12	2.59	2.89		38	1.17	0.79
13	2.89	3.36		39	1.33	0.75
14	0.55	0.31		40	1.06	0.74
15	0.41	0.18		41	2.61	3.45
16	5.33	3.83		42	2.05	1.38
17	1.52	0.74		43	1.36	0.72
18	1.82	1.96		44	0.79	0.34
19	1.84	1.98		45	1.01	0.84
20	0.95	0.76		46	2.06	1.59
21	2.93	4.76		47	0.40	0.20
22	1.10	0.60		48	0.55	0.22
23	1.02	0.66		49	2.03	1.09
24	0.07	0.01		50	1.85	2.99
25	1.56	2.65		51	1.54	1.15
26	1.01	0.61		52	1.48	1.60

The results showed the corrected insulin dose values to cover carbohydrate values within the range of 4.76 IU to 0.18 IU for the fifty-two (52) patients with TIDM. Table 3 indicates that fifty per cent (50%) of patients with TIDM exceeded 1.0 IU of the absolute error value. In contrast, the remaining patients with TIDM have lowest active insulin dose. From these values, it observes that any patients have null active insulin. Most patients have some active insulin dose which is still in action and have helped to adjust the next insulin values.

7 Conclusion and Future Work

In this study, we designed, developed and validated insulin dose to carbohydrate counting model, which allows an automatic estimate of the Carbohydrate from food that the insulin need to cover. In particular, we formulated a mathematical model based on insulin sensitivity, basal insulin, bolus insulin, correction factor, carbohydrate counts, bolus on board equations and continuous blood glucose levels. We have specified the conceptual view of the model using the Unified Modelling Language (UML) tools, which was also implemented as a mobile application. We evaluated the model by using MAE and RMSE as parameters to (i) ascertain the average error between the output predicted and actual input and (ii) measure the standard deviation of the differences in the output predicted.

The results showed the correct insulin dose values within the range of 4.76 IU to 0.18 IU for the fifty-two (52) patients with T1DM. A total of 156 meals data were recorded. The model evaluation indicates all 52 patients with T1DM and their insulin doses still in action. Therefore, half (50%) of the 52 patients with T1DM had big remaining insulin, while others had poor remaining insulin dose. These remaining insulin dose metrics can be taken into account when adjusting the next insulin dose during the pre or post-meal period. The developed model had reduced the incidence of hypoglycaemia and help to predict the next insulin dose.

Therefore, this research can be used to optimize the calculation of the correction insulin dose for postprandial and pre-prandial time. The algorithm performed better than the manual determination of insulin in the postprandial period and the prediction of remaining insulin dose, without exposing to a hypoglycaemic over-risk. In summary, the PMA meets the needs of people with diabetes (particularly T1D) for a more efficient, automated and precise way of estimating the grams of carbohydrates in the food, as well as controlling their blood glucose levels and improving their quality of life.

Additionally, this research can be used to optimize the calculation of the mealtime insulin dose. Moreover, it can be used as a decision support system for advanced carbohydrates counting for multiple daily injections (MDI) and continuous subcutaneous insulin infusion (CSII) therapy, which can be beneficial for people who cannot accurately estimate the carbohydrate content of meals and also for those who do not have adequate training in carbohydrate counting.

In our opinion, further research focusing on the accuracy of dietitians' recommendations for all macronutrients (carbohydrates, proteins, fats) is essential. The goal will be to validate the effectiveness of our approach for general use. Additionally, we hope that the types of food included in the current PMA could be expanded to cover a broader range of eating habits and cultural differences. In this case, the PMA can be an alternative dietary assessment tool for daily eating habits.

References

1. World Health Organization (WHO). *Global report on Diabetes 2016* Retrieve from http: www.who.intdiabetesglobal-report. Date consulted: 28th March 2019.
2. Soylu, S., Danisman, K., Sacu, I. E., & Alci, M. (2013). Closed-loop control of blood glucose level in type-1 diabetics: A simulation study. In *Electrical and Electronics Engineering (ELECO), 2013 8th International Conference on* (371–375). IEEE.
3. American Diabetes Association. (2010). Standards of medical care in diabetes—2010. *Diabetes Care, 33*(Supplement 1), S11–S61.
4. Imran, S. A., Rabasa-Lhoret, R., Ross, S., & Canadian Diabetes Association Clinical Practice Guidelines Expert Committee. (2013). Targets for glycemic control. *The Canadian Journal of Diabetes, 37*(Suppl 1), S31–34.
5. Cryer, P. E. (2008). The barrier of hypoglycemia in diabetes. *Diabetes, 57*(12), 3169–3176.
6. Miller, K. M., Xing, D., Tamborlane, W. V., Bergenstal, R. M., & Beck, R. W. (2013). Challenges and future directions of the T1D exchange clinic network and registry. *Journal of Diabetes Science and Technology, 7*(4), 963–969.
7. The Diabetes Control and Complications Trial Research Group. (1993). Effect of intensive treatment of diabetes on the development and progression of long-term complications in insulin-dependent diabetes mellitus. *New England Journal of Medicine, 329*(14), 977–986.
8. Gillespie, S. J., Kulkarni, K. A. R. M. E. E. N., & Daly, A. E. (1998). Using carbohydrate counting in diabetes clinical practice. *Journal of the American Dietetic Association, 98*(8), 897–905.
9. Wylie-Rosett, J., Albright, A. A., Apovian, C., Clark, N. G., Delahanty, L., Franz, M. J., et al. (2007). 2006–2007 American Diabetes Association nutrition recommendations: Issues for practice translation. *Journal of the American Dietetic Association, 107*(8), 1296–1304.
10. Rabasa-Lhoret, R., Garon, J., Langelier, H., Poisson, D., & Chiasson, J. L. (1999). Effects of meal carbohydrate content on insulin requirements in type 1 diabetic patients treated intensively with the basal-bolus (ultralente-regular) insulin regimen. *Diabetes Care, 22*(5), 667–673.
11. Delahanty, L. M., & Halford, B. N. (1993). The role of diet behaviors in achieving improved glycemic control in intensively treated patients in the diabetes control and complications trial. *Diabetes Care, 16*(11), 1453–1458.
12. Fu, S., Li, L., Deng, S., Zan, L., & Liu, Z. (2016). Effectiveness of advanced carbohydrate counting in type 1 diabetes mellitus: A systematic review and meta-analysis. *Scientific Reports, 6*, 37067.
13. Kawamura, T. (2007). The importance of carbohydrate counting in the treatment of children with diabetes. *Pediatric Diabetes, 8*, 57–62.
14. Sheard, N. F., Clark, N. G., Brand-Miller, J. C., Franz, M. J., Pi-Sunyer, F. X., Mayer-Davis, E., et al. (2004). Dietary Carbohydrate (amount and type) in the prevention and management of diabetes: a statement by the American Diabetes Association. *Diabetes Care, 27*(9), 2266–2271.
15. American Diabetes Association. (2008). Clinical practice recommendations: Diagnosis and classification of diabetes mellitus. *Diabetes Care, 31*(1), 55–60S.
16. Palerm, C. C., Zisser, H., Jovanovič, L., & Doyle, F. J., III. (2008). A run-to-run control strategy to adjust basal insulin infusion rates in type 1 diabetes. *Journal of Process Control, 18*(3–4), 258–265.

17. Weijman, I., Ros, W. J., Rutten, G. E., Schaufeli, W. B., Schabracq, M. J., & Winnubst, J. A. (2005). The role of work-related and personal factors in diabetes self-management. *Patient education and counselling, 59*(1), 87–96.
18. Morel, A., Lecoq, G., & Jourdain-Menninger, D. (2012). Evaluation de la prise en charge du diabète. *Inspection Général des Affaires sociales, RM2012-033P.*
19. Hovorka, R., Canonico, V., Chassin, L. J., Haueter, U., Massi-Benedetti, M., Federici, M. O., et al. (2004). Nonlinear model predictive control of glucose concentration in subjects with type 1 diabetes. *Physiological Measurement, 25*(4), 905.
20. Steil, G. M., & Reifman, J. (2009). Mathematical modelling research to support the development of automated insulin delivery systems. *Journal of Diabetes Science and Technology, 3*(2), 388–395.
21. Steil, G. M., Clark, B., Kanderian, S., & Rebrin, K. (2005). Modelling insulin action for development of a closed-loop artificial pancreas. *Diabetes Technology & Therapeutics, 7*(1), 94–108.
22. Souto, D. L., & Rosado, E. L. (2010). Use of carb counting in the dietary treatment of diabetes mellitus. *Nutricion Hospitalaria, 25*(1), 18–25.
23. Wilinska, M. E., Chassin, L. J., Schaller, H. C., Schaupp, L., Pieber, T. R., & Hovorka, R. (2004). Insulin kinetics in type-1 diabetes: continuous and bolus delivery of rapid acting insulin. *IEEE Transactions on Biomedical Engineering, 52*(1), 3–12.
24. Ellingsen, C., Dassau, E., Zisser, H., Grosman, B., Percival, M. W., Jovanovič, L., et al. (2009). Safety constraints in an artificial pancreatic β cell: an implementation of model predictive control with insulin on board. *Journal of Diabetes Science and Technology, 3*(3), 536–544.
25. Murphy, H. R., Elleri, D., Allen, J. M., Harris, J., Simmons, D., Rayman, G., et al. (2011). Closed-loop insulin delivery during pregnancy complicated by type 1 diabetes. *Diabetes Care, 34*(2), 406–411.
26. Percival, M. W., Wang, Y., Grosman, B., Dassau, E., Zisser, H., Jovanovič, L., et al. (2011). Development of a multi-parametric model predictive control algorithm for insulin delivery in type 1 diabetes mellitus using clinical parameters. *Journal of Process Control, 21*(3), 391–404.
27. Campos-Delgado, D. U., Femat, R., Hernández-Ordoñez, M., & Gordillo-Moscoso, A. (2005). Self-tuning insulin adjustment algorithm for type 1 diabetic patients based on multi-doses regime. *Applied Bionics and Biomechanics, 2*(2), 61–71.
28. Bishop, F. K., Maahs, D. M., Spiegel, G., Owen, D., Klingensmith, G. J., Bortsov, A., et al. (2009). The carbohydrate counting in adolescents with type 1 diabetes (CCAT) study. *Diabetes Spectrum, 22*(1), 56–62.
29. Lee, H., Buckingham, B. A., Wilson, D. M., & Bequette, B. W. (2009). A closed-loop artificial pancreas using model predictive control and a sliding meal size estimator.
30. Dias, V. M., Pandini, J. A., Nunes, R. R., Sperandei, S. L., Portella, E. S., Cobas, R. A., et al. (2010). Effect of the carbohydrate counting method on glycemic control in patients with type 1 diabetes. *Diabetology & Metabolic Syndrome, 2*(1), 54.
31. Bell, K. J., Barclay, A. W., Petocz, P., Colagiuri, S., & Brand-Miller, J. C. (2014). Efficacy of carbohydrate counting in type 1 diabetes: A systematic review and meta-analysis. *The Lancet Diabetes & Endocrinology, 2*(2), 133–140.
32. Finner, N., Quinn, A., Donovan, A., O'Leary, O., & O'Gorman, C. S. (2015). Knowledge of carbohydrate counting and insulin dose calculations in paediatric patients with type 1 diabetes mellitus. *BBA Clinical, 4,* 99–101.
33. Rhyner, D., Loher, H., Dehais, J., Anthimopoulos, M., Shevchik, S., Botwey, R. H., et al. (2016). Carbohydrate estimation by a mobile phone-based system versus self-estimations of individuals with type 1 diabetes mellitus: A comparative study. *Journal of Medical Internet Research, 18*(5), e101.
34. Reiterer, F., Freckmann, G., & del Re, L. (2018). Impact of carbohydrate counting errors on glycemic control in type 1 diabetes. *IFAC-PapersOnLine, 51*(27), 186–191.
35. Oviedo, S., Contreras, I., Bertachi, A., Quirós, C., Giménez, M., Conget, I., et al. (2019). Minimizing postprandial hypoglycemia in Type 1 diabetes patients using multiple insulin injections and capillary blood glucose self-monitoring with machine learning techniques. *Computer Methods and Programs in Biomedicine, 178,* 175–180.

36. Reiterer, F., & Freckmann, G. (2019). Advanced carbohydrate counting: An engineering perspective. *Annual Reviews in Control, 48*(2019), 401–422.
37. Ziegler, R., Waldenmaier, D., Kamecke, U., Mende, J., Haug, C., & Freckmann, G. (2020). Accuracy assessment of bolus and basal rate delivery of different insulin pump systems used in insulin pump therapy of children and adolescents. *Pediatric Diabetes, 21*(4), 649–656.
38. Yin, R. K. (2017). *Case study research and applications: Design and methods.* Sage publications.
39. Runeson, P., Host, M., Rainer, A., & Regnell, B. (2012). *Case study research in software engineering: Guidelines and examples.* Wiley.
40. Willmott, C. J., & Matsuura, K. (2005). Advantages of the mean absolute error (MAE) over the root mean square error (RMSE) in assessing average model performance. *Climate Research, 30*(1), 79–82.
41. Chai, T., & Draxler, R. R. (2014). Root mean square error (RMSE) or mean absolute error (MAE)?—Arguments against avoiding RMSE in the literature. *Geoscientific model development, 7*(3), 1247–1250.
42. Li, J., & Fernando, C. (2016). Smartphone-based personalized blood glucose prediction. *ICT Express, 2*(4), 150–154.
43. Pashkov, V. M., Gutorova, N. O., & Harkusha, A. (2016). Medical device software: defining key terms. *Wiadomości lekarskie, 6*(2016), 813–817.

An Automatic Classification Methods in Oral Cancer Detection

Vijaya Yaduvanshi, R. Murugan, and Tripti Goel

Abstract Oral cancer is a bunch of many related diseases and it is significantly important to diagnose the infected region with the efficient detection methods. This book chapter represented automatic classification segmentation methods for the detection of oral cancer especially ensemble-based segmentation methods. The estimated outcomes have been discussed with essential parameters. A relative study of segmentation methods have also been provided for the advancement of detection of infected regions. In addition, some best elementary approaches are also discussed to increase the recovery score. The goal is to increase the survival rate by diagnosing the oral cancer in less time duration and with more efficient detection methods which will be a significant step in the area of medical imaging.

Keywords Medical imaging · Radiography · Oral cancer · Automatic segmentation · Ensemble segmentation

1 Introduction

Oral cancer is a lethal tumor arising out of the oral crater through covering squamous epithelium. Oral cancers are assorted class of lumps which appear from unspecified biological section in oral crater. While explaining their anatomy, they are acknowledged in a group with a common form, where distinct features appear, likewise in their expansion, these characteristics are displayed through subsites [1]. Figures 1, 2, 3, and 4 represent different areas of oral cancer. Various emerging techniques were involved for the advancement in diagnosis and their profitable outcomes. This chapter demonstrates an organized learning of all aspects of oral cancer.

V. Yaduvanshi · R. Murugan (✉) · T. Goel
Bio-Medical Imaging Laboratory (BIOMIL), Department of Electronics and Communication Engineering, National Institute of Technology Silchar, Silchar, Assam 788010, India
e-mail: murugan.rmn@gmail.com

R. Patgiri et al. (eds.), *Health Informatics: A Computational Perspective in Healthcare*, Studies in Computational Intelligence 932,
https://doi.org/10.1007/978-981-15-9735-0_8

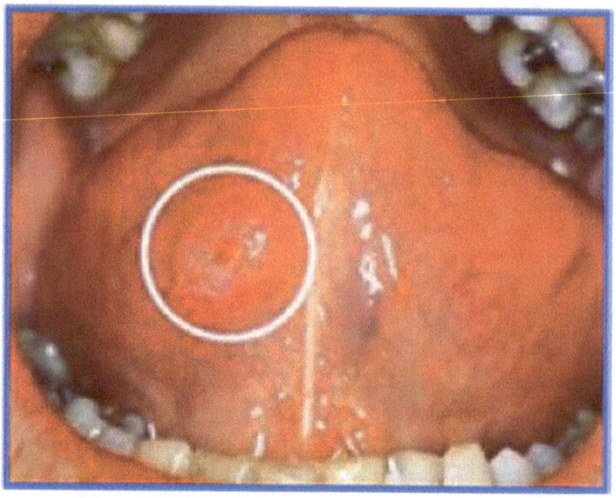

Fig. 1 A red patch under the tongue [2]

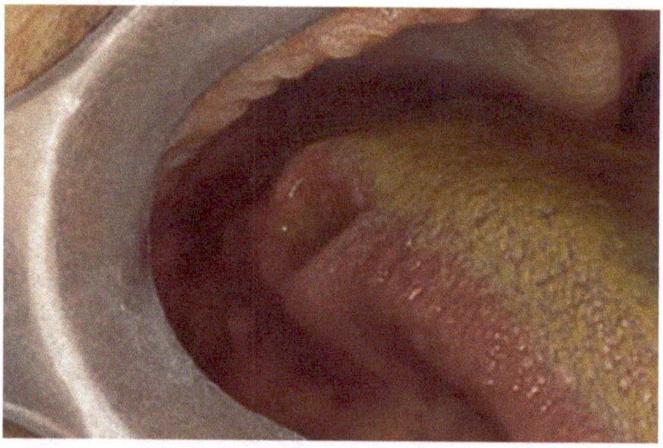

Fig. 2 A speckled ulcer inside the cheek [2]

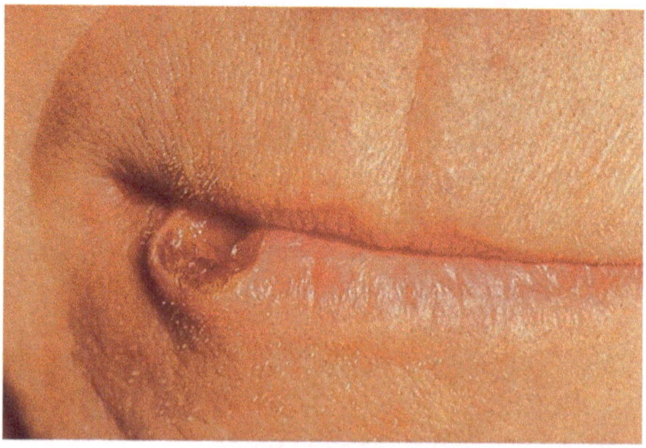

Fig. 3 Lip cancer [2]

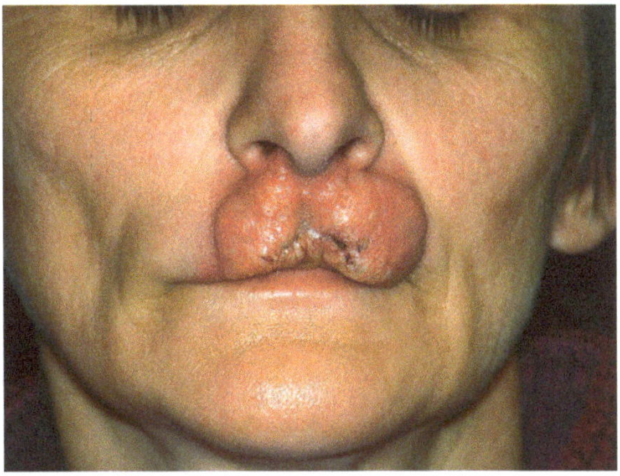

Fig. 4 Bloated area near the upper lip [2]

1.1 Dental X-Ray Images

Dental X-ray is a procedure which defines human dental classification and a vital element in the method of creating a specific analogy. It provides dental recognition of a defected person. It has been an emerging assignment in the field of forensic dentistry where dentist contributes a speedy and extremely cost-effective method of the sufferer recognition. On the other hand, numerous X-ray faults may also occur in forensic dentistry in comparison to normal dental procedures and assistances. Dental X-ray images can also be used in order to determine latent dental designs, banivolent and cancerous numbers, cartilage damage and crater. Dental X-ray images can be classified in two different ways, i.e., intraoral and extraoral [6].

Dental design segmentation is a challenging process in bitewing radiographs [7] because of large picture deviation and every now and then tooth are designed as backdrop (see Fig. 5) which produces many difficulties in the study process. For this challenging assignment, nine groups were listed, among them only two groups fairly presented the test outcomes. The mean F-score of the two groups (Ronneberger et al. and Lee et al.) is jointly 0.560 and 0.268 as well as Ronneberger et al. presented a *u*-shaped deep convolutional network which is more efficient and provides the better *F*-scores which is higher than the range 0.7 specifically for three elementary dental designs which are dentin, pulp, and enamel.

1.2 Background of Oral Cancer

Oral cancer is the sixth most popular cancer worldwide. Cancer of different regions of mouth like lips, palate, alveolar mucosa, oropharynx, floor of mouth, tongue, gingival, and buccal mucosa will give a description of almost 30,000 of the above listed malignancies (an occurrence of around 10 by 100,000).

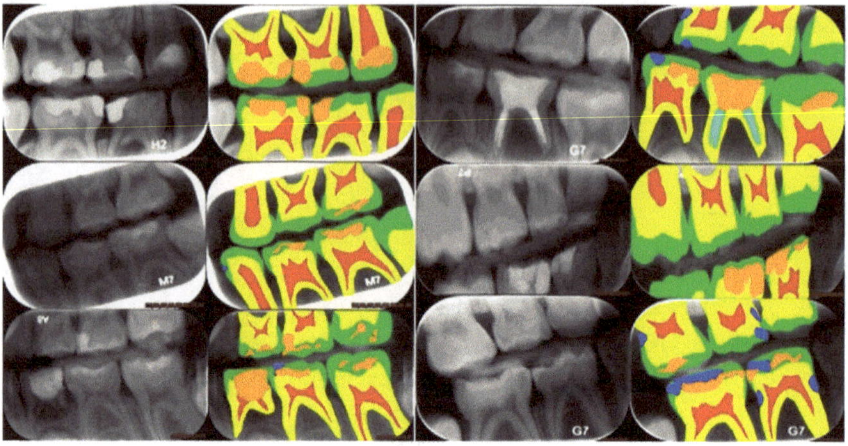

Fig. 5 Six patterns of seven dental designs in bitewing radiography accompanying rough image (left section) and manual segmentation outcome (right section) [7]

Oral cancer has a wide history. It becomes hazardous in the case of late diagnosis. This chapter tried to present much useful informations in order to have a better interpretation of oral cancer. Some of the databases are collected and explained with the help of relevant statistics. Here, Table 1 [8] illustrates oral cancer apportionment with age and sex. National Cancer Institute's Surveillance, Epidemiology and End Results (SEER) has submitted it. Since 1985–1996 from the bioanalytical data taken from nine different countries, these are the cancer investigated and handled cases. In addition to collar and head (nasopharynx, sinuses, primarily salivary glands) with the oral regions, then the cancer of these entire regions has been incorporated around 4% of total cancers detected annually in USA. The extremely ordinary and prevalent class of oral cancer is called squamous cell carcinoma which grows by the layered squamous epithelium that gives an edge to mouth and throat. This type of cancer is commonly detected in almost 9 of each 10 oral cancers. Therefore, it can be concluded that oral cancer issue is initially involved with the detection, medicine, and organization of squamous cell carcinoma.

Table 2 [8] represents the prominent regions of oral cancer. The National Cancer Institute's Surveillance, Epidemiology and End Results (SEER) set up has provided it in the year 1985–1996.*94% of lower lip.

Table 1 Age and gender dissemination for oral cancer [8]

Age (yr)	*N*	Percentage	Male-to-female ratio
<20	130	<1	1.0
20–39	1604	7	2.0
40–49	2432	11	2.5
50–64	7163	32	2.4
65+	11,170	50	1.6

Table 2 Oral cancer dominant sections [8]

Sections	Malignancy (%)	Male-to-female ratio	Average life
Tounge	30	2.0	61
Lip*	17	5.0	66
Mouth floor	14	2.2	62

1.3 Types of Oral Cancer

Oral cancer is classified into seven types which are epithelial cancers, bone cancers, odontogenic cancers, salivary gland cancers, hematologic cancers, mesenchymal cancers, etc. The most probable infection-prone areas of oral cancer are floor of mouth, palate, gingival, buccal/labial mucosa, mandible, alveolar mucosa, maxilla, tongue, and lip.

1.4 Contribution of This Chapter

- This chapter illustrates the basics of oral cancer and its various types.
- Statistical data represented in the chapter provides a better understanding of this cancer.
- Numerous comparative studies give a clear idea on a whole for the beginners in this field.
- Detection of oral cancer has been discussed for an accurate and efficient diagnostic because among all the cancers, the proper diagnostic of oral cancer has always been a hard nut to crack so in order to provide an excellent and fruitful solution to this problem, various segmentation techniques have been proposed.
- This chapter has discussed various segmentation methods for oral cancer which will definitely be very helpful in the field of medical imaging.
- Some best elementary approaches are also discussed to increase the recovery score.
- The goal is to increase the survival rate by diagnosing the oral cancer in less time duration and with more efficient detection methods which will be a significant step in dentistry.

1.5 Organization of the Chapter

The rest of this chapter is arranged as follows, Sect. 1 represents an introduction on oral cancer, its various types, related statistics to get a clear vision, and most importantly contribution of the chapter, in order to provide better diagnostics and treatments of oral cancer keeping the intention to serve the society in some of the other way. Section 2 illustrates the databases of the study in the field of medical imaging and their segmentation process with more efficient data from the previous researches. Section 3 describes the performance metrics in qualitative and quantitative manner. Section 4 presents a generic frame work of oral cancer segmentation workflow to get a systematic approach in order to understand the concept of the segmentation process which will be helpful for the beginners. Section 5 describes the related work keeping various segmentation methods for osteonecrosis of jaw bone which is a type of oral malignancy. Section 6 describes the discussion over oral cancer, its efficient diagnosis, and cure in order to decrease the death rate which will definitely be a valuable contribution in the domain of medical imaging. In Sect. 7, the gaps and future advancements in oral cancer segmentation process have been discussed. Section 8 represents the conclusion of the study.

2 Databases of the Study

In 2017, an oral cancer dataset is published by Mendeley. In this dataset, anonymized and deidentified panoramic dental X-rays of 116 sufferers has been taken, which are from Noor Medical Imaging Center, Qom, Iran. This dataset contains a large area of dental cases from normal, to fractional and exhaustive dull cases. The mandibles of total cases have been segmented manually with the help of two dental surgeons. This dataset consists of about 2000 BMP patterned computerized panoramic X-rays of ~2900 × 1250 pixels size which are obtained from Soredex CranexD computerized panoramic X-ray system. For the purpose of analysis as well as pharmaceutical interest, all the images have been utilized. For this analysis, no radiography report was employed. The link of the dataset is as follows: https://data.mendeley.com/datasets/hxt48yk462/1.

In 2020, for oral cancer, a histopathological imaging database has been given. Here, 1224 images were taken which are categorized in two groups with two separate resolutions. In the first group, 89 histopathological images were taken keeping oral crater's normal epithelium as well as 100 × amplified 439 oral squamous cell carcinoma (OSCC) images. In the second group, 201 images have been taken keeping oral crater's regular epithelium as well as 400 × amplified 495 histopathological images of OSCC. These images were collected in the distinction to hematoxylin and eosin (H & E) by the means of Leica ICC50 HD microscope, arranged and indexed by medical specialists from 230 sufferers. The link of their dataset is as follows: https://github.com/Tabassum2019/A-histopathological-image-repository-of-normal-epithelium-of-Oral-Cavity-and-OSCC/blob/master/README.md.

3 Performance Metrics

For screening process of oral images, primarily two practices are proposed called as subjective calculation and objective calculation [9]. In subjective calculation, definite cases were specified as those by fluorescence visualization loss (FVL) as well as negative cases as those by fluorescence visualization retention (FVR). This calculation is done by more than two inspectors and FVL standard were determined. Sensitivity and specificity are one of the performance metrics which can be evaluated as: sensitivity = (fluorescence visualization loss definite cases with SCC/total cases with SCC) × 100%; specificity = (fluorescence visualization loss negative cases after SCC/total cases after SCC) × 100%. In calculation, ROI average area (calculated in pixels), average luminance value (in candela per square meter, cd/m^2), luminance ratio, coefficient of variation of luminance, and standard deviation (SD) of luminance have been determined. The rate of standard deviation of luminance along with the average luminance value is used to determine the coefficient of variation of luminance. The rate of luminance of contusion ROI along with the luminance of regulated ROI determines the luminance ratio, which can be formulated as luminance ratio = (region of interest of contusion/Region of interest of regulation) × 100%.

By the receiver operating characteristics (ROC) contour in order to get SCC, numerous test has been executed [9] as well as cutoff rates were also addressed and finally achieving a differential analysis for oral mucosal disorders. With the help of ROC contour evaluation, area under the curve (AUC), specificity, and sensitivity has been evaluated. The rate of P less than 0.05 has been considered analytically critical.

Morikawa et al. [9] have presented the procedures of biased and unbiased assessment (Fig. 6). In biased assessment, dental images and fluorescence visualization (FV) images were analyzed (*A*, *B*), to calculate fluorescence visualization retention (FVR) or fluorescence visualization loss (FVL) in the contusion. FV is a non-intrusive, useful, and real-time examining procedure which uses optical instruments and experiments can be done in repetition. FV operates on blue radiation (400–460 nm) in order to highlight collagen cross-connections and nicotinamide adenine dinucleotide (NADH). Region of interest (ROI) of the contusion was specified like the region of FVL. At top of the contusion (*C*) in regular mucosa, dominant region of interest was fit in identical oral crater like a subsite beyond FVL. The region of interest has been presented in the surface plot (*D*) for the case of contusion.

Here in Fig. 7, the representation of various cases like stomatitis plus infection of right tongue has given a histopathological analysis for catarrhal stomatitis. Fluorescence visualization (FV) images represent a trimmed, homogeneous FVL over fibrin with fine borders of FVL. FVL is not clearly visible in case of mild carcinoma including fibroma in left buccal membrane. A histopathological analysis has been provided for the case of oral lichen planus (OLP) along a reticular contusion in the left buccal membrane. A regular FVL has been identified in the erythematous region in FV images and transparent FVL borders have been observed. In the regions of leukoderma, FV stimulation is detected. A histopathological analysis of hyperkeratosis is provided for the case of leukoplakia with homogeneous leukoderma in the

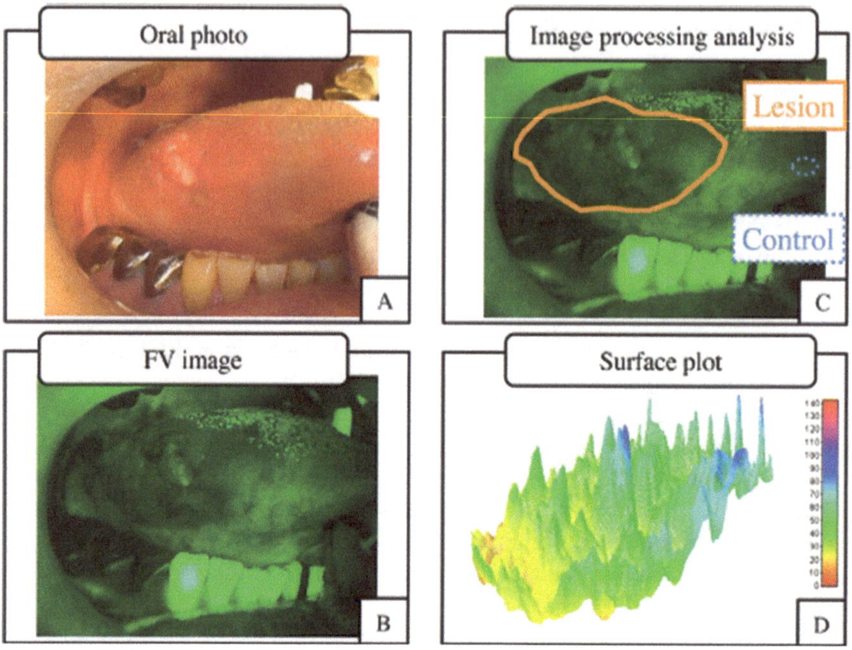

Fig. 6 Classification of systematic analysis of the contaminated region [9]

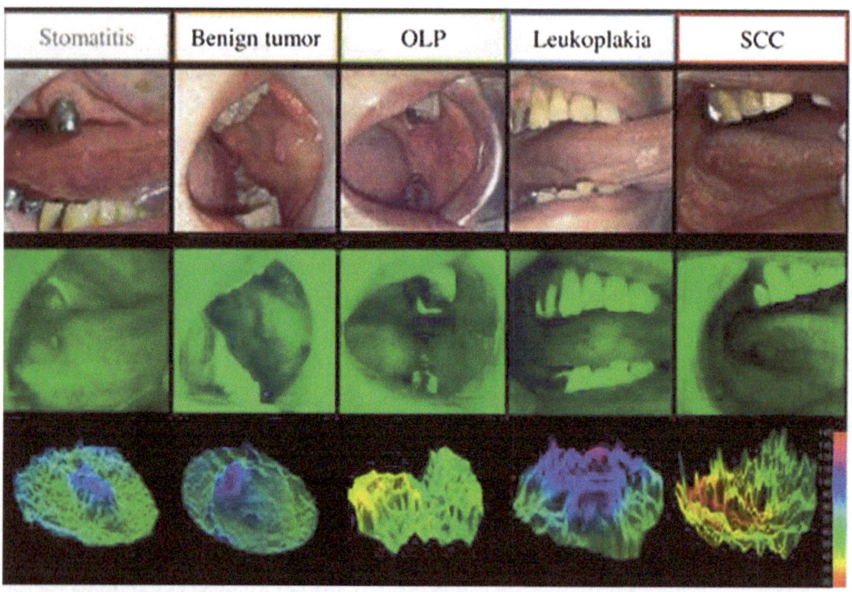

Fig. 7 Conventional cases of all types of oral malignancies [9]

right tongue. FVL is not possible in FV photographs whereas FV stimulation exists. A typical case of squamous cell carcinoma (SCC) provides a histopathological analysis of squamous cell carcinoma grade 1 with caustic contusion in the right tongue. FV photographs represent an irregular FVL with imprecise borders of fluorescence visualization loss (FVL) [9].

Leukoplakia represented essentially large value of average luminance in comparison of stomatitis and OLP. SCC represented essentially small value of average luminance in comparison of the other infections. Here in Figs. 8 and 9, meaningful

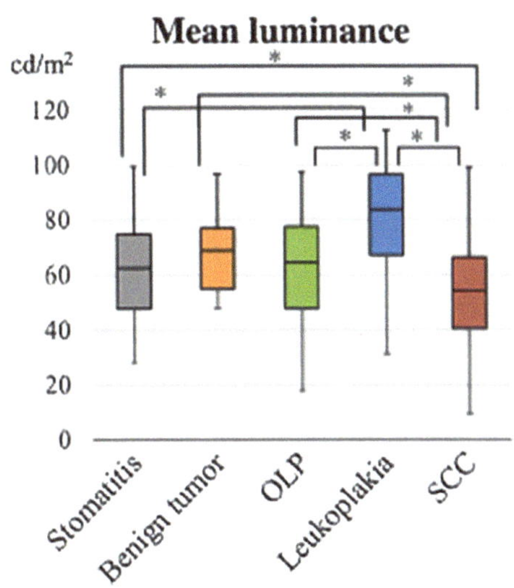

Fig. 8 Average Luminance as objective estimations [9]

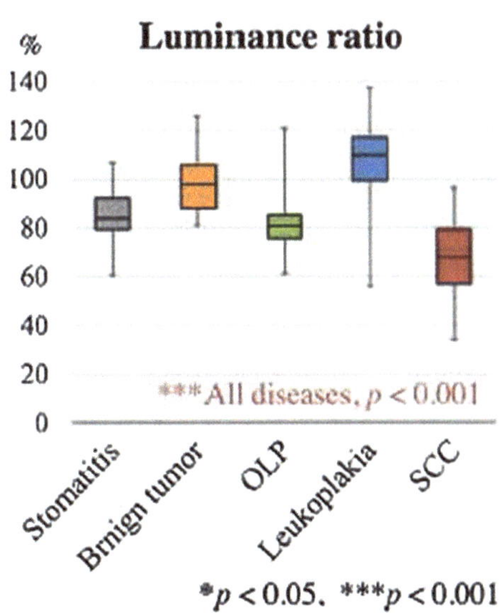

Fig. 9 Luminance ratio as objective estimations [9]

variations are represented for all infections in luminance ratio. Substantial differences in luminance ratio are represented by all the infections [9].

Here in Figs. 10 and 11, SCC represented essentially a large value of standard deviation for the luminance in comparison to OLP and leukoplakia. On the other hand, coefficient of variation of luminance has been observed 0.12 for mild malignancy,

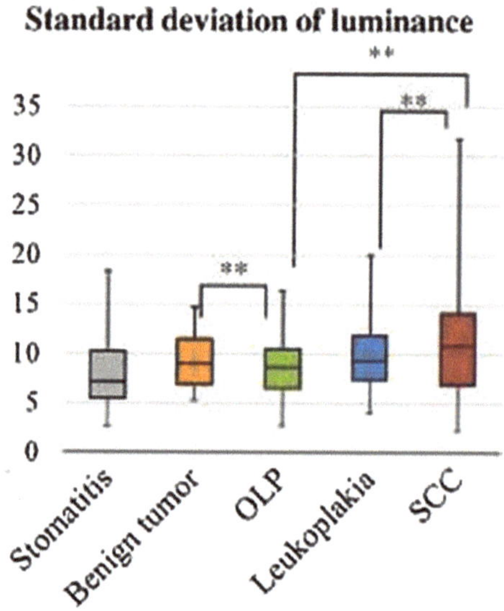

Fig. 10 Standard deviation of luminance as objective estimations [9]

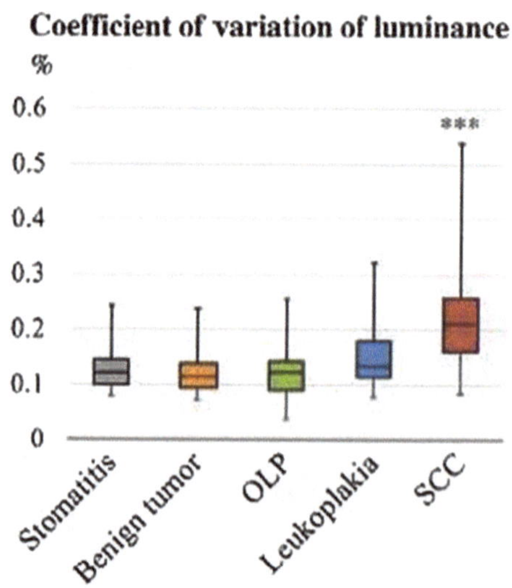

*$p < 0.05$, **$p < 0.01$, ***$p < 0.001$

Fig. 11 Coefficient of variation of luminance as objective estimations [9]

0.22 for SCC, 0.13 for stomatitis, 0.13 for OLP, and 0.13 for leukoplakia, representing essentially large value for SCC in comparison to other infections.

In AUC, the largest percentage is produced by the luminance coefficient of variation, pursued by the luminance ratio. For the average luminance, sensitivity and specificity are found to be 61.9% and 62.7%, coefficient of variation of luminance to be 72.5% and 85.4%, luminance ratio to be 90.3% and 55.7%, and standard deviation of luminance to be 56.5% and 67.7% (see Table 3).

In a research, segmentation of oral cancer images statistics in contrast of numerous segmentation processes has been presented [10]. Alarifi et al. [10] presented a work on computer aided cancer characterization method. They proposed a combined level-set image segmentation design for the betterment of segmentation process in medical imaging. A comparative study is shown in Fig. 12 for numerous segmentation techniques with some early methods.

Table 3 Objective estimation from receiver operating characteristic (ROC) curve analysis [9]

	AUC	*P* value	Cutoff	Sensitivity	Specificity
Luminance	**0.674**	**<0.001***	**60**	**61.9**	**62.7**
Luminance ratio	**0.828**	**<0.001***	**86.8**	**90.3**	**55.7**
Standard deviation	**0.616**	**0.001***	**9.1**	**56.5**	**67.7**
Coefficient of variation	**0.843**	**<0.001***	**0.18**	**72.5**	**85.4**

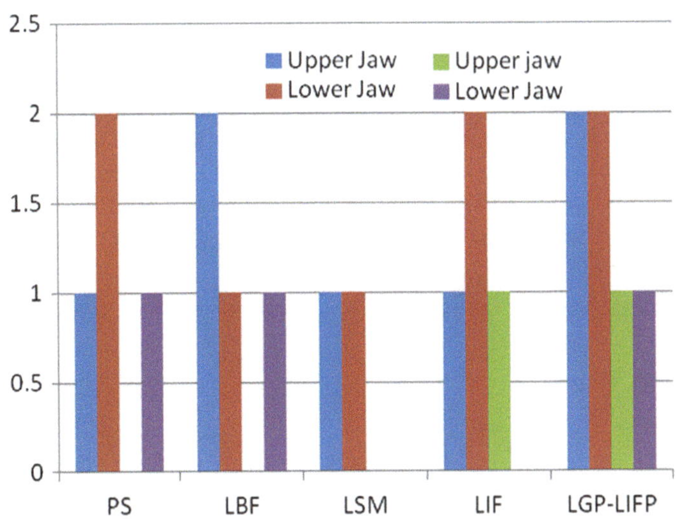

Fig. 12 Comparative study of various segmentation processes [10]

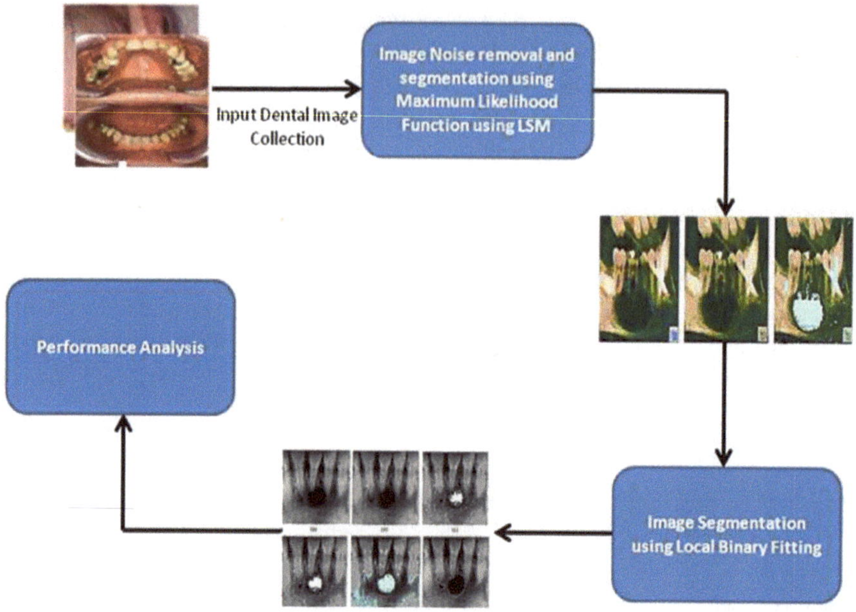

Fig. 13 A generic flow of oral cancer segmentation process using LGP-LIFP method [10]

4 General Frame Work of Oral Cancer Segmentation Workflow

From the previous studies of segmentation processes for oral images, Alarifi et al. [10] proposed a more accurate and efficient design in order to get easy diagnosis and treatment of oral malignancies in a short span of time. Figure 13 illustrates a workflow of their proposed segmentation process using LGP-LIFP methods. Their proposed method has been found more reliable in comparison of other conventional methods.

5 Related Works

In dentistry, panoramic X-ray is extremely prevailing extra oral radiography. The division of its biological architecture promotes identification of problems as well as enrollment of dental evidences. In order to provide a self-regulated apportionment of jaw in the panoramic X-rays, in 2015, Abdi et al. [11] proposed a work which provides an efficient design. Their proposed work has provided a four trail method in which an excellent boundary is extricated over horizontal elemental extension. An adjusted Canny edge pointer, guided through morphological driver, draws out auxiliary boundary of the jaw body. A contour discovering process has been used to extract the outer boundary of ramuses located on the typical design of mandible. A most suited paired pattern is obtained from directory of mandibles in order to finish the contour of both the sides (right and left). A total of 95 panoramic X-ray images has been used in this study and results are evaluated with the help of apportionment by three proficient dental surgeons and they demonstrated that the design is powerful and it has attained an average efficiency of more than 93%. The apportionment of biological systems is an essential move for numerous uses. Because of the various reasons like design inconsistency, usual abnormalities and low image approaches (e.g., flat divergence, irregular vulnerabilities, noise as well as distinct picture output); no steady method has been developed for pharmaceutical image analysis. By past decagon, numerous inventive designs have been suggested for pharmaceutical image and their equivalent design atlas [3–5], teeth apportionment and making a 'self-regulated dental testimony scheme' for the use of judicial doctrine [12–19]. Jain and Chen [13] were the first researchers to introduce a quasi-self-regulated probabilistic design for teeth apportionment and contour equalization in images which depends on elemental extensions. Bayes standard is used by Jain and Chen as well as radial scrutiny for extricating teeth profile even though primarily splitting every teeth against the opposite as well as neighboring tooth with elemental extensions.

Nowadays, panoramic radiography is widely used adjunct method in present dentistry because of its minimum expenditure, modesty, explanatory content, and nominal risk for the patient. This technique is very useful in the diagnosis of jaw rupture, methodical bone disorder, unexploded tooth, and intraosseous injury. This work divides cartilage into the panoramic radioactivity.

The real data file utilized in this work comprised of approximately 2000 computerized panoramic radioactivity in BMP pattern of ~2900 × 1250 pixels captured by the Soredex Cranex D computerized panoramic radioactivity system. Images were taken with the intention of investigation and analysis outlining. A four-layer segmentation has been suggested. In every move of this design, a subdomain of mandible contour was drawn out with the help of a specifically produced approach which was dependent on the previous information of the sub domain's structure.

5.1 *Superior Contour of Alveolar Method*

Abdi et al. [11] utilized the method of Jain and Chen [13] for dividing the uppermost and lowermost tooth on an intraoral X-ray called as bitewing. A block diagram (Fig. 14) is presented for the better understanding of this segmentation process.

Auxiliary boundary of mandible, outside boundary of ramuses, was the centric domains to work upon as well as methods of mandible. Apportionment efficiency is calculated for every condition with the consolidated gold measures manual apportionment. For this count, three performance metrics named specificity, dice similarity coefficient (DSC), and sensitivity have been calculated with the help of TP, TN, FP,

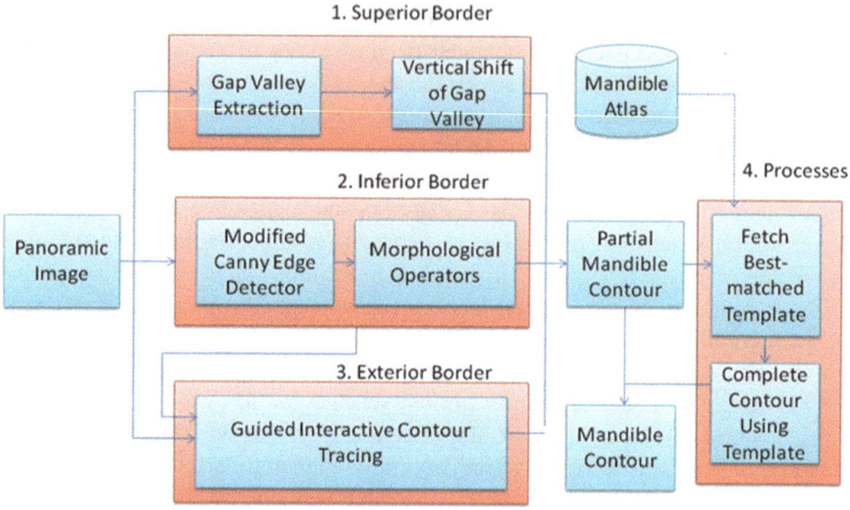

Fig. 14 Block diagram of the segmentation process [11]

FN rates (TP: true positive, TN: true negative, FP: false positive, and FN: false negative).

Tables 4 and 5, [11] compiled calculated metrics attained from analyzing the recommended design for 95 panoramic images. The suggested design is a four-layer process which is an efficient and strong method for automated apportionment of panoramic X-ray images in the absence of a dedicated input. An accurate application to this work has been drafted by Frejlichowski and Wanat [20]. This study can be further extended for the segmentation of various architectures in head and neck radiography procedures. The outcomes can be further extended in numerous outlines like developing enrollment of panoramic radio activities over the recent facts in distinction to a disjointed mandible. This process is also encouraging for

Table 4 Analysis outcomes of mandible segmentation equated with gold measures [11]

Standard	Average (%)
DSC	93.33% ± 1.52
Specificity	94.68% ± 2.17
Sensitivity	94.44% ± 2.29

Table 5 Analysis outcomes of Hausdorff range equated with gold measures [11]

Subregion	Average (%)
Superior border	12.68 ± 6.30
Inferior border	3.77 ± 2.14
Exterior border	6.19 ± 7.21
Processes	15.85 ± 3.88

personal recognition and for the detection of structural features but majorly used in the conditions of dental dialectic and exposure of periodical injury.

Nowadays, there is a huge demand of computerized medicinal analysis systems from X-ray images in order to perform an efficient decision making of feasible syndrome and its cure. In the year 2017, Son et al. [21] suggested an innovative structure which is named as dental diagnosis system (DDS) to present a compound method of segmentation, categorization, and decision making in dental diagnosis. For segmentation process, an efficient dental image distribution approach was established on quasi-supervised fuzzy clustering. A modern graph planted clustering design named APC + was recommended for the categorization task. With the help of this research, it has been made possible to find the ultimate affliction from the class of afflictions found from the section using the recent decision-making method.

Fuzzy inference system (FIS) is a widely used method in dental analysis for analyzing a bunch from an accustomed group of input data to a group of output data utilizing the concept of fuzzy logic [22, 23]. Likewise, Chattopadhyay et al. [24, 25] has given a function of Bayesian system for the detection of toothache. Kavitha et al. [26] have utilized support vector machine (SVM) to anticipate osteoporosis in dental images, and Oad et al. [27] recommended fuzzy-based approach to diagnose heart risk in 2014. In various dentistry issues, Castillo et al. [28] and Ramirez et al. [29] suggested fuzzy K-nearest neighbor (FKNN). To achieve an authentic efficient diagnosis in designing the fuzzy guidelines and expertise, it is quite needed to have specialist involvement and understanding to bypass insignificant methods [30]. These problems can be eliminated with the use of a compound segmentation, characterization, and important as well answerable methods in order to reduce the ineffectiveness and uncertainty in deciding the laws [31–35].

Segmenting a dental X-ray image is the primary action of this work in order to get more diagnosis check whether any disease exists or not. Creating many different sections in the image, where pixels in a section will have much analogy with the other groups [19] and this done by making groups of dental X-ray images. This issue has been considered broadly in [36–38] Bouchachia and Pedryzc [37]. Yasunori et al. [39] implemented SSSFC, i.e., semisupervised standard fuzzy clustering method. Yin et al. [40] presented eSFCM, i.e., semisupervised entropy regularized fuzzy clustering method to improve clustering efficiency. Portela et al. [41] have given semisupervised classifier which was dependent on clustering method in brain tissue disjunction for magnetic resonance.

In the secondary action, after getting the segmented groups, classification method [24, 26, 28, 42–46] is utilized for testing the segmented image in the database to diagnose whether the image is cancerous or non-cancerous and then a suitable method has been adapted for analyzing the conclusion for the diseased image.

In this research, panoramic images have been suggested because of their potential to give insurance for periodontal bone deficiency, peripheral injuries, and pathological jaw injuries, and for good patient acknowledgment, limited radiation vulnerability and infection restraint [47]. To handle numerous dental issues like odontoma, malocclusion, radicular cyst, dental cyst, periodontitis, and pulpitis, the recent DDS utilizes a compound design. This DDS is very much efficient to diagnose a suitable disease for all class of images and draw out required suggestions and information between an input image with actual disease design in the dataset. It is very crucial to get great attainment and efficiency, and this is because the recent work is limited in the experimental dataset for five standard diseases which are indisputable radio graphically and scientifically for the perfect validation of the accomplishment of the system [48].

5.2 *Dental Extricated Characteristics*

To attain an efficient and effective performance in medicinal domain [49], some elementary image functions, i.e., entropy, patch level feature (PAT), the gradient (GRA) [52], local binary patterns (LBP) [50], edge-value and intensity features (EEI) [51], and Red green blue (RGB) have been used to find the characteristics and hence producing a database of 56 input images. The opted characteristics provide remarkable accomplishment in the field of medical domain [49], among these five distinct characteristics gradient feature (GRA) is used to distinguish different small teeth's parts like as cementum, root canal, gum, and the enamel. Dental X-ray image characterization plays an important role in providing wide range applications which include dental age evaluation [18], forensic recognition, computerized dental recognition system, dental disease analysis, and teeth counting system. Clustering located characterization processes are very adaptable to noises and require advancement to get efficiently good performance. Hence, fuzzy clustering method is implemented to resolve this problem [36]. Here, a new clustering approach named semisupervised fuzzy clustering method is used [53] alongside other characteristics which helped to conduct and regulate clustering method. This method employs membership matrix for image disjunction issue as a supplementary fact.

5.3 *Semisupervised Fuzzy Clustering Method Employing Collective Fuzzy Satisficing (SSFC-FS)*

In advanced DDS approach [21], the segmentation of dental X-ray images has been done using the semisupervised fuzzy cluster with interactive fuzzy satisficing method which segments the images by integrating the characteristics of images keeping the supplementary facts produced through a membership matrix. Figure 15 displays that the ith portion keeping the disorder pattern 1 and 3 is located in the same cluster indicating that disorder could be one of the patterns named 1 and 3.

These disorder patterns are collected from a pattern database in which all the cases were present that have occurred in the past. In this way, this research provides a fruitful solution in the detection process of more related cases.

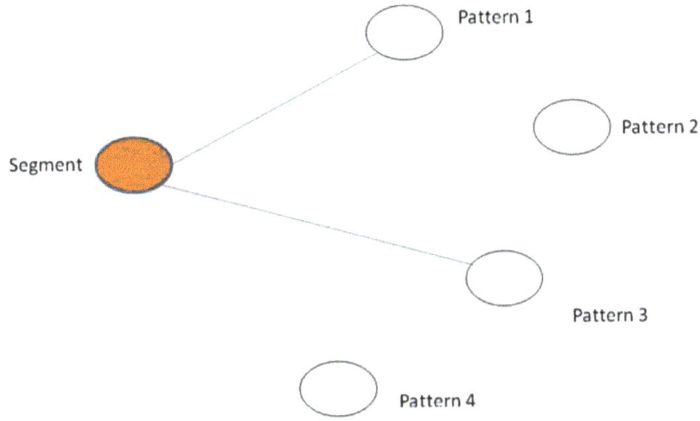

Fig. 15 Graph clustering results comparing one segment with four disorder patterns [21]

5.4 *The Recommended DDS Approach*

The recorded data is segmented within the testing sets through 10 runs. The attainment of these procedures evaluated and normalized by 10 runs [53]. It uses an advanced method for characterization and judgment.

In this way, this work using the DDS design is justified and examined in contrast by other related methods like: FIS [23], FKNN [28], GCP, GCK, APC [46] (FIS: fuzzy inference system, FKNN: fuzzy K-nearest neighbor, GCP: Prim's spanning tree, GCK: Kruskal spanning tree and APC: The affinity propagation clustering). The recent DDS design outperforms the other related methods (see Table 6) for detecting the five dental problems with efficiency of 92.74%. This paper also presented the future work on it in various ways. The preliminary outcomes on the original dental fact from Hanoi Medical University, Vietnam with 87 oral cancer images of five diseases authenticated that, the DDS is having an excellent performance to the appropriate units like FIS, FKNN, GCP, GCK, APC.

Image segmentation hits imperative representation in the field of computer perception. In images, the objects and their periphery can be found by image segmentation. In the field of medical imaging, the exercise of achieving pathological areas and automatic tracking down the disorder is a complex issue in the field of computer science engineering and image processing. Because of inadequate images, a huge difficulty

Table 6 Estimated Efficiency of all approaches [21]

	GCP	GCK	APC	FIS	FKNN	DDS
MSE	1.908	1.908	0.845	0.2098	0.2863	0.0804
MAE	1.002	1.007	0.805	0.1982	0.2346	0.0804
Efficiency (%)	58.46	58.46	90.01	89.67	80.05	92.74

exists in it. In medical images, the required characteristics of an exceptional segmentation algorithm are a huge level of segmentation preciseness, expertise, authenticity, and capacity to deal interferences or inhomogeneous magnitude. In the August 2019, Alarifi et al. [10] introduce an automated computer-aided structure with the help of a level-set region-based active contour segmentation method to find outline detection for two-dimensional medical images including and excluding inhomogeneous magnitude. With this method, cancer pictures are divided in a converted field to minimize the noise. This newly introduced design interfaces the local geometric integrity and local image fitting integrity to efficiently classify the picture element comparable to distinguish areas in a picture including and excluding magnitude inhomogeneity. This research introduces active contour segmentation method for diagnosing oral cancer in jaw bone area including as well as excluding magnitude inhomogeneity when integrating local geometric property (LGP) and local image fitting property (LIFP). A suitable contour segmentation method incorporates local statistical approach (LSM), local binary fitting (LBF), PS region-based active contour design, and local image fitting (LIF). These overhead designs have reduced computation performance as well as imprecise segmentation which are an extensive detriments. These detriments are inscribed in the advanced LGP-LIFP method (Fig. 12).

5.5 Advanced Composite LGP-LIFP Method to Codify Oral Cancer

Here on the basis of LSM, the most probable energy function is formulated and decreased. By the decrement of energy function planted on parameter set, the enforced parameters are approximated in scientific osteonecrosis for the two-dimensional cancer pictures of jaw bone region. With this research, LGP-LIFP methods obtained by unification of LSM and LIF for a concluding segmentation of two-dimensional jaw bone picture carrying a cancer distressed area. In this work, the maximum likelihood energy function employing LSM, LSM utilizing energy function, reduction of energy, and transformation code for level set, and finally LIF design and integrated LGP-LIFP method has been illustrated.

Alarifi et al. [10] described and performed the experiments on an original dataset for a two-dimensional oral cancer images which is discussed by the author [53], containing dataset of 116 patients [11, 54, 55]. Ten two-dimensional cancer images are also taken to describe tumors. In this case, author represented the results with area error metrics (Fig. 16). LIF, LSM, PS, and LBF region-dependent active contour region has issues related to performing arithmetic efficiency and faulty segmentation which has been described by the recommended LGP-LIFP method [56]. The results have been better illustrated (see Figs. 17, 18, 19 and 20) using the similarity index [21, 57], study of precision and PSNR, computation analysis [58], specificity, and sensitivity.

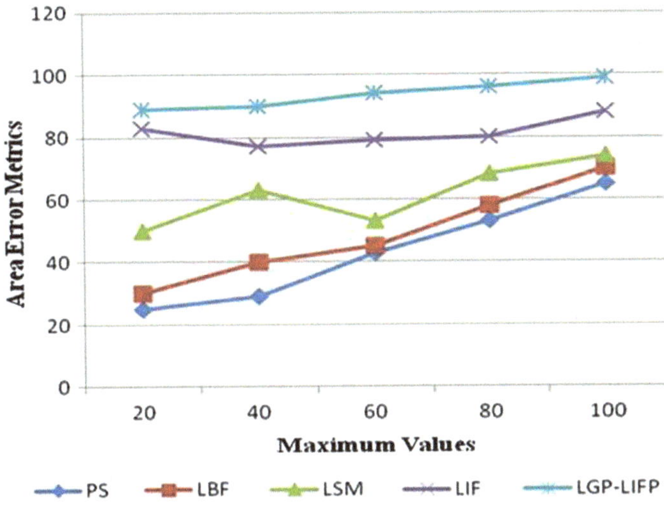

Fig. 16 Area error metrics test [10]

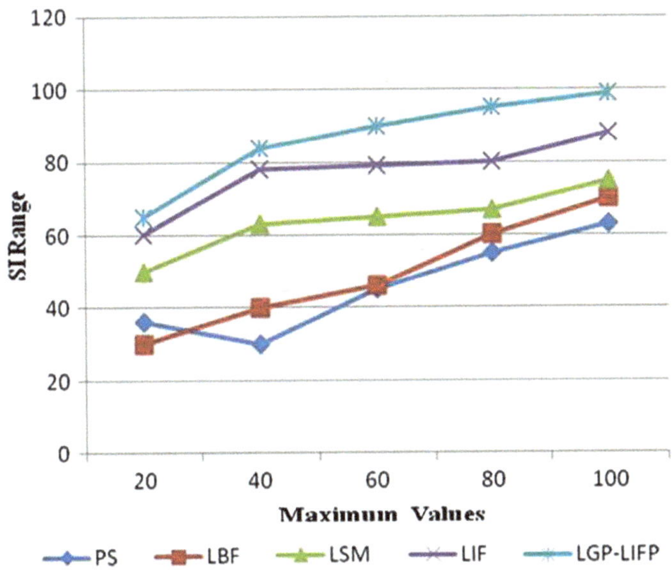

Fig. 17 Similarity index metrics test [10]

Table 7 represents a statistical comparison of lesion area and air gap area with numerous conventional methods and newly presented LGP-LIFP method which clearly represents that LGP-LIFP method produces more reliable and fine results than the previous methods of segmentation.

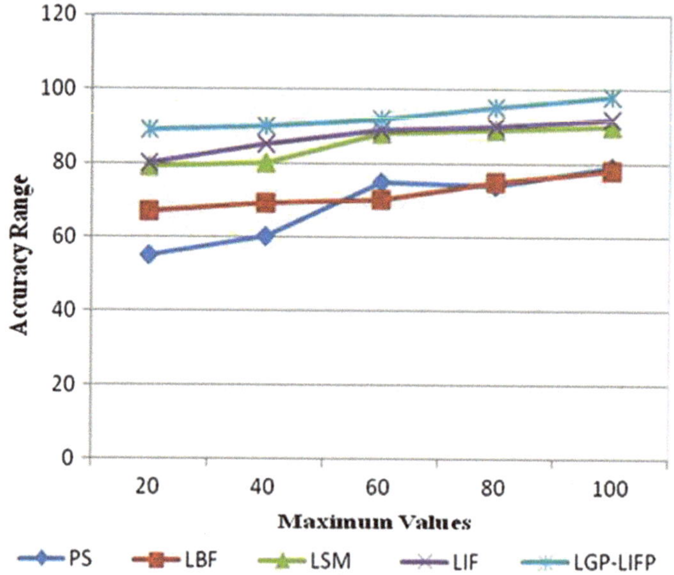

Fig. 18 Efficiency [10]

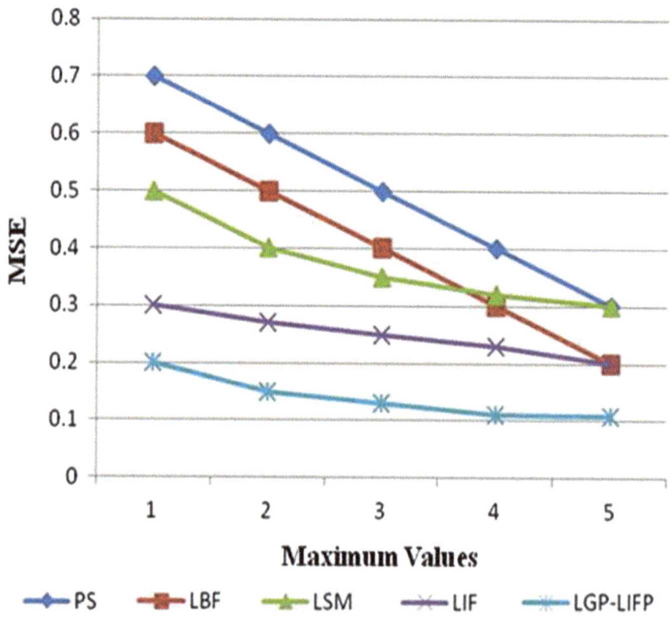

Fig. 19 Efficiency test [10]

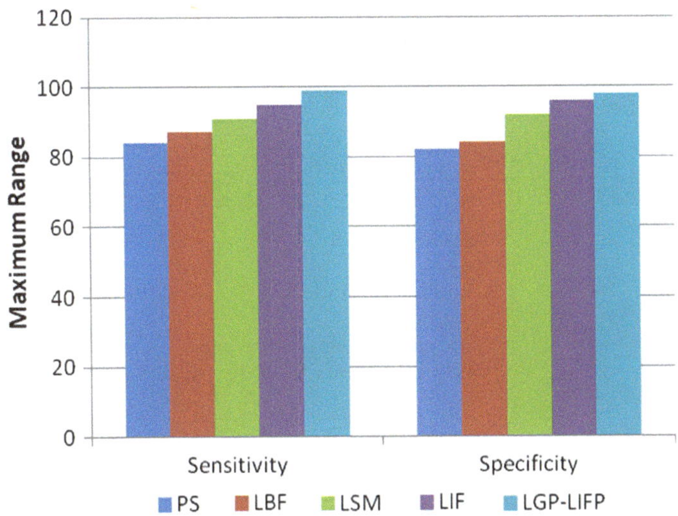

Fig. 20 Specificity and sensitivity scale [10]

Table 7 Lesion area and air gap area study [10]

Procedures	Lesion area		Air gap area	
Jaw types	Upper jaw	Lower jaw	Upper jaw	Lower Jaw
PS	1	2	0	1
LBF	2	1	0	1
LSM	1	1	0	0
LIF	1	2	1	0
LGP-LIFP	2	2	1	1

This research is eminently stronger to deal the image noise with less overlaps in the molded regions in terms of picture intensities and with intensity inhomogeneity. Author also suggested a future scope work for the betterment of image segmentation by using optimization methods to evaluate dental pictures pixel by pixel in a more efficient way.

In South-Central Asia, the oral cancer is widespread with 48.7% of overall cases in the year of 2012 [59]. In 2009, India committed to 33% of the universal oral cancer load in which 270,000 occurrences and 45,000 casualties [60, 61]. Health care was burdened with the dejection and fatality affiliated because of this disorder. Because of the extreme uses of tobacco and betel nut, oral squamous cell carcinomas (OSCC) provides up to 90% of the malignant growths. In the 2019, clinical testing fundamentals and findings after the application of essential stains for diagnostic treatments of patients carrying doubtful oral contusion like leukoplakia and erythroplakia has been provided by Panta et al. [57]. This work described an analysis on essential stains which are reachable in market and their significance for clinical use. Table 8

Table 8 Analysis of diagnostic power of a screening check [57]

Total reviews = 60	Analysis outcomes	
	Positive	Negative
Infected = 30	$V = 26$ (true positive)	$X = 4$ (false negative)
No infected = 30 i.e., regulations	$Y = 5$ (false positive)	$Z = 25$ (true negative)

Calculated Sensitivity–$V/V + X = 26/30 = 0.86$ or 86% (the true positive ratio)
Calculated Specificity–$Z/Y + Z = 25/30 = 0.83$ or 83% (the true negative ratio)
Calculated Positive predictive rate: $V/V + Y = 26/31 = 0.83$
Calculated Negative predictive rate: $Z/X + Z = 25/29 = 0.86$

represents an experimentation of detection power of the screening check with the performance metrics (sensitivity, specificity, positive predictive rate, negative predictive rate). A comparative study of their advantages, disadvantages and introduction of new shielding procedures have also been discussed.

Disclosure of oral malignant growth in the initial phase of (1st or 2nd) provides an important effect on the diagnosis and complete endurance of the sufferer. The five years endurance estimation for the sufferer carrying OSCC of movable tongue is about 80% in 1st phase and decrease to 15% in 4th phase [61]. Most of the oral malignant growth introduces primarily as oral potentially malignant disorders (OPMDs). 22 benchmarks addressed by the National Screening Board in the UK which should be fulfilled prior to the involvement of screening devices for analytic usage [62]. Table 9 represents performance analysis of various oral cancer procedures with the reference of gold measures.

Table 10 represents common ominous symptoms of oral cancer.

COE is the best elementary approach to enhance the recovery score and it is used for examining the sufferer with OPMDs and oral malignant disorder.

Table 9 Elementary efficiency analysis for various oral cancer procedures [57]

Efficiency spectrum	Oral cancer diagnostic approach	Remarks
1	Biopsy	Gold measures reference analysis
AUC < 0.1	Cytology	According to actual statistics, it is difficult to estimate which design is preferable over the other design and each design if practiced efficiently may help a competent and proficient therapist
	luminous designs	
	Critical stain	
	Mouth self-check	
	Typical oral check	

Table 10 General warning symptoms of oral cancer [57]

1. Non-curative oral lesion
2. Prevailing red/white lesion
3. A rough curdle
4. Intrusive sensation or tumor in mouth
5. Increase in trismus or decrease in tongue movability
6. Weak fit of teethes
7. Developing tooth movability or ache
8. Sound variation
9. Loss of weight/loss of appetite

6 Discussions

This Study talks about various forms of oral cancer and also touches upon the anatomical locations where oral cancers predominantly occur. Scientists and Researchers should not confine their attention to teeth but also analyze the oral mucosa for early detection of precancerous lesions which would drastically reduce the mortality and morbidity rate. Using image segmentation techniques in medical diagnosis of oral cancer, newly introduced technology has played a pivotal role.

Computer aided algorithms are crucial in automating the radiological jobs like segmented anatomical structures and the diseased regions in the body.

7 Gaps and Future Directions

Various designs from previous researches were not enough capable to strengthen local image fitting characteristic with an effective manner and it could have been revolutionary and more opposing to noise. It is required to have an accurate and efficient image segmentation design for the correct diagnosis of oral malignancy. In future, segmentation process can be made more fine and reliable by using various advanced and improved methods which will be capable of evaluating oral images pixel by pixel in an effective way.

8 Conclusion

A systematic review has been provided for automatic detection of oral cancer in this chapter. Various segmentation methods used for the detection of oral cancer have been discussed. A comparative study of different methods has been presented for better understanding. These methods are judged with sensitivity, specificity, efficiency, and other significant parameters. This study provides a clear hierarchy to understand the diverse designs and their algorithms to find the malignant lesions in jaw bone. A learning-based review for the detection of oral cancer has been provided. This further drives to attain a more efficient and accurate model for the segmentation of images in oral cancer and decrease of freedom for experimentation, discovering more strengthen and powerful segmentation algorithm for detection of oral cancer.

References

1. CRUK. https://www.cancerresearchuk.org 2017, Accessed on May 1, 2020.
2. Shivam, B. (2020). Oral cancer (lips and tongue) images, Version 1, Accessed on Dec 09, 2020 from https://www.kaggle.com/shivam17299/oral-cancer-lips-and-tongue-images.
3. Sabuncu, M. R., Yeo, B. T. T., Van Leemput, K., Fischl, B., & Golland, P. (2010). A generative model for image segmentation based on label fusion. *IEEE Transactions on Medical Imaging, 29*(10), 1714–1729.
4. Pohl, K. M., Fisher, J., Grimson, W. E. L., Kikinis, R., & Wells, W. M. (2006). A Bayesian model for joint segmentation and registration. *NeuroImage, 31*(1), 228–239.
5. Ashburner, J., & Friston, K. J. (2005). Unified segmentation. *NeuroImage, 26*(3), 839–851.
6. Kumar, R., Khambete, N., & Priya, E. (2011). Extraoral periapical radiography: an alternative approach to intraoral periapical radiography. *Imaging Science in Dentistry, 41*(4), 161
7. Wang, C.-W., Huang, C.-T., Lee, J.-H., Li, C.-H., Chang, S.-W., Siao, M.-J., et al. (2016). A benchmark for comparison of dental radiography analysis algorithms. *Medical Image Analysis, 31,* 63–76.
8. Silverman, S. (2003). Epidemiology. In *Oral Cancer* (pp. 1–6). American Cancer Society.
9. Morikawa, T., Kozakai, A., Kosugi, A., Bessho, H., & Shibahara, T. (2020). Image processing analysis of oral cancer, oral potentially malignant disorders, and other oral diseases using optical instruments. *International Journal of Oral and Maxillofacial Surgery, 49*(4), 515–521.
10. Alarifi, A., & Alwadain, A. (2019). Computer-aided cancer classification system using a hybrid level-set image segmentation. *Measurement, 148,* 106864.
11. Abdi, A. H., Kasaei, S., & Mehdizadeh, M. (2015). Automatic segmentation of mandible in panoramic x-ray. *Journal of Medical Imaging., 2*(4), 044003.
12. Fahmy, G. (2005). Toward an automated dental identification system. *Journal of Electronic Imaging, 14*(4), 043018.
13. Jain, A. K., & Chen, H. (2004). Matching of dental X-ray images for human identification. *Pattern Recognition, 37*(7), 1519–1532.
14. Lin, P. L., Lai, Y. H., & Huang, P. W. (2010). An effective classification and numbering system for dental bitewing radiographs using teeth region and contour information. *Pattern Recognition, 43*(4), 1380–1392.
15. Lin, P.-L., Lai, Y.-H., & Huang, P.-W. (2012). Dental biometrics: Human identification based on teeth and dental works in bitewing radiographs. *Pattern Recognition, 45*(3), 934–946.
16. Mahoor, M. H., & Abdel-Mottaleb, M. (2005). Classification and numbering of teeth in dental bitewing images. *Pattern Recognition, 38*(4), 577–586.
17. Nassar, D. E. M., & Ammar, H. H. (2007). A neural network system for matching dental radiographs. *Pattern Recognition, 40*(1), 65–79.
18. Nomir, O., & Abdel-Mottaleb, M. (2005). A system for human identification from X-ray dental radiographs. *Pattern Recognition, 38*(8), 1295–1305.
19. Zhou, J., & Abdel-Mottaleb, M. (2005). A content-based system for human identification based on bitewing dental X-ray images. *Pattern Recognition, 38*(11), 2132–2142.
20. Frejlichowski, D., & Czapiewski, P. (2013). An Application of the curvature scale space shape descriptor for forensic human identification based on orthopantomograms. In K. Saeed, R. Chaki, A. Cortesi, & S. Wierzchoń (Eds.), *Computer information systems and industrial*

management (Vol. 8104, pp. 67–76)., CISIM 2013, Lecture Notes in Computer Science Berlin, Heidelberg: Springer.
21. Son, L. H., Tuan, T. M., Fujita, H., Dey, N., Ashour, A. S., & Ngoc, V. T. N. (2018). Dental diagnosis from X-Ray images: An expert system based on fuzzy computing. *Biomedical Signal Processing and Control, 39,* 64–73.
22. Guillaume, S. (2001). Designing fuzzy inference systems from data: An interpretability-oriented review. *IEEE Transactions on Fuzzy Systems, 9*(3), 426–443.
23. Priyatharshini, R., & Chitrakala, S. (2018). A self-learning fuzzy rule-based system for risk-level assessment of coronary heart disease. *IETE Journal of Research, 65*(3), 288–297.
24. Chattopadhyay, S., Davis, R. M., Menezes, D. D., Singh, G., Acharya, R. U., & Tamura, T. (2010). Application of bayesian classifier for the diagnosis of dental pain. *Journal of Medical Systems, 36*(3), 1425–1439.
25. Chattopadhyay, C., Kim, D. W., Gombos, D. S., Oba, J., Qin, Y., Williams, M. D., et al. (2016). Uveal melanoma: From diagnosis to treatment and the science in between. *Cancer, 122*(15), 2299–2312.
26. Kavitha, M. S., Asano, A., Taguchi, A., Kurita, T., & Sanada, M. (2012). Diagnosis of osteoporosis from dental panoramic radiographs using the support vector machine method in a computer-aided system. *BMC Medical Imaging, 12*(1).
27. Oad, K. K., DeZhi, X., & Butt, P. K. (2014). A fuzzy rule based approach to predict risk level of heart disease. *Global Journal of Computer Science Technology, 14*(3), 16–22.
28. Castillo, O., Melin, P., Ramírez, E., & Soria, J. (2012). Hybrid intelligent system for cardiac arrhythmia classification with Fuzzy K-Nearest Neighbors and neural networks combined with a fuzzy system. *Expert Systems with Applications, 39*(3), 2947–2955.
29. Ramírez, J., Górriz, J. M., Salas-Gonzalez, D., Romero, A., López, M., Álvarez, I., et al. (2013). Computer-aided diagnosis of Alzheimer's type dementia combining support vector machines and discriminant set of features. *Information Sciences, 237,* 59–72.
30. Grabisch, M., Nguyen, H. T., & Walker, E. (1995). Introduction. In *Fundamentals of uncertainty calculi with applications to fuzzy inference* (pp. 1–3). Dordrecht Kluwer.
31. Doi, K. (2007). Computer-aided diagnosis in medical imaging: Historical review, current status and future potential. *Computerized Medical Imaging and Graphics, 31*(4–5), 198–211.
32. Pretty, I. A., & Maupomé, G. (2014). A closer look at diagnosis in clinical dental practice: Part 1. Reliability, validity, specificity and sensitivity of diagnostic procedures. *Journal (Canadian Dental Association), 70*(4), 251–255.
33. Priyono, A., Ridwan, M., Alias, A. J., Rahmat, R. A., Hassan, A., Mohd. Ali, M. A. (2005) Generation of Fuzzy Rules with Subtractive Clustering. *Jurnal Teknologi, 43*(1), 143–153.
34. Son, L. H., & Thong, N. T. (2015). Intuitionistic fuzzy recommender systems: An effective tool for medical diagnosis. *Knowledge-Based Systems, 74,* 133–150.
35. Thong, N. T., & Son, L. H. (2015). HIFCF: An effective hybrid model between picture fuzzy clustering and intuitionistic fuzzy recommender systems for medical diagnosis. *Expert Systems with Applications, 42*(7), 3682–3701.
36. Bezdek, J. C., Ehrlich, R., & Full, W. (1984). FCM: The fuzzy c-means clustering algorithm. *Computers & Geosciences, 10*(2–3), 191–203.
37. Bouchachia, A., & Pedrycz, W. (2006). Data Clustering with partial supervision. *Data Mining and Knowledge Discovery, 12*(1), 47–78.
38. Bouchachia, A., & Vanaret, C. (2014). GT2FC: An online growing interval type-2 self-learning fuzzy classifier. *IEEE Transactions on Fuzzy Systems, 22*(4), 999–1018.
39. Hamasuna, Y., & Endo, Y. (2012). On semi-supervised fuzzy c-means clustering for data with clusterwise tolerance by opposite criteria. *Soft Computing, 17*(1), 71–81.
40. Yin, X., Shu, T., & Huang, Q. (2012). Semi-supervised fuzzy clustering with metric learning and entropy regularization. *Knowledge-Based Systems, 35,* 304–311.
41. Portela, N. M., Cavalcanti, G. D. C., & Ren, T. I. (2014). Semi-supervised clustering for MR brain image segmentation. *Expert Systems with Applications, 41*(4), 1492–1497.
42. Belkin, M., & Niyogi, P. (2002). Laplacian eigenmaps and spectral techniques for embedding and clustering. *Advances in Neural Information Processing Systems, 14,* 585–591.

43. He, X., Cai, D., Wen, J.-R., Ma, W.-Y., & Zhang, H.-J. (2007). Clustering and searching WWW images using link and page layout analysis. *ACM Transactions on Multimedia Computing, Communications, and Applications., 3*(2), 10.
44. Hu, Y., Yu, N., Li, Z., & Li, M. (2007) Image search result clustering and re-ranking via partial grouping. In *2007 IEEE International Conference on Multimedia and Expo* (pp. 603–606).
45. Kavitha, N., Vijayarathna, S., Jothy, S. L., Oon, C. E., Chen, Y., Kanwar, J. R., et al. (2014). MicroRNAs: Biogenesis, roles for carcinogenesis and as potential biomarkers for cancer diagnosis and prognosis. *Asian Pacific Journal of Cancer Prevention, 15*(18), 7489–7497.
46. Manh Tuan, T., & Hoang Son, L. (2016). A novel framework using graph-based clustering for dental X-ray image search in medical diagnosis. *International Journal of Engineering and Technology., 8*(6), 422–427.
47. Valachovic, R. W., Douglass, C. W., Reiskin, A. B., Chauncey, H. H., & McNeil, B. J. (1986). The use of panoramic radiography in the evaluation of asymptomatic adult dental patients. *Oral Surgery, Oral Medicine, Oral Pathology., 61*(3), 289–296.
48. Greenstein, G., & Cavallaro, J. (2014). Failed dental implants. *The Journal of the American Dental Association, 145*(8), 835–841.
49. Narkhede, H. P. (2013). Review of image segmentation techniques. *Journal of Image and Graphics., 1*(8), 54–61.
50. Ahonen, T., Hadid, A., & Pietikainen, M. (2006). Face description with local binary patterns: Application to face recognition. *IEEE Transactions on Pattern Analysis and Machine Intelligence, 28*(12), 2037–2041.
51. Lai Y. H., & Lin P. L. (2008) Effective segmentation for dental X-ray images using texture-based fuzzy inference system. In J. Blanc-Talon, S. Bourennane, W. Philips, D. Popescu, & P. Scheunders (Eds.), *Advanced Concepts for Intelligent Vision Systems*. ACIVS 2008. Lecture Notes in Computer Science, Vol. 5259. Springer, Berlin, Heidelberg (2008)
52. Ghazali, K. H., Mustafa, M. M., Hussain, A., Bandar, M. E. C., Kuantan, G. (2007) Feature Extraction technique using SIFT keypoints descriptors. In *International Conference on Electrical and Engineering and Informatics Institute Technology* (pp. 17–19)
53. Tuan, T. M., Ngan, T. T., & Son, L. H. (2016). A novel semi-supervised fuzzy clustering method based on interactive fuzzy satisficing for dental x-ray image segmentation. *Applied Intelligence., 45*(2), 402–428.
54. Abdi, A., Kasaei, S. (2020) Panoramic dental X-rays with segmented mandibles. Mendeley Data, v2
55. Frejlichowski, D., & Wanat, R. (2011) Automatic segmentation of digital orthopantomograms for forensic human identification. In *Image Analysis and Processing-ICIAP 2011* (pp. 294–302). Springer, Berlin, Heidelberg.
56. Shi, S.-W., Li, B., Dong, Y., Ge, Y., Qu, X., Lu, L.-G., et al. (2019). In vitroand clinical studies of gene therapy with recombinant human adenovirus-p53Injection for malignant melanoma. *Human Gene Therapy Clinical Development., 30*(1), 7–18.
57. Panta, P (2019) Biopsy and oral squamous cell carcinoma histopathology. In *Oral Cancer Detection. Novel Strategies and Clinical Impact* (p. 142)
58. Muthulakshmi, M., & Kavitha, G. (2018) Analysis of myocardial ischemia from cardiac magnetic resonance images using adaptive fuzzy-based multiphase level set. In *Computational Signal Processing and Analysis* (pp. 11–22). Springer, Singapore
59. Shield, K. D., Ferlay, J., Jemal, A., Sankaranarayanan, R., Chaturvedi, A. K., Bray, F., et al. (2016) The global incidence of lip, oral cavity, and pharyngeal cancers by subsite in 2012. *CA: A Cancer Journal for Clinicians, 67*(1), 51–64
60. Subramanian, S. (2009). Cost-effectiveness of oral cancer screening: results from a cluster randomized controlled trial in India. *Bulletin of the World Health Organization, 87*(3), 200–206.
61. Warnakulasuriya, S. (2009). Global epidemiology of oral and oropharyngeal cancer. *Oral Oncology, 45*(4–5), 309–316.
62. Lingen, M. W., Kalmar, J. R., Karrison, T., & Speight, P. M. (2008). Critical evaluation of diagnostic aids for the detection of oral cancer. *Oral Oncology, 44*(1), 10–22.

IoT Based Healthcare Monitoring System Using 5G Communication and Machine Learning Models

Saswati Paramita, Himadri Nandini Das Bebartta, and Prabina Pattanayak

Abstract This chapter presents a smart healthcare monitoring system for patients by implanting wireless sensors on the body which collect different vital physiological parameters such as heart rate, blood pressure, body temperature, glucose level etc. The sensors are controlled by the Internet of Things devices and communicate the patient's health record to the monitoring station using 5G services. This 5G service helps to enable the immediate treatment for the critical patient with no time. In addition, the rate of detection of the critical condition of the patient is enhanced with the application of machine learning models for better and efficient prediction. Therefore, the improvement of healthcare monitoring system enhances human life value by integrating advanced and cutting edge technologies as a consequence of which the frequent visit of patients to the hospitals or emergency units can be reduced.

Keywords Healthcare monitoring system · Internet of things · 5G · Machine learning algorithms · IoT devices

1 Introduction

Intensive unhealthy life style of humanoid leads to various health issues and is noticeably increasing day after day. However, due to busy lifestyle schedule, visiting medical consultant or hospital at regular basis becomes difficult for patients. Therefore,

S. Paramita
Dayananda Sagar University, Bengaluru, India
e-mail: sparamita2007@gmail.com

H. N. D. Bebartta
ICFAI University, Hyderabad, India
e-mail: himadri.nandini@gmail.com

P. Pattanayak (✉)
Department of Electronics and Communication Engineering, National Institute of Technology Silchar, Silchar, India
e-mail: prabina.pattanayak@ieee.org

R. Patgiri et al. (eds.), *Health Informatics: A Computational Perspective in Healthcare*, Studies in Computational Intelligence 932,
https://doi.org/10.1007/978-981-15-9735-0_9

to minimize the need of human involvement in continuous health monitoring of a patient suffering from various health concerns such as heart disease, diabetes, blood pressure, cancer, stress etc. [10, 18], Internet of Things (IoT) plays an important role in health care monitoring system. The IoT devices monitor the health conditions of the patient remotely independently irrespective of the physical presence at the monitoring station, i.e., anywhere as well as anytime [19]. Again, 5G when used over current Long Term Evolution (LTE) networks, benefits IoT devices in achieving an increased transmission speed, a greater number of connected devices, a lower latency thereby increasing the capacity of remote execution [5, 15, 16]. This in turn motivated and enhanced the confidence of the providers in receiving the real time data when needed and provide care to the patient's requirement thereby fulfilling their expectations. Further, the disease of a sufferer can be predicted in the IoT systems using Machine learning (ML) algorithms by processing the measuring parameters such as pulse rate, temperature, blood pressure, etc. Therefore, IoT along with ML is used to alarm the situation when the patient is in real risk [1, 13]. ML predicts the health condition of a patient by using various supervised learning algorithms such as naive bayes, logistic regression, support vector machines, and decision trees etc. [7, 20]. Furthermore, evaluation of different ML models on predicted results can be analyzed using various performance metrics such as receiver operating characteristic (ROC) curve, confusion matrix etc. Ultimately, after data analysis using ML models, IoT implementing 5G is used to communicate the acute condition of the patient to the doctors present in monitoring station and the same is notified to the patient.

1.1 What Is IoT?

IoT is a dynamic, self configured and interoperable wireless network which has a capability to interconnect seamlessly billions of physical things or objects having physical identities and intelligent interfaces. These interconnected things are known as smart IoT devices as they are enabled by advanced communication technologies, smart sensor technologies and internet protocols. The advancement of IoT technology is capable of connecting anything, anyone at any time to any place by providing any services. The extensive applications of IoT are in several fields such as environmental monitoring, e-healthcare, motion monitoring in sports, smart city, smart vehicle, smart agriculture, smart grid and telemedicine etc. However, the future research estimates that around 40 billion of devices will be connected to the internet by 2021 [9, 10]. Therefore, there are requirements of large scale of connectivity, high security and privacy, large coverage of communication, low latency and high reliability for massive IoT devices in future wireless information network for different multitude of applications. So, the emerging technologies such as LTE and 5G are used for providing seamless connectivity as interfaces to the large number of IoT devices in the wireless network.

1.1.1 Design Requirement for IoT

The massive IoT devices are efficiently connected in a wireless network by implementing cellular low power wide area (LPWA) technology [5]. However, massive IoT network deployment for various services needs different design requirements [15] such as (shown in Fig. 1)

- Low cost IoT devices
- Low cost deployment technology
- Long life battery
- Extended coverage
- Highly secured and private network
- Support for massive number of IoT devices
- Device and data reliability

Low cost IoT devices: The cost of production of IoT devices should be optimized according to cellular low power wide area (LPWA) applications to support massive IoT devices deployment in a wireless network according to business or revenue generation perspective.

Low cost deployment technology: The connectivity of IoT devices in entire network should be cost effective for massive IoT applications. Therefore, software upgradation is required to connect massive IoT devices in existing cellular network and deploy for LPWA applications by maintaining the minimum capital expenditure.

Long life battery: Essentially, IoT devices are powered by battery as they are operated and controlled remotely from monitoring stations without intervention of human. As a scenario, it is also a challenging task to replace batteries within given interval of time when the fire management department receives the information from the fire alarm system. Therefore, it is necessary to consider the factor of energy efficiency while designing software and hardware for massive IoT applications. However, the battery life is extended by using efficient medium access (MAC) protocols to reduce duty cycle with the inclusion of sleep period in super-frame structure. So that the radio will be in sleep mode. Thus, the energy management techniques have great

Fig. 1 Application of IoT

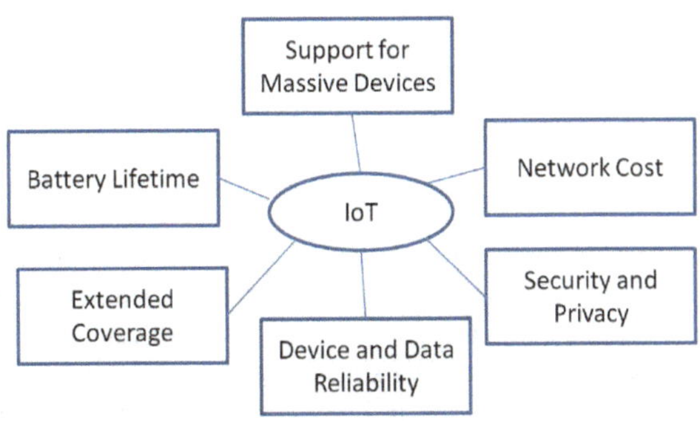

impact for low battery power operation by using efficient protocols and optimized routing algorithms for massive IoT applications. These techniques are also useful to reduce unnecessary energy harvesting by IoT devices from other sources as well as allow for connecting and deploying new smart IoT devices which are not in use to the various applications.

Extended Coverage: The massive IoT connectivity has a great design requirement to extend indoor coverage in case of smart basement electrical metering or water metering and applications inside elevator. Therefore, maximum coupling loss (MCL) is used to enhance the coverage for large connectivity of IoT devices. The amount of system coverage is measured by using MCL as per design requirements. It provides the service which can be delivered with limited value of coupling loss. In general, LTE cellular network operates upto 142 dB without enhancement of coverage of outdoor urban or suburban environments. However, this is a challenge to enhance the indoor coverage with adequate signal strength for penetrating walls or floors of the building for massive deployment of IoT devices. Therefore, a link budget for IoT connectivity is used to enhance the indoor coverage.

1.1.2 Existing Communication Technologies for IoT

Currently, the communication technologies are categorized for three networks such as long-range networks (LRNs), short-range networks (SRNs) and cellular networks (CNs) for massive IoT connectivity. Since, connectivity is the key enabler for successful deployment of IoT devices to a network. However, there is no availability of a one-size-fits-all communication solution for innumerable IoT use cases. Each communication technology has its own strengths and weaknesses according to range, scalability, cost and network requirements for best suited scenarios or environments. In general, massive and critical IoT connectivity uses fixed and short range communication through the traditional cellular networks and low power wide area networks (LPWAN) [5]. Because, LPWA technologies for IoT applications are having unique features such as high energy efficiency, high data rate, high channel bandwidth, wide-area coverage and low power consumption.

Long Range Networks: LPWA technologies such as SigFox, Ingenu RPMA, LoRa, Weightless, and DASH7 are used for connecting sensors and controllers to the internet for long range machine type communication (MTC) without intervention of existing communication technologies (traditional WiFi or Cellular). The above LPWA technologies are used for IoT to achieve machine type communication cases.

1. **LoRa**: LoRa is a low power, low cost and long range wireless communication technology based on LPWAN. Long Range Wide Area Network (LoRaWAN) provides long range communication by enabling LoRa physical layer and also manages data rate, frequencies and power for all devices connected to the network. However, the routing between the devices is decided by MAC protocol based on ALOHA in LoRaWAN. LoRa architecture has sensor nodes (devices)

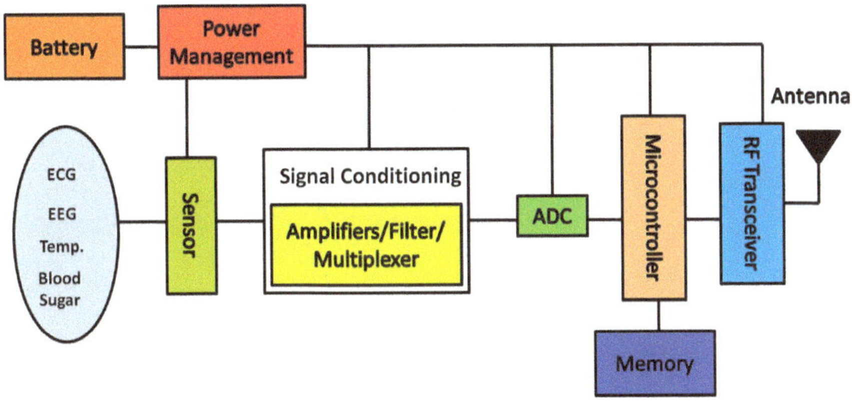

Fig. 2 Physical structure of IoT Device/Object

connected in star network topology, a server, a gateway and a remote terminal as shown in Fig. 2, in which the end devices communicate to the LoRa gateway with a direct single hop communication. LoRa provides bidirectional communication with unique modulation technique such as chirp spread spectrum (CSS) with various bandwidths of 7.8, 10.4, 15.6, 31.2, 41.7, 62.5, 125, 250 and 500 KHz. Frequency Hopping Spread Spectrum (FHSS) is used in LoRa to access the available channel for mitigating the effect of interference. It has been observed that LoRa achieves more than 15 km range of non-line of sight communication in urban environments. The network congestion between end devices and central nodes are handled based on LoRa and network layer of LoRaWAN. In addition, LoRaWAN 868 915 MHz communication band with maximum data rate of 50 Kbps for IoT applications. Thus, spreading factor and channel bandwidth decide the specific possible data rate for LoRa in case of IoT applications.

2. **SigFox**: IoT connectivity or machine to machine (M2M) communication has the requirement of efficient small amount of data transfer with low bandwidth. SigFox is the best suit for this kind of communication by providing low power complete end to end connectivity in wide are a network using ultra narrow band (UNB) technology. This technology uses cognitive software defined radio for configuring the base stations and connects each base station to back-end server based on Internet Protocol (IP)-based network infrastructure as shown in Fig. 3. The end devices of SigFox MTC network communicate to the base station in an UNB 100 Hz using Binary Phase Shift Keying (BPSK) modulation technique. SigFox with UNB technology provides long range communication, higher sensitivity and ultra low power consumption, efficient bandwidth utilization by compensating data rate, i.e., with limited data rate as most of the IoT applications do not have requirements of higher data rate. Moreover, SigFox network provides wide coverage by enabling Line-of-Sight communication using ISM (Industry, Scientific and Medical) band with frequency of operation 868–915

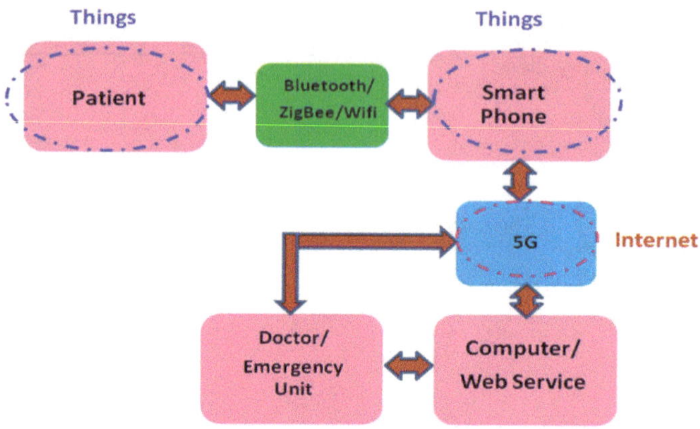

Fig. 3 Block diagram representation of IoT-5G health monitoring system

Table 1 SigFox uplink and downlink transmission specification details

	Uplink	Downlink
Modulation technique	GFSK	DBPSK
No. of messages/day	140	4
Packet size of each message	12 bytes	8 bytes
Total packet size of transmitted messages/day	1680 bytes	32 bytes

MHz. However, this network ranges from 30 to 50 km and beyond in rural areas using frequency hopping technique whereas 3–10 km in urban areas due to existence of obstacles like tall buildings, flyovers etc. Table 1 depicts the detail specifications of uplink and downlink data transmission in SigFox network. Furthermore, UNB signals are vulnerable to any aggressive noise. So, the bit duration exceeds 10 ms which causes a number of times retransmission of frames in SigFox network. Therefore, the traffic load is increased in this network. GFSK stands for gaussian frequency shift keying and DBPSK for differential binary phase shift keying as depicted in Table 1.

3. **Ingenu RPMA**: This LPWA technology has more flexibility as compared to LoRa and SigFox to use the spectrums all around different regions. This also provides better throughput and capacity as compared to other sub-GHz band technology. The communication is bidirectional in Ingenu. However, random phase multiple access (RPMA) direct sequence spread spectrum (DSSS) technique is used for uplink communication in Ingenu where multiple antennas are allowed to share a single time slot as a variable of code division multiple access (CDMA) by adding random offset delay to each of the transmitter within that time slot and avoiding consequent overlapping between the transmitters. Thus, signal to interference ratio increases for individual link. Furthermore, CDMA

is used for broadcasting spread signal of individual end connected devices in downlink communication by base station. Ingenu RPMA is adapted by legacy IEEE 802.15.4k specification with capability of achieving receiver sensitivity upto −142 dBm and a link budget of 168 dB.

4. **DASH7**: DASH7 is also used as a long range wireless technology for direct low power communication between the devices using extended radio frequency identification (RFID) based standards. A narrow band two-level GFSK modulation technique is employed in DASH7 according to SUB-GHz bands. It is offered for applications with noise upto the data rate of 167 Kbps and less data rate. This ranges upto 2 km and communicates to the end devices with 2 hops communication by default.
5. **Weightless**: The Weightless special interest group (SIP) has introduced a new wireless technology for long range low power communication. There are 3 LPWA standards such as:

   - Weightless-W
   - Weightless-N
   - Weightless-P.

   The above LPWA standards are operated in unlicensed as well as licensed spectrum for different ranges with low power consumption. Cognitive radio and TV white space are used by this technology according to the requirements of users. These bands are utilized by the opportunistic users without interfering with the licensed owners as primary user devices.

   - Weightless-W: differential binary phase shift keying (DBPSK) and 16-quadrature amplitude modulation (16-QAM) are supported modulation schemes for this standard with 10 Mbps data rate. The energy consumption is improved with narrow band, low power level signal transmission between the end devices and the base station.
   - Weightless-N: This standard supports one way UNB communication using DBPSK modulation technique from end device to the base station. It 470–790 MHz (TV white space or SUB-1 GHz).
   - Weightless-P: GMSK and QPSK modulation techniques are employed in this standard using narrow band channel 12.5 KHz with data rate of 100 Kbps. The main disadvantage of this standard is that the communication is one way. Therefore, this causes the limited use of various IoT applications. However, it has great merits of extending battery life as it does not support bidirectional communication. So, weightless-P and weightless-W support for long battery life.

Short Range Networks: Bluetooth, ZigBee and low power WiFi are M2M wireless communication technologies for short range wireless network. These technologies are used for IoT applications but does not support for industrial and other long range applications, i.e., beyond the capacity of the network.

1. **Bluetooth**: Bluetooth is a wireless technology which has been designed based on IEEE 802.15.1 standard for short range applications in a personal area network (PAN). It provides short range ad-hoc communication between the devices configured as Master and Slave structure with low Mbps data rate. This technology operates in 2.4 GHz ISM bands. Bluetooth special interest group (SIG) is responsible to manage the technical specifications and improvements like Smart bluetooth low energy (BLE) or Bluetooth 4.0 is used for improving the energy consumption of the connected devices. The Bluetooth standard has 40 channels 2 MHz of channel spacing. Gaussian frequency shift keying (GFSK) is used as modulation technique for Bluetooth 4.0. However, the Bluetooth mitigates interference and multipath fading by using frequency hopping spread spectrum (FHSS). The main drawback of this technology is that only two devices are enabled at a time for limited one to one communication. The bluetooth special group has proposed smart mesh network architecture for low energy Bluetooth technology by enhancing the communication coverage for IoT applications. Therefore, this technology provides the connectivity solution of IoT devices for healthcare, smart home, smart vehicle short range applications.
2. **IEEE 802.15.4 and ZigBee:** IEEE 802.15.4 standard defines the functioning of low rate wireless personal area network (LR-WPAN). This is the origin for ZigBee, 6LoWPAN, WirelessHART, MiWi, SNAP, Thread etc. specifications. IEEE 802.15.4 determines physical and MAC layer for LR-WPAN. This supports three different frequency bands such as 868 MHz, 914 MHz 2.4 GHz for 1, 10 and 16 channels respectively with each 2 MHz bandwidth and data rate of 250 Kbps. IEEE 802.15.4 standard is defined for physical layer (PHY) and data link layer (DLL) while ZigBee is defined for PHY and DLL as well as network layer by adding it on the top of PHY & DLL. The IEEE 802.15.4 uses direct sequence spread spectrum (DSSS) as a modulation technique and Carrier sense multiple accesses with collision avoidance (CMSA/CA) for channel access. The channel access is one of the important parameter for IoT communications. The basic differences between ZigBee and Lora are topology and range of communication.
3. **WiFi**: WiFi is defined as per IEEE 802.11 standard for wireless local area network (WLAN). This provides high bandwidth short range communication between the devices with high throughput connectivity. This technology was not designed for modern IoT communications. In general, the internet connectivity can be provided through wireless network access point within the ISM spectrum band 2.4 and 5 GHz maximum upto 1 km coverage area. The coverage area can be increased by overlapping multiple hotspots. Therefore, IEEE 802.11ac is released with enhanced features to improve the throughput and performance of network for highly dense and congested areas. Furthermore, IEEE has proposed a low power WiFi, known as IEEE 902.11ah, to achieve the IoT connectivity requirements such as massive IoT connected devices, enhancement of coverage area and reducing energy constraint for large scale of applications. This new WiFi standard targets to achieve a 100's milli Watts of lower energy consumption than other for IoT devices by providing large coverage area and data rate upto 347 Mbps.

Cellular Technology: The growth of cellular technology drives the enhancement of massive IoT applications as per the future requirements. This has been ensured by cellular LPWA technologies for various applications or services such as smart traffic, smart metering, smart home, smart grid, smart healthcare or health monitoring, smart vending machines, smart vehicular communication etc.

1. **2G Cellular Networks**: Second Generation (2G) cellular technology is introduced for signalling of low band digital data. Global system for mobile (GSM) is one of the important cellular technologies for 2G wireless communication. The GSM network operates in the frequency range 900–1800 MHz in all over world except in America. In America, GSM is used for operating frequency of 1900 MHz. This GSM technology for 2G wireless system is designed to use 25 MHz frequency spectrum from 900 MHz frequency band with frequency division multiple access (FDMA) or time division multiple access (TDMA). In FDMA, 25 MHz frequency band is divided into 124 carrier frequencies of each 200 KHz. So, multiple users can access the available radio frequency without interference of message signal because 200 KHz guard frequency band. In TDMA, each of this frequency is further divided into 8 time slots. This enables to access same frequency band by 8 different users simultaneously. This technology increases the number of users per single radio frequency at same time. Therefore, massive IoT devices can be deployed globally in cellular network based on GSM connectivity. This is used for limited data capacity applications such as short message and fax system which supports a data rate of 9.6 Kbps. In addition to, this technology does not support multimedia applications and web browsing. Therefore, 2.5G is developed to improve data capacity by adding the services like general packet radio service (GPRS) and wireless application protocol (WAP) to the existing GSM network. This supports 171.2 Kbps of data rate as per 3GPP (3rd Generation Partnership Project) standard for GPRS technology based GSM network.
2. **3G Cellular Network**: The third generation (3G) cellular communication network was introduced by the International Mobile Telecommunications-2000 (IMT-2000) of International telecommunication union (ITU) to provide wireless accessibility for the telecommunication infrastructure connected globally trough terrestrial and satellite system. Hence, this evolution helps to connect massive devices to the internet for various applications beyond multimedia like video conferencing with broadband connectivity even though the user is roaming. The data rate of this technology is as follows based on ITU:

   - 144 Kbps—for mobile users in wide area
   - 384 Kbps—for Pedestrian Users in Urban region
   - 2 Mbps—for fixed users.

   Massive IoT connectivity needs change in circuit based backhaul network, because 3G systems are IP-centric and justified for IP-based infrastructure. Therefore, this is not suitable for MTC for various massive IoT applications.

3. **4G Cellular Network**: Fourth generation (4G) broad band network provides massive connectivity for IoT devices with wide area coverage, low cost deployment, high security, dedicated spectrum allocation and efficient management system based on 3GPP LTE network standard. 4G technology also efficiently supports M2M applications based on 3GPP. Three main key standards are introduced in 3GPP Release-13 of 4G network to enhance the massive deployment of smart devices and services like smart cities, smart grid, smart connected home, smart building, smart traffic, smart hospital, smart health monitoring system etc. The three standards are: Enhanced machine-type communications (eMTC), narrowband-IoT (NB-IoT) and extended coverage GSM for the IoT (EC-GSM-IoT). eMTC is a cellular LPWA technology in Release-13 standardization for massive IoT deployment and coverage. This supports 10 years of long life battery with 5 Watt-Hour battery systems. Therefore, power management system (PSM) and extended discontinuous reception (eDRX) are used in this technology to achieve long life battery. The NB-IoT is a new low power wide area cellular technology. It is used to deploy massive IoT connectivity with existing operator, available spectrum and existing small portion of network. This technology is designed for ultra low end IoT applications such as smart remote sensing, smart metering, smart buildings etc. NB-IoT is a new technology for developing 5G radio network for new usage of IoT. EC-GSM-IoT is an emerging LPWA technology of high capacity, long range coverage, low energy and low complexity cellular network for IoT using enhanced GPRS (eGPRS). This also supports 10 years of battery life for wide range of use cases. Furthermore, the enhancement of this technology supports eDRX which results in the improvement of energy efficiency for the devices, minimization of idle mode processes and admission control for QoS. New logical channels are introduced in EC-GSM-IoT for effective massive deployment of IoT applications to extend the coverage. These channels are known as EC-Channels and are categorized as EC-shared channel, EC-access grant channel, EC-broadcast control channel, EC-packet data traffic channel, EC-paging channel and EC-packet associated control channel.

1.1.3 5G New Communication Technology for IoT

The future IoT system requires new applications and business models with new metrics of performance analysis such as massive connectivity, critical use, security and privacy, coverage range for wireless communication, ultra-low latency, high-throughput, and ultra-reliability for large number of IoT devices [21]. However, these requirements are achieved by the evolving LTE and 5G technologies which provide new connectivity interfaces for future mission-critical IoT applications.

1.2 What is Machine Learning?

The term "Machine Learning" was coined by an American Pioneer in the field of Artificial Intelligence and computer gaming. He defined ML as—**"Field of study that gives computers the capability to learn without being explicitly programmed"**. ML is a subsidiary of artificial intelligence based on the idea that systems can acquire knowledge from data, identify patterns and make decisions with minimum human interference. In a layperson term, ML is teaching computers to generate artificial knowledge by learning from experience. For example, let's say we want to create an app for Cancer patients that can predict whether he/she is cancerous or not based on the various facts such as Radius, Texture, etc which are termed as features. The app is designed in such a manner that it yields 1 for cancerous and 0 for non- cancerous patients. To yield the output we need to take actual data of some cancerous and non-cancerous people and feed it to some algorithms which are termed as training. Finally, when some unknown patient information is fed to the app, it can predict whether a person is suffering from cancer or not.

1.2.1 Applications of Machine Learning in IoT

Recently, IoT is at the pace of growth. Several implementations of IoT came out from industry and academics. ML can help the machines to analyze the data generated by human beings and predicting what they want from that data. ML plays an important role in the aspect of IoT to handle the data generated by those machines. Thereby, ML gives IoT and those machines a brain to think, which is called "embedded intelligence".

Due to the exponential widening of technology, we need high-performance tools to understand the current data and the upcoming data. To reach this objective we need to build intelligent machines. Today, companies are using ML in various fields such as weather forecasting, enhancing business decisions; detect diseases or medical diagnosis, image processing, etc. ML also plays a great role in manufacturing where IoT systems when used with cameras, controllers can save a lot of human resources. Also, it can predict if a particular field goes wrong at a certain time. In healthcare system, the issue is keeping track of personalized health history. Patients with several wearable devices that track those data can help doctors to make more accurate analysis [1].

1.3 IoT Based Health Monitoring System

Now-a-days Internet of Things has more importance in our daily life for different applications Healthcare monitoring system is one of the IoT applications for providing effective emergency services remotely to the patient irrespective of the physical presence. Hence, IoT based health care system enhances the access to care, strengthen to quality of care and reduced the cost of care day by day. As an example, e-health application is used to detect medical issues, emergency alerts and computer assisted instructions for patient healthcare monitoring [6].

Smart phones are connected to the sensors through short range communication technologies such as Bluetooth, ZigBee etc. for monitoring the health condition of the patient. The sensor sends various measured data such as blood pressure, heart rate, body temperature, blood glucose, oxygen level (SpO2) continuously to the smart devices like smart phones and these data are transmitted from the smart device to the cloud through wireless network to the cloud. The cloud stores, analyzes and allows accessing those data by the emergency unit or doctor. If there is an alarm condition then smart phone receives the information in form of message or image or sound alert then the communication redirected to the emergency unit for necessary and immediate action. Therefore, the acquired sensor data of the patient and diagnostic equipment are used for efficient automatic health care control as well as monitoring.

The physical IoT devices or objects are equipped with electronic sensors, micro-controllers, memory, signal processing unit, analog to digital converter (ADC), battery, power management system, transceivers as shown in Fig. 2. However, IoT devices are communicating with each other and users by building suitable protocol stacks. The IoT devices transmit the collected real time medical data to the cloud through the internet for storing, analyzing and activating alarm for abnormal medical information to the patient or doctor present at the monitoring station. These devices are having limited battery power. So, power consumption is required to reduce for continuous and ubiquitous health care monitoring system.

1.3.1 Provision of 5G Communication in IoT Based Health Monitoring System

The advancement of IoT based healthcare technology requires high performance of the system based on ultra reliability, low latency, high throughput, high security and fast communication for strengthening quality of care and cost of care [11, 17]. These requirements are achieved by using 5G wireless communication technology for transmitting various continuous measured data to the cloud for processing and accessing the data from the cloud by the emergency unit. This wireless technology reduces the wait time for taking immediate action against the emergency condition of the patient due to high rate of communication. Therefore, quality of life is improved by using this technology in IoT based healthcare applications. Hence, the revolution of 5G technology using IoT in medical healthcare applications enhances the quality and efficiency of wearable devices [16].

1.3.2 Benefits of Machine Learning in IoT for Healthcare Care Systems

ML is one of the most powerful automation systems that one would have ever come across. The value of ML in healthcare is its ability to process huge datasets, which is beyond the scope of human capability and ultimately provides assistance to a physician in devising and furnishing care which multiplies patient contentment by decreasing the cost of care and leading to better outcomes. ML technique can excellently enhance the degree of diagnosis in any health related issues. Research shows that experienced physicians can detect cancer by nearly 79% accuracy, while 91% (sometimes up to 97%) accuracy can be achieved using ML techniques. Thus IoT system on implementing ML techniques can aid physicians.

ML can be trained to see at images, locate anomalies for impactful treatment procedure. ML helps in providing the physician with critical information for proper diagnosis, testing and suggestions. ML, when used in IoT systems, helps to reduce diagnostic and therapeutic errors that are inevitable in the human clinical practice thereby making a transformation in the continuous monitoring system in healthcare.

Wearable sensor devices used in the IoT health monitoring system, continuously generate an enormous amount of data. The volume of data that gets generated by IoT sensor based health care system, is very high [16]. Thus, after the huge amount of individual health data is collected in the IoT system with help of 5G mobile network, ML algorithms can be applied to eliminate the unnecessary data from the data pool and also predict the health condition of a particular patient.

2 IoT-5G Based Health Monitoring System

The Internet of Things is a interconnected physical network of things or objects or devices with various technologies like bluetooth, wi-fi and cellular together on a single platform. In addition to 5G technology based IoT network are capable of downloading and uploading ultra high resolution data such as 3D videos, images within a fraction of seconds. This IoT-5G enabled system can enhance medical healthcare application drastically. However, IoT enabled healthcare system requires high data rate, high speed, reliable connectivity and long battery life for quality of life. These requirements are fulfilled by IoT based 5G Health Monitoring System. Therefore, patient can be able to avail the service of superfast diagnosis and treatment by implementing 5G communication in IoT based health monitoring system. Furthermore, the revolution of 5G in IoT based medical healthcare helps to enhance the quality and efficiency of wearable devices by reducing latency. Moreover, latency defines the time period for responding to a request or taking action for a service. This great challenge has overcome by using 5G communication in IoT healthcare system.

2.1 Architecture

The block diagram of IoT based health monitoring system by implementing 5G communication is depicted in Fig. 3. The patient's health condition is communicated to nearest smart device like smart phone through Bluetooth or ZigBee or Wi-Fi technology in message form of either text or image or video periodically. This information is stored in cloud computer using wireless communication technology of 5G communication. This is a continuous process of collecting and storing the data at cloud. If there is an emergency alert then the doctor or emergency unit will receive the information from smart phone through 5G communication. In addition, the concern doctor analyses the stored data periodically by accessing from the cloud. If he detects the emergency condition of the patient then the patient receives the immediate action alert from the doctor or emergency unit directly or provided the treatment solution through web services by activating smart ambulance service using 5G communication technology.

Figure 4 clearly shows that the things such as sensors attached to the patient's body and smart phone are connected to the Doctor or cloud through 5G wireless communication networks. The sensors attached to the patient's body continuously senses various parameters such as ECG, EEG, body temperature, insulin level, blood pressure etc. and sends to the master node which is one of the wearable IoT device like smart watch. This master node transmits the sensed data to the smart phone for communicating the health condition of the patient to the doctor or immediate family member or smart ambulance or cloud for storing. The received data are analyzed by the doctor and necessary action is used to be taken accordingly.

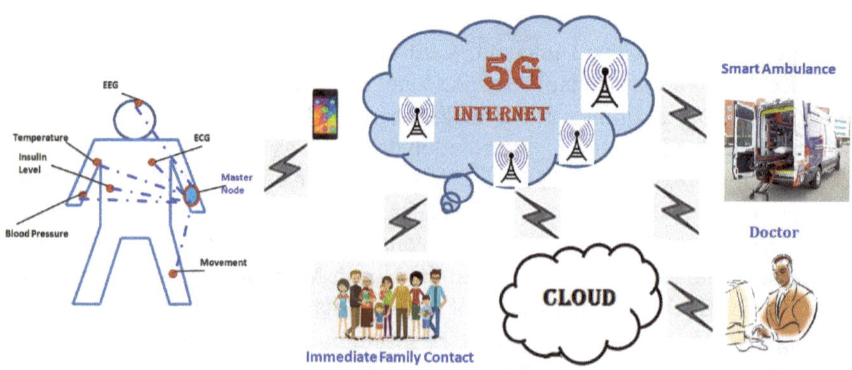

Fig. 4 IoT-5G based health monitoring system architecture

2.2 *Advantages and Limitations*

The advantages of IoT-5G based health monitoring system architecture depicted in Fig. 4 are as follows:

- quality of life improved
- faster services are available
- provides better connectivity, high reliability, low latency, high security
- strengthens cost of care and quality of care

Limitations

- The 5G-IoT healthcare system is lacking of consistency and standardization for IoT system as well as applications because of diversity of IoT-5G network and devices.
- The 5G enabled IoT system [14] has challenges based on following categories:
  - IoT devices: includes design and form of IoT products, big data analytic tools
  - Connectivity: includes communication protocols and networks connecting IoT devices
  - Business Models: includes satisfaction of commerce requirements, vertical, horizontal and consumable markets
  - Killer applications: includes data collection, control and analysis functions.

3 Machine Learning Algorithms for IoT Based System

Earlier in this chapter, we had a vivid discussion on how the 5G mobile networks are useful for supporting high volume of data generated by the IoT architecture. At present, we extend our discussion on how IoT System, when collaborated with Machine Learning Techniques can render its service more effectively. If technology is to enhance awareness in the future, then the digital facts provided to doctors via IoT system needs to be amplified by the power of analytics and ML. Needless to say, ML algorithms have so far been implemented successfully in various fields with outstanding performances. ML is quite efficient in making decisions and predictions and has achieved heights of success so far. It has the ability to deal with a large quantity of data generated by various sectors and healthcare industry is one of them.

Some popular ML Algorithms have been implemented successfully in health care systems. However, before discussing those algorithms let us have a look at the different categories of ML algorithms. This type of classification is important in identifying the role of the input data, the utility of the algorithms and learning models relative to the applications.

Supervised Learning: It is called supervised learning because the procedure of an algorithm while learning from a training dataset can be thought of as a teacher supervising the learning process. In Supervised Learning, we have input variables

(P) and an output variable (Q) and we use an algorithm to learn the mapping function from the input to the output.

$$Q = f(P) \tag{1}$$

The main goal is to approximate the mapping function well such that when we have a new input data (P) then we can predict the output variables (Q) for the data. For example, suppose a container consists of different types of objects such as a pencil, pen, eraser, and sharpener. The task is to arrange the same type of object in one place. Suppose a person assigned the task has prior experience on the shape of every object present in the container. Thus it is easy for him to arrange the similar type of objects in one place.

Unsupervised Learning: In Unsupervised Learning only the input data (P) is present without any output variables. We also stick to the same example considered in supervised learning where our job is to group the same type of objects at one place. This time there is no prior information or knowledge about those objects. As the objects are perceived for the first time, so any physical characteristic of a particular object is selected, say color, and then grouping commences.

Reinforcement Learning: In this type of learning the model acquires knowledge through hit and trial method. It involves an agent who explores the environment and learns how to live and adapt to living conditions on its own based on reward or penalty given for every action it performs. Even though there are a lot of ML algorithms, in this chapter let us explore some of the ML algorithms that are widely applied in the health care system as:

3.1 Logistic Regression

In terms of classifying things, logistic regression is one of the simplest, straightforward and a common algorithm [2]. It is easy to use and interpret. It is a supervised ML algorithm used for classification. Logistic Regression can be used to classify an observation of two classes (e.g., a person suffering from cancer or not or if suffering then he/she is in malignant or benign stage). LR can also be used to study on one of many classes also. But due to simplicity, we stick to two classes.

The goal of binary logistic regression is to train a classifier and create a linear decision boundary separating two classes from each other and also can predict the category to which a new instance belongs to based on the decision boundary. In LR, the decision boundary is given by a conditional probability. Conditional probabilities can help practitioners predict the probability of said tumor as being either Malignant (cancerous) or Benign (non- cancerous). For a binary logistic regression, the outcome can be a 0 or 1. Generally, in Logistic Regression, we are only concerned about the probability of the outcome of the dependent variable or target variable (malignant or benign). Logistic regression uses a sigmoid curve to output a probability value and thus performs the classification.

3.2 Support Vector Machine

One more ML technique that is widely used in health diagnosis is support vector machines (SVM). SVM was introduced by Vapnik [8]. Recent research shows SVM has achieved very high accuracy in cancer diagnosis. It is a very robust and flexible ML model that can effectively perform linear or nonlinear classification and regression. Initially, SVM was used on linearly separable data for binary classification. Detecting an optimal hyperplane is the prime objective of SVM. A decision boundary that helps in classifying the data between two classes is termed as a Hyperplane. There can be a number of Hyperplanes but the one whose aim is to maximize the margin between two classes is an optimal Hyperplane. The largest distance between the nearest data (support vector) and hyperplane in each class is the Margin. Realistically, the data are non linear in nature and hence cannot be linearly separable. However, by transforming the data space to a higher dimension through a non-linear mapping the data space can be linearly separable which is achieved by the use of kernel functions. Several types of kernel exists such as linear, sigmoid function, polynomial and Gaussian RBF. Both RBF and Linear kernel has the same performance on certain parameters [12].

3.3 Naive Bayes

Naive Bayes classifier has the capability to excel over many advanced classification methods and is based on Bayes theorem. Even though it is straightforward in nature, it can handle high dimensional inputs easily. Bayesian analysis believes in prior probability build on previous experiences. The Bayesian analysis is carried out by combining the both the concepts of likelihood and prior to form a posterior probability using Bayes' Rule (named after Rev. Thomas Bayes 1702–1761).

3.4 Deep Learning

Deep learning is an augmentation of the classical neural network. It uses multiple layers to gradually extract higher-level features from raw input. Deep learning, also known as hierarchical learning or deep structured learning, having extra abilities in comparison to classical ML algorithms, Deep Learning can explore more complex non-linear patterns in the data.

In the medical applications, Deep Learning algorithms successfully address both Machine Learning and Natural Language Processing tasks. Convolution neural network (CNN) is a widely used deep learning algorithm which has been successfully implemented in various fields and healthcare has not escaped from it.

Deep learning models consist of a cascade of multiple layers through which data is filtered. Being a pipeline of modules, each of the layers is trainable and can perform automatic feature extraction from the raw input data. In deep learning models, data filtration takes place through the multiple layers associated with it. Each succeeding layer uses the output generated by the previous layer. The hidden layer plays an important role by transforming the raw input to a significant output by implementing mathematical translations.

Recently, CNN has been successfully implemented in the medical area to assist disease diagnoses, such as skin cancer or cataracts. A study in the Annals of Oncology on June 2018 showed that when CNN trained with dermatology images, has the capability to identify melanoma with an increased efficacy of 10% as compared to human clinicians. Even after furnishing the background details of patients to the clinicians such as sex, age and the body site of the suspicious feature, dermatologists were left behind by nearly 7% in comparison to CNN.

In addition to being highly accurate, deep learning tools are fast. A deep neural network has been developed by the researchers at the Mount Sinai Icahn School of Medicine, which can diagnose critical neurological conditions such as brain haemorrhage and stroke by 150 times speed than human radiologists [4]. Similarly, deep learning models can analyze heart failures nine months prior than doctors can predict on the data stored in EHR. A deep learning model can also predict the dip and spikes of glucose levels in diabetic patients and advise them for injecting insulin or consuming sweet snacks [3].

In Fig. 5 manifested below, we can perceive that after collection of information from the edge devices, deep learning plays a great role for the health care system. It increases the capability of the edge nodes such as health care professional by making better and faster predictions in regard to the health condition of the patients.

4 Evaluation

Model evaluation is a mandatory step to check the performance of a machine learning or deep learning model. Through model evaluation, we can figure out the best model that depicts the data and how perfectly the particular model will function in near future. The main aim of the evaluation is to test a model on a different set of data than it was trained on. For easy understanding, we emphasize on binary classification problems. For example, if a patient suffering from cancer is in malignant (positive) or benign (negative) state. Before we start let us discuss four important terms to be focused on:

True Positives (TP): The cases in which we predicted positive and are actually positive.

True Negatives (TN): The cases in which we predicted negative and are actually negative.

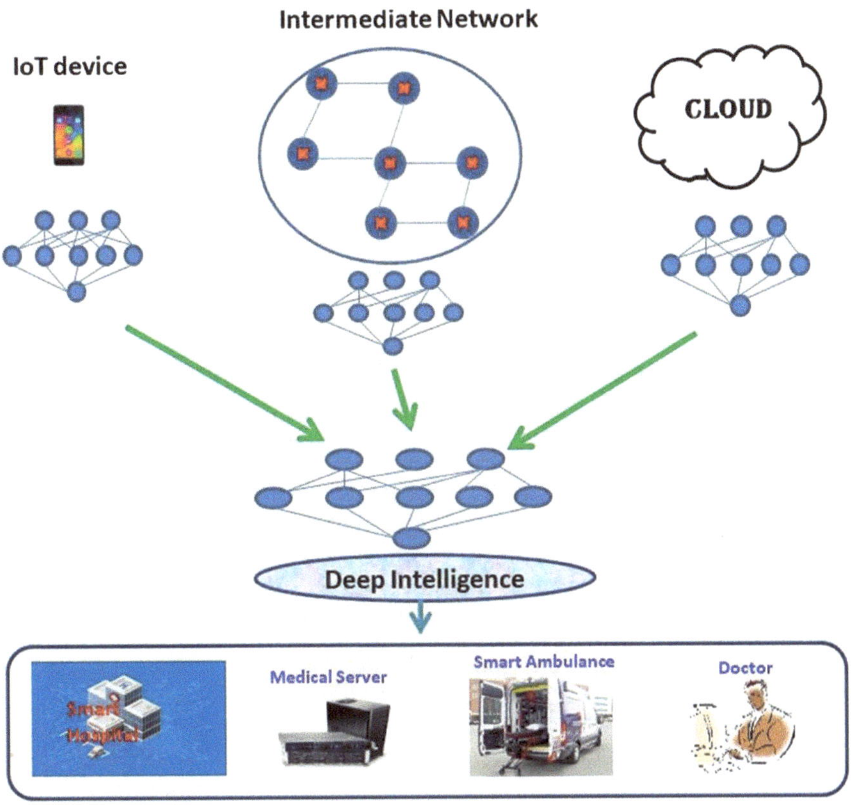

Fig. 5 Application of deep learning in healthcare system

False Positives (FP): The cases in which we predicted positive and are actually negative.

False Negatives (FN): The cases in which we predicted negative and are actually positive. Now we discuss the various metrics for evaluating the different models and when to use one in place of the other.

Accuracy: It is the most conventional and popularly used metric to measure the effectiveness of a model. It is formulated as shown below:

$$\text{Accuracy} = \frac{\text{Total number of correct predictions}}{\text{Total number of input samples or predictions made}} \tag{2}$$

Using the above four terms accuracy can be formulated as:

$$\text{Accuracy} = \frac{\text{TP+TN}}{\text{TP+TN+FP+FN}} \tag{3}$$

The particular cases during which the accuracy metric functions well is only when each class consists of an equal number of samples. The performance of the model terribly goes down when the classes are imbalanced and is thus not a clear indicator for analysis of model performance.

4.1 Confusion Matrix

It is a visual representation of the above said parameters in a matrix format. The confusion matrix shows how the classification model is confused when it makes predictions. Figure 6 represents the confusion made in predicting the disease as Malignant or Benign on Test data set. From the above confusion matrix, we conclude that a particular model has predicted in the following manner:

- 70 data points were correctly predicted as Benign tumors
- 43 data points were correctly predicted as Malignant tumors
- 01 data point was wrongly predicted as Malignant tumor
- 00 data point was not wrongly predicted as Benign tum.

F1 score: F1 score is the harmonic average of precision and recall. F1 Score is used to measure a test's accuracy. This score can range from 0 to 1, with 1 being the best possible F1 score, i.e., perfect precision and recall. And 0 is the worst F1 score.

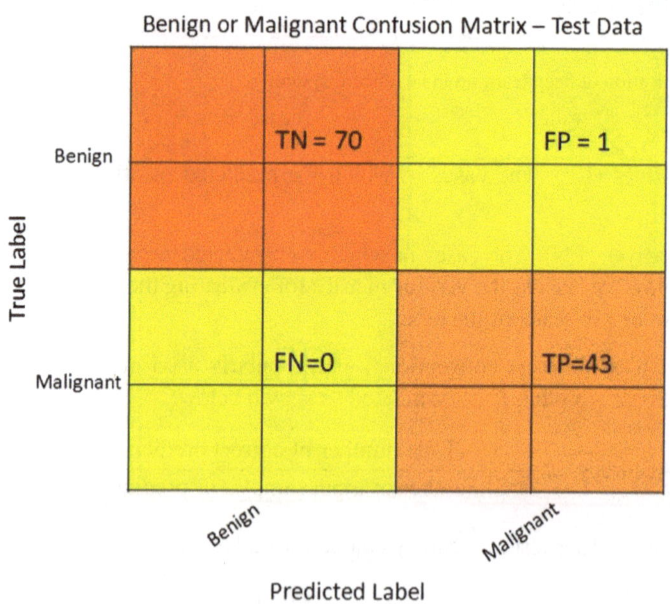

Fig. 6 Confusion matrix predicting malignant or benign stage of cancers

$$\text{F1} = 2 \times \left(\frac{\text{precision} \times \text{recall}}{\text{precision} + \text{recall}}\right) \tag{4}$$

where precision and recall is formulated as below:
Precision: It is the number of correct positive results divided by the number of positive results predicted by the classifier,

$$\text{Precision} = \frac{\text{TP}}{\text{TP+FP}} \tag{5}$$

Recall/ Sensitivity/ True Positive Rate: It is the number of correct positive results divided by the number of all relevant samples (all samples that should have been identified as positive),

$$\text{Recall} = \frac{\text{TP}}{\text{TP+FN}} \tag{6}$$

F1 score takes the contribution of both precision and recall. Higher values of F1 better. But for some applications F1 score may not fit to be the correct metric. Therefore ROC curve can help.

4.2 ROC Curve

A receiver operating characteristic (ROC) curve illustrates the performance of binary classifiers. The curve plots two parameters known as the true positive rate (TPR) and false positive rate (FPR) at different classification thresholds.
True Positive Rate (TPR): TPR is the measure of observations that are correctly predicted to be positive. As mentioned above the formula is:

$$\text{TPR} = \frac{\text{TP}}{\text{TP+FN}} \tag{7}$$

False Positive Rate (FPR): It is the measure of observations that are incorrectly predicted to be positive.

$$\text{FPR} = \frac{\text{FP}}{\text{TN+FP}} \tag{8}$$

TPR and FPR are different for different threshold values. Thus to predict the best threshold for the classifier, we need to plot the ROC curve. A typical ROC curve is shown in Fig. 7.

The diagonal line shows where the TPR is equal to the FPR. Any point in the line means that the proportion of correctly classified obese samples is the same as the proportion of the incorrectly classified sample that is not obese. The black dots

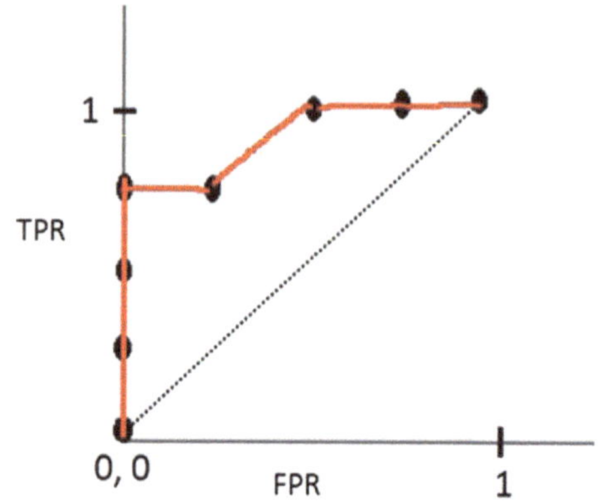

Fig. 7 A typical ROC curve for an obese dataset

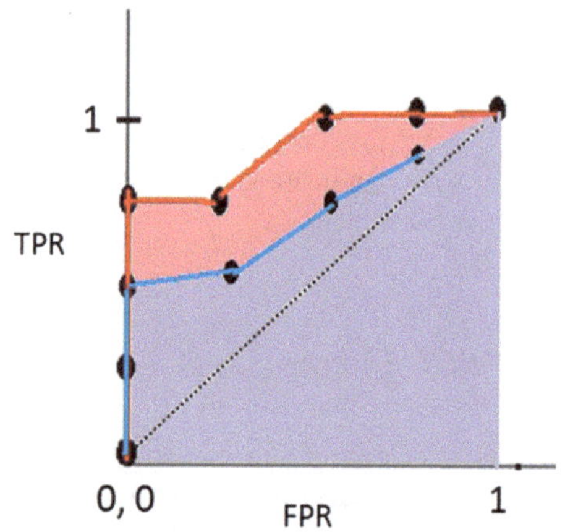

Fig. 8 AUC under ROC curve

show the different TPR and FPR values by changing the threshold values. The point 0,0 represents a threshold that results in zero TP and zero FP. FPR 1 means that every single sample that was not obese was incorrectly classified as obese. TPR 1 means that every single obese sample was correctly classified. A point 1,1 means even though we classified all of the obese samples, we incorrectly classified all of the samples that were not obese. Depending on how many false positive we are willing to accept, the optimal threshold is chosen.

ROC curves make it easy to identify the best threshold for making a decision. One can choose the threshold according to the application at hand. AUC can help to decide which categorization method is better. AUC stands for "Area under the ROC Curve". The AUC makes easy to compare one ROC curve to another. The AUC for the Red ROC curve in Fig. 8 is greater than the AUC for the Blue ROC curve, suggesting that the red ROC curve is better. So if the red ROC curve represents logistic regression and the Blue ROC curve represents Naive Bayes, then we would use Logistic Regression.

5 Conclusion

In this chapter, the authors' attention is towards the application of 5G services on IoT devices used in health care monitoring system. Further to assist the physicians, several ML techniques are implemented such that a patient is being alerted at the real risk period. This chapter introduces some practical usages of several methods that will be favourable for different people. Research directions are talked about how the integration of 5G services in IoT healthcare system amplifies the capacity of remote execution and use of ML techniques provides a backing to the doctors for accurate health predictions of patients. The algorithms explained above in Sect. 3 can be implemented using various open source programming languages such as Python and R. SciKit-Learn and NumPy are some free machine learning libraries for python. Tensor Flow is an open-source software library for numerical computation using data flow graphs and is very popular in deep learning and computer vision.

References

1. (2015). Recent Machine Learning Applications to Internet of Things (IoT). https://www.cse.wustl.edu/~jain/cse570-15/ftp/iot_ml/.
2. (2015). Simple Guide to Logistic Regression in R and Python. https://www.analyticsvidhya.com/blog/2015/11/beginners-guide-on-logistic-regression-in-r/.
3. (2018). Deep Learning in Healthcare. https://missinglink.ai/guides/deep-learning-healthcare/deep-learning-healthcare/.
4. (2018). What is Deep Learning and How Will it Change Healthcare? . https://healthitanalytics.com/features/what-is-deep-learning-and-how-will-it-change-healthcare.
5. Akpakwu, G. A., Silva, B. J., Hancke, G. P., & Abu-Mahfouz, A. M. (2018). A survey on 5G networks for the internet of things: Communication technologies and challenges. *IEEE Access*, *6*, 3619–3647.
6. Ananth, S., Sathya, P., & Madhan Mohan, P. (2019). Smart health monitoring system through IoT. In *2019 International Conference on Communication and Signal Processing (ICCSP)* (pp. 0968–0970).
7. Bhuvaneswari, R., & Kalaiselvi, K. (2012). Naive Bayesian classification approach in healthcare applications.
8. Cortes, C., & Vapnik, V. (1995). Support-vector networks. *Machine Learning*, *20*, 273–297. https://doi.org/10.1007/BF00994018.
9. Darshan, K. R., & Anandakumar, K. R. (2015). A comprehensive review on usage of internet of things (IoT) in healthcare system. In *2015 International Conference on Emerging Research in Electronics, Computer Science and Technology (ICERECT)* (pp. 132–136).
10. Dhanvijay, M. M., & Patil, S. C. (2019). Internet of things: A survey of enabling technologies in healthcare and its applications. *Computer Networks*, *153*, 113–131. https://doi.org/10.1016/j.comnet.2019.03.006, http://www.sciencedirect.com/science/article/pii/S1389128619302695.
11. Goudos, S., Dallas, P., Chatziefthymiou, S., & Kyriazakos, S. (2017). A survey of IoT key enabling and future technologies: 5G, mobile IoT, sematic web and applications. *Wireless Personal Communications*. https://doi.org/10.1007/s11277-017-4647-8.

12. Hassanien, A. E., & hoon Kim, T. (2012). Breast cancer MRI diagnosis approach using support vector machine and pulse coupled neural networks. *Journal of Applied Logic, 10*(4), 277–284. https://doi.org/10.1016/j.jal.2012.07.003, http://www.sciencedirect.com/science/article/pii/S1570868312000523, selected papers from the 6th International Conference on Soft Computing Models in Industrial and Environmental Applications.
13. Kumar, P. M., & Gandhi, U. D. (2018). A novel three-tier internet of things architecture with machine learning algorithm for early detection of heart diseases. *Computers & Electrical Engineering, 65*, 222–235. https://doi.org/10.1016/j.compeleceng.2017.09.001, http://www.sciencedirect.com/science/article/pii/S0045790617328410.
14. Li, S., Xu, L. D., & Zhao, S. (2018). 5G internet of things: A survey. *Journal of Industrial Information Integration, 10*, 1–9. https://doi.org/10.1016/j.jii.2018.01.005, http://www.sciencedirect.com/science/article/pii/S2452414X18300037.
15. Luo, E., Bhuiyan, M. Z. A., Wang, G., Rahman, M. A., Wu, J., & Atiquzzaman, M. (2018). Privacyprotector: Privacy-protected patient data collection in IoT-based healthcare systems. *IEEE Communications Magazine, 56*(2), 163–168.
16. Magsi, H., Sodhro, A. H., Chachar, F. A., Abro, S. A. K., Sodhro, G. H., & Pirbhulal, S. (2018). Evolution of 5G in internet of medical things. In *2018 International Conference on Computing, Mathematics and Engineering Technologies (iCoMET)* (pp. 1–7).
17. Nasri, F., & Abdellatif, M. (2017). Smart mobile healthcare system based on WBSN and 5G. *International Journal of Advanced Computer Science and Applications, 8*. https://doi.org/10.14569/IJACSA.2017.081020.
18. Onasanya, A., & Elshakankiri, M. (2019). Smart integrated IoT healthcare system for cancer care. *Wireless Networks*. https://doi.org/10.1007/s11276-018-01932-1, https://link.springer.com/content/pdf/10.1007/s11276-018-01932-1.pdf.
19. Pal, D., Funilkul, S., Charoenkitkarn, N., & Kanthamanon, P. (2018). Internet-of-things and smart homes for elderly healthcare: An end user perspective. *IEEE Access, 6*, 10483–10496.
20. Rathi, M. (2012). *Breast cancer prediction using naïve bayes classifier, 1*, 77–80.
21. Selvaraj, S., & Sundaravaradhan, S. (2019). Challenges and opportunities in IoT healthcare systems: A systematic review. *SN Applied Sciences*. https://doi.org/10.1007/s42452-019-1925-y, https://link.springer.com/article/10.1007/s42452-019-1925-y.

Forecasting Probable Spread Estimation of COVID-19 Using Exponential Smoothing Technique and Basic Reproduction Number in Indian Context

Zakir Hussain and Malaya Dutta Borah

Abstract The ongoing pandemic of COVID-19 has shut down almost everything and it has become troublesome for smooth running of social life. The infections are increasing day by day. It is important to predict and forecast upcoming increase in infections to plan better. Predicting the possible spread can alert the COVID-19 fighters fighting from the front end as well as the common people. This study is about forecasting possible spread of COVID-19 in India using Exponential Smoothing technique and estimated spread based on Basic Reproduction Number (R_0). R_0 is a sign of transmissibility of a virus. It represents the average number of new infections produced by an infectious person in a completely naive population. Also, this study has focused on forecasting the number of future infections to occur in various states of India. The forecasting and estimation has been carried out for 12 (Twelve) days from August 18, 2020 to August 29, 2020. These forecasted and estimated values show that Maharashtra will experience highest number of confirmed cases followed by Tamil Nadu, Andhra Pradesh, Uttar Pradesh, Delhi and West Bengal. Mizoram will experience least number of cases. This study can help the government and concerned authorities to make good work plan and prepare them for executing the same as per the requirement of states.

Keywords COVID-19 · CoronaVirus · Forecasting COVID-19 · Exponential smoothing · Basic reproduction number · COVID-19 forecasting in India

---

Z. Hussain (✉) · M. Dutta Borah
Department of Computer Science and Engineering, National Institute of Technology Silchar, Silchar, Assam, India
e-mail: zak08hussain@gmail.com

M. Dutta Borah
e-mail: malayaduttaborah@gmail.com

R. Patgiri et al. (eds.), *Health Informatics: A Computational Perspective in Healthcare*, Studies in Computational Intelligence 932,
https://doi.org/10.1007/978-981-15-9735-0_10

1 Introduction

COVID-19 is a highly contagious disease engendered by the 2019 novel corona virus (2019-nCoV) [6]. This virus causes a different type of pneumonia which is very infectious [6]. The pneumonia caused by COVID-19 was initially turned up in Wuhan city in December 2019. Wuhan city is in Hubei Province of China. This disease appeared with an breakout covering Hubei Province and some other areas of the country [6]. World Health Organization (WHO) declared the ongoing outbreak of 2019-nCoV as a public health emergency globally [6]. A study about the death in Italy has claimed that older people with history of diabetes, cardiovascular diseases, cancer and smoking are more susceptible to get infected by Severe Acute Respiratory Syndrome Coronavirus 2 (SARS-CoV-2) [3]. Coronavirus is one of the major microorganisms that predominantly targets the respiratory system of human [11]. The world has experienced the outbreaks of coronavirus (CoVs) in the form of Severe Acute Respiratory syndrome (SARS)–CoV and Middle East Respiratory Syndrome (MERS)–CoV earlier. These were characterized as representatives of a great threat to public health [11]. The interval from the outset of symptoms of COVID-19 to death is 6 to 41 days with an average time frame of 14 days. The indications of COVID-19 contamination emerges after an fecundation period of roughly 5.2 days [11].

Most of the COVID-19 virus infected people will confront mild to moderate respiratory ailment and recover without particular treatment [20]. The COVID-19 virus outspreads predominantly via droplets of spittle or discharge from nose when an infected individual sneezes or coughs [20]. Till date there are no specific vaccine or treatments for this disease [20]. Many organizations have developed many drugs and vaccine and also tested but no drug and vaccine has shown 100% positive result. WHO has suggested to maintain personal hygiene, social distancing, frequently washing hand as a preventive measure. For infected persons, quarantine has been suggested along with healthy diet to increase immunity. Coronaviruses are a family of allied RNA viruses that causes infection in mammals and birds [21]. In human, these viruses infect respiratory tract [21]. Symptoms of these viruses are different in different species [21]. In chickens, they infect upper respiratory tract, in cows and pigs they cause diarrhea [21]. Coronaviruses were first discovered in 1930s in new-born chicks. The chicks' mortality rate was 40–90% [21]. Human coronavirus were discovered in 1960s [21].

Till date the increment of infection is exponential and so in India. In India, initially the infection didn't spread so fast but now it has geared up and the spread has peaked around 47,000 infections per day. As on 21st August 2020, a total of 22,993,104 corona virus cases have been recorded worldwide. Death toll from the pandemic is 799,359. At least 15,616,649 patients recovered. In India a total of 2,969,125 cases have been confirmed, 55,902 death cases and 2,213,887 patients have recovered.

1.1 Motivation and Research Objectives

Recent outbreak of 2019 novel corona virus has shown an exponential growth in number of infections per day. This virus infects all sort of people, however it has been seen that number of male adult persons have been infected the most. This virus has infected adult female, child of all gender, older of all gender. It has been reported that this virus is dangerous to the older and child. Most number of infected senior citizens and child have deceased due to COVID-19. Along with the world, India is also experiencing significant rise in number of new cases per day. It is very important to predict the possible number of infections for next few days in India and its individual states such that administration, doctors, family members, political leaders, health organizations can prepare themselves to combat the situation. They can plan better for reducing the number of new infections such that no one faces the casualty due to COVID-19.

The objectives of this study is to predict and forecast the number of infections supposed to cause in next few days in India as well as in different states of India. The following research questions have to be addressed to fulfill the objectives of this research:

- What is the current trend in infections due to nCoV-19 globally?
- What is the current trend of infections due to nCoV-19 in India and its states?
- Can we correctly predict and forecast the number of infections due to nCoV-19 in India and its states?

To answer the first research questions, we have referred the situation report published by WHO every 24 h. This report contains laboratory confirmed cases globally. To answer the second research questions, we have referred the situation report published by WHO once in a week for each of the countries affected by coronavirus. Also, the Ministry of Health and Social Welfare, Government of India publishes the status of India every day. We have referred that also. For the last question, we have collected the required data and applied a model.

The remaining portion of this study has been arranged into four sections. Section 2 is about the review of literature survey, Sect. 3 presents methodology, Sect. 4 discusses the results and findings while Sect. 5 concludes the study.

2 Literature Review

For this research, we have extensively reviewed the previous works. 2019 novel corona virus (2019-nCoV) is a new study and hence there are limited number of publications and information. For this study, we have focused on the review of the previous studies related to the forecasting as well as estimation of possible spread of coronavirus across the globe. The study in [2] has mentioned that they have provided the approximation of prime epidemiological parameters established on the basis of epidemiological data for Hubei province of People's Republic of China from 11 January to 10 February, 2020. They have also provided an estimation for ratio of fatality and recovery cases with 90% confidence intervals [2]. They have further provided an approximation of Basic Reproduction Number (R_0) as well as per day infection recovery and mortality rates on the basis of Susceptible-Infectious-Recovered-Dead (SIDR) model [2]. They also attempted to forecast the growth of epidemic at the epicenter three weeks up front by calibration of SIRD model parameters [2]. They have also claimed that their forecasting signals a cautionary note for presently evolving outbreak in China [2]. The paper in [15] presents an objective approach to predict the prolongation of COVID-19. Assuming the reliability of data and continuation of past pattern of infection, their forecasts indicate a pick up in the COVID-19 confirmed cases with substantial analogous unpredictability [15]. This paper also outlines the schedule for a real time forecasting effort with enormous potential indication for decision making, planning and imparts objective forecasts for COVID-19 confirmed cases [15].

As mentioned in study [17], the researchers have used formerly validated phenomenological models to make short-term estimates of accumulative cases that are reported in Guangdong and Zhejiang of People's Republic of China. They have reported 5 to 10 days ahead forecasts of cumulative cases using day-to-day reported accumulative cases until February 13, 2020 from National Health Commission of China [17]. They have made forecasts using Richards Growth model, Generalized Logistic Growth model and a Sub-epidemic Wave model [17]. All these models were earlier employed for forecasting outbreaks because of different communicable diseases [17]. Forecasts from these models show nearing extinction of outbreak in both Zhejiang and Guangdong [17]. Additionally, the Sub-epidemic model estimates comprises the possibility of further sustained transmission, specially in Zhejiang [17]. In study [1], they have presented forecasting using an upgraded Adaptive Neuro-Fuzzy Inference System (ANFIS) that uses enhanced Flower Pollination Algorithm (FPA) along with Salp Swarm Algorithm (SSA) [1]. The principal idea of the initiated model named FPASSA-ANFIS is to enhance the efficiency of ANFIS by determination of parameters of ANFIS using FPASSA [1]. Their FPASSA-ANFIS model has been assessed using WHO official data of COVID-19 for forecasting confirmed cases of forthcoming ten days [1]. The study in [14] has shown forecasts with a simple iteration method that uses only day-to-day confirmed cases and the method considers expected recoveries and deaths [14]. Their forecasts suggest to maintain daily growth rates below 5% [14].

In study [18], they have used an age-structured SIR model taking social contact matrices that were got from Bayesian imputation and surveys with an intention to study the headway of COVID-19 pandemic in India. The basic reproduction number (R_0) and its generalization dependent on time are evaluated on the basis of social contact structure, case data and age distribution [18]. They have found that a three week lock down is not sufficient for revival [18]. They have provided forecasts for reduction in age-structured morbidity and mortality [18]. In [13], they predicted the number of infections for next 2 weeks. They have used SEIR and Regression model on the data collected from John Hopkins University depository for the span of

January 30 to March 30, 2020 [13]. RMSLE was used to evaluate the performance and obtained 1.52 for SEIR and 1.75 for regression model [13]. They obtained an RMSLE error rate of 2.01 between SEIR and Regression model [13]. Also, they have found the value of R_0 to be 2.02 [13]. The work in [7] is about the COVID-19 outspread analysis in different nations and principal features for growing COVID-19 [7]. They have hard coded a distinct algorithm in python using Scipy [7]. They have claimed that their algorithm learns the social-contact structure [7]. Their forecasting reveals that strictness to maintain social distancing in India is not sufficient to contain the growth of COVID-19 [7]. The study on forecasting in [19] shows an ascending tendency for the cases in forthcoming days [19]. The study in [9] uses exploratory data analysis for reporting present situation and they have made use of time series forecasting to predict future trends in India and its states. Their findings indicate the quick rise in number of infected cases averaging 10 to 73 cases per day for first 300th case [9]. They have found the mortality rate around 1.9 with Kerala and Maharashtra being the top two contaminated states reporting cases beyond 100 [9]. The paper in [5] have aimed to elucidate the outspreading potentiality of COVID-19 virus in India considering 21 days lock down data. They have fitted the Linear and Polynomial function with the finest fitted plot of daily fresh cases along with number of days exhausted after lock down [5]. They have discussed the forecast of maximum chances of spread with Linear and 4-degree Polynomial fitting parameters [5].

The study in [4] predicts the unfolding of the COVID-19 epidemic in several nations by using a Regression-Based Predictive model. The growth rate of the infection has been inputted as an exponential decay and the model estimates the approximate number of total infections after the outbreak is over [4]. The study in [16] used phenomenological models to produce and evaluate short-term forecasts of accumulative confirmed cases in Hubei province and for inclusive trajectory in China [16]. They collected day-to-day accumulative confirmed cases from National Health Commission of China for each Chinese province [16]. They have used quantified uncertainty that is based on Richards growth model, a generalized logistic growth model and a sub-epidemic wave model to forecast for five successive days starting from 05 February to 09 February 2020 [16]. The study in [8] has analyzed the temporal dynamics of coronavirus in China, Italy and France. Based on their calculation they have estimated that 2500 ventilation units will be required to tackle the peak spread in Italy [8]. The study in [10] proposed a method inspired by artificial intelligence (AI) for forewarning of Covid-19 in real-time. They have expected to estimate lengths, size and terminating time of Covid-19 all over China [10]. They have developed an altered stacked auto-encoder for designing the transmission dynamics of the pandemics [10]. They have used this model for forecasting the confirmed cases across China in real-time [10]. For grouping the provinces or cities to investigate the transmission structure, they used the latent variables in the auto-encoder and clustering algorithms [10]. They predicted the accumulative confirmed cases all over China from 20 January to 20 April, 2020 [10]. They have used multiple-step forecasting to estimate average errors and found 1.64% for 6-step, 2.27% for 7-step, 2.14% for 8-step, 2.08% for 9-step and 0.73% for 10-step forecasting [10]. This shows high accuracy of AI-based methods for forecasting the trajectory [10]. The study in [12] has used a statistical model and predicts an excess demand of 64,175 total beds, 17,380 ICU beds and 19,481 ventilators at the culmination of COVID-19 [12]. They have predicted second of April as the period for peak demand and also estimated death of 81,114 people in the United States from COVID-19 over the next four months [12].

2.1 Research Gap

Form the literature review it has been found that a significant number of studies have been carried out on 2019 novel corona virus (nCoV-19) that causes COVID-19. Most of the studies could not reach an exact conclusion as this study is new and more is there to explore. A limited number of studies regarding prediction and forecasting the number of future infections has been carried out. Out of these studies it has been found that forecasting using Exponential Smoothing is yet to be carried out. So, this research has been aimed to predict and project the probable number of nCoV-19 infection in India and its states using Exponential Smoothing. Also this forecasted value will be compared with the estimated future infections using Basic Reproduction Number. This will help the concerned departments and organizations to take better decision to combat the possible situation to be arisen due to nCoV-19 In India.

3 Methodology

3.1 Proposed Architecture

The workflow of the proposed work is shown in Fig. 1. We have started our work with data collection. The collected data has been accumulated in a format to create the dataset called CORONA.csv. We have collected the data from concerned ministry website of Government of India. We have also downloaded one more dataset from www.kaggle.com. After creating the dataset we have pre-processed as per our need. We have seen that the requirement of both of our proposed methods are a bit different. But the required parameters are available in the same dataset. So, we have selected the required parameters for both the used methods. Then we have found the Basic Reproduction Number (R_0) disclosed by Indian Council of Medical Research (ICMR). We have applied Exponential Smoothing technique for forecasting and R_0 has been used to estimate. Then we have planned to validate the forecasting to check whether the forecasting is actually working or not. Then we have planned to compare the forecasted value and estimated value. At last we have planned to find the fluctuation or error in prediction.

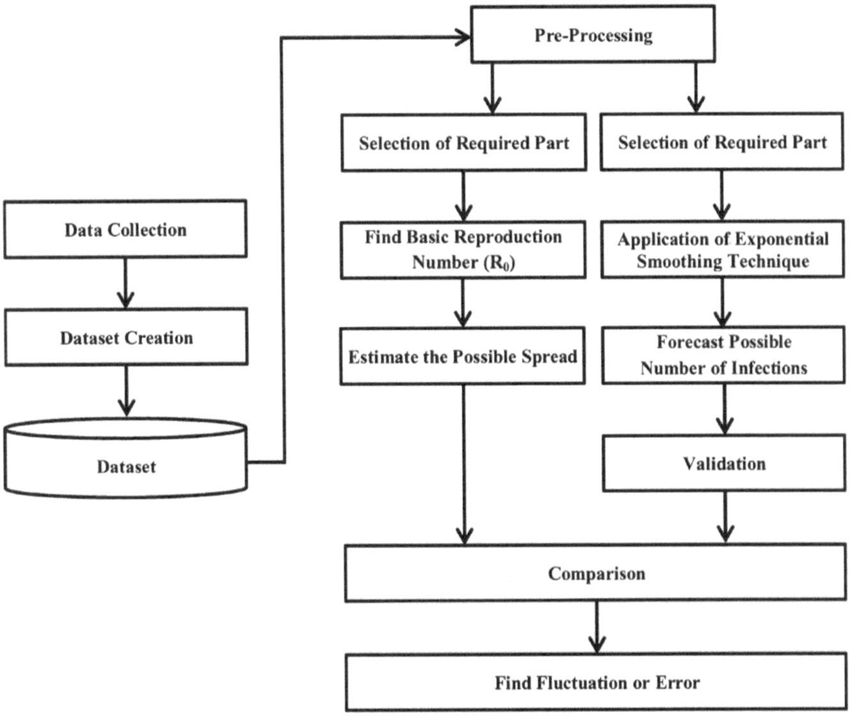

Fig. 1 Proposed architecture

3.2 Dataset Details

Our aim is to forecast the number of future infections in India and different states of India. Also we will estimate the possible future infections using Basic Reproduction Number. We have collected the active cases on daily basis. Also, we have downloaded one more dataset from www.kaggle.com which was last updated on August 17, 2020. The details of the downloaded dataset can be found in Table 1.

Table 1 Dataset detail

Name of dataset:	covid_19_india.csv
No. of instances:	5335
No. of attributes:	09.
Source:	www.kaggle.com
Last update:	August 17, 2020

3.3 Used Methods

3.3.1 Basic Reproduction Number

The basic reproduction number (R_0) can be defined as the number of secondary case(s) (expected) generated by an individual infectious case in a totally susceptible population. R_0 is a number without dimension (not a rate) and it can have units of $time^{-1}$.

Mathematical representation of basic reproduction number is as follows:

$R_0 \propto \left(\frac{\text{infection}}{\text{contact}}\right) \cdot \left(\frac{\text{contact}}{\text{time}}\right) \cdot \left(\frac{\text{time}}{\text{infection}}\right)$

More specifically it can be written as:

$R_0 = T \cdot C \cdot D$

where,

T denotes the transmissibility, that means the probability of infection with respect to contact between infected individual and susceptible population.

C denotes the average rate of contact between infected individual and susceptible population

D denotes the required time for infectiousness. That means it is the duration for infection to sustain.

Effective Reproductive Number: The basic reproduction number is the capacity of infected individual to contaminate further population that comes into contact. In real life situation, every contact will not be infected as some of them will have good immune system to fight the infection. So, the actual number of contamination that is supposed will reduce. The actual average number of infections due to the individual will be termed as effective reproductive number. So,

$R = R_0 \times x$

where, R = Effective Reproductive Number

R_0 = Basic Reproduction Number

x = Fraction of host population that is actually susceptible.

If we consider that nobody gets cured during forecasting period then the following formula can be used to calculate the possible number of infected people:

$C_T = C_0 \times R_0^T$

where, $C_T \rightarrow$ number of active cases on day T

$C_0 \rightarrow$ number of active cases day before first day of forecasting

$R_0 \rightarrow$ Basic Reproduction Number

$T \rightarrow$ number of day for forecasting.

If we consider Recovery, Death and Migration, then the active case on day T will be,

$C_T = C_{T-1} \times R_0$ and

$C_{T-1} = C_T - R_T - D_T - M_T$

where, $C_T \rightarrow$ number of active case on day T,

$C_{T-1} \rightarrow$ number of active case on day $T - 1$,

$R_0 \rightarrow$ Basic Reproduction Number,

$R_T \rightarrow$ number of Recovery on day T,

$D_T \rightarrow$ number of death on day T, and
$M_T \rightarrow$ number of Migration of active case on day T.

3.3.2 Exponential Smoothing Technique

It is a time series forecasting technique for univariate data. It has the extension capacity to support data with a well ordered fashion or seasonal component. It is a robust forecasting method and can be used as an substitute to ARIMA model. Following three methods can be used to estimate exponential smoothing:

- Single Exponential Smoothing: If the data doesn't have trend and seasonal pattern, then this method is used and it uses weighted moving averages where the weights exponentially decreases. Formula for this method is:
  $S_t = AX_t + (1 - A)S_{t-1}$; A is the smoothing factor or smoothing coefficient.
- Double Exponential Smoothing: If the data has linear trend and seasonal smoothing is absent then this method is used. Formula for this method is:
  $S_t = AX_t + (1 - A)(S_{t-1} + K_{t-1})$
  $K_t = B(S_t - S_{t-1}) + (1 - B)K_{t-1}$
  where, A is the smoothing factor or smoothing coefficient for the level
  B is smoothing factor to control the decay for the influence of trend
- Triple Exponential Smoothing: If the data has both linear trend and seasonal pattern then this method is used. Formula for this method is:
  $S_t = A\frac{X_t}{L_t - H} + (1 - A)(S_{t-1} + K_{t-1})$
  $K_t = B(S_t - S_{t-1}) + (1 - B)K_{t-1}$
  $L_t = C\frac{X_t}{S_t} + (1 - C)L_t - H$
  where, A is the smoothing factor for the level
  B is the smoothing factor the trend
  C is the smoothing factor for the seasonality.

4 Results and Discussions

In our proposed architecture, we have planned that the forecasting will be based on Exponential Smoothing and estimation will be based on Basic Reproduction Number (R_0). Then we have planned to compare both forecasted value and estimated value. Now, let us see the results obtained.

Results based on Basic Reproduction Number (R_0): The basic reproduction number of any disease changes time to time as it depends on factors like transmissibility, average rate of contact between infected individuals and susceptible population and duration to sustain the infection. In India, ICMR monitors these changes and calculates the value of R_0. The changes in R_0 for corona virus in India can be found in Table 2. From Table 2 it has been seen that the R_0 was maximum in the last week of March 2020. As on April 13, 2020 R_0 has been reduced to 1.36 and it remains same

Table 2 Change in basic reproduction number (R_0) in India

Date	Basic reproduction number (R_0) in India
March 4, 2020	1.83
March 23, 2020	4.00
April 6, 2020	1.83
April 9, 2020	1.27
April 11, 2020	1.55
April 13, 2020	1.36
May 3, 2020	1.27
June 26, 2020	1.11
July 7, 2020	1.19
July 29, 2020	1.11

up to the end of April 2020. Further it reduced to 1.27 in the first week of May 2020 and then in the month of June 2020 it reduced to 1.11. Again it increased to 1.19 in the first week of July 2020 and then reduced to 1.11 in the last week of July 2020. Also it is mention worthy that, R_0 may have different value for different states. For the case of COVID-19, it has been reported that 95% of infected people gets cured and there is only 5% fatality rate. Table 3 can be referred for the estimated confirmed cases for different states of India using basic reproduction number. Please note that this estimation has been done ignoring the recovery, death and migration of infected people.

Results based on Exponential Smoothing: Tableau is a software which implements the exponential smoothing with an interactive window. Using Tableau we have implemented exponential smoothing which has forecasted the possible confirmed cases for next 12 (Twelve) days from 18th August 2020. From Fig. 2 it can be seen that the model has forecasted highest possibility of confirmed cases of 34,08,138 on 29 August 2020 with a Mean Absolute Scaled Error (MASE) of 0.15. This value of MASE shows that it is a good model. The value of MASE varies from 0 to 1. 0 means the best model and 1 means the worst model. A value of MASE less than 0.50 is considered good model. Figure 2 is for the forecasting of possible spread in India considering all the states together. Considering the same software, it was possible to forecast the future confirmed cases in individual states. Forecasting for individual states can be found in Table 3 The forecasted and estimated values in Table 3 has shown a range of minimum and maximum value. The forecasting and the estimation have been carried out for the period of August 18, 2020 to August 29, 2020 as we have used a dataset updated till August 17, 2020. The forecasting and estimation is about the possible confirmed cases. From the forecasted values it has been found that there will be an increment of 2.49% on 18th August 2020, 2.33% on 19th August 2020, 2.27% on 20th August 2020, 2.22% on 21st August 2020, 2.17% on 22th August 2020, 2.13% on 23rd August 2020, 2.08% on 24th August 2020, 2.04% on 25th August 2020, 2.00% on 26th August 2020, 1.96% on 27th August

Table 3 Forecasted and estimated COVID-19 confirmed cases for individual states of India

States with active cases	Date	Forecasted value (Min to Max)	Estimated value using R_0
Andaman and Nicobar Islands	Aug 18–29, 2020	2552 to 3929	2639 to 7529
Andhra Pradesh	Aug 18–29, 2020	299,293 to 395,684	318,812 to 909,608
Arunachal Pradesh	Aug 18–29, 2020	2799 to 3562	2971 to 8477
Assam	Aug 18–29, 2020	80,288 to 104,644	84,563 to 241,267
Bihar	Aug 18–29, 2020	108,051 to 145,159	114,228 to 325,907
Chandigarh	Aug 18–29, 2020	2205 to 3617	2312 to 6597
Chhattisgarh	Aug 18–29, 2020	15,984 to 21,647	17,018 to 48,555
Dadar Nagar Haveli	Aug 18–29, 2020	1931 to 2417	2066 to 5894
Delhi	Aug 18–29, 2020	153,796 to 165,143	167,838 to 478,861
Goa	Aug 18–29, 2020	12,179 to 16,893	12,803 to 36,528
Gujarat	Aug 18–29, 2020	79,780 to 91,848	86,548 to 246,932
Haryana	Aug 18–29, 2020	47,967 to 56,590	51,868 to 147,986
Himachal Pradesh	Aug 18–29, 2020	4257 to 5639	4572 to 13,043
Jammu and Kashmir	Aug 18–29, 2020	29,021 to 34,698	31,317 to 89,351
Jharkhand	Aug 18–29, 2020	23,849 to 32,346	25,361 to 72,356
Karnataka	Aug 18–29, 2020	234,516 to 321,436	249,663 to 712,317
Kerala	Aug 18–29, 2020	45,894 to 63,128	48,857 to 139,393
Ladakh	Aug 18–29, 2020	1986 to 2372	2143 to 6114
Madhya Pradesh	Aug 18–29, 2020	46,348 to 56,959	50,001 to 142,657
Maharashtra	Aug 18–29, 2020	608,234 to 740,174	655,452 to 1,870,080
Manipur	Aug 18–29, 2020	4642 to 6063	5026 to 14,339
Meghalaya	Aug 18–29, 2020	1397 to 1977	1511 to 4312
Mizoram	Aug 18–29, 2020	797 to 1096	868 to 2476
Nagaland	Aug 18–29, 2020	3479 to 4107	3733 to 10,652
Odisha	Aug 18–29, 2020	61,778 to 88,014	66,055 to 188,463
Puducherry	Aug 18–29, 2020	8077 to 12,059	8505 to 24,266
Punjab	Aug 18–29, 2020	32,215 to 44,038	34,327 to 97,938
Rajasthan	Aug 18–29, 2020	62,549 to 76,831	67,426 to 192,373
Sikkim	Aug 18–29, 2020	1201 to 1703	1284 to 3663
Tamil Nadu	Aug 18–29, 2020	343,924 to 408,642	371,861 to 1,060,961
Telengana	Aug 18–29, 2020	94,860 to 118,095	101,481 to 289,536
Tripura	Aug 18–29, 2020	7354 to 8988	7924 to 22,609
Uttar Pradesh	Aug 18–29, 2020	159,089 to 209,315	169,860 to 484,630
Uttarakhand	Aug 18–29, 2020	12,597 to 16,153	13,393 to 38,210
West Bengal	Aug 18–29, 2020	119,481 to 152,993	128,148 to 365,621

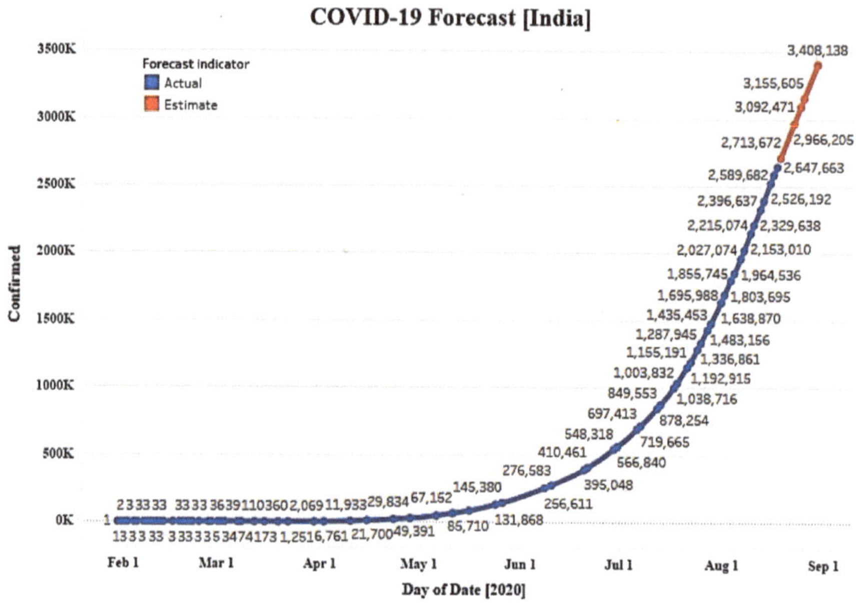

Fig. 2 COVID-19 forecast for confirmed cases in India for 12 days from 18th August 2020

2020, 1.92% on 28th August 2020 and 1.89% on 29th August 2020. From Table 3, it has been seen that the number of estimated cases using R_0 has very high value compared to forecasted value using exponential smoothing. This is because we have ignored recovery, death and migration and considered that all cases are live for next 12 (Twelve) days. We have considered the basic reproduction number of July 29, 2020, i.e. 1.11. Which is the lowest of all R_0 values in India till date.

4.1 *Comparison with Other Studies*

Many studies have been accomplished to predict and forecast the future number of infections in various countries. Likewise, in India many researchers have carried out the work to forecast the future infections. The researchers have primarily focused on the most infected states. They have ignored the forecasting for the states with less number of infections. All the researchers have used different methods and techniques for forecasting. In our case, we have used exponential smoothing and the forecasting have been considered for all the states of India.

5 Conclusion

COVID-19 has been proclaimed a pandemic all over the world. It has shut down most of the outdoor activities for the survival. It has created a havoc in the world. Even the country with strongest economy of the world failed to contain the spread of corona virus. forecasting and estimation of possible future number of new infections, confirmed cases can help the administration and concerned department as well as individual to plan better to stay safe. In this study an effort has been invested to forecast the values using exponential smoothing and estimation using basic reproduction number. The estimation has been carried out ignoring recovery, death and migration. As a future work we planned to develop a mathematical model to estimate considering recovery, death and migration of the infected people.

Acknowledgements The dataset required for this study has been downloaded from www.kaggle.com. It was freely and publicly available for use. A part of the required data has also been collected from the website of Ministry of Health and Family Welfare, Government of India. The authors would like offer heartfelt gratitude to the concerned of both websites for their splendid work.

References

1. Al-qaness, M. A. A., Ewees, A. A., Fan, H., & Abd El Aziz, M. (2020). Optimization method for forecasting confirmed cases of Covid-19 in China. *Journal of Clinical Medicine*, *9*(3). https://doi.org/10.3390/jcm9030674, https://www.mdpi.com/2077-0383/9/3/674.
2. Anastassopoulou, C., Russo, L., Tsakris, A., & Siettos, C. (2020). Data-based analysis, modelling and forecasting of the Covid-19 outbreak. *PLOS ONE*, *15*(3), 1–21. https://doi.org/10.1371/journal.pone.0230405, https://doi.org/10.1371/journal.pone.0230405.
3. Andrea Remuzzi, G. R. (2020). Covid-19 and Italy: What next? *The Lancet*, *395*, 1225–28. https://doi.org/10.1016/S0140-6736(20)30627-9.
4. Bhardwaj, R. (2020). A predictive model for the evolution of Covid-19. medRxiv. https://doi.org/10.1101/2020.04.13.20063271, https://www.medrxiv.org/content/early/2020/04/17/2020.04.13.20063271.
5. Bhattacharyya, A., Bhowmik, D., & Mukherjee, J. (2020). Forecast and interpretation of daily affected people during 21 days lockdown due to Covid 19 pandemic in India. medRxiv. https://doi.org/10.1101/2020.04.22.20075572, https://www.medrxiv.org/content/early/2020/04/25/2020.04.22.20075572.
6. Chen, H., Guo, J., Wang, C., Luo, F., Yu, X., Zhang, W., et al. (2020). Clinical characteristics and intrauterine vertical transmission potential of Covid-19 infection in nine pregnant women: A retrospective review of medical records. *The Lancet*, *395*, 809–15. https://doi.org/10.1016/S0140-6736(20)30360-3.
7. Dhanwant, J. N., & Ramanathan, V. (2020). Forecasting Covid 19 growth in India using susceptible-infected-recovered (S.I.R) model.
8. Fanelli, D., & Piazza, F. (2020). Analysis and forecast of Covid-19 spreading in China, Italy and France. *Chaos, Solitons & Fractals*, *134*, 109,761. https://doi.org/10.1016/j.chaos.2020.109761, http://www.sciencedirect.com/science/article/pii/S0960077920301636.
9. Gupta, R., & Pal, S. K. (2020). Trend analysis and forecasting of Covid-19 outbreak in India. medRxiv. https://doi.org/10.1101/2020.03.26.20044511, https://www.medrxiv.org/content/early/2020/03/30/2020.03.26.20044511.

10. Hu, Z., Ge, Q., Li, S., Jin, L., & Xiong, M. (2020). Artificial intelligence forecasting of Covid-19 in China.
11. Hussin A. Rothana, S. N. B., (2020). The epidemiology and pathogenesis of coronavirus disease (Covid-19) outbreak. *Journal of Autoimmunity*, *109*(102), 433. https://doi.org/10.1016/j.jaut.2020.102433.
12. Murray, C. J. (2020). Forecasting Covid-19 impact on hospital bed-days, ICU-days, ventilator-days and deaths by US state in the next 4 months. medRxiv. https://doi.org/10.1101/2020.03.27.20043752, https://www.medrxiv.org/content/early/2020/03/30/2020.03.27.20043752.
13. Pandey, G., Chaudhary, P., Gupta, R., & Pal, S. (2020). SEIR and regression model based Covid-19 outbreak predictions in India.
14. Perc, M., Gorišek Miksić, N., Slavinec, M., & Stožer, A. (2020). Forecasting Covid-19. *Frontiers in Physics*, *8*, 127. https://doi.org/10.3389/fphy.2020.00127, https://www.frontiersin.org/article/10.3389/fphy.2020.00127.
15. Petropoulos, F., & Makridakis, S. (2020). Forecasting the novel coronavirus Covid-19. *PLOS ONE*, *15*(3), 1–8. https://doi.org/10.1371/journal.pone.0231236, https://doi.org/10.1371/journal.pone.0231236.
16. Roosa, K., Lee, Y., Luo, R., Kirpich, A., Rothenberg, R., Hyman, J., et al. (2020). Real-time forecasts of the Covid-19 epidemic in china from February 5th to February 24th, 2020. *Infectious Disease Modelling*, *5*, 256–263. https://doi.org/10.1016/j.idm.2020.02.002, http://www.sciencedirect.com/science/article/pii/S2468042720300051.
17. Roosa, K., Lee, Y., Luo, R., Kirpich, A., Rothenberg, R., Hyman, J. M. et al. (2020). Short-term forecasts of the Covid-19 epidemic in Guangdong and Zhejiang, China: February 13–23, 2020. *Journal of Clinical Medicine*, *9*(2). https://doi.org/10.3390/jcm9020596, https://www.mdpi.com/2077-0383/9/2/596.
18. Singh, R., & Adhikari, R. (2020). Age-structured impact of social distancing on the Covid-19 epidemic in India.
19. Tandon, H., Ranjan, P., Chakraborty, T., & Suhag, V. (2020). Coronavirus (Covid-19): ARIMA based time-series analysis to forecast near future.
20. WHO. Coronavirus (2020). https://www.who.int/health-topics/coronavirus. Last accessed May 13, 2020,
21. Wikipedia. Coronavirus (2020). https://en.wikipedia.org/wiki/Coronavirus. Last accessed May 13, 2020.

Realization of Objectivity in Pain: An Empirical Approach

K. Shankar and A. Abudhahir

Abstract It is well known that feeling pain is very common. If anyone does not feel the pain for any causes, then it is considered as a disease or disorder; s(he) requires immediate medical attention. Since pain is an advance informer about the disease, it is considered as a fifth vital sign of the human body. Pain is felt by an excellent mechanism of the human body, and this mechanism transmits the information from the location of tissue damage to the cortex of the brain for further response. In pain management, the priority always goes to control the pain than to cure the disease. Pain measurement is a tool which helps the physicians to control the pain by prescribing the right dosage of pain killers. The dosage of pain killers which are prescribed to alleviate the pain is decided based on the patient's subjective responses. It is hard to hide the fact that the pain killers leave their side effects on the patient while controlling the pain. So, the pain is still one of the most challenging problems in clinical practices. It is essential to adopt a method to measure the pain to control it. There are two methods to measure pain: subjective method and objective method. In the present scenario, almost all physicians use any of the subjective methods. This method is totally dependent on patients' external responses which are not reliable; the prescribed dosage of pain killer could also not be an accurate one. Hence, it is necessary to propose an alternate method which could overcome the challenges posed by pain killers in the name of side effects. This chapter presents a few experimental attempts made to propose an objective method which is reliable and hence could be used to prescribe the correct dosage of pain killer to the patient.

K. Shankar (✉)
Department of Electronics and Instrumentation Engineering, National Institute of Technology Silchar, Assam 788010, India
e-mail: shankar@ei.nits.ac.in

A. Abudhahir
Department of Electrical and Electronics Engineering, Vel Tech Rangarajan Dr. Sagunthala R&D Institute of Science and Technology, Avadi, Chennai 600062, India

R. Patgiri et al. (eds.), *Health Informatics: A Computational Perspective in Healthcare*, Studies in Computational Intelligence 932,
https://doi.org/10.1007/978-981-15-9735-0_11

1 Introduction

"Disease, its cause, what may abate the ill:
Let leech examine these, then use his skill."
– Thirukural No. 948

The meaning of above said Thirukural written by the great Tamil Poet Thiruvalluvar, a 2000 years ago, is "Let the physician enquire into the (nature of the) disease, its cause and its method of cure and treat it faithfully according to (medical rule)". It is explained as identify the disease by understanding the changes in patient's body; know the cause for disease; choose an appropriate therapy to alleviate the cause and cure the disease.

These great lines made me think beyond the point about my son's habit. He used to yell every morning after the holidays. It was also one such very fantastic morning, a little bit busy too. After an enjoyable weekend, all at home were preparing themselves for their another week-long business except my cute little son. It was his habit that everyday morning he made our home as circus ground and made us as ring masters. He had a habit of denying going to school. The reason would be really considerable and doubtful, as it was his routine every Monday morning to bunk the school. At the start of every week, he had different pains as reasons. That Monday, the reason, for not going to school, he stated was a stomach ache. It was neither believable nor verifiable. So, most of Monday mornings, he tried to succeed in his mission by not going to school. But, we never failed to put our efforts in sending him to school.

A thought sparked in my mind to explore "What is pain?" and the possibilities of measuring pain. However, I was reluctant to hear the words from my son about his pain, as I believed that the pain he reported every time was for the reason of not going to school. And I wished to know more about pain, its physiology and related theories.

Once after started exploring the pain and its management procedures only, I came to understand that pain is not a disease; it is one of the five vital signs of the human body [1].

If it is so, what is the necessity of treating this as a disease? The reason is simple that it hurts, it disturbs our routine, and it changes our mindset. But, the fact is that it is possible to manage the pain psychologically. A same quantum of pain is felt differently by different individuals based on their pain tolerance level. Pain tolerance level is not only based on physical strength but also based on psychological strength.

So the pain of any kind of a person is managed by a physician based on the level of pain expressed by the sufferer. Here, I understand that this is a subjective phenomenon. But, upon my experience, I raised a question in my mind that how come it is possible for an infant, a deaf, and a mentally retarded person to communicate effectively about their pain level? The clinical science has its own answer that if a person is not able to express his pain through any one of the subjective methods like Visual Analog Scale (VAS), Color Analog Scale (CAS), Numeric Pain Scale (NPS), or questionnaire, then they would use Face Pain Scale (FPS), where the patients' facial expression would be read by the physician, and the pain management procedure would be started [2].

So, I concluded that I could apply any one of the above methods or all the methods on my son and know whether he was in pain or not? My son would respond equally same for all the methods whatever we applied that "Yes, it is paining much." But, is that a correct answer? Is it correct to react or respond him by considering his statement? If it is so, would it be a right decision? One cannot correctly/exactly express his/her feeling about pain subjectively. So, I decided to go for alternate options to know the feel of pain.

The alternative would be objective method. That is, the pain should be measured/known upon the source of pain. For this, I should know first "What is Pain? A leading international pain forum "International Association for Study of Pain (IASP)" defines pain as "An unpleasant sensory and emotional experience associated with actual or potential tissue damage or described in terms of such damage" [3]. So, it is a symptom or informer of diseases; transmits the information from the location of tissue damage to the cortex of brain for further response which is diagrammatically shown in Fig. 1.

So, the tissue damage of any kind causes pain. Once the tissue is damaged, there must be physiological changes. But, we cannot expect a significant change in all the physiological parameters. So, it is needed to identify the parameters which show the significant change for pain.

But, again a question is raised in my mind that "are these all possible?" Have any of the researchers tried to do this? My journey started in exploring the possibilities of objective pain measurement. All along my journey, to date, I have been reading technical articles of many researchers who work on it. I understood that all the researchers are not experimenting with humans; they predominantly experiment with animals. I am not trying to say that the experiments with animals would not yield good results which could be used for human beings. Instead, performing experiments with humans for these types of studies would yield better results to conclude.

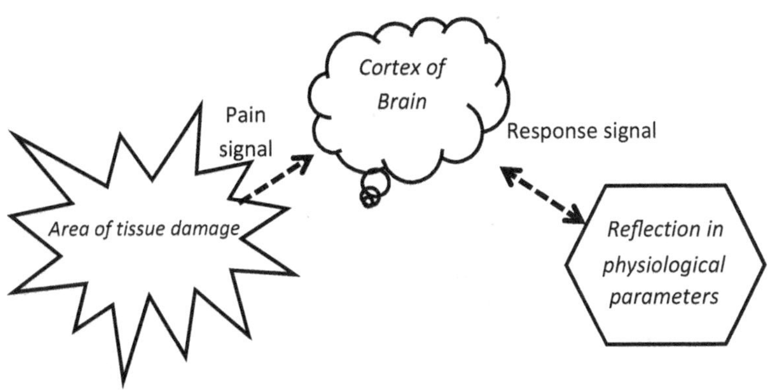

Fig. 1 Pain pathway

In his research paper, Ikeda (1995) concluded that the pain threshold level should be considered to measure the pain objectively, and also it is quite difficult to judge the pain from a single physiological datum. He also addressed that a powerful analytical method would certainly help the researchers to obtain an objective pain measure [4]. In recent research done with thermal pain stimulator and Electro Encephalo Gram (EEG) setup by Yelena Granovsky et al. (2008), it is reported that outcome has a strong correlation with stimulated pain [5]. Rissacher et al. (2007) also confirmed the correlation between pain and EEG [6]. Li D et al. (2008) summarized that objective pain measures would be very useful in assessing the pain of critically ill adult patients who unable to self-report [7]. Mobascher et al. (2010) found that Electro Dermal Activity (EDA) is a useful additional objective index when pain is studied with functional Magnetic Resonance Imaging (fMRI)/EEG [8]. An Electro Myo Gram (EMG) study was conducted by Schasfoort et al. (2008) with hospitalized infants, and they concluded that long-term, objective and continuous measurement of peripheral motor parameters is feasible, has high potential, and is promising to assess pain in pre-verbal hospitalized infants [9].

The research is going on in the imaging/mapping area also to quantify the pain (First objective measure of pain discovered in brain scan patterns by CU-Boulder study and Brauer et al. 2000) [10, 11]. Researchers are trying to examine the neurophysiologic response to pain by using fMRI techniques also. A research group in Liverpool University (Pain Imaging) and Pande et al. (1996) have been trying to find an objective pain measure by correlating pain with fMRI and MRI—pain drawing, respectively, [12, 13]. In the pain management area, Shankar et al. (2006) confirmed the relationship between hypnosis and one of the physiological parameters Galvanic Skin Response (GSR). It shows the response of pain in GSR [14].

The researchers who have been doing this research are using various types of pain stimuli such as nociceptive and neuropathic pain stimuli. Whatever may be the pain on which the experiment would be done that should be existing or created. Now, let us imagine that a patient who is suffering from any sort of acute pain would prefer to be experimented with him/her? If I am a patient, then I shall not prefer. Then, how could we expect others? So, it is needed to develop such a pain on normal human beings for experimental purpose. There comes a question that would the developed pain be as same as the pain experienced by the patient in real clinical practice? It cannot be expected. But, it is possible to obtain more than 99% accuracy of creating the real pain experimentally. So, I decided to develop a pain inducer of thermal and mechanical type.

While carefully going through these reported research findings hitherto, it is very hard to conclude that a specific physiological parameter alone is sufficient for pain measurement. Also, implementing the already proposed objective pain measurement methods would not be a cost effective, and they failed to address in reducing the dosage of painkillers.

Hence, it has been attempted to measure the pain objectively at a reasonable cost. This chapter discusses the significance of objective pain measurement procedure, pain inducers, and experiments performed to confirm the objectivity of pain.

2 Pain Measurement

The measurement of pain is essential for controlling the pain [15], as well as in controlling the dosage of pain killers. There are few pain clinics which use Patient Controlled Analgesia (PCA) device to administer the required amount of pain killers during the pain management procedure [16]. The PCA devices do not involve in the measurement of pain at all and the dosage of analgesia injected completely under the subjective control of patients. Also, in the present scenario, almost all the physicians use any of the subjective pain measurement methods to determine the patients' pain level and to prescribe the pain killers. The commonly practised-unidimensional-subjective methods are Visual Analog Scale (VAS), Color Analog Scale (CAS), Numerical Pain Scale (NPS), Verbal Rating Scales (VRS), Numerical Rating Scales (NRS), Descriptor Differential Scale of Pain Intensity (DDSI), Face Pain Scale (FPS), Behavioral Measurements, and Pain Diary. The multidimensional subjective methods are interviews and questionnaire.

A patient who is suffering from the pain of any kind would respond equally same for all the subjective methods whatever we applied that "Yes, it is paining much", as everybody wants to get rid of the pain as soon as possible. So, the statement what a patient gives about his/her pain would not be a reliable one. The dosage of pain killer prescribed by the doctor, based on the patient's statement, could also not be an accurate one. Because it is hard to express his/her feeling correctly/exactly about the intensity of pain orally.

> Though things diverse from divers sages' lips we learn,
> 'Tis wisdom's part in each the true thing to discern.
> —Thirukural No. 423

The explanation of this Thirukural goes as "To discern the truth in everything, by whomsoever spoken, is wisdom" which is simply explained in Karl Marx's words,

> "Everything must be doubted."

So, it is concluded that choosing the pain management procedure and prescribing pain killers to alleviate the pain based on subjective methods are not a reliable one. Hence, it is decided to propose an alternate method which is simple, cost-effective, and reliable to measure the pain level. As it is aimed to propose a method which is cost effective and to be used in regular clinical practice to measure pain, the objective pain measurement methods based on brain cortex imaging techniques [17] are not taken as reference in this study. Proposing such a method would involve many experimental procedures. This has been achieved by designing and conducting different experiments in a laboratory environment with thermally and mechanically induced pain of nociceptive in nature.

3 Objective Pain Measurement

The objective measurement is defined as "Objective measurement is the repetition of a unit amount that maintains its size, within an allowable range of error, no matter which instrument, intended to measure the variable of interest, is used and no matter who or what relevant person or thing is measured" [18]. This definition clearly says that the result of any measurement of a particular variable of a process should be the same for any type of instrument and a person who is using the instrument. So, in this case also, the level of pain should be correctly reflected by the measurement procedure what we adopt to. This could be achieved with the Objective Pain Measurement (OPM) procedure only. The OPM method involves measurement and analysis of physiological parameters for the pain input.

These types of researches normally do not involve the patients who are in hospital for treatment, as they would not allow conducting experiments on them. So the healthy subjects were chosen, and the pain was induced on them for experimental purpose. The subjects who volunteered themselves were asked for their consent by explaining the nature of experiments, and they consented to be the subjects. The experiments were conducted with subjects by following the relevant ethical guidelines.

4 Pain Iducers

Two types of pain inducers (i) Mechanical Pain Inducer (MPI) and (ii) Thermal Pain Inducer (TPI) developed in our laboratory are shown in Fig. 2.

The Peltier device and a set of iron disks of specific weight on a cube of 1 × 1 cm dimension are used to fabricate TPI and MPI, respectively. The former is used to induce thermal pain, and the latter is used to induce mechanical pain on healthy human subjects. The temperature generated by the TPI could be varied by controlling

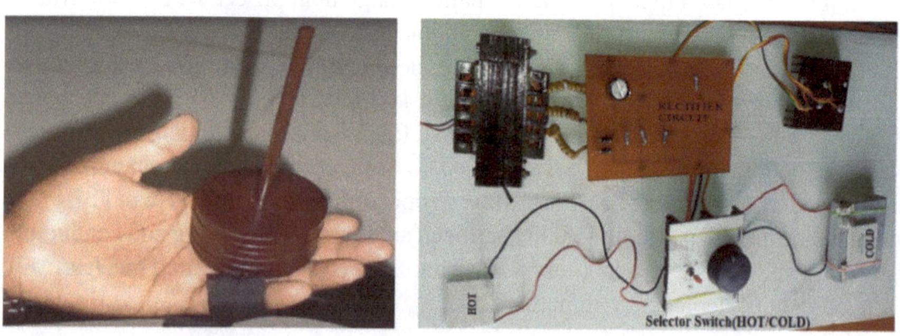

(a) (b)

Fig. 2 Pain inducers **a** MPI, **b** TPI

the current passed through the Peltier device. The mechanical force applied to the subject is varied by adding or removing the weights on the metal cube. Even though the Peltier device can generate both cold and hot temperatures, in this work, we use the hot temperature only. The suitable signal conditioning circuits have also been constructed to read the output appropriately. The performance of thermal pain inducer was tested for different current inputs, and the results were discussed. The performance of the inducers was checked by conducting pain threshold/tolerance experiments with few healthy human subjects.

5 Experiments and Results

The Peltier-based thermal pain inducer, indigenously developed in our laboratory and was used to induce the thermal pain on subjects' wrist. The changes on certain physiological parameters, heart rate and body temperature, for the induced thermal pain were noted and analyzed. All the experiments were conducted in three different stages, namely pre-pain, during pain, and post-pain stages.

The results of experiments conducted for heart rate versus thermal pain and body temperature versus thermal pain are graphically represented in Figs. 3 and 4, respectively. The results shown here are of the experiments conducted for thermal pain of 30 °C. But, the experiments were conducted for thermal pain of 35 and 40 °C also. The results show the variation of heart rate and body temperature in "During Pain" stage of the experiment. The body temperature rises up to about 55% of female subjects. The heart rate also shows a variation on the higher side for almost 75% of male subjects in the "During Pain" stage of experiments. The rise in the value of heart rate and body temperature for thermal pain stimuli in "During Pain" stage of the experiment is indicated with an arrow mark in the graph. The anxiety, about the procedure, before starting the experiment might have made other subjects to show their heart rate and body temperature in higher values even in the "pre-pain" stage of the experiment.

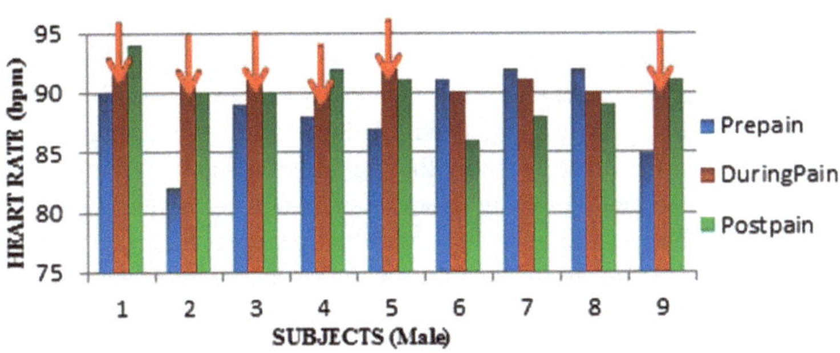

Fig. 3 Response of heart rate to thermal pain of 30 °C for male subjects

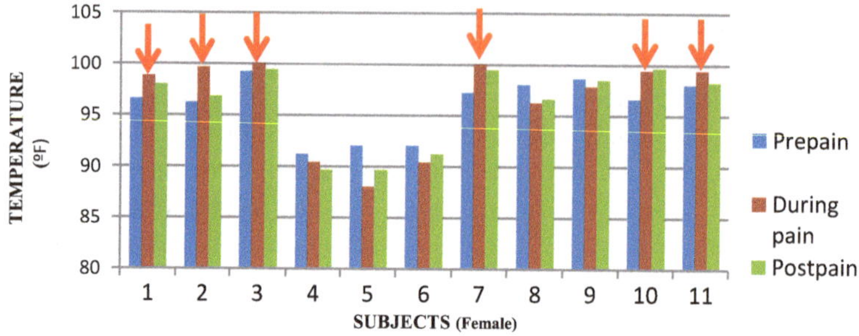

Fig. 4 Response of body temperature to thermal pain of 30 °C for female subjects

Also, for the subjects whose normal body temperature was lower than other subjects, especially the fifth and sixth female subjects, the body temperature responded in the opposite way for thermal pain stimuli in "During Pain" stage. But in both the experiments, all the subjects showed variations between all the three stages of experiments [19]. As an outcome, it was concluded that there are significant changes in physiological parameters, and a valid objective pain measure could be suggested for better pain management procedure.

An experimental setup to acquire Vata-nadi (Radial Artery Pulse), whose characters get changed for the pain felt, was also made, and using this setup, the experiments were conducted to measure stimulated pain objectively. Vata-nadi has been considered as an only reflector of pain in Indian traditional medical system [20]. The Nadi (Pulse) is sensed by placing the fingers with necessary pressure on the patient's wrist. The same three stages of the experiment were also conducted for acquiring and analyzing the Vata-nadi for induced mechanical pain. The response of Vata-nadi in terms of the amplitude of a percusion wave and a dicrotic wave was also verified for stimulated mechanical pain, and the pain what subject felt was calculated using neural network.

6 Conclusion

An attempt has been made to study the objectivity nature of pain by conducting experiments on healthy human subjects with induced thermal and mechanical pain. The two types of pain inducers, namely thermal pain inducer and mechanical pain inducer were developed indigenously in our laboratory. The conducted experiments showed significant changes in heart rate, body temperature, and Vata-nadi (Radial Artery Pulse) when the subjects were applied with thermal and mechanical pain. Even though we have realized that there are more possibilities to measure pain objectively, it is necessary to analyze the changes, caused in physiological parameters due to induced thermal and mechanical pain, in other ways also. Also, it is needed to conduct experiments with actual clinical pain on patients who are suffering from a specific type of pain for validating the proposed method.

References

1. Morone, N. E., & Weiner, D. K. (2013, November). Pain as the 5th vital sign: Exposing the vital need for pain education. *Clinical Therapeutics, 35*(11), 1728–1732. https://doi.org/10.1016/j.clinthera.2013.10.001.
2. Cohen, L. L., Lemanek, K., Blount, R. L., Dahlquist, L. M., Lim, C. S., Palermo, T. M., et al. (2008) Evidence-based assessment of pediatric pain. *Journal of Pediatric Psychology, 33*(9), 939–955. https://doi.org/10.1093/jpepsy/jsm103.
3. Merskey, H., & Bogduk, N. (2002). *Classification of chronic pain descriptions of chronic pain syndromes and definitions of pain terms* (2nd ed.). IASP PRESS SEATTLE.
4. Ikeda, K. (1995). Quantitative evaluation of pain by analyzing non-invasively obtained physiological data with particular reference to joint healing with continuous passive motion. In *Proceeding RC IEEE-EMBS*. https://doi.org/10.1109/RCEMBS.1995.532959.
5. Granovsky, Y., Granot, M., Nir, R.-R., & Yarnitsky, D. (2008). Objective correlate of subjective pain perception by contact heat-evoked potentials. *The Journal of Pain, 9*(1), 53–63.
6. Rissacher, D., Dowman, R., & Schuckers, S. A. C. (2007). Identifying frequency—domain features for an EEG-based pain measurement system. In *Bioengineering Conference, NEBC, IEEE 33rd Annual Northeast*. https://doi.org/10.1109/NEBC.2007.4413305.
7. Li, D., Puntillo, K., & Miaskowski, C. (2008, January). A review of objective pain measures for use with critical care adult patients unable to self-report. *Journal of Pain, 9*(1), 2–10. Epub 2007 Nov 5.
8. Mobascher, A., Brinkmeyer, J., Warbrick, T., Musso, F., Schlemper, V., & Wittsack, H. (2010). Brain activation patterns underlying fast habituation to painful laser stimuli. *International Journal of Psychophysiology, 75,* 16–24. https://doi.org/10.1016/j.ijpsycho.2009.10.008.
9. Schasfoort, F. C., Formanoy, M. A., Bussmann, J. B., Peters, J. W., Tibboel, D., & Stam, H. J. (2008, July). Objective and continuous measurement of peripheral motor indicators of pain in hospitalized infants: A feasibility study. *Pain, 15,* 137(2), 323–331.
10. First objective measure of pain discovered in brain scan patterns by CU-Boulder study. Available from: https://www.colorado.edu/today/2013/04/10/first-objective-measure-pain-discovered-brain-scan-patterns-cu-boulder-study. January 28, 2015.
11. Brauer, F., Dick, B. D., Stroink, G., Connolly, J. F, McGrath, P. J., & Finley, G. A. (2000). KLT analysis of brain potential maps during pain. In *Proceedings of the 22nd Annual International Conference of the IEEE*. Engineering in Medicine and Biology Society.
12. PainImaging. Available from: https://www.liverpool.ac.uk/pain-research-institute/our-research/pain-imaging/. September 23, 2016.
13. Pande, A. C., Pyke, R. E., Greiner, M., Cooper, S. A., Benjamin, R., & Pierce, M.W. (1996, February). Analgesic efficacy of the kappa-receptor agonist, enadoline, in dental surgery pain. *Clinical Neuropharmacology, 19*(1), 92–97.
14. Shankar, K., Manivannan, M., & Frenandez, P. (2006, January). GSR analysis of hypnotic analgesia. *International Journal of Systemics, Cybernetics and Infomatics*, ISBN 0973-4864.
15. Turk, D. C., & Melzack, R. (2011). *The hand book of pain assessment*. New York: The Guilford Press.
16. Rudolph, H., Packer, J. S., Cade, J. F., Lee, B., & Morley, P. (1999, March). Pain relief using smart technology: An overview of a new patient—Controlled analgesia device. *IEEE Transaction on Information Technology in Biomedicine, 3*(1), 20–27.
17. Brown, J. E., Chatterjee, N., Younger, J., & Mackey, S. (2011). Towards a physiology-based measure of pain: Patterns of human brain activity distinguish painful from non-painful thermal stimulation. *PLoS ONE, 6*(9), e24124. https://doi.org/10.1371/journal.pone.0024124.

18. Definition of Objective Measurement. Available from: https://www.rasch.org/define.htm. May 21, 2016.
19. Strigo, I. A., Carli, F., & Catherine Bushnell, M. (2000). Effect of ambient temperature on human pain and temperature perception. *Anesthesiology, 92*, 699–707.
20. Ayurvedic Treatment of Arthritis (Painful Joints). Available from. https://www.boloji.com/index.cfm?md=Content&sd=Articles&ArticleID=1185. May 21, 2016.

Detail Study of Different Algorithms for Early Detection of Cancer

Prasenjit Dhar, K. Suganya Devi, Satish Kumar Satti, and P. Srinivasan

Abstract Cancer is one of the most dangerous disease in human life. Diagnosing the cancer cell in early stages plays an important (valuable) role in saving human life and for successful treatment. At an early stage the spreading of cancer cells of the body can be stopped by removing the benign cells (cancer cells in the early stage). Whereas, malignant tumor (cancer cells in later stages) which are having aggressive spreading capacity, affects different other parts of the body and cannot be controlled. This paper presents a study on five different types of cancer viz., breast, brain, lung, liver and skin; and different published techniques of detecting these cancers, which help the students (researcher) to understand the current ongoing techniques and aids to develop new structure that gives better and accurate result. It also focuses on different segmentation (ACM, PSO, UNet, watershed etc), cancer feature extraction, cancer features reduction (PCA, LDA, SVD). Also, it discusses different cancer classification using machine learning and clustering (SVM, KNN, Bayesian, Neuro fuzzy, k-mean algorithm, GANs etc.), deep learning (CNN, ResNet, VGG etc) technique, also discuss about different evaluating method.

Keywords Early cancer detection · Cancer segmentation and feature extraction · Cancer classification clustering and deep learning.

P. Dhar · K. Suganya Devi (✉) · S. K. Satti
Computer Science and Engineering, National Institute of Technology Silchar, Silchar, India
e-mail: suganya@cse.nits.ac.in

P. Dhar
e-mail: prasenjitdhar.cse@gmail.com

S. K. Satti
e-mail: sskumar789@gmail.com

P. Srinivasan
Physics, National Institute of Technology, Silchar, India
e-mail: srininits@gmail.com

R. Patgiri et al. (eds.), *Health Informatics: A Computational Perspective in Healthcare*,
Studies in Computational Intelligence 932,
https://doi.org/10.1007/978-981-15-9735-0_12

1 Introduction

In different parts of human body Cancer is the uncontrolled growth of abnormal cells [1]. The human body always provides balance into cells but when some the unbalance is happening in any cell that cells become uncontrollable. In an uncontrollable situation, the human body's cell production capacity falls down. At that time one type of mass was formed which is known as a tumor. If the cancer is diagnosed in earlier stage, the human body can overcome that, otherwise in later stage this tumor is converted into a cancer cell. According to the WHO report, across the world is the second deadly disease. As per the report, 9.6 million people were dying in 2018 approximately 1 out of 6 died because of the different types of cancer. Approximately 22% of people is dying due to cancer mainly because of tobacco; which increases the risk factor of cancer. Apart from this, some other behaviors and dietary risks such as high Body Mass Index, intake of low fruits and vegetables, lack of physical activity, alcohol and tobacco usage is also led to cancer [2]. According to the WHO report, out of 9.6 million deaths, 1.76 million deaths are from lung cancer, 7.8 lakhs deaths are with liver cancer, 62.7 lakhs deaths are by breast cancer and 7.83 lakhs are by stomach cancer. Based on a WHO 2018 report, in India both male and female the person was affected by cancer and from 135 crores population 11 lakhs new cases were registered out of that 78 were dying.

There are different modalities of imaging are available, viz., structural and functional find the most suitable treatment opinion for each patient. To name a few Computer Tomography (CT),Positron Emission Tomography (PET), ultra-sound, Magnetic Resonance Imaging (MRI), X-ray mammogram.These imaging techniques are often used in combination to obtain sufficient information for diagnosis. Each imaging technique has its own merits and procedure. Computer Tomography (CT) is the best useful medical imaging which gives better clarity of blood vessels, bones or other internal parts of the human body compared to other imaging. CT provides cross-sectional imaging by computer and it uses X-ray. MRI is another useful type of medical imaging. It also helps to understand viewing the different inside joint or ligament of the human body which cannot be seen by X-ray or CT images. Especially, it helps to identify spinal cord injuries, tumors, and diagnose strokes. MRI is used for examining cancer in head and neck region and its uses powerful magnetic fields. Positron emission tomography (PET) scans images helps the doctor to check the blood flow of the body, oxygen intake, the sugar level in our body. PET uses a radioactive tracer, which finds spreads of cancer cells by a faster metabolic rate which is shown as bright spots. This can be combined with CT, called PET-CT scan images. PET-CT scan images used for accurate diagnosis and to locate abnormal activity within the human body. This scan helps to detect cancer, blood flow, heart attack area, brain disorder, etc. Ultrasound is used to examine centre, prostrate, head, neck bladder region by inspecting the gastrointestinal tract. Mammography is used for saving the breast cancer by capturing the inside structure of the breast and it uses X-ray images. X-ray is used to find the bone structure, presence of any abnormal masses and to detect dental problems.

2 Literature Survey

Early cancer detection is very important for survival of human life and it helps the society, family and everyone. It reduces the risk factor of death and it helps in finding more treatment options. Sometimes, cancer (false negative) cannot be detected at early stages which would be harmful for the patient a later. This paper discusses the different methodologies used for detecting different types of prevalent cancers along with the imaging modalities and different learning techniques and classifiers that are used for caner detecting at an early stage. This survey aids the researcher in understanding and analyzing different techniques that can be used for detecting cancers and aids in choosing imaging modality suitable for specific cancers.

2.1 Breast Cancer

Agarwal et al. [3] has proposed a patch-based CNN methodology for automatic mass detection on mammogram. Li et al. [4] identified benign and malignant stages on mammogram images using DenseNet-II. The proposed method of Saba et al. [5] was working on the cloud system. In this for experimental purposes, microscopic cytology based breast images are used. Also, they used ANN and Naïve Bayes classifier had been used for classifying benign and malignant breast cancer images. Li et al. [6] used CNN methodology in their work in identifying normal, benign, malignant on histology images. Araujo et al. [7] worked on histology images and they classified histology images into four categories such as benign, normal, invasive carcinoma and in suit carcinoma by combining CNN and SVM. They also used binary classifier for identifying carcinoma and non-carcinoma category. Devi and Devi [8] used decision tree-based J48 classifier on WBDC and WDBC histology image data sets for classifying benign and malignant breast cancer. Zemouri et al. [9] diagnosed breast cancer diseases on WBCD histology data set using constructive DNN and joint selection methods. STRASS and mRMR selection variables are useful for reducing clinical variables. Shenbagavalli and Thangarjan [10] used a combination of multi scale shearlet transformation with Neural Network on DDSM mammogram images for classifying benign and malignant breast cancer. The Shearlet transformation, enhancement technique gives more details about shift invariance, data phase and directionality when compared to wavelet transform. As a result, the proposed method received a good accuracy rate for classifying benign and malignant breast images.Ting et al. [11]had made some improvement in CNN and applied that CNN method with Neural Network technique for classifying breast cancer lesion on MIAS 2018 data set. Khan et al. [12] used three types of CNN network such as ResNet, VGGNet, and Google Net for classifying breast cancers images on own microscopic cytology data set and tested their work with the bench mark data set [13]. It is observed that, they achieved the highest classification rate.

2.2 Brain Cancer

Muneer and Joseph [14] used MRI images for classifying normal or abnormal brain cancer images. In their proposed methodology, PCA technique has been used for feature reduction and for selecting the most valuable features from the images. Finally, they have used three types of classifier namely KNN, SVM, and ANN and it was observed that ANN gives a better result compare with the other two classifiers. Ayadi et al. [15] worked on two techniques such as DWT (Discrete Wavelet Transform) and BoG (Bag-of-Words) for detecting the brain cancer cells. This technology helps to reduce the computational time and it was easy to operate. Natarajan and Kumarasamy [16] detected an unpredictable or irregular tumor size using the combination of fuzzy logic and spiking neuron model. Which gives a much better result compare with the previously existing method. Sajjad et al. [17] used CNN technique for classifying multigrade brain tumor images. In their methodology, deep learning techniques are used to identify the feature values and before classification data augmentation also done. Zacharaki et al. [18] used pattern recognition method to categories different types of brain tumor say identifying primary gliomas component from metastases, grading component from gliomas. Sriramakrishnan et al. [19] used PLTP (probabilistic local ternary patterns) technique for segmenting cancerous region from MRI images. PLTP technique is based on the probability density value and it takes the density value from histogram bins. Al-handi et al. [20]classified brain cancer using texture and KNN classifier. Texture analysis differentiated cancer lesion such that, if it is cancer then the texture of a particular region has high correlation. Vishnuvarthanan and Rajasekaran [21] segment brain tumor region with the help of a fuzzy system. The PSNR and MSE show the segmented images are correctly identified. Zhang et al. [22] used multi spectral based images for segmented brain tumor and feature selection case kernel feature was used. Sing et al. [23] modified FCM technique for a segmented brain tumor on MRI images. This technique was helpful if there is a high level of noise present or intensity inhomogeneity was present in an image. Usha and Perumal [24] used SVM for classifying brain image after applying morphological transform and some mathematical operation performed for segmentation. Alzubi et al. [25] applied ANN and Naïve Bayes classifiers for detecting brain tumors and the proposed method also help to find the actual position of the tumor in the brain MRI images. Talo et al. [26] applied ResNet 34 based CNN deep learning the technique for classifying normal or abnormal tumor on MRI brain image data set. In the proposed technique data augmentation, and an optimization based deep learning technique also used before the classification process.

2.3 Lung Cancer

Bhuwaneswari and Theresa [27] used a mixture of the Genetic Algorithm (GA) and KNN classifier for detecting early lung cancer images. This combination method was applied to CT images. Asuntha et al. [28] pro posed the PSO technique for early lung image detection purposes and Genetic Algorithm and SVM classifier is used for feature extraction and classification respectively. This technique works on CT, MRI as well as Ultrasound images. Kumar et al. [29] used the different pre processing techniques for image enhancement, out of that adaptive median filter gives a better result. Segmentation is made by different technique and it was observed that guaranteed convergence PSO (particle Swam Optimization) gives a better segmentation result comparing with [27, 28]. Kaser et al. [30] used region growing segmentation method for extracting the Region Of Interest (ROI) i.e. cancers part from CT based lung images. Sangamithraa and Govindaraju [31] segmented the tumor region based on K-mean clustering and later BPN classifier applied for classification purposes. Aggarwal et al. [32] segmented the ROI based optimal thresholding and geometric features help to differentiate between the cancer nodules and blood vessels. Later stage LDA classifier has been used for classifying the normal nodules and anatomy structure. Jin et al. [33] used a circular filter as well as morphological operations for extracting ROI. Circular filter reduced the false positive rate and tries to increase the integrity rate of ROI and finally CNN has been used for classification purposes. Roy et al. [34] extracted the region of cancers part by using ACM (Active Contour Model) and classification by fuzzy logic. It also compares with SVM method and it was observed that the proposed method gives the better result. Ignatious and Joseph [35] used watershed algorithm and region growing algorithm for segmentation and different types of statistical features are extracted for lung cancer detection purposes. Gonzalez and Ponomaryov [36] used morphological operation as well as a thresholding method for removing background and unwanted tissue from lung tumor images. Finally, SVM classification is applied to the classification stage. Makaju et al. [37] used watershed segmentation method in the segmentation stage and different types of statistical features are extracted and in the final stage SVM classifier help to detect benign and malignant cancer. Paing and Choomchuay [38] used morphological method and otsu's method for nodules segmentation and MLP has been used for classification purposes. Tariq et al. [39] has been used neuro-fuzzy classifying for classifier cancers region. Dandil et al. [40] used ANN classifier for classifying cancer cells and SOM (Self Organizing Maps) has been used for segmentation purposes. Manickavasagam and Selvan [41] used Naïve Bayes classifier for identifying normal and abnormal cancer cells and from abnormal cancer cells, In this, Neuro fuzzy and Cuckoo search algorithm helps to find the stages of cancers. Palani and Venkatalakshmi [42] developed an IOT based model for detecting lung cancer in this model they used fuzzy classifier for segmentation and CNN based decision tree for classification. Ke et al. [43] used Ant Lion and Moth-Flame based heuristic algorithm for extracting lung diseases from X-ray images. Prabu et al. [44] used optimal DNN and LDA for classifying lung cancer. Keshani et al. [45] used ACM and SVM for segmentation and recognition of Lung cancer.

2.4 Liver Cancer

Das et al. [46] applied two segmentation methods Gaussian Mixture and Watershed for segmentating cancer region and later DNN classifier has been used for classification purposes. Anter and Hassenian [47] used different types of segmentation approach such as fuzzy c-mean, watershed and neutrosophic sets for improving and correctly identifying the liver tumor. Liu et al. [48] used U-Net and graph cutting method for correctly segmented liver cancer parts. DoGantekin et al. [49] proposed a method which will help to reduce the execution time as well as space. In [49] CNN based classifier, as well as a combination of SVD and Discrete Wavelet, Transform based hash function was used. Anwar et al. [50] applied a fuzzy c mean based algorithm that has been used for extracting cancer regions from the CT liver images. Wu et al. [51] classified the benign and malignant liver tumor using deep learning-based method. Khan et al. [52] applied different types of segmentation algorithms for automatic liver cancer detection purposes. In [52] Otsu, morphological and H-minima transform has been used in the segmentation technique. Raj and Jayasree [53] used a graph cut method for correctly detecting liver cancer and SVM classifier has been used for classification purpose.

2.5 Skin Cancer

Khan et al. [54] used PSO for segmentation and SVM classifier has been used for classification purposes. Tschandl et al. [55] classified skin cancer based on ResNet 34 based deep neural network and U-Net based technique. Yang et al. [56] proposed a technique based on three-stages. In the pre processing stage Otsu, segmentation stage Gabor wavelet transform and in post processing stage morphological operator has been used. Mahbod et al. [57] applied various types of CNN such as AlexNet, VGGNet, ResNet and also used SVM classifier for classifying skin cancer. Garcia-Arroyo et al. [58] used a fuzzy classifier for classifying skin cancer. In [58]they used before classifying like segmentation, extracting feature (texture and color). Gavrilov et al. [59] used several techniques the Inception V3 method for classifying skin diseases. Hameed et al. [60] has applied AlexNet classifier for feature extraction and SVM classifier for classifying purposed. Shoieb and Youssef [61] has used CNN classifiers for feature extraction as well as for classification purposes. Shahin et al. [62] used ResNet 50 and Inception V3 method for classifing seven skin lesion types. Hosny et al. [63] used the AlexNet method for classifying by modifying the last layer with softmax activation function. In [63] they used data augmentation as well as a transfer learning technique. Riaz et al. [64] used ACM based segmentation method and later periphery analysis (local boundary patterns) issued to extract skin lesions. Soudani and Barhoumi [65] has been used VGG16 and ResNet 50 for feature extraction as well as for classification purposes. Hu et al. [66] applied adaptive threshold based wavelet transform for segmentation purpose and later morphological operation has been used to make more clear segmented results.

3 Segmentation Technique on Different Cancer Detection

Segmentation is an important technique in medical imaging where the digital image is split into multiple parts, i.e. regions and extract the meaningful region namely ROI (Region Of Interest). If the aim of the doctor is to analysis the tumor or cancer cell in computer tomography (CT) or any other imaging, then the tumor in the image is the region of interest. Another example is that, if an image application aims to find the iris in an eye image, then in this particular task ROI is iris part in an image. Segmentation of perfect ROI in real world images is the first process of getting success. Hence, the success rate or failure rate of the extraction of ROI from digital images ultimately influences the success of the image processing applications. No universal segmentation is built for all images processing application therefore, every one try with different method to extract their ROI. According to the image processing application, segmentation method also changed.

3.1 Region Growing Technique

The paper [22] uses region growing for final tumor detection and for segmentation use in papers [30, 35]. The region growing mainly build the similarity principle. The principle of the similarity state that a region is merge if all the pixels of that region are homogeneous in nature with respect to some of their characteristics like colour, texture, intensity, other statistical properties. Idea of region growing is that choose a pixel within the region which is called the starting or seed point of the ROI. Merge all the neighbor pixel together whose pixel value is matching the seed pixel values. The process is repeated until no merge possible. This results in the segmentation(merging part), known a region of interest.

3.2 Active Contour Model

In papers [34, 45, 66], they use Active Contour Model (ACM) for cancer segmentation. Active contour models are a segmentation method. It is also known as snakes, dynamic contours or deformable model. Most of the case active contour the model is named as a snake model. The segmentation of real images like medical imaging, it is very complicated task as they are covered by noise and artefacts. The performance of the ACM in medical imaging is very impressive. The advantages of snakes are that this approach is immune to noise, boundaries, and gaps present in the image. The main idea behind ACM is that it computes the minimum energy paths. Snakes follow the region growing approach method. Initially, a contour is placed like a seed or starting point inside the ROI. The contour is a small curve which, like an elastic band, grows or shrinks to fit the region of interest.

The contour is moving by forces or energy functions to the boundary of the object. These force or energy functions are derived from the images itself. By controlling the energy function, one can have control over the snakes. In digital imaging snakes are divided into external energy and internal energy. Internal energy depends on some essential properties such as the boundary length or curvature. The minimization of these forces leads to shrinkage of the contour. To counteract the shrinkage of snakes, external energy is used. The external energy is derived from the image structures and it determines the relationship between the snake and the image. This can be the sum of the grey levels or any complicated function of the grey scale gradients. If it is the sum of the grey levels, then the snake latches onto the brightness. External energy depends on the image structure and user-supplied constraints based factors. These constraints are also controlled by external force. The total energy is the sum of the internal, the external and the constraint energies.

3.3 Thresholding

In papers [35, 39, 58], they use thresholding for segmentation where in [36] they used it for image enhancement. Thresholding is the easiest and most popular segmentation technique in image processing. In this technique first gray level image is converted into a binary image. This segmentation mainly separate the background and foreground based on some thresholding value T. All of the pixels a value greater than the thresholding value T considers as a foreground and the values less than thresholding value T consider as a background. Thresholding can be categorized into three classes local, global and adaptive thresholding. In global thresholding with the help of single threshold value it divides the entered image into two dominant classes [67]. Otsu's global method use in papers [7, 38, 42, 50, 53, 56] is one of the popular single thresholding value algorithm. Additive thresholding used in papers [47, 66] and Optimal thresholding use of paper [32].

3.4 Genetic Algorithms (GA)

After feature extraction, optimization purpose papers [27, 28, 54] follow this method. The main idea behind Genetic Algorithm (GA) is biology. It is working on the Charles Darwin principle. As per natural selection, organisms that are able to survive, adapt, and prosper, continue their ability to maintain their offspring. Here the notion of 'fitness' is defined as how well the organism is able to adapt to the environment and able to survive. Evolutionary computing methods use this principle to solve optimization problems. Then an exhaustive the search is performed for the best solutions for the given optimal solution. Genetic algorithms are part of evolutionary algorithms, but are more realistic. Genetic operations are derived using biological principles.

3.5 Watershed Algorithm

Watershed algorithm is used for segmentation purpose in papers [35, 37, 46]. A watershed is one type of segmentation algorithm, it locates the object using watershed. This algorithm has separated the objects from the images. User first identified the marker value then the algorithm works and it takes pixel values for local elevation. The algorithm flood within the marker value and it was stopped until other marker line meets. The maximum case markers are chosen as a local minima of the image. The algorithm fill the basins inside the marker line. The watershed lines mark the boundaries of the watershed lines. The problem with this method is that this algorithm leads to over segmentation. This is caused because of noise. Hence it is better if the images are smoothed before the segmentation process. The post segmentation algorithms can be invoked within the smaller regions to prevent over segmentation. It requires low computational times and it is easy, intuitive method.

3.6 Morphological Operation

To improve the quality of the image, the papers [24, 36] follow Morphological Operation method and whereas papers [30, 33, 34, 39, 47] use for segmentation. The basic morphological operation is dilation and erosion. Dilation operator is applied on binary and grey scale images. The basic effect of dilation operator on a binary image is that it increases the boundaries of the region, because of that the small holes present in the image becomes smaller. Erosion is another important operation by morphological operation. The main objective of this operator is it make an object smaller by removing its outer layer of pixels. If a black pixel has a white neighbor, then all the pixels is made white. The erosion operator takes the image and the structuring element as inputs and thins the objects.

3.7 Particle Swarm Optimization (PSO)

Particle Swarm Optimization (PSO) is used for feature selection purpose in papers [28, 29] and for segmentation purpose of paper [54]. PSO is one of the optimization technique which can solve hard computational problems. PSO is robust (can solve the problem in different condition with different situation) stochastic optimization method which works based on the movement of objects and intelligence of object swarms. Set of n individual particle communicate to each other directly or indirectly using search directions (gradients). Set of n individual's particles flying over and searching space to locate global optimal value. During every iteration of PSO all particles update their position based on previous experience and neighbors experience value. PSO composed by three vectors.

(a) X-Vector: This vector store the current location (position) of a particular particle.
(b) P-Vector: It is known as p best. It stores the location (position) which was given a best solution among all the particle.
(c) V-Vector: It stores a direction (gradient) where the particle will travel undisturbed.

Every particle has local best and it moves towards the global best. All particles are the members of the whole population throughout every iteration operation of PSO.

4 Feature Reduction or Dimension Reduction Technique

Reduction of dimension into our input data feature set matrix is called dimension or feature reduction. When we try to work on big dimension value, it is difficult to visualize and the computation time as well as iteration value and only keeps most important feature value.

4.1 Principal Component Analysis (PCA)

The papers [14, 40, 54] use Principal Component Analysis (PCA) for feature reduction. PCA is a dimension reduction technique. In real data values are multi dimensional. The PCA technique helps to reduce the dimension such a way that the small dimension must have most important and useful information which is useful in later stage. The working principle of PCA is discussed in below:

(a) First calculate covariance matrix (C_x) on the input datasets matrix (X) $C_x = \frac{1}{(n-1)}(X - \mu_x).(X - \mu_x)^T$ Where $\mu_x$mean of X data value and T indicate transpose of matrix.
(b) Find the Eigen value and corresponding Eigen vectors of the covariance matrix (C_x)
(c) Sort this Eigen vectors along with their Eigen value in decreasing order.
(d) Chose m Eigen vector and that will gives new m dimensions.
(e) Finally, convert this n dimensional data matrix to m dimensional value.

4.2 Single Value Decomposition (SVD)

In papers [18, 49] use SVD for feature reduction. SVD also known as a matrix decomposition method. It reduces matrix constituent parts to make easy calculation purpose.

Mathematically, the SVD can write as-
$A = U.S.V^T$

where
orthogonal matrix U of size $x \times y$ $[x \geq y]$
A is a $x \times y$ matrix.
S is $x \times y$ diagonal matrix. V is $x \times y$ another orthogonal matrix.
'S' (a diagonal matrix) store the singular values of the matrix A. left singular vector values of matrix A represent by column of U and right singular value of matrix A represent by column of V. SVD is calculated through iteration. SVD is used for dimension reduction purpose. From the high dimensional feature data value we extract the performance of our next work.

4.3 *Linear Discriminant Analysis (LDA)*

Linear Discriminant Analysis (LDA) uses as a classifier in papers [18, 32] and for reduction purpose in paper [44]. For discriminating the input features LDA method used decision functions. The LDA is the model that does the distribution of predictors separately in each of the response classes, and then it uses bayes' theorem to estimate the probability [68]. It is used for supervised classification problems which takes, labels for consideration. This is used in bio metrics, chemistry and bio informatics. It projects the higher dimensional space into a lower dimensional space.

5 Classification and Clustering Technique for Cancer Detection

Classification is a supervised learning method. If we want to classify between apple and banana then some parameters such as color, size, and shape are required. Thus a data set needs to be constructed to train a classifier on apple looks or a banana looks. These attributes are called input features, attributes, or independent variables. The input also includes labels of known instances. So a classifier takes a set of features as input and learns what features characterize an apple or a banana. Then it takes an unknown instance and assigns the label 'apple' or 'banana'. This label is a dependent variable and this process is called classification, prediction, or recognition. A class is supposed to be predefined and non-overlapping, and should completely partition the entire data set evenly.

A classifier model is supposed to 'learn' the complex relationships that exist between the input image features using the training data. This resultant learning the process is known as a concept or model. After the learning stage is over, the classifier is called a 'learn system' and produces a classification model. So when an unknown instance is given as input, and if the classifier assigns the label correctly, it is known as a correct classification; otherwise it is termed as an incorrect classification and implies that more inputs are required to train the classifier.

5.1 Support Vector Machine (SVM)

The papers [6, 14, 15, 18, 19, 22, 24, 28, 30, 31, 33, 37, 45, 53] uses Support Vector Machine (SVM) for classification (supervised algorithm). SVM used to separate the data values by hyper plane. The main aim of SVM is to find the optimal hyper plane, which helps to maximize the margin value of the training image data set values. Show in Fig. 1 about SVM hyper plane.

The hyper plane may be drawn into the different way which may be optimal or not. To solve this optimal hyper plane problem introduce a new concept called margin. After computing the closet data set point to the hyper plane, the double this distance value and drawn another hyper plane is called margin. If the hyper plane is much chosen for the given data point, then its margin is big. The main objective which generates the maximizing the margin values of the training data sets.

5.2 Bayesian Classifier

The papers [5, 25, 41] use Bayesian for classification. Bayesian classifier one of the popular classifier in image processing. Total three types of Bayesian classifier available in image processing. They are maximum likelihood classifier, minimum distance classifier and minimum risk classifier. Compare this three maximum likelihood is most popular version.

(a) $P(i)-$ is class i prior probability.
(b) $p(x/i)-$ is class i Conditional probability has x. This conditional probability value is calculated from the training data set.

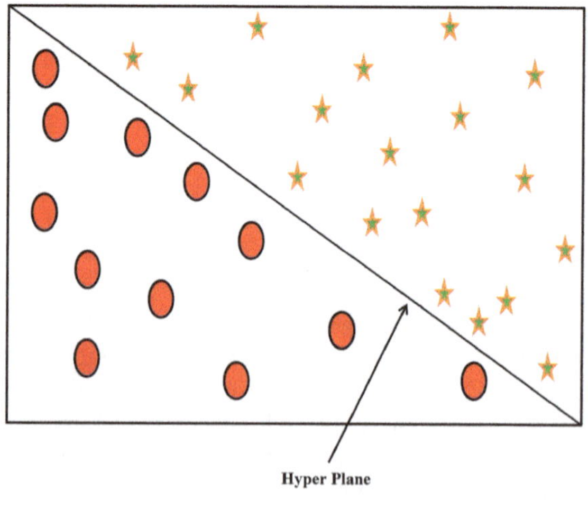

Fig. 1 Support Vector Machine (SVM)

(c) $P(x)-$ and $P(x/i)$ over the entire data sets. This is not a probabilistic information, but it considers as a normalization factor. As per the Bayesian principle, one can find the inverse probability $P(i/x)$from$P(x/i)$ and $P(i)$

$\therefore P(i/x) = \frac{P(\frac{x}{i})P(i)}{P(x)}$

The prior probability of the class is obtained from the training data set.

5.3 K-Nearest Neighbour (KNN) Classification

The papers [14, 15, 18, 20, 27] use K-Nearest Neighbour (KNN) for classification. KNN is an unsupervised learning method. In KNN classifier the input is an unknown and it classified the different group based on similarity measurement. Classification was done based on the majority vote of neighbours.

In Fig. 2 nearest neighbour value is 3 for new object star. It was noticed that out of 3 neighbors majority vote is given by circle so, new object belongs to circle group.

Figure 3 depicts nearest neighbor value of 5 and majority vote given by circle, so, the new objects belongs to circle group. K-NN gives better results on big data sets and odd numbers of neighbours, because even number of nearest neighbour value the tested object may be goes into wrong group.

5.4 Neuro Fuzzy

The Neuro fuzzy system uses in papers [34, 39, 41, 48] for classifier and papers [16, 21] uses for segmentation. The Neuro fuzzy system is one of a good approach for

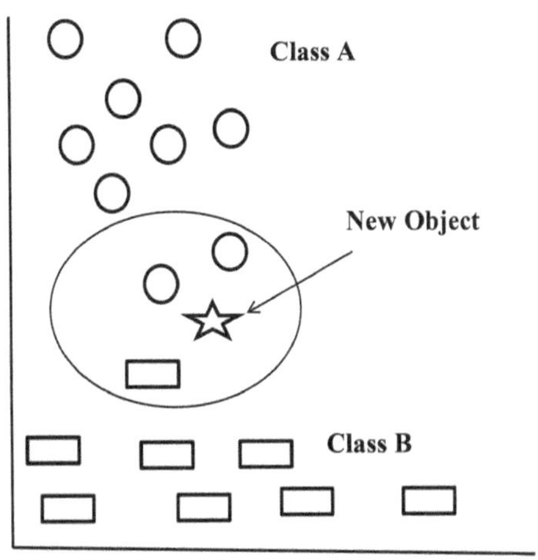

Fig. 2 nearest neighbour equal to 3

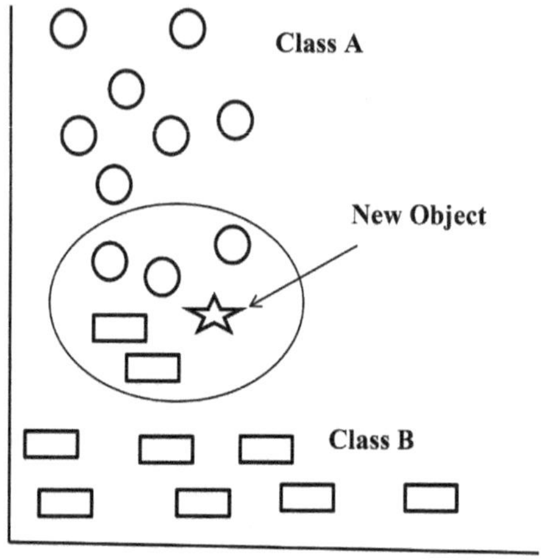

Fig. 3 Nearest neighbour equal to 5

learning fuzzy system from data. The learning algorithm was derived from the neural network (NN) theory. The neuro fuzzy classifier has three layer, all the layers are feed forward. This classifier not used activation function, its use t-norms. The first layer of the classifier simply indicates input variables, middle layer indicate hidden layer and the outer layer use for output variables. Fuzzy rules are applied into hidden layer with weight value. Data flow parallels in nature.

5.5 K-Mean Clustering

The papers [25, 29, 31] use this method as classifier. K-Mean is another useful clustering algorithm. Let us assume that there are n observations or instances, $\{x_1, x_2, \ldots x_n\}$. The procedure for the k-means technique is as follows:

(a) Calculate the distance between cluster means and the observation.
(b) Assign observation value or the instance value to the minimum distance Cluster.
(c) New mean has to be calculated after observation value added to the cluster.
(d) Repeat the above steps till a predefined threshold is met.

5.6 Fuzzy C-Means

Feature extraction purpose papers [19, 23, 25, 42, 60, 61] uses fuzzy c-means whereas, paper [47] use as a classifier. This is another useful fuzzy technique. Similar to k-means algorithm, clustering is done by comparing the instance with the centroid of a cluster. If the distance is minimal, the instance is added to the cluster. As soon as the instance is added, the cluster centroid is recomputed and this is done iteratively till there are no instances that change clusters.

6 Machine Learning Technique for Cancer Detection

Machine learning is one of the best applications of artificial intelligence. Artificial intelligence proves a system which has a capacity to learn automatically and improving the learning capacity based on experience not by human interference. Different categories of a machine learning algorithm are available such as supervised, unsupervised, semi-supervised and reinforcement.

In a supervised learning model, the training was done on labeled data. Feature of labeled data has extracted and it is compared with feature values of new data. The unsupervised method trains the system without labeling the data. It draws a function based on a hidden structure of unlabeled data and classified based on this function value. Semi-supervised model placed between supervised and unsupervised learning. In this model, the training was done based on small labeled data and large unlabeled data set. Reinforcement is another type of model, which learn based on train error search and delayed reward technique.

6.1 Back Propagation Neural Network (BPN)

Back Propagation Neural Network (BPN) is a supervised learning algorithm where, for training the model using multiple perceptron's value in paper[31]. At the starting we have chosen random weight value for designing the neural network. This random value may be correct or incorrect. BPN was introduced for solving this type of problem. BPN working principle is that, it first looks into error function for minimum the error rate in weight space. This is done with gradient descent or delta rule technique. The weight value which minimizes the value of the error function considers to be the solution of particular learning problem.

In BPN, we first initializes some random value into the weight (W) and propagated forward. If some error value is found, then it reduce that error value, we propagated the model background and increase the weight value W. if we the found error value has increased then we cannot increase the weight value W, we propagate the model backward and reducing the error value W.

6.2 Decision Tree (DT)

Papers [8, 42] use Decision Tree (DT) as classifier. DT is a supervised learning algorithm. It looks like the similar structure of the tree. Where each internal node value gives class attribute value, the outcome of the class test indicating by branch, leaf or terminal node gives the class label value. Below pseudo code of DT given is

Pseudo code:

(a) Find the distance between the observation and cluster means.
(b) Divide the training data sets value into subsets such that each subset consists of data with the same value for an attribute.
(c) Repeat step a and b on each subset before we get leaf nodes or a terminal nodes in all the branches of the tree.

In starting, the whole training data sets are considered as the root of the decision tree. Categorical feature values are preferable. If these feature values are continued value then has been built the model. The distributed attribute value is recorded respectively. Based on some statistical technique the place attributes values are decided i.e. it may place into the root or internal node or leaf node.

6.3 Multilayer Perceptron (MLP)

The papers [37, 40] use Multi Layer Perceptron (MLP) as classifier. A multilayer perceptron is a feed for-ward artificial neural network. MLP generates sets of outputs when it taken sets of input value. MLP uses back propagation technique for training the network. An MLP considers as logistic regression classifier group. The input of the model is first transformation projects input data value into some space where the input data value becomes linearly separable. This middle (intermediate) layer is known as hidden layer. A single intermediate layer is comfortable to make a multilayer perceptron neural network. Figure 4 shows the graphical representation of MLP. Here, one input, hidden or intermediate and one output layer present. MLP generally applied in supervised learning problems. This model train on the sets of input and output pairs. It is also learn't the correlation between inputs data value and the output value. Training parts help for adjusting some parameters like weight value and biases with the help of back propagation technique.

6.4 Artificial Neural Networks (ANN)

The papers [5, 10, 14, 25, 61] use Artificial Neural Networks (ANN) as classifier. The Artificial Neural Network (ANN) worked on biological functioning of the human brain. The visualization of human brain as a model showing that the input value is obtained through millions of neurons. Hence the human brain can be visualized as a large interconnection processing unit and the activation function of this model is fires when the neurons will cross the some threshold value. The diagram of ANN model is shown in Fig. 5.

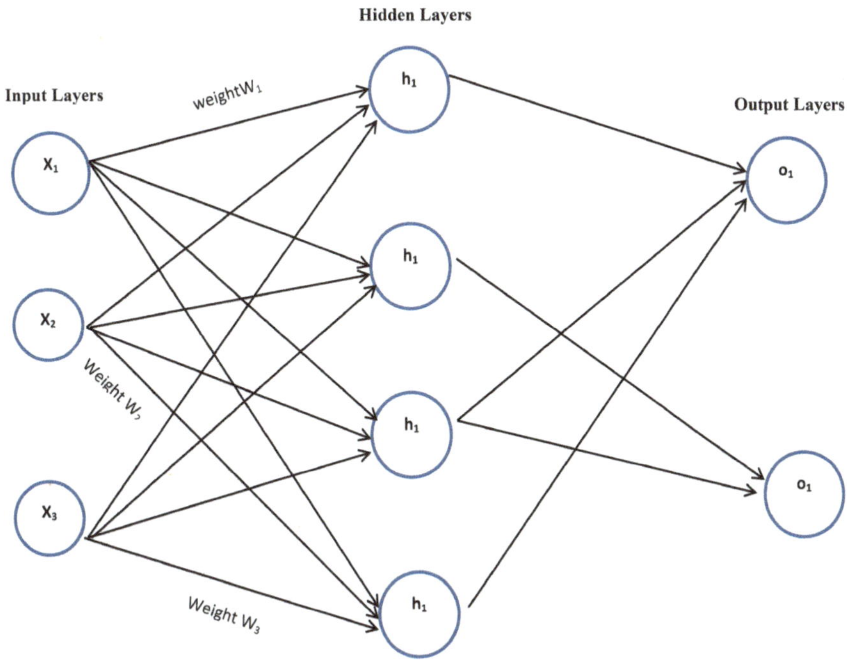

Fig. 4 Graphical representation of MLP

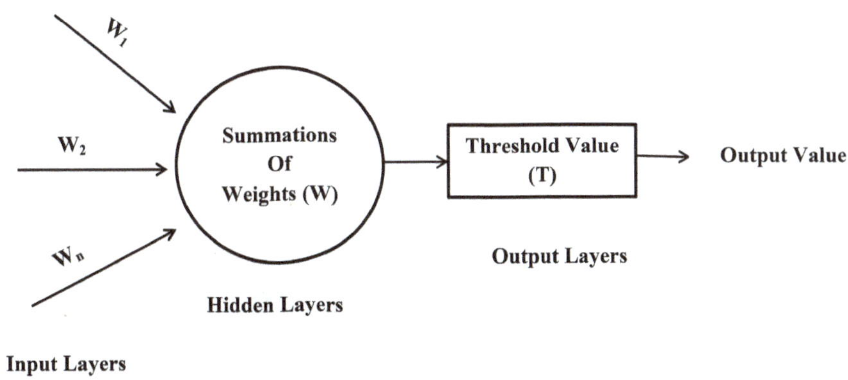

Fig. 5 Neural Network (NN) diagram

6.5 Deep Neural Network (DNN)

The papers [9, 44, 46, 51] use Deep Neural Network (DNN) as classifier. The deep neural network is the foundation of many artificial intelligence. Now different DNNs method increases the human accuracy in many image processing applications. On input space, after using statistical approach into larger input image data set, deep neural network extracted higher level feature values and it is an effective representation. It is the very good approach than previous method. DNN belongs to artificial intelligence and machine learning. Science and engineering together create an intelligent machine which can do similar classification as human done.

The relationship between DNN with machine learning and artificial intelligence shown in Fig. 6. In neural network there are three layer one is input, output and one hidden layer. In deep neural network, input and output the layer is same but it uses more than one hidden layer. Now, maximum model used many hidden layers of increasing better performance. DNN methods are capable to learn higher-level features from complex or a simple data set. The basic learning the process of DNNs is same as the machine learning process. In some of the special types of DNNs, this learning takes responsibility to determine the weight value and the bias value in the network and this technique is called as a training the network. Once the training process is complete, the network is ready to perform its task and it gives the output

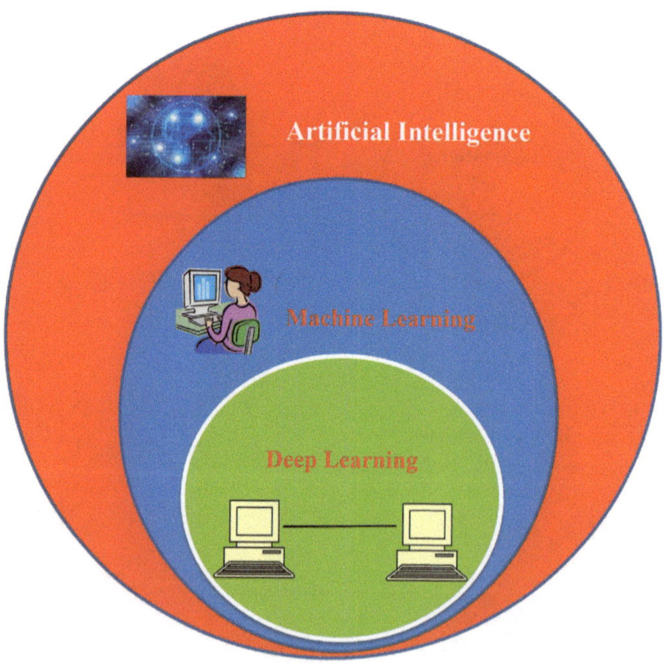

Fig. 6 Structure of Neural Network (NN)

value based on the weight value which is determined during the training process [69]. The methods run with these weights is referred to as interference [69].

6.6 *Convolution Neural Network (CNN)*

The papers [7, 11, 17, 33, 49] use Convolution Neural Network (CNN) method. Convolution is also known as ConvNet. It is deep neural network and designed for image recognition. We divided our entire method into two main category feature extraction and classification. The image first enter into the feature extraction the network then these extracted features are entering into classification network. The classification then operates based on the images feature values and finally CNN model gives the output value. The feature extraction neural network consists of the piles of the convolutional layer and pooling layer pairs. Convolutional layer of CNN converted images into convolution operation. It collected digital filters. The pooling operation combines all the neighboring pixel into one single pixel. So, the pooling layer reduces the size of the image. As per the primary point in view of ConvNet in the image, the two operations pooling and convolution are conceptual in 2D (two-dimension) plane. This is one main difference between CNN and other neural network.

6.7 *AlexNet*

The papers [57, 60] use AlexNet method. AlexNet was the first CNN to win the ImageNet challenge in 2012 [69]. In AlexNet model five convolution layers and three fully connected layers were used. Each convolution layer built with 96 to 384 filters and size of the filters vary between (3×3 to 11×11) with 3 to 256 channels each. Three channels of first layer indicates red, green, blue components of the input data image. The activation function ReLu i.e. non-linear function was used in each and every layer. The 3×3 max pooling function applied on the output layers 1, 2 and 5. Pooling function was used for reducing the size and 4 stride method is applied for this. AlexNet first used the local response normalization in the first two layers before use of the max pooling function. Reducing the size and computation time, the first layer's 96 output channels was divided into two parts and each group has 48 channels and so on. Finally AlexNet needs 61 million weights and total 724 million multiply and accumulates (MACs) to process one 227×227 input image [69].

6.8 VGG-16

The papers [3, 6, 12, 57, 65] use VGG method. In VGG-16 out of total 16 layers 13 are used as a convolutional layer and three layers used as a fully connected layer. To balance the cost the 5×5 filter layers are reduced into 3 × 3 filter shown into Fig. 20 and which have light weights. All convolutional layers used 3×3 filters and total VGG-16 required 138 million weights. The input image data size will be 224×224 with 15.5G MACs process. Two types of VGG Net are available VGG-16 and VGG-19. Compare with VGG-16, VGG-19 gives a 0.1 lower top-5 error rate, at the cost of 1.27 more MACs [69].

6.9 Google Net

The paper [12] uses GoogleNet method. Total 22 layers are used in GoogleNet network. It introduced a parallel connection inception module shown in below Fig. 21. Here three different size filters 1 × 1, 2 × 2 and 5 × 5 with 3 × 3 max-pooling functions are used in different parallel connection and outputs of parallel connection is joined together and generate a final network output value. Multiple filter sizes have the effect on processing the input at multiple scales [69]. GoogleNet using back propagation method of training time to get weights and activation function value and it improves the training seed. In order to reduce weights, 1 × 1 filters are applied as a 'bottleneck' to reduce the number of channels for each filter [69]. In 22 layers three are convolution layers, 9 inceptions layer (each has two deep convolution layers) and one fully-connected layer. GoogleNet has different version such as V1, V3, and V4.

6.10 Inception V3

The papers [3, 59, 62, 63] use Inception method. It reduces the convolution layer by using small one dimensional filters. MACs number is reduced and weights go to deep into 42 layers. In conjunction with batch normalization [70], V3 achieves over 3% lower top-5 error than V1 with 2.5 increase in computation [71]. Inception V4 uses residual connections [72] for a 0.4 % reduction in error [69].

6.11 ResNet

The articles [3, 6, 12, 55, 57, 62, 65] use ResNet method. It is also popular with the name Residual Net. It uses 34 or more layers to go deeper. It was the first entry DNN in ImageNet challenge that exceeded the human level accuracy with a top-5 error rate below 5% [69] the challenge task of deep networks is to vanish gradient value during training period, the error back propagates with the help of network gradient shrinks, which will affect the ability to update the weight- it is the problem of all deep learning networks. ResNet includes 'shortcut' module. These shortcut modules contain an identity connections namely convolution layer (weight layers).

For learning purposes ResNet using residual mapping function $[F(x) = H(x) - x]$. Initially $F(x)$ is considered as a zero and identity connection is taken during training, the weight layer is used in actual forward connection. Reducing the weight parameters, ResNet using 1×1 filter named as 'bottle neck'. Therefore, two layers of the shortcut module are replace with three layers such as 1×1, 3×3, 1×1. Where 1×1 is used for reduce purpose and 3×3 used to increase the weight value. ResNet-50 used one convolution layer and 16 shortcut layers and one fully connected layers.

6.12 U-Net

In paper [48], this technique is use for segmentation and paper [55] use this as a classifier. The U-Net model is built based on fully convolutional network. U-Net method modified such a way that, it can properly segment the medical imaging. U-Net architecture is symmetric. U-Net segmentation method have three architectures namely- down-sampling path or the contracting, bottleneck and up-sampling path or the expanding. This architecture uses concatenation operation be-tween down-sampling and up-sampling path for skip connection purpose.

6.13 Generative Adversarial Networks (GANs)

The papers [73–76, 76, 77] use GANs model. GANs are the recently introduced powerful unsupervised learning technique. GANs technique actually consists of a system where two neural networks model compete, i.e., fighting between each other or try to build a systematic such a way that it able to capture, analyses or copy the data set variations.

In deep neural nets, if some noise or other unwanted material added to the original data, then it may miss classify the data. Because the maximum machine learning models used limited amount of data and it creates the over fitting problem. Another way the machine learning can miss classify the data is that machine always maintain a linear map between input and output data, i.e., the boundary of different classes separate by linearly, but in reality the classes are composed of linearities. If any small changes happen in feature value then it will automatically miss classify. GANs system tries to overcome this miss classification problem. GANs are separated by three parts First part G (Generative) help to understand the model from where we know how that data has been generated through probabilistic model. Adversarial is the second portion which helps to train the model. DNN based third (networks) part is used for the training the model.

GANs model has one generator and one discriminator. Generator simple, take face value (like video data, audio data) and tries to fool discriminator on the other hand discriminator tries to find the distinguish between real and fake data. Both discriminator and generator is a neural network model and both are run at the training time. In training several iterations have done and during this time discriminator and generator tries to get better and better result in ever iteration.

In GANs model generator tries to capture the distributed data in such a way that the mistake probability value of discriminator will increase and discriminator tries to estimate probability function such that every time it receive the sample of training data not from the generator created data.

7 Conclusion

This paper an intensive review on different types of cancer like breast, skin, lung, liver and brain has been discussed. Also different types of segmentation algorithms and its evaluation techniques; it's different dimension reduction techniques; different classification-clustering and machine learning techniques with their various evaluation techniques have also been discussed.

References

1. Davis, C. P., MedicineNet:Cancer 29-1-2019.
2. News-room. World Health Organization; 12 September 2018
3. Agarwal, R., Diaz, O., Lladó, X., Yap, M. H., & Martí, R. (2019). Automatic mass detection in mammograms using deep convolutional neural networks. *Journal of Medical Imaging*, *6*(3), 031409.
4. Li, H., Zhuang, S., Li, D., Zhao, J., & Ma, Y. (2019). Benign and malignant classification of mammogram images based on deep learning. *Biomedical Signal Processing and Control*, *51*, 347–354.
5. Saba, T., Khan, S. U., Islam, N., Abbas, N., Rehman, A., Javaid, N., et al. (2019). Cloud-based decision support system for the detection and classification of malignant cells in breast cancer using breast cytology images. *Microscopy Research and Technique*.
6. Li, Y., Junmin, W., & Qisong, W. (2019). Classification of breast cancer histology images using multi-size and discriminative patches based on deep learning. *IEEE Access*, *7*, 21400–21408.
7. Araújo, T., Aresta, G., Castro, E., Rouco, J., Aguiar, P., Eloy, C., et al. (2017). Classification of breast cancer histology images using convolutional neural networks. *PloS One*, *12*(6), e0177544.
8. Delshi Howsalya Devi, R., & Indra Devi, M. (2016, April–June). Outlier detection algorithm combined with decision tree classifier for early diagnosis of breast cancer. *International Journal of Advanced Engineering Technology*, *93*, 98.
9. Zemouri, R., Omri, N., Devalland, C., Arnould, L., Morello, B., Zerhouni, N., et al. (2018). Breast cancer diagnosis based on joint variable selection and Constructive Deep Neural Net-

work. In *2018 IEEE 4th Middle East Conference on Biomedical Engineering (MECBME)* (pp. 159–164). New York: IEEE.
10. Shenbagavalli, P., & Thangarajan, R. (2018). Aiding the digital mammogram for detecting the breast cancer using Shearlet transform and neural network. *Asian Pacific Journal of Cancer Prevention: APJCP, 19*(9), 2665.
11. Ting, F. F., Tan, Y. J., & Sim, K. S. (2019). Convolutional neural network improvement for breast cancer classification. *Expert Systems with Applications, 120*, 103–115.
12. Khan, S. U., Islam, N., Jan, Z., Ud Din, I., & Rodrigues, J. J. P. C. (2019). A novel deep learning based framework for the detection and classification of breast cancer using transfer learning. *Pattern Recognition Letters.*
13. http://www.medinfo.cs.ucy.ac.cy/index.php/32-software/218-datasets .
14. Ahammed Muneer, K. V., & Paul Joseph, K. (2019). Automation of MR brain image classification for malignancy detection. *Journal of Mechanics in Medicine and Biology, 19*(01), 1940002.
15. Ayadi, W., Elhamzi, W., Charfi, I., & Atri, M. (2019). A hybrid feature extraction approach for brain MRI classification based on Bag-of-words. *Biomedical Signal Processing and Control, 48*, 144–152.
16. Natarajan, A., & Kumarasamy, S. (2019). Efficient segmentation of brain tumor using FL-SNM with a metaheuristic approach to optimization. *Journal of Medical Systems, 43*(2), 25.
17. Sajjad, M., Khan, S., Muhammad, K., Wu, W., Ullah, A., & Baik, S. W. (2019). Multi-grade brain tumor classification using deep CNN with extensive data augmentation. *Journal of Computational Science, 30*, 174–182.
18. Zacharaki, E. I., Wang, S., Chawla, S., Yoo, D. S., Wolf, R., Melhem, E. R., et al. (2009). Classification of brain tumor type and grade using MRI texture and shape in a machine learning scheme. *Magnetic Resonance in Medicine: An Official Journal of the International Society for Magnetic Resonance in Medicine, 62*(6), 1609–1618.
19. Sriramakrishnan, P., Kalaiselvi, T., & Rajeswaran, R. (2019). Modified local ternary patterns technique for brain tumour segmentation and volume estimation from MRI multi-sequence scans with GPU CUDA machine. *Biocybernetics and Biomedical Engineering, 39*(2), 470–487.
20. Ali, A. H., Al-hadi, S. A., Naeemah, M. R., & Mazher, A. N. (2019). Classification of brain lesion using K-nearest neighbor technique and texture analysis. *Journal of Physics: Conference Series, 1178*(1), 012018 (IOP Publishing) .
21. Vishnuvarthanan, G., & Rajasekaran, M. P. (2013). Segmentation of MR brain images for tumor extraction using fuzzy. *Current Medical Imaging Reviews, 9*(1), 2–6.
22. Zhang, N., Ruan, S., Lebonvallet, S., Liao, Q., & Zhu, Y. (2011). Kernel feature selection to fuse multi-spectral MRI images for brain tumor segmentation. *Computer Vision and Image Understanding, 115*(2), 256–269.
23. Sing, J. K., Adhikari, S. K., & Basu, D. K. (2015). A modified fuzzy C-means algorithm using scale control spatial information for MRI image segmentation in the presence of noise. *Journal of Chemometrics, 29*(9), 492–505.
24. Usha, R., & Perumal, K. (2019). SVM classification of brain images from MRI scans using morphological transformation and GLCM texture features. *International Journal of Computational Systems Engineering, 5*(1), 18–23.
25. Alzubi, J. A., Kumar, A., Alzubi, O. A., & Manikandan, R. (2019). Efficient approaches for prediction of brain tumor using machine learning techniques. *Indian Journal of Public Health, 10*(2), 279.
26. Talo, M., Baloglu, U. B., Yıldırım, Ö., & Rajendra Acharya, U. (2019). Application of deep transfer learning for automated brain abnormality classification using MR images. *Cognitive Systems Research, 54*, 176–188.
27. Bhuvaneswari, P., & Brintha Therese, A. (2015). Detection of cancer in lung with k-NN classification using genetic algorithm. *Procedia Materials Science, 10*, 433–440.
28. Asuntha, A., Singh, N., & Srinivasan, A. (2016). PSO, genetic optimization and SVM algorithm used for lung cancer detection. *Journal of Chemical and Pharmaceutical Research, 8*(6), 351–359.

29. Senthil Kumar, K., Venkatalakshmi, K., & Karthikeyan, K. (2019). Lung cancer detection using image segmentation by means of various evolutionary algorithms. *Computational and Mathematical Methods in Medicine*.
30. Kaur, J., Garg, N., & Kaur, D. (2014). Segmentation and feature extraction of lung region for the early detection of lung tumor. *International Journal of Science and Research (IJSR), 3*(6), 2327–2330.
31. Sangamithraa, P. B., & Govindaraju, S. (2016). Lung tumour detection and classification using EK-Mean clustering. In *2016 International Conference on Wireless Communications, Signal Processing and Networking (WiSPNET)* (pp. 2201–2206). New York: IEEE.
32. Aggarwal, T., Furqan, A., & Kalra, K. (2015). Feature extraction and LDA based classification of lung nodules in chest CT scan images. In *2015 International Conference on Advances in Computing, Communications and Informatics (ICACCI)* (pp. 1189–1193). New York: IEEE.
33. Jin, X.-Y., Zhang, Y.-C., & Jin, Q.-L. (2016). Pulmonary nodule detection based on CT images using convolution neural network. In *2016 9th International Symposium on Computational Intelligence and Design (ISCID)* (vol. 1, pp. 202–204). New York: IEEE.
34. Roy, T. S., Sirohi, N., & Patle, A. (2015). Classification of lung image and nodule detection using fuzzy inference system. In *International Conference on Computing, Communication and Automation* (pp. 1204–1207). New York: IEEE.
35. Ignatious, S., & Joseph, R. (2015). Computer aided lung cancer detection system. In *2015 Global Conference on Communication Technologies (GCCT)* (pp. 555–558). New York: IEEE.
36. Rendon-Gonzalez, E., & Ponomaryov, V. (2016). Automatic lung nodule segmentation and classification in CT images based on SVM. In *2016 9th International Kharkiv Symposium on Physics and Engineering of Microwaves, Millimeter and Submillimeter Waves (MSMW)* (pp. 1–4). New York: IEEE.
37. Makaju, S., Prasad, P. W. C., Alsadoon, A., Singh, A. K., & Elchouemi, A. (2018). Lung cancer detection using CT scan images. *Procedia Computer Science, 125*, 107–114.
38. Paing, M. P., & Choomchuay, S. (2017). A computer aided diagnosis system for detection of lung nodules from series of CT slices. In *2017 14th International Conference on Electrical Engineering/Electronics, Computer, Telecommunications and Information Technology (ECTI-CON)* (pp. 302–305). New York: IEEE.
39. Tariq, A., Usman Akram, M., & Younus Javed, M. (2013). Lung nodule detection in CT images using neuro fuzzy classifier. In *2013 Fourth International Workshop on Computational Intelligence in Medical Imaging (CIMI)* (pp. 49–53). New York: IEEE.
40. Dandıl, E., Çakiroğlu, M., Ekşi, Z., Özkan, M., Kurt, Ö. K., & Canan, A. (2014). Artificial neural network-based classification system for lung nodules on computed tomography scans. In *2014 6th International Conference of Soft Computing and Pattern Recognition (SoCPaR)* (pp. 382–386). New York: IEEE.
41. Manickavasagam, R., & Selvan, S. (2019). Automatic detection and classification of lung nodules in CT image using optimized neuro fuzzy classifier with Cuckoo search algorithm. *Journal of Medical Systems, 43*(3), 77.
42. Palani, D., & Venkatalakshmi, K. (2019). An IoT based predictive modelling for predicting lung cancer using fuzzy cluster based segmentation and classification. *Journal of Medical Systems, 43*(2), 21.
43. Ke, Q., Zhang, J., Wei, W., Połap, D., Woźniak, M., Kośmider, L., et al. (2019). A neuro-heuristic approach for recognition of lung diseases from X-ray images. *Expert Systems with Applications, 126*, 218–232.
44. Lakshmanaprabu, S. K., Mohanty, S. N., Shankar, K., Arunkumar, N., & Ramirez, G. (2019). Optimal deep learning model for classification of lung cancer on CT images. *Future Generation Computer Systems, 92*, 374–382.
45. Keshani, M., Azimifar, Z., Tajeripour, F., & Boostani, R. (2013). Lung nodule segmentation and recognition using SVM classifier and active contour modeling: A complete intelligent system. *Computers in Biology and Medicine, 43*(4), 287–300.
46. Das, A., Rajendra Acharya, U., Panda, S. S., & Sabut, S. (2019). Deep learning based liver cancer detection using watershed transform and Gaussian mixture model techniques. *Cognitive Systems Research, 54*, 165–175.

47. Anter, A. M., & Hassenian, A. E. (2018). CT liver tumor segmentation hybrid approach using neutrosophic sets, fast fuzzy c-means and adaptive watershed algorithm. *Artificial Intelligence in Medicine*.
48. Liu, Z., Song, Y.-Q., Sheng, V. S., Wang, L., Jiang, R., Zhang, X., et al. (2019). Liver CT sequence segmentation based with improved U-Net and graph cut. *Expert Systems with Applications*, *126*, 54–63.
49. Doğantekin, A., Özyurt, F., Avcı, E., & Koç, M. (2019). A novel approach for liver image classification: PH-C-ELM. *Measurement*, *137*, 332–338.
50. Anwar, S. M., Awan, S., Yousaf, S., & Majid, M. (2018). Segmentation of liver tumor for computer aided diagnosis. In *2018 IEEE-EMBS Conference on Biomedical Engineering and Sciences (IECBES)* (pp. 366–370). New York: IEEE.
51. Wu, K., Chen, X., & Ding, M. (2014). Deep learning based classification of focal liver lesions with contrast-enhanced ultrasound. *Optik-International Journal for Light and Electron Optics*, *125*(15), 4057–4063.
52. Khan, N., Ahmed, I., Kiran, M., Rehman, H., Din, S., Paul, A., et al. (2019). Automatic segmentation of liver and lesion detection using H-minima transform and connecting component labeling. *Multimedia Tools and Applications*, 1–23.
53. Raj, A., & Jayasree, M. (2016). Automated liver tumor detection using Markov random field segmentation. *Procedia Technology*, *24*, 1305–1310.
54. Khan, M. A., Akram, T., Sharif, M., Saba, T., Javed, K., Lali, I. U., et al. (2019). Construction of saliency map and hybrid set of features for efficient segmentation and classification of skin lesion. *Microscopy Research and Technique*.
55. Tschandl, P., Sinz, C., & Kittler, H. (2019). Domain-specific classification-pretrained fully convolutional network encoders for skin lesion segmentation. *Computers in Biology and Medicine*, *104*, 111–116.
56. Yang, T., Chen, Y., Jiewei, L., & Fan, Z. (2019). Sampling with level set for pigmented skin lesion segmentation. Signal, Image and Video Processing, 1–9.
57. Mahbod, A., Schaefer, G., Ellinger, I., Ecker, R., Pitiot, A., & Wang, C. (2019). Fusing fine-tuned deep features for skin lesion classification. *Computerized Medical Imaging and Graphics*, *71*, 19–29.
58. Garcia-Arroyo, J. L., & Garcia-Zapirain, B. (2019). Segmentation of skin lesions in dermoscopy images using fuzzy classification of pixels and histogram thresholding. *Computer Methods and Programs in Biomedicine*, *168*, 11–19.
59. Gavrilov, D. A., Melerzanov, A. V., Shchelkunov, N. N., & Zakirov, E. I. (2019). Use of neural network-based deep learning techniques for the diagnostics of skin diseases. *Biomedical Engineering*, *52*(5), 348–352.
60. Hameed, N., Shabut, A. M., & Hossain, M. A. (2018). Multi-class skin diseases classification using deep convolutional neural network and support vector machine. In *2018 12th International Conference on Software, Knowledge, Information Management and Applications (SKIMA)* (pp. 1–7). New York: IEEE.
61. Shoieb, D. A., & Youssef, S. M. (2018). An enhanced hybrid model for skin diagnosis using deep convolution neural network. In *2018 9th Cairo International Biomedical Engineering Conference (CIBEC)* (pp. 37–40). New York: IEEE.
62. Shahin, A. H., Kamal, A., & Elattar, M. A. (2018). Deep ensemble learning for skin lesion classification from dermoscopic images. In *2018 9th Cairo International Biomedical Engineering Conference (CIBEC)* (pp. 150–153). New York: IEEE.
63. Hosny, K. M., Kassem, M. A., & Foaud, M. M. (2018). Skin cancer classification using deep learning and transfer learning. In *2018 9th Cairo International Biomedical Engineering Conference (CIBEC)* (pp. 90–93). New York: IEEE.
64. Riaz, F., Naeem, S., Nawaz, R., & Coimbra, M. (2019). Active contours based segmentation and lesion periphery analysis for characterization of skin lesions in dermoscopy images. *IEEE Journal of Biomedical and Health Informatics*, *23*(2), 489–500.
65. Soudani, A., & Barhoumi, W. (2019). An image-based segmentation recommender using crowdsourcing and transfer learning for skin lesion extraction. *Expert Systems with Applications*, *118*, 400–410.

66. Hu, K., Liu, S., Zhang, Y., Cao, C., Xiao, F., Huang, W., et al. (2018). A skin lesion segmentation method based on saliency and adaptive thresholding in wavelet domain. In *International Symposium on Artificial Intelligence and Robotics* (pp. 445–453). Cham: Springer.
67. Renukalatha, S., & Suresh, K. (2018). A review on biomedical image analysis. *Biomedical Engineering: Applications, Basis and Communications, 30*(04), 1830001.
68. Peixeiro, M. (2018) Classification: Linear Discriminant Analysis; Dec 11, 2018, https://towardsdatascience.com/classification-part-linear-discriminant-analysis.
69. Sze, V., Chen, Y. H., Yang, T. J., & Emer, J. S. (2017). Efficient processing of deep neural networks: A tutorial and survey. *Proceedings of the IEEE, 105*(12), 2295–2329.
70. Ioffe, S., & Szegedy, C. (2015). Batch normalization: Accelerating deep network training by reducing internal covariate shift. arXiv preprint arXiv:150203167.
71. Szegedy, C., Vanhoucke, V., Ioffe, S., Shlens, J., & Wojna, Z. (2016). Rethinking the inception architecture for computer vision. In *Proceedings of the IEEE Conference on Computer Vision and Pattern Recognition* (pp. 2818–2826).
72. Szegedy, C., Ioffe, S., Vanhoucke, V., & Alemi, A. A. (2017). Inception-v4, inception-resnet and the impact of residual connections on learning. In *Thirty-First AAAI Conference on Artificial Intelligence*.
73. Frid-Adar, M., Diamant, I., Klang, E., Amitai, M., Goldberger, J., & Greenspan, H. (2018). GAN-based synthetic medical image augmentation for increased CNN performance in liver lesion classification. *Neurocomputing, 321*, 321–331.
74. Chuquicusma, M. J. M., Hussein, S., Burt, J., & Bagci, U. (2018). How to fool radiologists with generative adversarial networks? A visual turing test for lung cancer diagnosis. In *2018 IEEE 15th International Symposium on Biomedical Imaging (ISBI 2018)* (pp. 240–244). New York: IEEE.
75. Frid-Adar, M., Klang, E., Amitai, M., Goldberger, J., & Greenspan, H. (2018). Synthetic data augmentation using GAN for improved liver lesion classification. In *2018 IEEE 15th International Symposium on Biomedical Imaging (ISBI 2018)* (pp. 289–293). New York: IEEE.
76. Salehinejad, H., Valaee, S., Dowdell, T., Colak, E., & Barfett, J. (2018). Generalization of deep neural networks for chest pathology classification in x-rays using generative adversarial networks. In *2018 IEEE International Conference on Acoustics, Speech and Signal Processing (ICASSP)* (pp. 990–994). New York: IEEE.
77. Wu, E., Wu, K., Cox, D., & Lotter, W. (2018). Conditional infilling Gans for data augmentation in mammogram classification. In *Image Analysis for Moving Organ, Breast, and Thoracic Images* (pp. 98–106). Cham: Springer.

Medical Image Classification Techniques and Analysis Using Deep Learning Networks: A Review

Arpit Kumar Sharma, Amita Nandal, Arvind Dhaka, and Rahul Dixit

Abstract Medical is a sector all different from other sectors, it is always the highest demanding sector. The days we look back, medical experts are the one who can process medical images such as X-rays etc. Deep learning nowadays has involved deeply into medical sector. If the processing or analyzing of medical image is concerned, it mostly varies according to the knowledge of the analyzer. Thus to avoid this variation and get more accurate results in the analysis of medical images, deep learning can play a major role. This paper discusses about the use of deep learning for medical processing. This paper aims to provide an introduction of deep learning in the medical sector for image processing. Firstly, the process of image processing neural network has been discussed and then a review of machine learning architectures about CNN, learning with CNN, RNN, Boltzmann machine is presented. The application of neural networks in medical image analysis has also been discussed such as detection, segmentation, registration and localization etc. This paper is concluded by adding some points about challenges and future applications of deep learning networks. The advantage of deep learning in terms of accuracy over machine learning and artificial intelligence has also been presented. Although, the machine learning algorithms are able to provide a great knowledge and information about medical image analysis because it has so efficient and accurate algorithms which are able to interact with image detection.

Keywords Deep learning · Machine learning · CNN · RNN · Analysis of medical image · Image detection and segmentation

A. K. Sharma · A. Nandal · A. Dhaka (✉)
Department of Computer and Communication Engineering, Manipal University Jaipur, Jaipur, India
e-mail: arvind.neomatrix@gmail.com

R. Dixit
Department of Computer Science Engineering, IIIT Pune, Pune, India

R. Patgiri et al. (eds.), *Health Informatics: A Computational Perspective in Healthcare*, Studies in Computational Intelligence 932,
https://doi.org/10.1007/978-981-15-9735-0_13

1 Introduction

In the current era, medical sector has become more convenient with the use of artificial intelligence (AI), machine learning (ML) and deep learning (DL). ML is a subset of AI and DL is a subset of ML [1]. Deep learning has progressed rapidly in current years. It plays a vital role in medical image analysis, image interpretation, image segmentation, image fusion and image registration. ML algorithms can be used for medical image analysis to make it more accurate [1]. With the help of AI and ML, doctors can predict the risk of diseases more accurately which helps in resolving the disease better. But nowadays, deep learning has become a better choice over ML and AI in medical field due to its efficiency and accuracy. Deep learning makes use of neural networks that means study of human brain that takes input, process it and gives output [2]. Medical image classification is a five step process as given below

1. Image acquisition: It selects image range from X-rays, magnetic resonance imaging (MRI) and computed tomography (CT).
2. Preprocessing: It gives the best data results by executing raw dataset. It has some phases like image cropping, filtering and scaling.
3. Feature extraction: It describes the image content by using feature estimation and feature selection methods.
4. Classification: For classification we use data instances process.
5. Evaluation: The most accurate example of this is coincidence matrix and contingency.

In this paper we have discussed many applications and tools of deep learning which are helpful in medical image processing. Every tool or application has its own role. Deep learning can be used in CT, MRI and X-Ray radiology process for detecting and processing the medical image with the best dataset. Besides it, we have algorithms and processes to define and to analyze an image. Restricted Boltzman Machine (RBM) and Deep Boltzman Machine (DBM) play very fantastic role in clinical image analyzing [3–5]. There exist CNNs that are used to train the whole dataset. Convolutional neural network (ConvNet) is mostly used to train the dataset of large amount of medical image. We have also used black boxing process to train dataset.

As we know that medical sector is not a small industry today, in fact, it is one of the tremendously increasing sectors. The data or medical images are increasing in such a wide format that it is leading to big data in coming times [6]. Thus, to handle such large data by human experts can lead to many errors and mishandlings, thus deep learning brings different machine learning algorithms with high computation that can meet the needs and could be more efficient in many ways. Deep learning not only helps to exhibit known methods but it helps to discover new methods too. It also helps the physician to analyze the problem and provides appropriate solution to it. This will also help doctors to analyze the variation in genetic level which can lead to the cause of certain diseases. Deep learning includes [7] the methods such as support vector machine (SVM), neural network (NN), k-nearest neighbor

(KNN), etc. These methods are slow and performed by medical experts. They lack in processing raw images. Deep learning methods such as convolutional neural network (CNN), recurrent neural network (RNN), long short term memory (LSTM) etc. These methods are relatively faster. The deep learning methods use the large set of images from database to analyze the images.

The rest of the paper is organized as follows: Sect. 2 discusses medical imaging; Sect. 3 presents literature overview of deep learning for healthcare; Sect. 4 details about neural networks and algorithms; Sect. 5 discusses the use of different CNN models and techniques in medical imaging; Sect. 6 presents research challenges and future scope; and finally, Sect. 7 concludes this chapter.

2 Medical Imaging

Machine learning, artificial intelligence and deep learning have approached very fast for healthcare industries in every manner from detection to diagnosis level [8]. Machine learning algorithms and artificial intelligence techniques use datasets to analyze medical images with the help of different classification techniques. In medical imaging various methods and techniques are processed to create a visualization so that the internal and external parts of the human structure with specific issues are analyzed for medical diagnosis. These images include accidental images, cardio images, injuries, heart pipe images, stepping image of any diseases, CT Scan images etc. Machine learning and deep learning techniques use MRI scans, ECG, CT scans to diagnose heart disease, cancer and brain tumor [3]. Analyzing the size of tumor and level of cancer are done by medical imaging using deep learning.

The corporate sector that is related to medical field is making devices to analyze the image of body part or via sensors. Many organizations are incorporating medical imaging devices in hospitals and clinics to provide the free standing radiology and pathology facilities for the patients. Samsung, Lenovo and other similar type of company are making fitness bands relate to medical sector. Healthineers, Fituji, and other Japanese or Chinese companies are making medical devices for analysis purpose [6, 8]. These devices can also give medical recommendations through medical images to the patients.

The uses of the medical imaging techniques are highly important for treatment and analysis of patient's medical condition. The diagnostic services are related to the significant security of the history of the patients and ailments related to treatment. Sometimes the use of high definition images can reduce the treatment process time for a doctor. In other manner, if anyone has a tumor then its type, size and complete analysis is detected through the machine learning algorithms which is a great help in diagnosis and treatment [9, 10]. The initial level diagnosis and exploratory procedures can find out the issues and problems of aging human, chronic pain on children, and can detect the sugar level and can detect type of the cancer. In the medical imaging process, the information regarding type of cancer, way of bleeding, type of brain injuries, and many more diseases, in a timely manner can help the patient in different ways of their treatment [2].

Famous study of medical imaging in the breast cancer has helped the doctors and medical experts to suggest the way of treatment to decrease the level of breast cancer from 34 to 22%. With the help of early imaging in colon cancer, the treatment to stop blood clotting got an approximate 20% decrease in death percentage rate [11, 12]. The detection techniques through beneficial clinical picturing are known to medical experts in terms of diagnosis of disease set effectively.

Medical imaging is a new insight of computer vision field that increases the result accuracy through different modeling techniques. Computer vision modeling will improve the efficiency and working style of medical experts to get results through medical imaging. Medical experts determine the treatment for patient's early recovery by studying the status of organs. Imaging techniques relay on the human body tests and concerns regarding the patient's health. Medical experts and pharmaceuticals use it for the disease investigation and organ study so that the required treatment can be suggested [6, 8].

Researchers are consistently researching on the new technologies and DL/ML models for higher accuracy. Labeling is done by the researchers and inventors of the model with the help of image dataset, pharmaceutical condition and type of traditional image processing and DL approaches.

3 Deep Learning for Healthcare: A Review

Many researchers have done work in past related to the development of methodologies and concepts for the purpose of medical imaging to diagnose and to recognize the medical abnormalities in a patient. In this manner, deep learning model is an efficient method to find out the best result and accuracy in diagnosis. Deep Learning finds applications in body care industry, medical industry and it provides answers to the many types of problems so that an effective treatment to patients can be suggested. In sequence study of various methods, sometimes the generated data is useful and sometimes it is not useful. Deep learning models analyze the graphs and charts to achieve the higher result accuracy.

According to World Health Organisation (WHO) total count of humans suffering with insulin and diabetes in 1980 were up to 108 million and this count has increased to 422 millions in 2014 [13]. According to WHO's diabetes graph this increase in the count is from low to medium level of countries side [13]. Insulin can cause a type of blindness, a type of stroke, a type of heart attacks, a type of kidney failure and a type of lower limb amputation etc. 1.6 million people died in 2016 due to insulin and this estimate will likely increase up to 2.2 million in 2022 due to high blood sugar in patient of diabetes. Diabetic retinopathy [14] is an important cause of blindness that occurs as a result of long-term accumulated damage to the small blood vessels in the retina. 2.6% of global blindness can be attributed to diabetes. It is caused by damage to the blood vessels of the light-sensitive tissue at the back of the eye (retina). At first, diabetic retinopathy may cause no symptoms or only mild vision problems. Diabetic retinopathy can be revered and carried if diagnosed at earlier stage by retinal screening of the initial level. If diabetic retinopathy is done manually then its detection is very time consuming. In the initial stage none of symptoms shows owing ophthalmologists need a good count of analysis with time the images and delay the treatment [15]. Therefore, medical experts need some tools and techniques to diagnose it at an earlier stage.

Gulshan et al. [14] discussed Deep Convolutional Neural Network (DCNN) model that followed the multiple dataset for classification techniques and output between moderate and referable diabetic (Insulin) retinopathy (RDR): eye picture archive communication system (EyePACS-1) dataset with resultant images as:

- EyePACS-1 Dataset detail is 9963 total count of images and out of 4997 images means patients.
- Messidor-1 dataset: 874 images out of 1748 images.

This algorithm had an approximate sensitivity of 97.5% and accuracy of 93.4% on EyePACS-1 Data, and 96.1% sensitivity and 93.9% specificity on Messidor-1 Data.

Szegedy et al. [16] presented Inception-v3 architecture as specific neural network as shown in Fig. 1.

The images taken to screen for Diabetic retinopathy (DR) were used as examples of retinal fundus photographs. Left side picture of the Fig. 2 is A and it shows healthy retina, in mean a retina with referable diabetic retinopathy, B shows a number of red spots (hemorrhages) present.

Kathirvel et al. [17] trained a Deep convolutional neural network (DCNN) as shown in Fig. 3 with added dropout layer on publicly available Kaggle data set online. They have achieved accuracy count of 94%. Kaggle dataset includes pharmaceutical labeled images across 5 types of multiple classes, i.e., Class-1 No DR, Class-2 Mild, Class-3 Moderate, Class-4 Severe and Class-5 Proliferative DR.

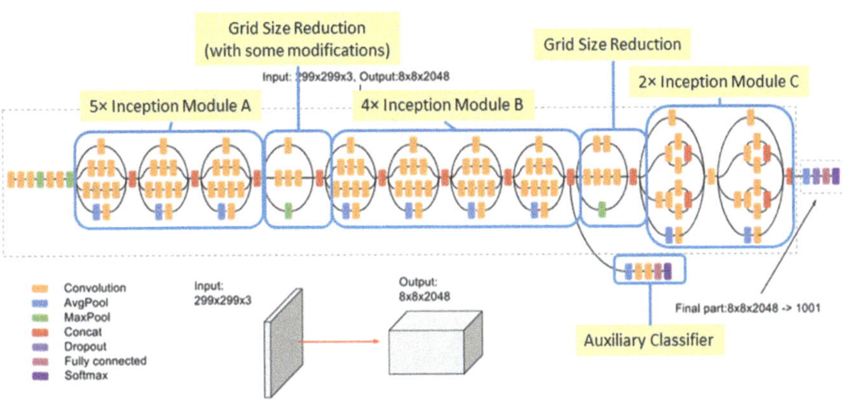

Fig. 1 Inception-v3 architecture [16]

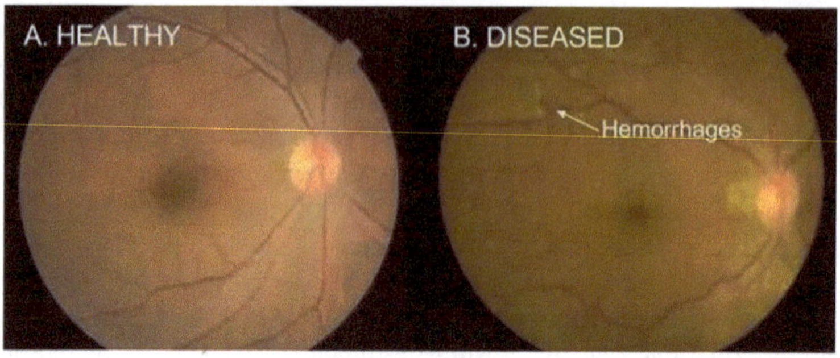

Fig. 2 Representation of diabetic retinopathy

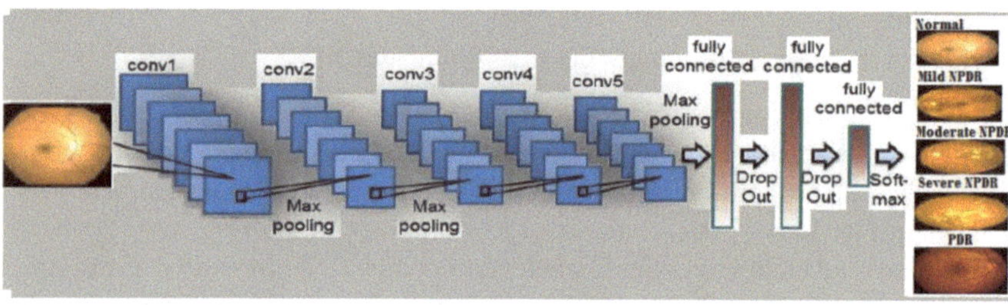

Fig. 3 DCNN architecture [17]

The advancements in automated diabetic retinopathy screening methods pose very powerful and potential metric to assist the medical experts to evaluate the patients more accurately and to speed up the diagnostic methodology that can decrease the time gap for treatments. The working process with Food and Drug Administration (FDA) and other regulatory agencies are in process of evaluating these technologies in medical studies to make a standard part of the procedure. Google is trying a screening process that can benefit to both for patients as well as medical expert as well.

Sirinukunwattana et al. [11] presented patches of different types of object found in the used dataset as shown in the Fig. 4. The figure includes epithelial nuclei, inflammatory object nuclei, fibroblasts and miscellaneous nuclei object.

According to Bayramoglu et al. [12] the main problem is that the training dataset is available in limited mode. The authors used the concept of transfer learning and checked the possibilities of the less data and obtained a representation with limited data set.

Quinn et al. [18] developed a new setup to capture blood smear images, blood stain pictures, slaver samples pictures and stool exampled pictures.

The experts identified bounding boxes around each object of interest in every image. In thick blood stain images, plasmodium were annotated and outed from total datset (1182 images out of 7245 objects). In sputum samples, tuberculosis bacilli were annotated (928 images out of 3734 objects). In stool samples, Hookwarm

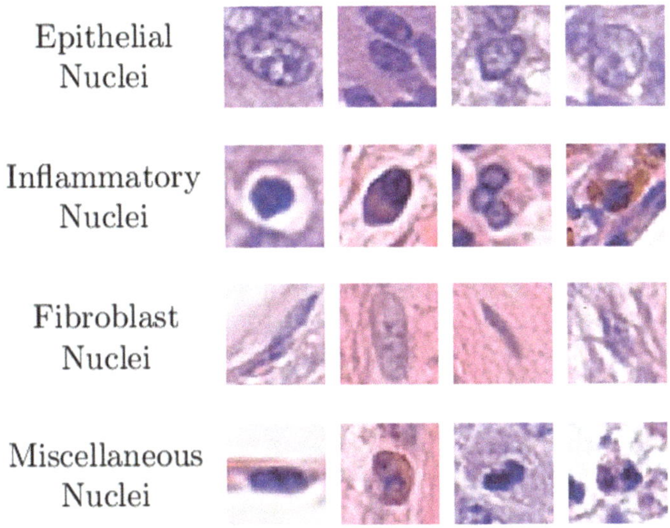

Fig. 4 Patches of different types of object

eggs were annotated (162 images out of 1217 objects). Deep Convolutional Neural Networks (DCCNs) can detect Maleria disease by individually training all particular plasmodium objects of the dataset for Automatic Microscopic Diagnostic (AMD) analysis with a resultant score of 0.99. Figure 5 shows plots of region of convergence e (ROC). The DCNN was comprised of multiple levels of 4 hidden layers:

1. Layer one Convolution used 3 * 3 size 7 filter.
2. Layer two with pooling factor 2.
3. Layer three Convolution layer used 2 * 2 size 12 filters.
4. Fully connected layer with 500 hidden units.

Qu et al. [19] used DCNN Model with data set Wireless Capsule Endoscopy (WCE) with resultant score is 0.9955 F1 Score. Qu et al. [19] DCNN model is shown in Fig. 6. Figure 7 shows three types of objects:

1. A normal WCE Object (Fig. 7a)
2. Vital bleeding wireless capsule endoscopy object (Fig. 7b)
3. Unviable bleeding wireless capsule endoscopy object (Fig. 7c).

The Urban et al. [6] proposed an algorithm for cancer detection. The method got an area under curve (AUC) of 0.991 and resultant accuracy of 96.4%. In this method authors developed a self mean automated diagnostic system by adenoma detection rate (ADR). This method reduced the interval type of cancer and needed the validation in the large form of multiple cantered trials. Figure 8 shows the dataset used by Urban et al. [6]. The top row shows images containing a polyp and bottom row shows nonpolyp images.

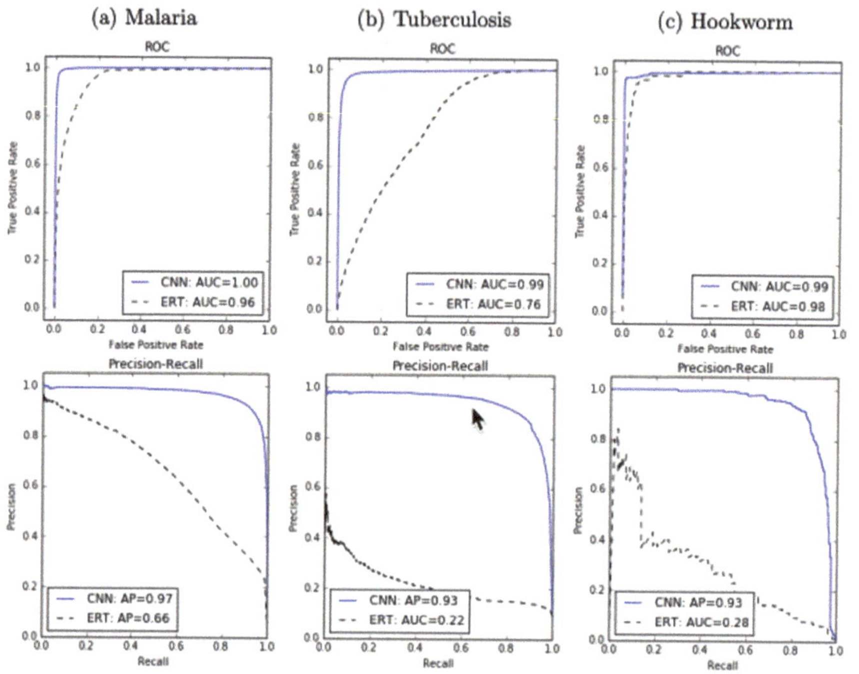

Fig. 5 Plots of ROC [18]

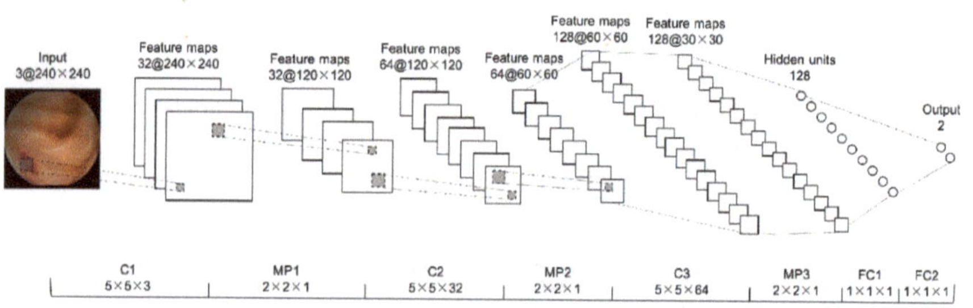

Fig. 6 Qu et al. [19] Model DCNN architecture

Jha et al. [20] employed sparse auto encoders structure as shown in Fig. 9 for the detection of Alzheimer's disease. The method needs a less labeled dataset for training model. The authors have used deep learning model that consisted of auto encoder and soft max function with the layer of output to classify the conditions being in the mild stage of methodology. The proposed algorithm resulted in sensitivity of 98% and specificity of 84% approximately.

Ortiz et al. [21] used DaTSCAN images from PPMI (Parkinson's Progression Markers Initiative) database for the process of detection. Dataset Count was 269 and out of 269, 158 were suffering from Parkinson's disease and 111 were normal

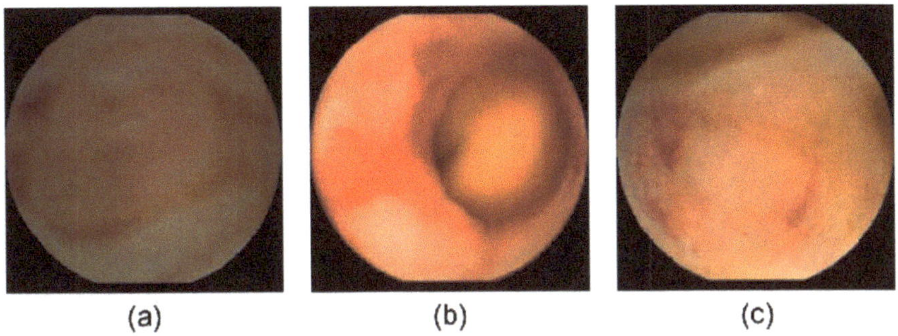

Fig. 7 WCE Object Dataset

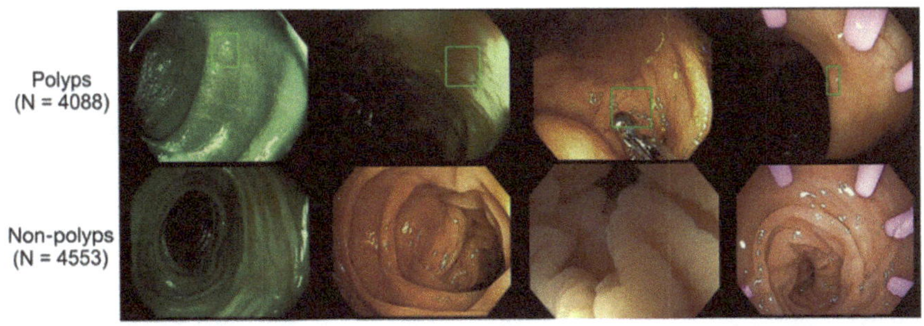

Fig. 8 Imaging data used by Urban et al. [6]

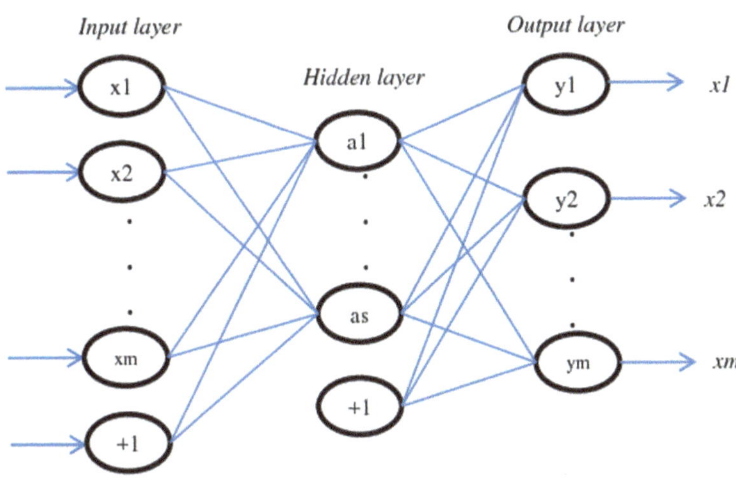

Fig. 9 Auto-encoder structure [20]

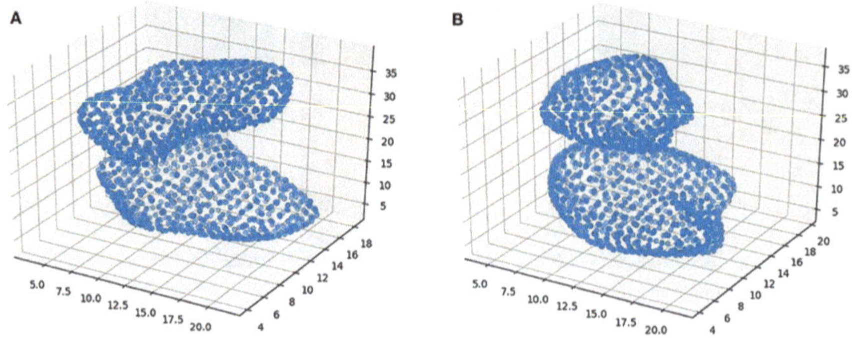

Fig. 10 Isosurfaces example with threshold = 0.5 for a NC subject (a) and PD, patient (b)

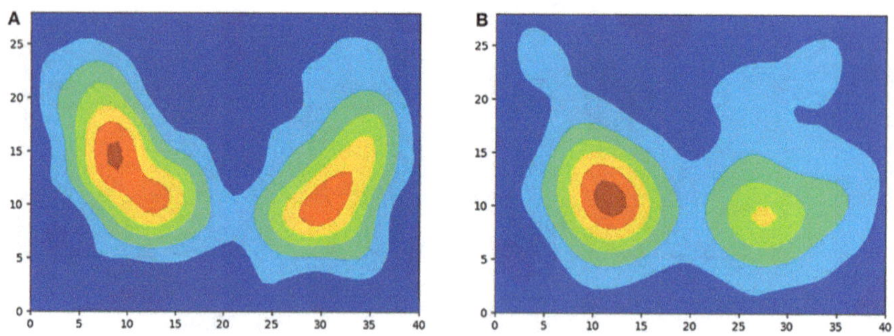

Fig. 11 Isolines example with different threshold for a NC subject (a) and PD, patient (b)

according to methodology. According to Fig. 10 in different methods different thresholds were used. This approach creates isosurfaces from the dataset of DaTSCAN images as waste or raw images for the architecture like LeNet-5, AlexNet. This approach achieved mean accuracy of 95.1% and AUC of 0.97. It was concluded that computation of isosurfaces helped in better then convergence of CNN which in turn resulted in better and faster automated detection Parkinson's disease in dataset of DaTSCAN images. Figure 11 shows results for Isolines surface with different threshold.

A subpart of biological imaging is medical imaging that incorporates radiology and it includes various technologies such as Radiography, MRI, Ultrasound, Endoscopy, Thermography, Nuclear Medicine Imaging and Tomography.

3.1 MRI

MRI means magnetic resonance imaging that is a scanning process of medical image used in radiology to detect and form the pictures of organs and tissues of body. It has scanner which have a huge size tube of magnet and uses radio waves and magnetic field for scanning. MRI is mainly used to check inner organs like womb or prostate gland, brain, breasts and heart, bones and joint.

3.2 Ultrasound

It is a medical image capturing process of organs and inner body parts that uses sound waves for detection. It is also called sonography that is mostly use to check the unborn child by imaging. It is used to check the brain, eyes, kidney, womb, testicles, blood vessels of unborns.

3.3 Endoscopy

Endoscopy is one of the best investigation, confirmation and treatment technique in medical science. In this technique a long tube is directly inserted into the patient's body to observe internal wounds and organs, so that doctors can treat them easily. It is one of the quick and safe medical procedures to treat patients. It is helpful in diseases like tumors, ulcer, stone etc. as it can track out digestive tract.

3.4 Thermography

Thermography is a procedure of clicking images from an device that can find the flow and procedure of blood in body. In this procedure, infrared camera can sense infrared rays and heat waves from our body and produce images that are called as Thermograms. Digital infrared thermal imaging (DITI) is the type of thermography that is used to diagnose breast cancer. It is used to detect Tumors and cancer in patient's body. Once image is obtained we can apply computer vision algorithms to detect the infected parts. Applications of thermography lies in diagnose of lower extremity vessel disease, neuro-Musculo-skeletal, breast pathologies, digestive disorder, urinary disease and respiratory dysfunctions.

3.5 Nuclear Medical Imaging

It is a process of detecting and producing images of different inner body parts and organs by using radioactive tracers. It make graphical picture on computer when we perform process of nuclear imaging. It is different from other process because it gives the information about organ's functioning.

3.6 Tomography

It is a process of getting X-rays of body parts. In this a X-ray tube and a film is moved in opposite side so that it can detect a clear image of object lying at plane in the pivot direction and capture blurred image of rest of the body. The main advantage of tomography is that infected part appears sharp and other parts remain blurred. Deep learning implementation in medical imaging makes it more disruptive technology in the field of radiology [1, 4]. Medical fields which have shown promises to be revolutionized using deep learning are Ophthalmology, Pathology and Cancer diagnosis.

3.7 Ophthalmology

It is study of eye surgery which is helpful to diagnose any eye disorder. It is concerned about the symptoms about eye infection and their surgery. There are so many procedures that are performed by ophthalmologist such as Cataract surgery, Neoplasm, Glaucoma surgery, injection around the eye, repairing torn and retinas.

3.8 Pathology

Pathology is the investigation of ailment. It is the extension among science and medication. It supports each part of patient's consideration, from demonstrative testing and treatment.

3.9 Cancer Diagnosis

We use many approaches for cancer diagnosis such as:

Laboratory test: In this we perform urine and blood tests to identify symptoms of cancer.
Biopsy: This is the most affecting way of diagnosing the cancer by taking cells' sample and checking its size.
Imaging Tests: In imaging we perform X-Ray, CT scan, ultrasound and MRI to examine internal organs and tissues.

Any diagnosis of medical image consists of image acquisition and image interpretation. Traditional acquisition methods are best in their ways, but the traditional interpretation involving experts are less reliable. The best of machine learning algorithm is the computer vision, but the fact that traditional methods require expert guidance cannot be denied. This can be proved by the fact that expert guidance is always required in tumor detection for extracting the structure feature [1]. Due to the various advanced features of deep learning it is preferred in medical imaging. According to a fact there will be more than 300 million images in medical sector by 2021. Deep learning uses deep neural network model instead of neural network by traditional learning, thus uses neurons as the smallest unit. Human brain gets linear signals, collects them and uses them to control nonlinear output actions [3]. Various applications of deep learning include its impact on MRI field as well [3]. The stepwise processing of deep learning with MRI scans is as follows:

Step 1: Taking the data from image acquisition to image registration:

It includes various steps that lead to image segmentation and classification of image after reconstruction. It includes:

1. Acquisition of data and reconstruction.
2. Fingerprinting of quantitative parameters.
3. Restoration of image that includes denoising and detection of artifact.
4. Super resolution of images.
5. Image synthesis.
6. Registration of image.

Step 2: The process of diagnosis starts from the segmented images [3]. This includes:

1. Image segmentation

There are various methods proposed for the segmentation of image, some of them is discussed below:

(a) *Manual segmentation method*:
It uses different experience and training qualification of the radiologist, to go through different slices of segmented image slice by slice.
(b) *Semi-automatic method*:
It requires user involvement in three major steps that are, initialization, feedback response, and evaluation.
(c) *Fully automatic method*:
In this the algorithms and prior knowledge database are combined to help in segmentation and no user interaction is required.

2. Depending upon segmented image the diagnosis is done.

Step 3: Content based retrieval of image is the last step for the MRI part. It gives the report of similar cases to the radiologist so that the detection of problem could be solved.

4 Neural Networks and Algorithms

The concept and structure of artificial neural network is totally inspired from human neural network. One of the oldest known artificial neural networks is perceptron which uses input layers and they are directly connected to output layer thus making it convenient for linearly separable patterns [22]. But the problem for complex problem is to solve by making layered structure which consists of many input layers, output layers and some hidden layers in inter connection. Each layer takes input, performs suitable operation on it and gives output which acts as input for the coming layers.

There is a growing trend in deep learning as the achievement in these fields are remarkable whether it is the case of computer vision, or detecting cancer in blood or for checking for tumor in MRI scans. The increase in hidden layers helped in increase in solving more complex problems that has considerably improved medical imaging and abstraction techniques.

The deep neural network is made up of layers of neurons, which could be up to 1000 layers. Thus this large network body could store every possible case if it is stored in a proper manner and dataset. There are numerous deep learning algorithms such as Deep Neural Network (DNN), Deep Boltzmann Machine (DBM), Deep Conventional Extreme Learning Technique (DC-ELT), Convolutional Neural Network (CNN), Deep Belief Network (DBN), Recurrent Neural Network (RNN) and Deep Autoencoder (DA). The CNN also contains many sub architectures such asVGGNet, alexnet, googleNEt, lenet, ResNEt, ZFnet, faster R-CNN, etc. [23–26].

4.1 CNN (Convolutional Neural Network)

A CNN has a special relationship with data and different layers connections [2]. In the CNN, input is arranged in a compact structure and is fed to different layers because each layer operation has an operating relation on other previous layers. CNN performs process of filtering and scaling to the radiological image. There are different layers like convolutional layer, activation layer and pooling layer which converts or transforms raw pixel of an image into high pixel by processing. CNN has an efficient input data representation. CNN takes input and processes it as 2-D and 3-D image. Nowadays CNN is the most popular machine learning algorithm. It relates an image by capturing its important features. ML algorithms are classified as supervised learning algorithms and unsupervised learning algorithms [2]. Deep belief network (DBN), restricted Boltzmann machine and Generative adversarial network (GAN) are unsupervised learning algorithms.

4.1.1 Convolutional Layer

Convolutional layer is a layer that provides the network its name. It performs convolution operation that operates on two functions, i.e., input value (pixel) in an image and filtering. It operates multiplication of a set with the given input for 2-D and 3-D array of weight. The filter is a dot product of filter and multiplication between inputs. It is also called scalar product because it gives single output as result. This computation is repeated till it covers whole image that gives an activation map or featured map. This map is used to check that the filter is completely activated or not. In CNN an image is firstly analyzed by having a line and a dot at this layer then all others subsequent features precede to other layers in CNN architecture [2]. Convolutional layer has following three operations to perform machine learning.

1. Sparse connection
   It means every neural network layer is connected to other neural network layer to every neuron which is called sparse connection.
2. Parameter or weight share
   Only some inputs have sparse connection, i.e., fully featured map so as to increase the efficiency of algorithms. It decreases number of weights so CNN reduces memory storage and is called weight share.
3. Equivalent representation.

We use an equivalent representation in which input is defined by * symbol and output is defined by dot product of input which is single valued.

4.1.2 Restricted Linear Unit (RLU) Layer

RLU layer is also called activation function because it is used to transform the weight input to the activation node. It provides output if it is positive otherwise output will zero. In this layer activation function solves the vanishing gradient problem. It also works as default automation for developing multilayer perception.

4.1.3 Pooling Layer

Down sampling is an approach to address a problem using single processing. Down sampling can be achieved using CNN if the convolutional stride of image is changed. If we want to create a new number of pooled feature maps then we use pooling layer. The operation of pooling layer is like filter on feature map. It is the mid-part of convolutional layer and RLU layer. Max pooling and average pooling are two types of pooling. These are used to measure the size of image with its width or length [22].

4.1.4 Fully Connected Layer

It is also an important component of CNN, which provides results by successfully recognizing and classifying image. It is called fully connected because it is connected to the preceding layer like convolutional layer and pooling layer. It takes output of preceding layer as an input and provides output by analyzing successfully an image as result. It may be *N* vector featured layer which contains *N* directional information. This layer is used for regression and classification from input to other because all other layers contain edge, line, dot of image but this layer contains aggregation, classification [22]. Figure 12 represents the neural network model for detection of tumor cells in the DNA.

4.2 Transfer Learning with CNN

It is a process in which a model is trained to solve problems which have relation with other problems to solve it. Transfer learning takes a model which is trained on large dataset and then transfers its knowledge to smallest dataset [22]. Then, CNN is used to identify the object in an image. If we want to apply transfer learning then we can use pre built and pre trained model. In Fig. 13, we can see that the difference between infected lung and normal lung can help to predict pneumonia. This can be achieved by training the CNN.

The basic premise of transfer learning is to apply the transfer learning knowledge of large dataset to small dataset [9]. By holding starting layer of CNN, we use last few layers for perfect prediction. The idea is that the convolutional layer will extract the general, low level features that are applicable across the image edges, patterns, and gradients. The last layers will identify specific features like eyes and wheels. Thus, CNN can be used on unrelated category in massive dataset, and can be applied to any problem, because there are some universal low level features shared between the images [5].

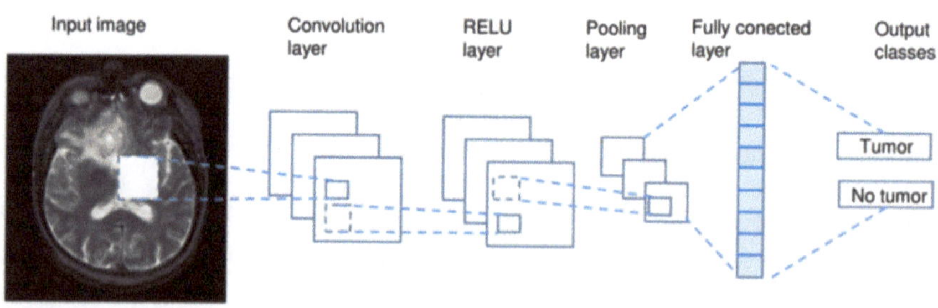

Fig. 12 Neural network basic model

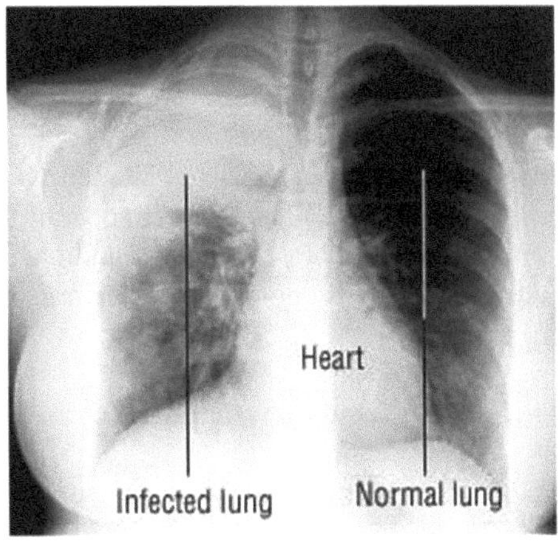

Fig. 13 Training CNN to detect pneumonia using deep learning

4.3 Recurrent Neural Network (RNN)

RNN is classified in two network classes-

1. Finite impulse RNN
   It is used as a feed forward neural network so it is a directed acyclic graph.
2. Infinite impulse RNN
   It is not used as an acyclic graph. So it is directional cyclic graph.

RNN is also called feedback neural network because it is used for sequential data that means it analyzes word by word in sentences [3]. Due to this feature RNN is also used in speech recognition, text prediction, image caption generator, language making and word translation. It is called feedback neural network because it combines output with next inputs and reprocess it and stores result in memory. There may be a problem like vanishing gradient problem while storing in memory. Therefore, Long Short Term Memory (LSTM) and Gated Recurrent Unit (GRU) are used. Other process which RNN performs is segmentation [3–5]. If we want to segment neural network and fungal structure from 3-D electron microscope image then we combine CNN and RNN. The multidirectional LSTM can be performed with brain MRI scans.

4.4 Unsupervised Learning Model

4.4.1 Auto Encoder

In supervised learning we have known about an image with label but in unsupervised learning there is no label data in an image, i.e., we don't describe any label data in an image. We perform reconstruction by taking input and coding to reconstruction output. The main logic of encoder is that the output must be similar to the input values because there is a function that does not permit any input to have different output values. It has so many features like it has an image in unsupervised model, i.e., without label and it has low complexity. It can reconstruct the output data from input data. A hidden layer is present in the auto encoder that is called stacked auto encoder. It has a symmetric architecture model where hidden layer is equivalent to reflection layer [4]. Some different operations like sharing weight from decoder layer to encoder layer before stacking and transfer leaving, trains the different subsets of auto encoder. This optimizes the performance of auto encoder [5].

4.4.2 Restricted Boltzmann Machine (RBM) and Deep Belief Networks

RBM is firstly invented by Ackley in 1985 but it is modified by Paul Smolensky in 1986. RBM is a stochastic neural network that is generative, probabilistic and provides bidirectional graphical representation. It is a set of visible and hidden layers that learns distribution over inputs. According to its name, this Boltzmann machine has some restriction like a bipartite graph must be formed by its neurons [5]. Figure 14 shows Restricted Boltzmann Machine with three visible and four hidden units. There is a pair of node which has symmetric connection between nodes that are taken from each group unit that is visible or hidden. It is a contrast that there is a connection between hidden layers in unrestricted Boltzmann machine. RBMs can tell information about fibro fed, ground glass tissue, micro nodular and lung tissue. We know that convolution RBMs are trained to learn filter. These are trained with objective like purely generative, purely discriminative or mixed generative and mixed discriminative. With the help of this filter feature activation map is created and feature extraction is performed. Contrast divergence algorithms train the part of RBMs that are stacked in the DBNs [5]. Figure 15 shows the structure of a DBN. The output of hidden layer

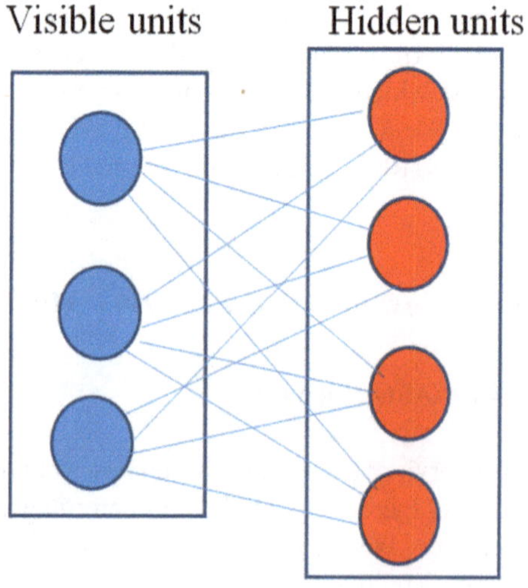

Fig. 14 Restricted Boltzmann Machine with three visible and four hidden units

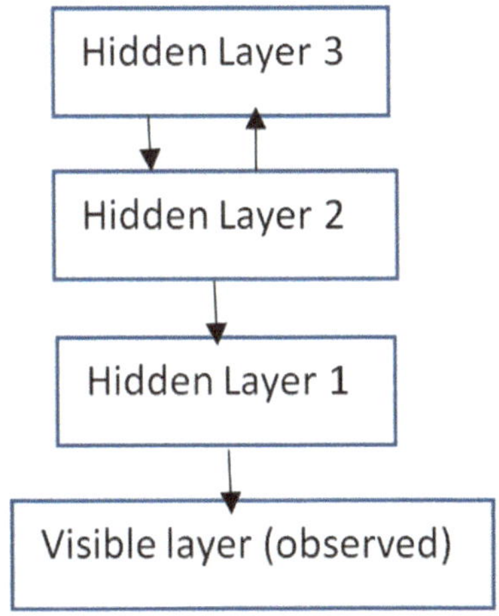

Fig. 15 Structure of deep belief network

behaves like input in visible layer which is on the second RBM stack. We can train DBN layer with two types. The low level featuring is done layer by layer and higher level featuring is done by using mirroring (i.e., real-world data hierarchy). We can produce a semi supervised deep learning architecture with the couple of supervised layers of RBMs and DBNs. After training DBNs with supervision, it performs classification and without supervision it probabilistically reconstructs its input [5]. DBNs are considered as a composition of RBNs and auto encoder. The main use of DBNs in medical image analysis is electroencephalography and drug discovery [8].

4.5 Generative Adversarial Network (GAN)

Generative adversarial network helps to make an unsupervised learning that can hold medical image analysis tasks efficiently. It is a generative model which can generate an artificial image as well. Generative adversarial network works in multilayer model of CNN [10]. In this model the first CNN is a generator that generates an artificial image and the other CNN is called discriminator, which classifies that the image as real or artificial [23]. The desired end point of this system is that it cannot take out the difference between the real and artificial image [24]. The probability of assigning an image to either data distribution is 1/2. The advantage of this network is that the both generator and discriminator can be trained with back propagation [25]. Table 1 presents comparison of network types.

Table 1 Comparison of network types

Type of network	Detail of network	Pros	Cons
Convolutional neural network	Consists of convolutional filter to transfer 2D to 3D	Good model, learning at good rate	Needs a large data
Deep conventional extreme learning machine	Uses Gaussian probability function for sampling of local connection	–	–
Deep belief network	All hidden layers in sub network are visible	The strategy used in each layer minimizes the likelihood	It is expensive in terms of training purpose
Deep neural network	Consists of more than 2 layers which helps in complex non-linear relationship	Due to its accuracy, it is widely used	Learning is slow
Recurrent Neural Network	Sequence learning is one of the important capability	Due to its various available states it provides accuracy	Issues arise due to requirement of big datasets
Deep Boltzmann machine	Contains connection in single direction among all the hidden layers	Provides robust interference	Optimization is not possible for large dataset in terms of parameter
Deep auto-encoder	Used for unsupervised learning, and extraction and reduction of dimensions	Does not require label data	Suffers in training step

5 Use of Different CNN Models and Techniques in Medical Imaging

We are very much aware that deep learning has a great impact on society due to its various properties and features. Deep learning follows below steps-

Step 1: Sensor receives the data collected in imaging.

Step 2: The processors working on deep learning algorithm start working and try to extract the right information which can be useful for further recognition and imaging of disease.

Step 3: The processed features that are extracted from the data set are now used to find the classification of the disease from the set of features it belongs to.

Step 4: On the basis of classification done, the particular class of disease is chosen that has the highest possibility of having the same set of features as present in the data set.

The results of the above steps are repeated in a manner that lead to the success of many fields in medical science such as image detection and recognition, image segmentation, image registration, computer aided diagnosis, physical simulation, and image reconstruction.

5.1 *Image Detection and Recognition*

It utilizes machine vision innovations with man-made brainpower and prepared calculations to perceive pictures through a camera framework. Picture affirmation is the route toward recognizing and perceiving a thing or a part in a mechanized picture or video.

5.2 *Image Segmentation*

With digital image processing and computer vision, image classification is the process of separating digital image into multiple categories. Image classification is often used to find objects and borders (lines, curves, etc.) in images.

5.3 *Image Registration*

Image registration is the process of converting different sets of data into a single link system. Data can be multiple images, data can be from different sensors, times, depth, or views. It is used in computer vision, medical thinking automatic war recognition, and the design and analysis of images and data from satellites. Registration is required to be able to compare or combine data obtained from these different scales.

5.4 *Computer Aided Diagnosis (CAD)*

In clinical imaging field, PC supported location (CADe) or PC supported determination (CADx) is the PC based framework that encourages specialists to take choices quickly [28, 29]. Clinical imaging manages data in pictures that the clinical specialist and specialists needs to assess in brief timeframe.

5.5 *Physical Simulation*

Physical simulation of materials includes the specific proliferation of the warm and mechanical procedures in the research center that the material is exposed to in the genuine manufacture or end use. A little example of the real material is utilized in the re-enactment. Physical re-enactments are done by forcing various weights on man-made coupons to discover the basic pressure distinction that can empower the counterfeit crack to enter the hindrance from the oil layer.

5.6 Image Reconstruction

Picture reproduction in CT is a numerical procedure that creates tomographic pictures from X-beam projection information procured at a wide range of edges around the patient. Two significant classes of recreation strategies exist, systematic reproduction and iterative remaking (IR). Picture reproduction can be performed either by sifted backprojection, as in CT, or by utilizing iterative strategies.

As we are aware that medical imaging can be done through CNN techniques. One of the features of this method is that it learns on its own. Thus it does not need to state the same code again and again [2]. In order to use CNN technique the environment that we need to setup requires a normal high performance machine and python programs, VM GPU on cloud servers and the platforms for testing. This setup further includes data augmentation design, oriented fast and rotated binary (ORB) and support vector machine (SVM) application environment design, transfer learning experiments design and capsule neural network design.

The effect of CNN technology on anatomy based classification of image includes ConvNets, which work on various fields to improve the quality and enhance the property of medical imaging, with the help of various GPUs. The ConvNet has become one of fast processors to process the medical image [2]. The method of ConvNet includes convolutional network which becomes the keys to anatomic approach in many medical imaging like CT images. It contains convolutional filter that classifies the image by its five layered structure. It is far better than traditional CAD method. Next stage is the data mining of key images. It includes searching for some key words in the radiological images that are provided in particular format. Next stages are data augmentation, random translation, non-rigid deformation, and rotations; which are used to enrich the dataset using spatial deformation [2].

One of the major applications of deep learning lies in tumor detection, which is a combination of various processes that use different features of deep learning algorithm in their various steps. The process of detection of tumor consists of following steps:

Step 1: Tumor implantation.

Iatrogenic tumor implantation is a condition that outcomes from different clinical methods utilized during determination of treatment. It includes desquamation and dispersal of tumor cells that form into a neighborhood.

Step 2: Texture feature extraction.

A fundamental stage to accumulate such features through surface examination process is called as surface segment extraction. Due to the significance of surface information, surface part extraction is a key limit in various pictures for recognizing, clinical imaging and substance based picture recuperation [30]. Surface is a component used to parcel pictures into districts of intrigue and to characterize those areas. Texture gives data in the spatial course of action of hues or forces in a picture. Texture is portrayed by the spatial appropriation of force levels in an area.

Step 3: Selecting model for tumor extraction.

In the medical imaging of tumor, the image of tumor is extracted through extreme point and an analysis is done.

Step 4: Prediction of tumor growth rate.

The proportionality study depicts the development pace of the tumor. Various models are used for early examination of tumor development.

Step 5: Collecting statistical data and analyzing performance of model.

There are so many tasks which can be accomplished by CNN. Few of them are listed below:

1. *Classification*: Classifying an image according to its inputs or presence of things inside input. For example- a disease or panic is present or not in our body means that if blood is present in MRI brain scan that we can say there is a hemorrhagic stroke in mind.
2. *Localization*: In this, we draw a bounding box around only and only single input is present in image. If we want to find kidney in ultrasound image this is called localization.
3. *Detection*: In this, we draw bounding box around multiple different types of input present in an image.
4. *Segmentation*: This means drawing outlines and labels. We draw around the edge of input and define input as label (e.g., the label is there is a cat inside an image). If we segment an outline around lung tumor, it helps to determine its distance from main part of body, i.e., heart [26]. In the different applications of medical images, segmentation plays a vital role in computer aided diagnosis like- X-ray, ultrasound, computed tomography (CT) and Magnetic Resonance image (MRI). We use segmentation because it partitions the image into many coherent regions, besides it the gradient information is used in image segmentation [7].
5. *Registration*: It is a process in which we fit an image onto other image that may be 2-D and 3-D [27].

6 Research Challenges and Future Scope

As we know that research on deep learning is more preferred due to presence of its three basic capabilities which are, the amount of data leading to big data, the impact that created on society by deep learning and the processing speed it will offer. Thus, there are many aspects which should be kept in mind for the future references. Deep learning requires high inter organizational collaboration, capitalization of big data images, legalization and privacy of data and high accuracy and better development.

The analysis of classification techniques can we done by machine Learning algorithms & Deep Learning Model and Networks. These network are CNN, Transfer Learning with CNN, RNN, Unsupervised Model, ANN, SVM, Bayesian Network etc. Out of all this networks the CNN is highly efficient for healthcare analysis. Here CNN is replacement of Transfer Learning Model which includes limited parameters (Layer) for analysis purpose. If we include all positive attributes of Transfer Learning Model with CNN then it can prove more efficient model for healthcare & medical image analysis.

7 Conclusion

We all know about the tremendous performance of deep learning. However, some researchers say that after some years it will take the position of all old machine learning algorithms and there will be all autonomous machines. If we want to produce accurate results then it is clear that deep learning provides accurate dataset but there may be some technical challenges like lack of mathematical and theoretical models. There may be some social challenges like spreading and maximizing technological benefits all around. By this way we can say if deep learning works like as its original way then it will be a good active research for future.

In this paper we have discussed that CNNs are good for brain tumor diagnose because CNN can help in providing advantages to complex feature of brain tissues through MRI. One of the challenges is that there is lack of general data set and labeled data set. Besides it, deep learning is more feasible and usable process. There exist so many applications of deep learning, and we can say that deep learning is so useful in medical image analysis. Thus, we have seen that deep learning will have a deep impact in future's medical imaging sector. But the speed in doing so is very slow as compared to other sectors. In this paper we have also discussed the barriers that might come in the progression and the solutions we could have for that. We have provided introduction about deep learning algorithms and we have concluded about its effect in medical imaging processes. In this paper we also attempted to discuss the topic of medical imaging process through different algorithms but the main focus was given to CNN because of its versatility and features.

References

1. Razzak, M. I., Naz, S., & Zaib, A. (2017) .Deep learning for medical image processing: Overview, challenges and future. Lecture Notes in Computational Vision and Biomechanics, 2.

2. Yadav, S. S., & Jadhav, S. M. (2019, December). Deep convolutional neural network based medical image classification for disease diagnosis. *Journal of Big Data, 6*(113).
3. Lundervold, A. S., & Lundervold, A. (2019, May). An overview of deep learning in medical imaging focusing on MRI. *Zeitschrift Für Medizinische Physik, 29*(2), 102–127.
4. Maier, A., Syben, C., Lasser, T., & Riess, C. (2019, May). A gentle introduction to deep learning in medical image processing. *Zeitschrift Für Medizinische Physik, 29*(2), 86–101.
5. Işın, A., Direkoğlu, C., & Şah, M. (2016). Review of MRI-based brain tumor image segmentation using deep learning methods. *Procedia Computer Science, 102,* 317–324.
6. Urban, G. L., Amyx, C., & Lo renzon, A. (May 2009). Online trust: State of the art, new frontiers, and research potential. *Journal of Interactive Marketing, 23*(2), 179–190.
7. Ker, J., Wang, L., Rao, J., & Lim, T. (2017, December). Deep learning applications in medical image analysis. *IEEE Access, 6,* 9375–9389.
8. Cao, C., Liu, F., Tan, H., Song, D., Shu, W., Li, W., et al. (2018, February). Deep learning and its applications in biomedicine. *Genomics, Proteomics & Bioinformatics, 16*(1), 17–32.
9. Tang, T. T., Zawaski, J. A., Francis, K. N., et al. (2019). Image-based classification of tumor type and growth rate using machine learning: A preclinical study. *Science Reports, 9.*
10. Neelaja, K., Kumar, A., & Minavathi. (2017). Medical image classification techniques for early cancer diagnosis: A comprehensive study. *International Journal of Advanced Research in Computer and Communication Engineering, 6*(5), 778–782.
11. Sirinukunwattana, K., et al. (2016). Gland segmentation in colon histology images: The GlaS challenge contest.
12. Bayramoglu, N., Kannala, J., & Heikkilä, J. (2016). Deep learning for magnification independent breast cancer histopathology image classification. In *23rd International Conference on Pattern Recognition (ICPR)* (pp. 2440–2445). Cancun.
13. WHO Homepage. https://www.who.int/.
14. Gulshan V., Peng L., Coram M., et al. (2016). Development and validation of a deep learning algorithm for detection of diabetic retinopathy in retinal fundus photographs, *316*(22), 2402–2410.
15. Wani, N., & Malik, N. (2019). Complications of sight threatening diabetic retinopathy: A review. *International Journal of Advanced Trends in Computer Science and Engineering, 8*(4), 1038–1044.
16. Szegedy, C., Vanhoucke, V., Ioffe, S., & Shlens, J. (2015). Rethinking the inception architecture for computer vision. *CVPR Foundation*, pp. 2828–2826.
17. Chandrakumar, T., & Kathirvel, R. (2016). Classifying diabetic retinopathy using deep learning architecture. *International Journal of Engineering Research Technology, 5*(6).
18. Quinn, J. A., Nakasi, R., Mugagga, P. KB., Byanyima, P., Lubega, W., & Andama, A. (2016). Deep convolutional neural networks for microscopy-based point of care diagnostics. In *Machine Learning and Healthcare Conference*, Los Angeles, CA.
19. Qu, J., Hiruta, N., Terai, K., Nosato H., Murakawa, M., & Sakanashi, H. (June 2018). Gastric pathology image classification using stepwise fine-tuning for deep neural networks. *Vision Based Computing Systems for Healthcare Applications..*
20. Jha, D., & Kwon, G. (2017). Alzheimer's disease detection using sparse autoencoder, scale conjugate gradient and softmax output layer with fine tunin. *International Journal of Machine Learning and Computing, 7*(1), 13–17.
21. Ortiz, A., Palacio, A. A., Górriz, J. M., Ramírez, J., & González, D. S. (2013). Segmentation of brain MRI using SOM-FCM-based method and 3D statistical descriptors. *Computational and Mathematical Methods in Medicine,* (1).
22. Lai, Z., & Deng, H. (2018). Medical image classification based on deep features extracted by deep model and statistic feature fusion with multilayer perceptron. *Computational Intelligence and Neuroscience,* (1).
23. Lashari S. A., & Ibrahim, R. (2013). A framework for medical images classification using soft set. In *4th International Conference on Electrical Engineering and Informatics (ICEEI)* (vol. 11, pp. 548–556), Selangor, Malaysia.

24. Roth, H. R. et al. (2015). Anatomy-specific classification of medical images using deep convolutional nets. In *IEEE 12th International Symposium on Biomedical Imaging (ISBI)*, New York, USA.
25. Lau, P. Y., & Ozawa, S. (2003). Image classification for different imaging modalities in image-guided medical diagnosis model. In IEEE EMBS Asian-Pacific conference on biomedical engineering (pp. 150–151). Kyoto, Japan.
26. Gao, L., Pan, H., Han, J., Xie, X., Zhang, Z., & Zhai, X. (2016). Corner detection and matching methods for brain medical image classification. In *IEEE International Conference on Bioinformatics and Biomedicine (BIBM)* (pp. 475–478). Shenzhen, China.
27. Gu, Y., Chanussot, J., Jia, X., & Benediktsson, J. A. (2017). Multiple kernel learning for hyperspectral image classification: A review. *IEEE Transactions on Geoscience and Remote Sensing, 55*(11), 6547–6565.
28. Kontos, M., Wilson, R., & Fentiman, I. (2011). Digital infrared thermal imaging (DITI) of breast lesions: Sensitivity and specificity of detection of primary breast cancers. *Clinical Radiology.*
29. RCPATH Homepage. https://www.rcpath.org/discover-pathology/what-is-pathology.html.
30. Humeau-Heurtier, A. (2019). Texture feature extraction methods: A survey. *IEEE Access, 7,* 8975–9000.

Protein Interaction and Disease Gene Prioritization

Brijendra Gupta

Abstract Gene prioritization is a new approach for extending our knowledge about diseases and phenotypic information each gene encodes. The general notion of gene prioritization assumes that one has a set of candidates and he wants to order the candidates from the most promising to the least promising one. A primary motivation for prioritization of candidate disease genes comes from the analysis of linkage regions that contain genetic elements of diseases. The notion of a disease gene is unambiguous: a genetic element that confers disease susceptibility if its variants are present in the genome. For a particular disease phenotype, we often have a list of candidate genes usually genes located in a linkage interval associated with the disease. Finding the actual gene and candidate can be a subject of expensive experimental validations; however, once identified as real, these disease-associated genes or their protein products can be considered as a therapeutic target or a diagnostic biomarker. Online Mendelian Inheritance in Man (OMIM) is a representative database that links phenotypes, genomic regions, and genes. To make effective use of biological resources, computational gene prioritization allows us to choose the best candidate genes for subsequent experimental validations. In this chapter, we represent the methodology for the pathway of the candidate genes related to ADHD, dementia, mood disorder, OCD, and schizophrenia. The pathway is required because of since not all genes affect significantly for the cause of the disease. Hence, they should be prioritized according to their significance. We have taken that gene–gene interaction data and their corresponding network are used to prioritize these genes according to their interaction with the targeted genes mapped to a particular disease pathway. Section 1 represents the prioritization using interaction network. Section 2 discusses for the pathways. Section 3 represents the target, mapped, and reference genes for ADHD, dementia, mood disorder, OCD, and schizophrenia. Section 4 represents disease gene prioritization using random walk with restart. Section 5 concludes RWR method to help us find genes and to reach to the conclusion of the highly interacted genes network formation for the above disease prioritization.

B. Gupta (✉)
Department of CSE, Siddhant College of Engineering, Pune, India
e-mail: Gupbrij@rediffmail.com

R. Patgiri et al. (eds.), *Health Informatics: A Computational Perspective in Healthcare*, Studies in Computational Intelligence 932,
https://doi.org/10.1007/978-981-15-9735-0_14

1 Prioritization Using Interaction Networks

Many methods using interactions in prioritizing candidate genes are fundamentally counting and comparing "qualified" interactions under the following underlying assumptions

1. Causative genes for a disease reside in the same biological module;
2. Genes in the module have many interactions with other members within the module and relatively few interactions with nonmembers outside the module.

The observation that disease genes share interactions at a much higher rate than random gene pairs was made when protein–protein interaction (PPI) networks were assembled [1].

2 Pathways

Research efforts are therefore currently focusing on the discovery of more precise markers, which are needed so that appropriate treatment decisions can be made for individual patients, and on the characterization of genetic pathways involved in the development and progression of the disease. However, simply identifying the list of genes involved in a disease is only a first step in the process. There is the need for identifying more refined information (e.g., the interaction between the various steps in the pathway). The target proteins include enzymes (e.g., glycogen synthase and other kinases); transcription factors (e.g., c-Jun), and non-enzymatic proteins (e.g., histones) that are involved in distinct signaling pathways linked to metabolism, gene expression, cell motility, cell division, cell differentiation, and apoptosis.

A set of genes has a high chance of participating in a common biological pathway if they form a module in both the gene–gene and protein–protein interaction networks (PPINs) [2]. Sometimes, these networks are constructed by combining multiple sources of information by way of investigating associations between them. Thus, we can obtain a robust and integrated view of the underlying biology. This chapter focuses exclusively on the topological properties of interaction networks of proteins and their significance in the systems level. Instead of pursuing a piecemeal study of the single components, we pay attention to the more global analyzes of the structure, function, and dynamics of the networks in which macromolecules work.

3 Target, Mapped, and Reference Genes for ADHD, Dementia, Mood Disorder, OCD, and Schizophrenia

We have taken data from NCBI which are the allelic variants out of many other available genes for those given diseases. So, these genes are taken as target genes whose interactions we are taking into consideration with other many genes who are experimentally tested and verified from STRING DATABASE and ENRICHNET for the functional, molecular, and cellular bindings with other genes [3, 4]. So, the available datasets in these databases are taken as reference genes. The pathway under which we observed the connections of genes in ENRICHNET tool are mapped genes which are highly interacted [5] and with which we have to target other interactions under the available database and the targeted ones to get interaction scores and summed together to determine the priorities out of those targeted genes on behalf of distance minimization and interaction score maximization [6].

3.1 Gene–Gene Interaction for ADHD

See Fig. 1.

HTR1B: 5-hydroxytryptamine (serotonin) receptor 1B—This is one of the several different receptors for 5-hydroxytryptamine (serotonin), a biogenic hormone that functions as a neurotransmitter, a hormone, and a mitogen. The activity of this receptor is mediated by G proteins that inhibit adenylate cyclase activity.

ADRA2A: Adrenergic,alpha-2A-, receptor—Alpha-2 adrenergic receptors mediate the catecholamine-induced inhibition of adenylate cyclase through the action of

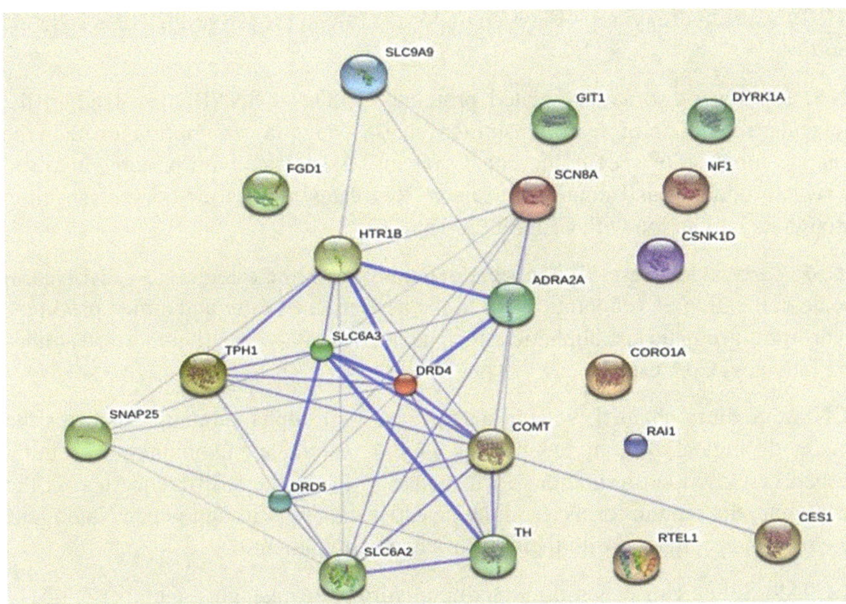

Fig. 1 Thicker lines represent strong interaction between the genes

G proteins. The rank order of potency for agonists of this receptor is oxymeta—zoline > clonidine > epinephrine > norepinephrine > phenylephrine > dopamine > p-synephrine > p-tyramine > serotonin = p-octopamine. For 4 antagonists, the rank order is yohimbine > phentolamine = mianserine > chlorpromazine = spiperone = prazosin > propanolol > alprenolol = pindolol.

TPH1: Tryptophan hydroxylase 1.

SLC6A3: Solute carrier family 6 (neurotransmitter transporter, dopamine), member 3—amine transporter. Terminates the action of dopamine by its high-affinity sodium-dependent reuptake into presynaptic terminals.

DRD4: dopamine receptor D4.

COMT: Catechol-O-methyltransferase—Catalyzes the O-methylation, and thereby the inactivation, of catecholamine neurotransmitters and catechol hormones. Also, shortens the biological half-lives of certain neuroactive drugs, like L-DOPA, alpha-methyl DOPA, and isoproterenol.

DRD5: Dopamine receptor D5—This is one of the five types (D1 to D5) of receptors for dopamine. The activity of this receptor is mediated by G proteins which activate adenylyl cyclase.

SLC6A2: Solute carrier family 6(neurotransmitter transporter, noradrenaline), member 2—Amine transporter. Terminates the action of noradrenaline by its high-affinity sodium-dependent reuptake into presynaptic terminals.

TH: Tyrosine hydroxylase—Plays an important role in the physiology of adrenergic neurons.

SNAP25: Synaptosomal-associated protein, 25 kDa—t-SNARE involved in the molecular regulation of neurotransmitter release. May play an important role in the synaptic function of specific neuronal systems. Associates with proteins involved in vesicle docking and membrane fusion. Regulates plasma membrane recycling through its interaction with CENPF (206 aa).

CES1: Carboxylesterase 1 (monocyte/macrophage serine esterase 1)—Involved in the detoxification of xenobiotics and in the activation of ester and amide prodrugs. Hydrolyzes aromatic and aliphatic esters, but has no catalytic activity toward amides or a fatty acyl CoA ester.

SCN8A: Sodium channel, voltage gated, type VIII, alpha subunit—Mediates the voltage-dependent sodium ion permeability of excitable membranes. Assuming opened or closed conformations in response to the voltage difference across the membrane, the protein forms a sodium-selective channel through which Na(+) ions may pass in accordance with their electrochemical gradient.

SLC9A9: Solute carrier family 9 (sodium/hydrogen exchanger), member 9—May act in electroneutral exchange of protons for Na(+) across membranes. Involved in the effusion of Golgi luminal H(+) in exchange for cytosolic cations. Involved in organelle ion homeostasis by contributing to the maintenance of the unique acidic pH values of the Golgi and post-Golgi compartments in the cell.

3.2 Gene–Gene Interaction for Dementia

See Fig. 2.

PDGFRB: Platelet-derived growth factor receptor, beta polypeptide—Receptor that binds specifically to PDGFB and PDGFD and has a tyrosine-protein kinase activity. Phosphorylates Tyr residues at the C-terminus of PTPN11 create a binding site for the SH2 domain of GRB2

HTRA1: HtrA serine peptidase 1—Protease that regulate the availability of IGFs by cleaving IGF-binding proteins

CLN3: ceroid-lipofuscinosis, neuronal 3.

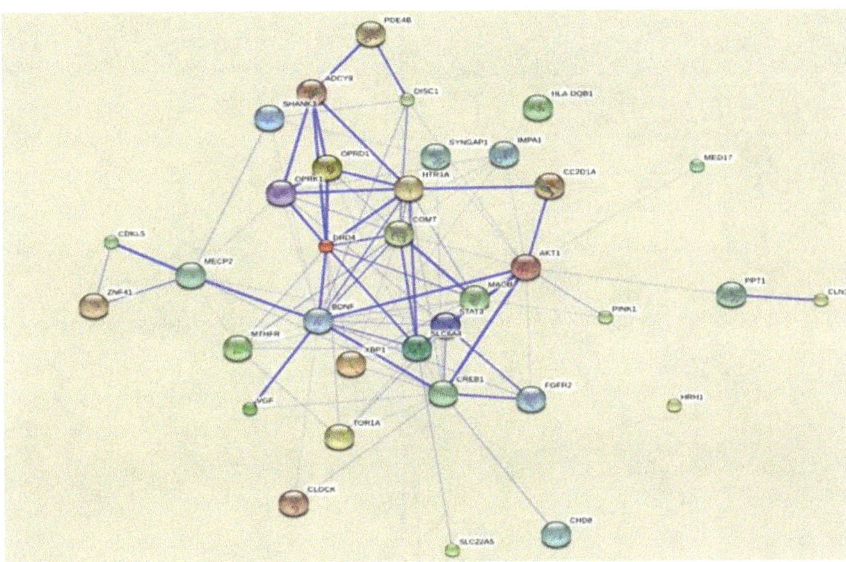

Fig. 2 Thicker lines represent strong interaction between the genes

3.3 Gene–Gene Interaction for Mood Disorder

The protein-protein interaction subnetworks for target and reference set are shown which guides us to analyze the interacted genes for mood disorder, a disease whose target genes are tested (Fig. 3).

PDE4B: Phosphodiesterase 4B, cAMP-specific (phosphodiesterase E4 dunce homolog, Drosophila)—May be involved in mediating central nervous system effects of therapeutic agents ranging from antidepressants to anti-asthmatic and anti-inflammatory agents

DISC1: Disrupted in schizophrenia 1

ADCY9: Adenylate cyclase 9—May play a fundamental role in situations where fine interplay between intracellular calcium and cAMP determines the cellular function. May be a physiologically relevant docking site for calcineurin (By similarity)

COMT: catechol-O-methyltransferase—Catalyzes the O-methylation, and thereby the inactivation of catecholamine neurotransmitters and catechol hormones. Also,

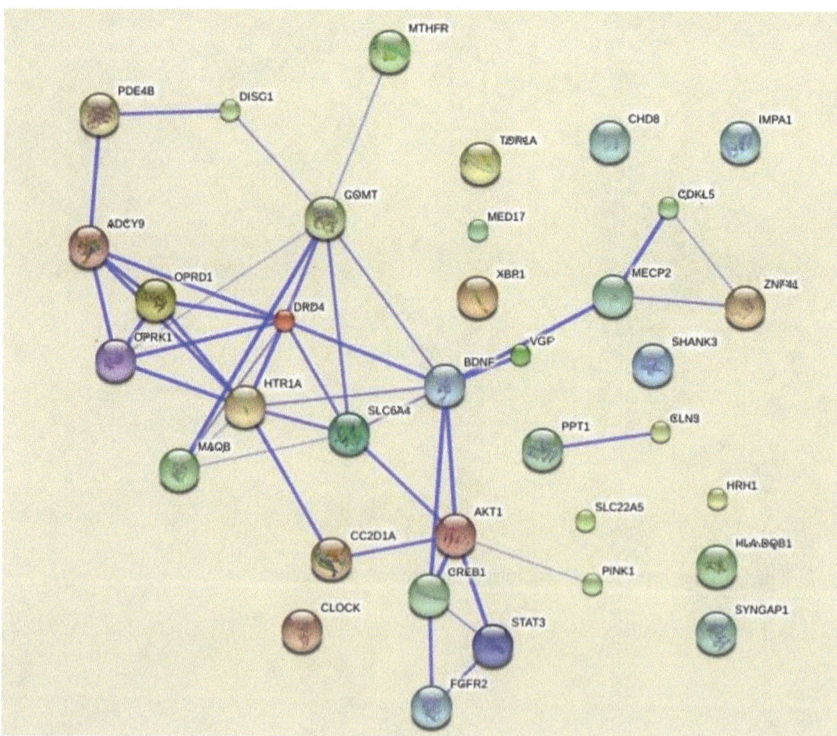

Fig. 3 Thicker lines represent strong interaction between the genes

shortens the biological half-lives of certain neuroactive drugs, like L-DOPA, alpha-methyl DOPA, and isoproterenol

MTHFR: 5,10-methylenetetrahydrofolate reductase (NADPH)—Catalyzes the conversion of 5,10-methylenetetrahydrofolate to 5-methyltetrahydrofolate, a co-substrate for homocysteine remethylation to methionine

OPRK1: Opioid receptor, kappa 1—Inhibits neurotransmitter release by reducing calcium ion currents and increasing potassium ion conductance. Receptor for dynorphins. May play a role in arousal and regulation of autonomic and neuroendocrine functions

OPRD1: Opioid receptor, delta 1—Inhibits neurotransmitter release by reducing calcium ion currents and increasing potassium ion conductance. Highly stereoselective receptor for enkephalins

MAOB: Monoamine oxidase B—Catalyzes the oxidative deamination of biogenic and xenobiotic amines and has important functions in the metabolism of neuroactive and vasoactive amines in the central nervous system and peripheral tissues. MAOB preferentially degrades benzylamine and phenylethylamine

HTR1A: 5-hydroxytryptamine (serotonin) receptor 1A—This is one of the several different receptors for 5-hydroxytryptamine (serotonin), a biogenic hormone that functions as a neurotransmitter, a hormone, and a mitogen. The activity of this receptor is mediated by G proteins that inhibit adenylate cyclase activity

DRD4: Dopamine receptor D4

CC2D1A: coiled-coil and C2 domain containing 1A—Transcription factor that binds specifically to the five repressor element (FRE) and represses HTR1A gene transcription in neuronal cells. The combination of calcium and ATP specifically inactivates the binding with FRE. May play a role in the altered regulation of HTR1A associated with anxiety and major depression. Mediates HDAC-independent repression of HTR1A promoter in neuronal cell

SLC6A4: solute carrier family 6 (neurotransmitter transporter, serotonin), member 4—Terminates the action of serotonin by its high-affinity sodium-dependent reuptake into presynaptic terminals

BDNF: brain-derived neurotrophic factor—During development, promotes the survival and differentiation of selected neuronal populations of the peripheral and central 9 nervous systems. Participates in axonal growth, pathfinding, and in the modulation of dendritic growth and morphology. Major regulator of synaptic transmission and plasticity at adult synapses in many regions of the CNS. The versatility of BDNF is emphasized by its contribution to a range of adaptive neuronal responses including long-term potentiation (LTP), long-term depression (LTD), and certain forms of short-term synaptic plastic.

VGF: VGF nerve growth factor inducible—May be involved in the regulation of cell–cell interactions or in synatogenesis during the maturation of the nervous system

MECP2: methyl CpG binding protein 2 (Rett syndrome)—Chromosomal protein that binds to methylated DNA. It can bind specifically to a single methyl-CpG pair. It is not influenced by sequences flanking the methyl-CpGs. Mediates transcriptional repression through interaction with histone deacetylase and the corepressor SIN3A

ZNF41: zinc finger protein 41—May be involved in transcriptional regulation

AKT1: v-akt murine thymoma viral oncogene homolog 1—General protein kinase capable of phosphorylating several known proteins. Phosphorylates TBC1D1. Signals downstream of phosphatidylinositol 3-kinase (PI(3)K) to mediate the effects of various growth factors such as platelet-derived growth factor (PDGF), epidermal growth factor (EGF), insulin, and insulin-like growth factor I (IGF-I). Plays a role in glucose transport by mediating insulin-induced translocation of the GLUT4 glucose transporter to the cell surface. Mediates the antiapoptotic effects of IGF-I. Mediates insulin-stimulated protein.

CREB1: cAMP responsive element binding protein 1—This protein binds the cAMP response element (CRE), a sequence present in many viral and cellular promoters. CREB stimulates transcription on binding to the CRE. Transcription activation is enhanced by the TORC coactivators which act independently of Ser-133 phosphorylation. Implicated in synchronization of circadian rhythmicity

STAT3: signal transducer and activator of transcription 3 (acute-phase response factor)—Transcription factor that binds to the interleukin-6 (IL-6)-responsive elements identified in the promoters of various acute-phase protein genes. Activated by 10 IL31 through IL31RA FGFR2fibroblast growth factor receptor 2. Receptor for acidic and basic fibroblast growth factors

PPT1: palmitoyl-protein thioesterase 1—Removes thioester-linked fatty acyl groups such as palmitate from modified cysteine residues in proteins or peptides during lysosomal degradation. Prefers acyl chain lengths of 14 to 18 carbons

CLN3: ceroid-lipofuscinosis, neuronal 3.

3.4 Gene–Gene Interaction for OCD

The protein–protein interaction subnetworks for target and reference set is shown which guides us to analyze the interacted genes for OCD disease whose target genes is tested (Fig. 4).

HTR2A: 5-hydroxytryptamine (serotonin) receptor 2A—This is one of the several different receptors for 5-hydroxytryptamine (serotonin), a biogenic hormone that functions as a neurotransmitter, a hormone, and a mitogen. This receptor mediates its action by association with G proteins that activate a phosphatidylinositol–calcium second messenger system. This receptor is involved in tracheal smooth muscle contraction, bronchoconstriction, and control of aldosterone production

COMT: catechol-O-methyltransferase–Catalyzes the O-methylation, and thereby the inactivation, of catecholamine neurotransmitters and catechol hormones. Also,

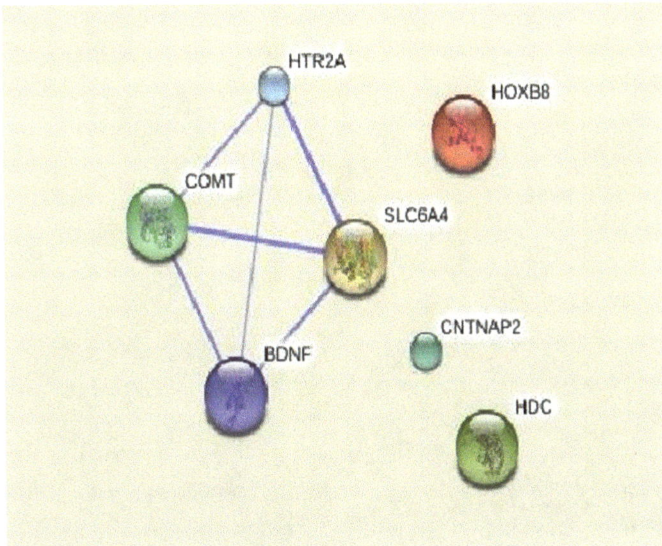

Fig. 4 Thicker lines represent strong interaction between the genes

shortens the biological half-lives of certain neuroactive drugs, like L-DOPA, alpha-methyl DOPA, and isoproterenol

SLC6A4: solute carrier family 6 (neurotransmitter transporter, serotonin), member 4–Terminates the action of serotonin by its high-affinity sodium-dependent reuptake into presynaptic terminals

BDNF: brain-derived neurotrophic factor–During development, promotes the survival and differentiation of selected neuronal populations of the peripheral and central nervous systems. Participates in axonal growth, pathfinding, and in the modulation of dendritic growth and morphology. Major regulator of synaptic transmission and plasticity at adult synapses in many regions of the CNS. The versatility of BDNF is emphasized by its contribution to a range of adaptive neuronal responses including long-term potentiation (LTP), long-term depression (LTD), and certain forms of short-term synaptic plastic

3.5 Gene–Gene Interaction for Schizophrenia

The protein–protein interaction subnetworks for target and reference set is shown which guides us to analyze the interacted genes for schizophrenia, disease whose target genes is tested (Fig. 5).

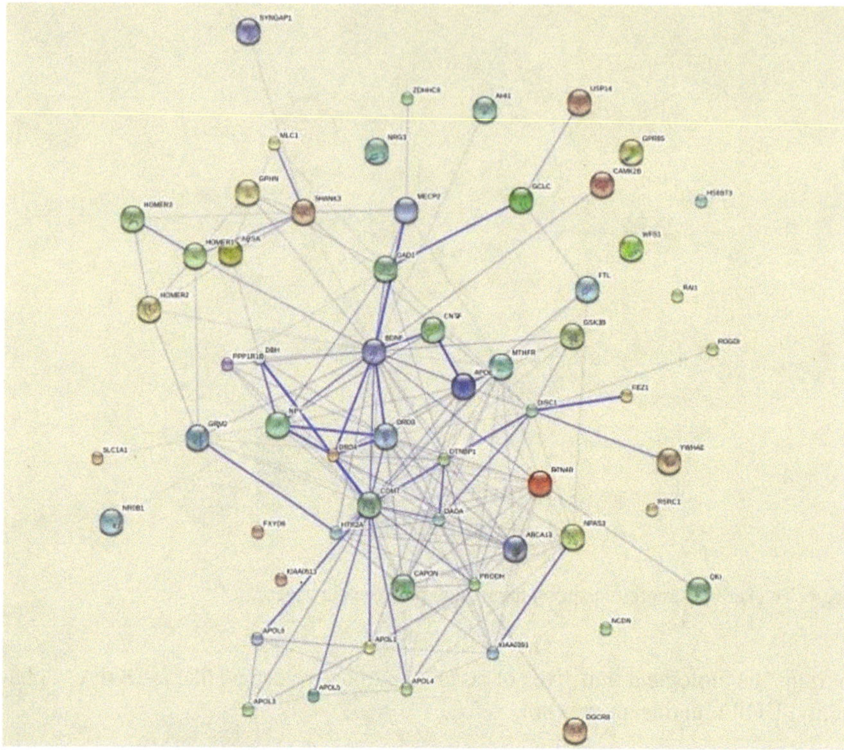

Fig. 5 Thicker lines represent strong interaction between the genes

MECP2: methyl CpG binding protein 2 (Rett syndrome)—Chromosomal protein that binds to methylated DNA. It can bind specifically to a single methyl-CpG pair. It is not influenced by sequences flanking the methyl-CpGs. Mediates transcriptional repression through interaction with histone deacetylase and the corepressor SIN3A

GOLG: A-7 complex is a palmitoyltransferase specific for HRAS and NRAS

GAD1: glutamate decarboxylase 1 (brain, 67 kDa)—Catalyzes the production of GABA

APOE: apolipoprotein E—Mediates the binding, internalization, and catabolism of lipoprotein particles. It can serve as a ligand for the LDL (apo B/E) receptor and for the specific apo-E receptor (chylomicron remnant) of hepatic tissues

MTHFR: 5,10-methylenetetrahydrofolate reductase (NADPH)—Catalyzes the conversion of 5,10-methylenetetrahydrofolate to 5-methyltetrahydrofolate, a co-substrate for homocysteine remethylation to methionine

DRD4: dopamine receptor D4

FEZ1: fasciculation and elongation protein zeta 1 (zygin I)—May be involved in axonal outgrowth as component of the network of molecules that regulate cellular morphology and axon guidance machinery. Able to restore partial locomotion and axonal fasciculation to C.elegans unc-76 mutants in germline transformation experiments

DISC1: disrupted in schizophrenia 1

APOL1: apolipoprotein L, 1—May play a role in lipid exchange and transport throughout the body. May participate in reverse cholesterol transport from peripheral cells to the liver

APOL4: apolipoprotein L, 4—May play a role in lipid exchange and transport throughout the body. May participate in reverse cholesterol transport from peripheral cells to the liver

APOL5: apolipoprotein L, 5—May affect the movement of lipids in the cytoplasm or allow the binding of lipids to organelles

APOL6: apolipoprotein L, 6—May affect the movement of lipids in the cytoplasm or allow the binding of lipids to organelles

NPY: neuropeptide Y—NPY is implicated in the control of feeding and in secretion of gonadotrophin-release hormone

DTNBP1: dystrobrevin binding protein 1—Plays a role in the biogenesis of lysosome-related organelles such as platelet dense granule and melanosomes

HTR2A: 5-hydroxytryptamine (serotonin) receptor 2A—This is one of the several different receptors for 5-hydroxytryptamine (serotonin), a biogenic hormone that functions as a neurotransmitter, a hormone, and a mitogen. This receptor mediates its action by association with G proteins that activates a phosphatidylinositol–calcium second messenger system. This receptor is involved in tracheal smooth muscle contraction, bronchoconstriction, and control of aldosterone production

YWHAE: tyrosine 3-monooxygenase/tryptophan 5-monooxygenase activation protein, epsilon polypeptide–Adapter protein implicated in the regulation of a large spectrum of both general and specialized signaling pathway. Binds to a large number of partners, usually by recognition of a phosphoserine or phosphothreonine motif. Binding generally results in the modulation of the activity of the binding partner

4 Disease Gene Prioritization Using Random Walk with Restart

Random Walk with Restart for Disease Gene Prioritization

- Method is used to prioritize genes based on cumulative interaction score corresponding to mapped genes of target and reference in a pathway regarding disease. The network is traversed starting from a gene to find its cumulative score with high restart probability to find its cumulative score in interaction of pathway.

Random Walk with Restart Steps

- INPUT—List of target genes/proteins L, list of reference datasets P, molecular interaction adjacency matrix A for graph $G = V, E$, restart probability $p(0.9)$
- OUTPUT—vector of cumulative distance scores for each reference dataset in P
- STEP1—map pathway sets P and the gene/protein list L onto graph G
- STEP2—v: = vector of length IVI with enies for mapped elements of L set o 1, otherwise 0;
- STEP3—u:= v;
- STEP4—u(old):= vector of length IVI with all entries set to 0;
- STEP5—A:= normalize(A), so that each column sums to 1;
- STEP6—while (sum|u-u(old)|) >=1E-06, do
  - U(old): = u;
  - $u := (1 - p)$Au(old) $+ pv$;
- STEP7—distance scores:= vector of length IPI;
- STEP8—for i <= 1 to IPI do
  - Distance*scores*[i]:= 1 − u [P[i]], *converttodistancescores*

4.1 Random Walk with Restart-ADHD

INPUT-L = 21 GENE-GIT1 SLC9A9 RAI1 CORO1A CSNK1D DYRK1A SCN8A SNAP25 FGD1 TH TPH1 HTR1B SLC6A2 NF1 SLC6A3 DRD5 DRD4 COMT CES1 ADRA2A

- $P = 124$ gene—Parkinson's data are similar so need to be tested all its genes.
- includes three target genes (SLC6A3, TH, COMT)
- Mapped number of genes in desired pathways = 3, i.e., (SLC6A3, TH, COMT)
- Now $v = 145$ in which three genes are target and are used for random walk over the v nodes. STEP1: map pathway sets P and L onto graph G STEP2: $V =$ [101000100010000111111]
  STEP3: $U =$ [0 0 0 0 0 0 0 0 0 0 0 0 0 0 0 0 0 0 0 0 0 0 0], (U initiates to V) STEP 4:

Uold = [0 0 0 0 0 0 0 0 0 0 0 0 0 0 0 0 0 0 0 0 0], STEP5: The normalization Table A is given under:

ADHD G	ADRA2A	CES1	COMT	CORO1A	CSNK1D	DRD4	DRD5	DYRK1A	FGD1	GIT1	HTR1B	NF1	RAI1	RTEL1	SCN8A	SLC6A2	SLC6A3	SLC9A9	SNAP25	TH	TPH1
ADRA2A	0	0	0.0911	0	0	0	0	0	0	0	0.22	0	0	0	0	0.16	0	0.51	0	0.17	0
CES1	0	0	0.113	0	0	0	0	0	0	0	0	0	0	0	0	0	0	0	0	0	0
COMT	0	0	0	0	0	0	0	0	0	0	0.09	0	0	0	0	0.21	0	0	0	0.17	0
CORO1A	0	0	0	0	0	0	0	0	0	0	0	0	0	0	0	0	0	0	0	0	0
CSNK1D	0	0	0	0	0	0	0	0	0	0	0	0	0	0	0	0	0	0	0	0	0
DRD4	0.707584	0	0.218	0	0	0	0.16	0	0	0	0.22	0	0	0	0	0.16	0.52	0	1	0.14	1
DRD5	0	0	0.15	0	0	0	0	0	0	0	0	0	0	0	0	0.15	0	0	0	0.09	0
DYRK1A	0	0	0	0	0	0	0	0	0	0	0	0	0	0	0	0	0	0	0	0	0
FGD1	0	0	0	0	0	0	0	0	0	0	0	0	0	0	0	0	0	0	0	0	0
GIT1	0	0	0	0	0	0	0	0	0	0	0	0	0	0	0	0	0	0	0	0	0
HTR1B	0	0	0	0	0	0	0	0	0	0	0	0	0	0	0	0.09	0	0	0	0	0
NF1	0	0	0	0	0	0	0	0	0	0	0	0	0	0	0	0	0	0	0	0	0
RAI1	0	0	0	0	0	0	0	0	0	0	0	0	0	0	0	0	0	0	0	0	0
RTEL1	0	0	0	0	0	0	0	0	0	0	0	0	0	0	0	0	0	0	0	0	0
SCN8A	0	0	0.07	0	0	0	0	0	0	0	0.09	0	0	0	0	0	0	0	0	0	0
SLC6A2	0	0	0	0	0	0	0	0	0	0	0	0	0	0	0	0	0	0	0	0.19	0
SLC6A3	0.292416	0	0.21	0	0	0	0.48	0	0	0	0.1	0	0	0	0	0	0	0.49	0	0.25	0
SLC9A9	0	0	0	0	0	0	0	0	0	0	0.05	0	0	0	0	0	0	0	0	0	0
SNAP25	0	0	0	0	0	0	0.24	0	0	0	0.06	0	0	0	0	0.09	0.17	0	0	0	0
TH	0	0	0	0	0	0	0	0	0	0	0	0	0	0	0	0	0	0	0	0	0
TPH1	0	0	0.15	0	0	0	0.13	0	0	0	0.16	0	0	0	0	0.16	0.3	0	0	0	0

4.1.1 Filters for Scoring Interaction

In Table 1, we have taken the set of candidate genes and they are scored with the reference gene lists in which the filter helps us give us the selected number of genes which are interacted with the filtered candidate genes.

This filter scoring is taken from STRING database and it is then used to update the scores with the target genes to form higher interactive network by the formula:

$$u := (1 - p)\mathrm{Au(old)} + pv.$$

STEP 7: distance score minimization and interaction score maximization

STEP 8: distance score for all nodes is taken and interaction score is listed by STRING.

Using sene–gene interaction score, we first find significant disease pathway and overall gene in the pathway network and then mapping our candidate gene, we find the highest correlated genes that are called the “target genes.”

4.1.2 Interaction Score for ADHD

In Table 2, the interaction score is calculated for each gene through RWR and each node (genes) is taken with equal probability. Distance score is minimized and interaction score is maximized for ADHD.

Table 1 score filters for candidate genes

#node	node2	combined_sco
HTR1B	ADRA2A	0.906
COMT	SCN8A	0.247
COMT	TPH1	0.532
SLC6A2	SNAP25	0.235
TH	DRD4	0.514
TH	DRD5	0.318
SLC6A2	HTR1B	0.262
HTR1B	COMT	0.374
COMT	DRD5	0.54
HTR1B	TPH1	0.675
SLC6A3	DRD4	0.965
SCN8A	DRD5	0.286
SCN8A	SLC6A3	0.229
SCN8A	SLC9A9	0.21
COMT	CES1	0.407
DRD5	SNAP25	0.371
COMT	DRD4	0.784
SLC6A2	ADRA2A	0.428
SNAP25	DRD4	0.34
SLC9A9	SLC6A3	0.269
TH	SLC6A2	0.693
SCN8A	DRD4	0.296
SCN8A	ADRA2A	0.462
DRD5	DRD4	0.253

4.1.3 Updated Interaction Score for ADHD

In Table 3, the interaction score is updated and summed for each genes through RWR having interactions with the target genes for ADHD.

Here, the target gene TH score is taken for the candidate genes ADRA2A, COMT, DRD4, DRD5, SLC6A2, and SLC6A3. The target gene SLC6A3 score is taken for the candidate gene DRD1. The target gene COMT score is taken for the candidate genes ADRA2A, CES1, COMT, DRD4, DRD5, SCN8A, SLC6A2, and SLC6A3.

Table 2 Interaction score for ADHD

ADHD GE	ADRA2	CES1	COMT	CORO1A	CSNK	DRD	DRD5	DYRK1A	FGD1	GIT1	HTR1B	NF1	RAI1	RTEL1	SCN8A	SLC6A2	SLC6A3	SLC9A9	SNAP25	TH	TPH1
ADRA2A	0	0	0.327	0	0	0	0	0	0	0	0.906	0	0	0	0	0.428	0	0.281	0	0.613	0
CES1	0	0	0.407	0	0	0	0	0	0	0	0	0	0	0	0	0	0	0	0	0	0
COMT	0	0	0	0	0	0	0	0	0	0	0.374	0	0	0	0	0.567	0	0	0	0.613	0
CORO1A	0	0	0	0	0	0	0	0	0	0	0	0	0	0	0	0	0	0	0	0	0
CSNK1D	0	0	0	0	0	0	0	0	0	0	0	0	0	0	0	0	0	0	0	0	0
DRD4	0.905	0	0.784	0	0	0	0.253	0	0	0	0.911	0	0	0	0	0.432	0.965	0	0.34	0.514	0.581
DRD5	0	0	0.54	0	0	0	0	0	0	0	0	0	0	0	0	0.399	0	0	0	0.318	0
DYRK1A	0	0	0	0	0	0	0	0	0	0	0	0	0	0	0	0	0	0	0	0	0
FGD1	0	0	0	0	0	0	0	0	0	0	0	0	0	0	0	0	0	0	0	0	0
GIT1	0	0	0	0	0	0	0	0	0	0	0	0	0	0	0	0	0	0	0	0	0
HTR1B	0	0	0	0	0	0	0	0	0	0	0	0	0	0	0	0.262	0	0	0	0	0
NF1	0	0	0	0	0	0	0	0	0	0	0	0	0	0	0	0	0	0	0	0	0
RAI1	0	0	0	0	0	0	0	0	0	0	0	0	0	0	0	0	0	0	0	0	0
RTEL1	0	0	0	0	0	0	0	0	0	0	0	0	0	0	0	0	0	0	0	0	0
SCN8A	0	0	0.247	0	0	0	0	0	0	0	0.371	0	0	0	0	0	0	0	0	0	0
SLC6A2	0	0	0	0	0	0	0	0	0	0	0	0	0	0	0	0	0	0	0	0.693	0
SLC6A3	0.374	0	0.752	0	0	0	0.75	0	0	0	0.43	0	0	0	0	0	0	0.269	0	0.898	0
SLC9A9	0	0	0	0	0	0	0	0	0	0	0.228	0	0	0	0	0	0	0	0	0	0
SNAP25	0	0	0	0	0	0	0.371	0	0	0	0.263	0	0	0	0	0.235	0.319	0	0	0	0
TH	0	0	0	0	0	0	0	0	0	0	0	0	0	0	0	0	0	0	0	0	0
TPH1	0	0	0.532	0	0	0	0.202	0	0	0	0.675	0	0	0	0	0.428	0.563	0	0	0	0

4.1.4 Prioritized Genes for ADHD

In Table 4, genes expanded sorting for ADHD is done and the highly interacted genes are sorted with the gene names and prioritized in network generation resulting for ADHD.

The genes are prioritized according to their overall interaction score during RWR from a candidate gene to all target genes. Adding scores corresponding to walk of the target genes is presented in Table 2.

4.1.5 Results and Discussions

Firstly, Sect. 1.1.1.1 gives the interaction scores of the 21 genes. Secondly, in Sect. 1.1.1.2, the target genes (three genes, i.e., TH, SLC6A3, and COMT) are selected from the pathway interaction use from ENRICHNET tools and the interaction score is calculated with RWR method. Finally, in Sect. 1.1.1.3, the scores are updated according to the targeted. Here, it is total 10 genes to interact and fame the network for disease prioritization.

4.2 Random Walk with Restart-Dementia

- $L = 71$ GENE-MAPT VCP PRNP TARDBP GRN PSEN1 SNCA TNF FUS APP CETP SNCB CLN6 C10ORF2 DCTN1 PSEN2 LAMA2 DNMT1 CP SERPINA3 DARC LRRK2 PINK1 NPC1 ARSA EPM2A CLN3 EIF2B5 HSD11B1 PLP1

Table 3 Interaction score updation for ADHD

ADHD GENE	TH	SLC6A3	COMT	INTERACTION SCORE SUM
ADRA2A	0.613	0	0.327	0.94
CES1	0	0	0.407	0.407
COMT	0.613	0	0	0.613
CORO1A	0	0	0	0
CSNK1D	0	0	0	0
DRD4	0.514	0.965	0.784	2.263
DRD5	0.318	0	0.54	0.858
DYRK1A	0	0	0	0
FGD1	0	0	0	0
GIT1	0	0	0	0
HTR1B	0	0	0	0
NF1	0	0	0	0
RAI1	0	0	0	0
RTEL1	0	0	0	0
SCN8A	0	0	0.247	0.247
SLC6A2	0.693	0	0	0.693
SLC6A3	0.898	0	0.752	1.65
SLC9A9	0	0	0	0
SNAP25	0	0.319	0	0.319
TH	0	0	0	0
TPH1	0	0.563	0.532	1.095

ARX POLG PDGFRB FTL ANG ROGDI C9ORF72 OTUD4 DNAJC5 NPC1 SAITOHIN NPEPPS CYP27A1 PARK7 NCKAP1 CXCL11 APBA3 TYROBP SNCAIP CTSF SNCG APBB1 KLK6 SORT1 NEDD4 HTRA1 NOVA2 SIGMAR1 ISCHEMIC HAP1 DYRK1A CXCL12 VSNL1 MEOX2 RELN NR1H2 NOTCH3 HNRNPA2B1 PARK2 KSS FMR1

- $P = 124$ gene-Parkinson's data are similar so need to test all their genes which include three target genes (PARK7, LRRK2, SNCA)
- Mapped number of genes in desired pathways = 3, i.e., (PARK7, LRRK2, SNCA) now $v = 195$ in which three genes are target and are used for random walk over the v nodes.

  Similarly, the algorithm is executed for dementia, the result comes with interaction score, then updation and then prioritization of gene network for disease.

Table 4 Genes expanded sorting for ADHD

S.NO.	ADHD GENE	SUM
1	DRD4	2.263
2	SLC6A3	1.65
3	TPH1	1.095
4	ADRA2A	0.94
5	DRD5	0.858
6	SLC6A2	0.693
7	COMT	0.613
8	CES1	0.407
9	SNAP25	0.319
10	SCN8A	0.247
11	CORO1A	0
12	CSNK1D	0
13	DYRK1A	0
14	FGD1	0
15	GIT1	0
16	HTR1B	0
17	NF1	0
18	RAI1	0
19	RTEL1	0
20	SLC9A9	0
21	TH	0

Using gene–gene interaction score, we first find significant disease pathway and overall gene in the pathway network and then mapping our candidate gene, we find the highest correlated genes that are called the "target genes."

4.2.1 Interaction Score for Dementia

In Table 5, the interaction score is calculated for each gene through RWR and each node (genes) is taken with equal probability. Distance score is minimized and interaction score is maximized for dementia.

Table 5 Interaction score for dementia

dementia	MAPT	CP	PRNP	TARDBP	GRN	PSEN1	SNCA	TNF	FUS	APP	CETP	SNCB	CLN6	C10ORF	DCTN1	PSEN2	LAMA2	DNMT1	CP	SERPINA	DARC	LRRK2	PINK1
MAPT	0	0.467	0.429	0	0	0	0	0	0	0	0	0	0	0	0.736	0.528	0	0	0	0	0	0	0.307
VCP	0	0	0	0	0	0	0	0	0	0	0	0	0	0	0.308	0	0	0	0	0	0	0	0
PRNP	0	0	0	0	0	0	0	0	0	0	0	0	0	0	0	0	0	0	0	0	0	0	0
TARDBP	0.609	0.862	0	0	0	0.319	0.317	0	0.302	0	0	0	0	0	0.379	0.263	0	0	0	0	0	0.344	0
GRN	0.657	0.561	0.221	0.752	0	0.372	0.29	0.281	0.373	0.266	0	0	0	0	0	0.318	0	0	0	0	0	0.301	0
PSEN1	0.862	0.303	0.516	0	0	0	0.374	0.256	0	0	0	0	0	0	0.238	0.655	0	0	0	0	0	0	0.26
SNCA	0.943	0	0.318	0	0	0	0	0	0	0	0	0	0	0	0	0.308	0	0	0	0	0	0	0.657
TNF	0	0	0	0	0	0	0	0	0	0	0	0	0	0	0	0	0	0	0	0	0	0	0
FUS	0.34	0.347	0	0	0	0	0	0.201	0	0	0	0	0	0	0.305	0	0	0	0	0	0	0	0
APP	0.836	0	0.803	0	0	0.338	0.371	0.337	0	0	0	0.688	0	0	0	0.345	0	0	0	0	0	0.241	0
CETP	0	0	0	0	0	0	0	0.241	0	0	0	0	0	0	0	0	0	0	0	0	0	0	0
SNCB	0	0	0.361	0	0	0.318	0.641	0	0	0	0	0	0	0	0	0.307	0	0	0	0	0	0	0
CLN6	0	0.621	0	0	0	0	0	0	0	0	0	0	0	0	0	0	0	0	0	0	0	0	0
C10ORF	0	0	0	0	0	0	0	0	0	0	0	0	0	0	0	0	0	0	0	0	0	0	0
DCTN1	0	0	0	0	0	0	0	0	0	0	0	0	0	0	0	0	0	0	0	0	0	0	0
PSEN2	0	0	0.404	0	0	0	0	0	0	0	0	0	0	0	0	0	0	0	0	0	0	0	0
LAMA2	0	0	0	0	0	0	0	0	0	0	0	0	0	0	0	0	0	0	0	0	0	0	0
DNMT1	0	0	0	0	0	0	0	0	0	0	0	0	0	0	0	0	0	0	0	0	0	0	0
CP	0	0	0.2	0	0	0	0	0.239	0	0.272	0	0	0	0	0	0	0	0	0	0	0	0	0
SERPINA	0	0	0	0	0	0	0	0	0	0.623	0	0	0	0.374	0	0	0	0	0	0	0	0	0
DARC	0	0	0	0	0	0	0	0.463	0	0	0	0	0	0	0	0	0	0	0	0	0	0	0
LRRK2	0.567	0.241	0.212	0	0	0.374	0.381	0	0	0	0	0.324	0	0	0	0.271	0	0	0	0	0	0	0.439
PINK1	0	0	0	0	0	0	0	0	0	0	0	0	0	0	0	0	0	0	0	0	0	0	0
NPC1	0.223	0	0	0	0	0	0	0	0	0	0	0	0	0	0	0	0	0	0	0	0	0	0
ARSA	0	0	0	0	0	0	0	0	0	0	0	0	0.374	0	0	0	0	0	0	0	0	0	0
EPM2A	0	0	0	0	0	0	0	0	0	0	0	0	0	0	0	0	0	0	0	0	0	0	0
CLN3	0	0	0	0	0	0	0	0	0	0	0	0	0	0	0	0.266	0	0	0	0	0	0	0
EIF2B5	0.271	0	0	0	0	0	0	0	0	0	0	0	0	0	0	0	0	0	0	0	0	0	0
HSD11B1	0.201	0	0	0	0	0.221	0	0.825	0	0	0	0	0	0	0	0.245	0	0	0	0	0	0	0
PLP1	0.209	0	0	0	0	0	0	0.201	0	0	0	0	0	0	0	0	0	0	0	0	0	0	0
ARX	0	0	0	0	0	0	0	0	0	0	0	0	0	0	0	0	0	0	0	0	0	0	0
POLG	0	0	0	0	0	0	0	0	0	0	0	0	0	0.853	0	0	0	0	0	0	0	0	0
PDGFRB	0	0	0	0	0	0	0	0.238	0	0	0	0	0	0	0	0	0	0	0	0	0	0	0
FTL	0	0	0.838	0	0	0	0	0.379	0	0	0	0	0	0	0	0	0	0	0	0	0	0	0
ANG	0	0	0	0	0	0	0	0.305	0	0	0	0	0	0	0.293	0	0	0	0	0	0	0	0
ROGDI	0	0	0	0	0	0	0	0	0	0	0	0	0	0	0	0	0	0	0	0	0	0	0
C9ORF	0	0	0	0	0	0	0	0	0	0	0	0	0	0	0	0	0	0	0	0	0	0	0

4.2.2 Updated Interaction Score for Dementia

In Table 6, the interaction score is updated and summed for each genes through RWR having interactions with the target genes for dementia.

Here, the target gene PARK7 score is taken for the candidate genes PSEN1, SNCA and LRRK2. The target gene LRRK2 score is taken for the candidate genes TARDBP, GRN and APP. The target gene PARK2 score is taken for the candidate gene SNCB. The target gene LRRK2 score is taken for the candidate genes TARDBP, GRN and APP. The target gene PARK2 score is taken for the candidate gene SNCB. The target gene PINK1 score is taken for the candidate genes PSEN1, SNCA and LRRK2. The target gene SNCA score is taken for the candidate gene TARDBP, GRN, PSEN1, APP, SNCB and LRRK2. The target gene SNCAIP score is not taken as it is not interacting with other candidate genes. The target gene APBB1 score is taken for the candidate gene APP. The target gene APP score is taken for the candidate genes GRN, CP and SERPINA3. The target gene PSEN1 score is taken for the candidate genes GRN, APP, SNCB, LRRK2 and HSD11B1. The target gene PSEN2 score is taken for the candidate genes TARDBP, GRN, SNCA, TNF, APP, SNCB, LRRK2, CLN3 and HSD11B1.

Table 6 Interaction score updation for dementia

dementia	MAPT	CP	PRNP	TARDB	GRN	PSEN1	SNCA	TNF	FUS	APP	CETP	SNCB	CLN6	C10ORF	DCTN1	PSEN2	LAMA2	DNMT1	CP	SERPIN	DARC	LRRK2	PINK1
MAPT	0	0.467	0.429	0	0	0	0	0	0	0	0	0	0	0	0.736	0.528	0	0	0	0	0	0	0.307
VCP	0	0	0	0	0	0	0	0	0	0	0	0	0	0	0.308	0	0	0	0	0	0	0	0
PRNP	0	0	0	0	0	0	0	0	0	0	0	0	0	0	0	0	0	0	0	0	0	0	0
TARDB	0.609	0.862	0	0	0	0.319	0.317	0	0.302	0	0	0	0	0	0.379	0.263	0	0	0	0	0	0.344	0
GRN	0.657	0.561	0.221	0.752	0	0.372	0.29	0.281	0.373	0.266	0	0	0	0	0	0.318	0	0	0	0	0	0.301	0
PSEN1	0.862	0.303	0.516	0	0	0	0.374	0.256	0	0	0	0	0	0	0.238	0.655	0	0	0	0	0	0	0.26
SNCA	0.343	0	0.318	0	0	0	0	0	0	0	0	0	0	0	0	0.308	0	0	0	0	0	0	0.657
TNF	0	0	0	0	0	0	0	0	0	0	0	0	0	0	0	0	0	0	0	0	0	0	0
FUS	0.34	0.347	0	0	0	0	0	0.201	0	0	0	0	0	0	0.305	0	0	0	0	0	0	0	0
APP	0.836	0	0.803	0	0	0.338	0.971	0.337	0	0	0	0.688	0	0	0	0.345	0	0	0	0	0	0.241	0
CETP	0	0	0	0	0	0	0	0.241	0	0	0	0	0	0	0	0	0	0	0	0	0	0	0
SNCB	0	0	0.361	0	0	0.318	0.641	0	0	0	0	0	0	0	0	0.307	0	0	0	0	0	0	0
CLN6	0	0.621	0	0	0	0	0	0	0	0	0	0	0	0	0	0	0	0	0	0	0	0	0
C10ORF	0	0	0	0	0	0	0	0	0	0	0	0	0	0	0	0	0	0	0	0	0	0	0
DCTN1	0	0	0	0	0	0	0	0	0	0	0	0	0	0	0	0	0	0	0	0	0	0	0
PSEN2	0	0	0.404	0	0	0	0	0	0	0	0	0	0	0	0	0	0	0	0	0	0	0	0
LAMA2	0	0	0	0	0	0	0	0	0	0	0	0	0	0	0	0	0	0	0	0	0	0	0
DNMT1	0	0	0	0	0	0	0	0	0	0	0	0	0	0	0	0	0	0	0	0	0	0	0
CP	0	0	0.2	0	0	0	0	0.239	0	0.272	0	0	0	0	0	0	0	0	0	0	0	0	0
SERPIN	0	0	0	0	0	0	0	0	0	0.629	0	0	0	0.374	0	0	0	0	0	0	0	0	0
DARC	0	0	0	0	0	0	0	0.463	0	0	0	0	0	0	0	0	0	0	0	0	0	0	0
LRRK2	0.567	0.241	0.212	0	0	0.374	0.381	0	0	0	0	0.324	0	0	0	0.271	0	0	0	0	0	0	0.439
PINK1	0	0	0	0	0	0	0	0	0	0	0	0	0	0	0	0	0	0	0	0	0	0	0
NPC1	0.229	0	0	0	0	0	0	0	0	0	0	0	0	0	0	0	0	0	0	0	0	0	0
ARSA	0	0	0	0	0	0	0	0	0	0	0	0	0.374	0	0	0	0	0	0	0	0	0	0
EPM2A	0	0	0	0	0	0	0	0	0	0	0	0	0	0	0	0	0	0	0	0	0	0	0
CLN3	0	0	0	0	0	0	0	0	0	0	0	0	0	0	0	0.266	0	0	0	0	0	0	0
EIF2B5	0.271	0	0	0	0	0	0	0	0	0	0	0	0	0	0	0	0	0	0	0	0	0	0
HSD11B1	0.201	0	0	0	0	0.221	0	0.825	0	0	0	0	0	0	0	0.245	0	0	0	0	0	0	0
PLP1	0.209	0	0	0	0	0	0	0.201	0	0	0	0	0	0	0	0	0	0	0	0	0	0	0
ARX	0	0	0	0	0	0	0	0	0	0	0	0	0	0	0	0	0	0	0	0	0	0	0
POLG	0	0	0	0	0	0	0	0	0	0	0	0	0	0.853	0	0	0	0	0	0	0	0	0
PDGFRB	0	0	0	0	0	0	0	0.238	0	0	0	0	0	0	0	0	0	0	0	0	0	0	0
FTL	0	0	0.838	0	0	0	0	0.379	0	0	0	0	0	0	0	0	0	0	0	0	0	0	0
ANG	0	0	0	0	0	0	0	0.305	0	0	0	0	0	0	0.293	0	0	0	0	0	0	0	0
ROGDI	0	0	0	0	0	0	0	0	0	0	0	0	0	0	0	0	0	0	0	0	0	0	0
C9ORF	0	0	0	0	0	0	0	0	0	0	0	0	0	0	0	0	0	0	0	0	0	0	0

4.2.3 Prioritized Genes for Dementia

In Table 7, genes expanded Sorting for Dementia is done and the highly interacted genes are sorted with the gene names and prioritized in network generation resulting for Dementia.

4.2.4 Results and Discussions

Firstly, Sect. 1.1.2.1 gives the interaction scores of the 71 genes. Secondly, in Sect. 1.1.2.2, the target genes (10 genes, i.e., PARK7, LRRK2, PARK2, PINK1, SNCA, SNCAIP, APBB1, APP, PSEN1, and PSEN2) are selected from the pathway interaction use from ENRICHNET tools and the interaction score is calculated with RWR method. Finally, in Sect. 1.1.2.3, the scores are updated according to the targeted. Here, it is total 23 genes to interact and fame the network for disease prioritization.

Table 7 Genes expanded sorting for DEMENTIA

S.NO.	Dementia	Interaction score sum
1	APP	1.154
2	LRRK2	2.815
3	SNCAIP	2.445
4	NOTCH3	2.156
5	SNCA	1.948
6	GRN	1.547
7	PSEN1	1.518
8	SNCB	1.512
9	TARDBP	1.243
10	KLK6	0.969
11	PARK2	0.946
12	APBB1	0.92
13	SORT1	0.907
14	MAPT	0.835
15	PARK7	0.778
16	HSD11B1	0.695
17	APBA3	0.636
18	SERPINA3	0.629
19	NEDD4	0.563
20	NR1H2	0.427
21	CP	0.272
22	CLN3	0.266
23	POLG	0.24
24	VCP	0
25	PRNP	0
26	TNF	0
27	FUS	0
28	CETP	0
29	CLN6	0
30	C10ORF2	0
31	DCTN1	0
32	PSEN2	0
33	LAMA2	0
34	DNMT1	0
35	DARC	0
36	PINK1	0
37	NPC1	0

(continued)

Table 7 (continued)

S.NO.	Dementia	Interaction score sum
38	ARSA	0
39	EPM2A	0
40	EIF2B5	0
41	PLP1	0
42	ARX	0
43	PDGFRB	0
44	FTL	0
45	ANG	0
46	ROGDI	0
47	C9ORF72	0
48	OTUD4	0
49	DNAJC5	0
50	NPC1	0
51	SAITOHIN	0
52	NPEPPS	0
53	CYP27A1	0
54	NCKAP1	0
55	CXCL11	0
56	TYROBP	0
57	CTSF	0
58	SNCG	0
59	HTRA1	0
60	NOVA2	0
61	SIGMAR1	0
62	ISCHEMIC	0
63	HAP1	0
64	DYRK1A	0
65	CXCL12	0
66	VSNL1	0
67	MEOX2	0
68	RELN	0
69	HNRNPA2B1	0
70	KSS	0
71	FMR1	0

Table 8 Interaction score for mood disorder

mood	CHD8	PINK1	MTHFR	SHANK3	DISC1	TOR1A	HLA-DQ	SYNGAP	SLC22A	IMPA1	CLOCK	ZNF41	CDKL5	MECP2	CLN3	CHAC	XBP1	SLC6A4	PD	AKT1	DRD4	CREB1	COMT	BDNF
CHD8	0	0	0	0	0	0	0	0	0	0	0	0	0	0	0	0	0	0	0	0	0	0	0	0
PINK1	0	0	0	0	0	0	0	0	0	0	0	0	0	0	0	0	0	0	0	0	0	0	0	0
MTHFR	0	0	0	0	0	0	0	0	0	0	0	0	0	0.2	0	0	0	0	0	0	0	0	0	0.202
SHANK3	0	0	0	0	0.307	0	0	0.236	0	0	0	0	0	0.374	0	0	0	0	0	0	0	0	0	0.2
DISC1	0	0	0	0	0	0	0	0	0	0	0	0	0	0	0	0	0	0	0	0	0	0	0	0.373
TOR1A	0	0	0.236	0	0	0	0	0	0	0	0	0	0	0	0	0	0	0	0	0	0	0.208	0	0
HLA-DQ	0	0	0	0	0	0	0	0	0	0	0	0	0	0	0	0	0	0	0	0	0	0	0	0
SYNGAP	0	0	0	0	0	0	0	0	0	0	0	0	0	0	0	0	0	0	0	0	0	0	0	0
SLC22A	0	0	0	0	0	0	0	0	0	0	0	0	0	0	0	0	0	0.326	0	0	0	0	0	0
IMPA1	0	0	0	0	0	0	0	0	0	0	0	0	0	0	0	0	0	0	0	0	0	0	0	0
CLOCK	0	0	0	0	0	0	0	0	0	0	0	0	0	0	0	0	0	0	0	0	0	0.318	0	0.2
ZNF41	0	0	0	0	0	0	0	0	0	0	0	0	0.443	0.603	0	0	0	0	0	0	0	0	0	0
CDKL5	0	0	0	0	0	0	0	0	0	0	0	0	0	0.384	0	0	0	0	0	0	0	0	0	0.243
MECP2	0	0	0	0	0	0	0	0	0	0	0	0	0	0	0	0	0	0	0	0	0	0	0	0.346
CLN3	0	0	0	0	0	0	0	0	0	0	0	0	0	0	0	0	0	0	0	0	0	0	0	0
CHAC	0	0	0	0	0	0	0	0	0	0	0	0	0	0	0	0	0	0	0	0	0	0	0	0
XBP1	0	0	0	0	0	0	0	0	0	0.229	0	0	0	0	0	0	0	0	0	0.35	0	0.333	0	0
SLC6A4	0	0	0.346	0	0	0.26	0	0	0	0	0	0	0	0	0	0	0	0	0	0.827	0	0.241	0	0.615
PD	0	0	0	0	0	0	0	0	0	0	0	0	0	0	0	0	0	0	0	0	0	0	0	0
AKT1	0	0.416	0	0	0.238	0	0	0.25	0	0.228	0	0	0	0	0	0	0	0	0	0	0	0.336	0.26	0.328
DRD4	0	0	0.361	0	0	0.308	0	0	0	0.229	0	0	0	0	0	0	0.243	0.784	0	0	0	0	0.784	0.884
CREB1	0.334	0	0	0	0	0	0	0.252	0	0	0	0	0	0.307	0	0	0	0	0	0	0	0	0	0.347
COMT	0	0	0.468	0	0.54	0	0	0	0	0	0	0	0	0	0	0	0	0	0	0	0	0	0	0.609
BDNF	0	0	0	0	0	0	0	0	0	0	0	0	0	0	0	0	0	0	0	0	0	0	0	0
HTR1A	0	0	0	0	0	0	0	0	0	0	0	0	0	0	0	0	0	0	0	0	0	0.307	0.461	0.609
STAT3	0	0	0	0	0	0	0	0	0	0	0	0	0	0.265	0	0	0	0	0	0	0	0.517	0	0.334
ANXIET	0	0	0	0	0	0	0	0	0	0	0	0	0	0	0	0	0	0	0	0	0	0	0	0
DISC1	0	0	0	0	0	0	0	0	0	0	0	0	0	0	0	0	0	0	0	0	0	0	0	0.379
ADCY9	0	0	0	0	0	0	0	0	0	0	0	0	0	0	0	0	0	0	0	0	0	0	0	0
VGF	0	0	0	0	0	0	0	0	0	0	0	0	0	0	0	0	0	0	0	0	0	0.276	0	0.836
IMPA1	0	0	0	0	0	0	0	0	0	0	0	0	0	0	0	0	0	0	0	0	0	0	0	0
PPT1	0	0	0	0	0	0	0	0	0	0	0	0	0	0	0	0	0	0	0	0	0	0	0	0
HRH1	0	0	0	0	0	0	0	0	0	0	0	0	0	0	0	0	0	0	0	0	0	0	0	0
PDE4B	0	0	0	0	0.774	0	0	0	0	0	0	0	0	0	0	0	0	0	0	0	0	0	0	0
ZNF41	0	0	0	0	0	0	0	0	0	0	0	0	0	0	0	0	0	0	0	0	0	0	0	0
MAOB	0	0	0	0	0	0	0	0	0	0	0	0	0	0	0	0	0	0	0	0	0	0	0	0.34
CDKL5	0	0	0	0	0	0	0	0	0	0	0	0	0	0	0	0	0	0	0	0	0	0	0	0.243

4.3 Random Walk with Restart-Mood Disorder

- $L = 46$ GENE-CHD8 PINK1 MTHFR SHANK3 DISC1 TOR1A HLA-DQB1 SYNGAP1 SLC22A5 IMPA1 CLOCK ZNF41 CDKL5 MECP2 CLN3 CHAC XBP1 SLC6A4 PD AKT1 DRD4 CREB1 COMT BDNF HTR1A STAT3 ANXIETY DISC1 ADCY9 VGF IMPA1 PPT1 HRH1 PDE4B ZNF41 MAOB CDKL5 CHAC XBP1 FGFR2 OPRK1 OPRD1 PINK1 CLN3 DRD4 COMT
- $P = 124$ gene-Parkinson's data are similar so need to test all their genes which include three target genes (MAOB, AKT1, BDNF)
- Mapped number of genes in desired pathways = 3, i.e., (MAOB, AKT1, BDNF)
- Now $v = 170$ in which three genes are target and are used for random walk over the v nodes.

  Similarly, the algorithm is executed for, the result comes with interaction score, then updation and then prioritization of gene network for disease using gene–gene interaction score, we first find significant disease pathway and overall gene in the pathway network and then mapping our candidate gene, we find the highest correlated genes that are called the "target genes."

4.3.1 Interaction Score for Mood Disorder

In Table 8, the interaction score is calculated for each gene through RWR and each node (genes) is taken with equal probability. Distance score is minimized and interaction score is maximized for mood disorder.

4.3.2 Updated Interaction Score for Mood Disorder

In Table 9, the interaction score is updated and summed for each genes through RWR having interactions with the target genes for mood disorder.

The target gene MAOB score is taken for the candidate genes MTHFR, TOR1A, SLC6A4, DRD4, COMT, HTR1A, and PINK1. The target gene AKT1 score is taken for the candidate gene XBP1 and SLC6A1. Similarly, it is done for all candidate genes in respect of the target genes.

4.3.3 Prioritized Genes for Mood Disorder

In Table 10, genes expanded sorting for mood disorder is done and the highly interacted genes are sorted with the gene names and prioritized in network generation resulting for MOOD DISORDER.

4.3.4 Results and Discussions

Firstly, Sect. 1.1.3.1 gives the interaction scores of the 46 genes. Secondly, in Sect. 1.1.3.2, the target genes (6 genes, i.e., MAOB, AKT1, STAT3, BDNF, CREB1, and PINK1) are selected from the pathway interaction use from ENRICHNET tools and the interaction score is calculated with RWR method. Finally, in Sect. 1.1.3.3, the scores are updated according to the targeted. Here, it is total 25 genes to interact and fame the network for disease prioritization.

4.4 Random Walk with Restart-OCD

- $L = 8$ GENE-CNTNAP2 SLC6A4 HTR2A HOXB8 HDC COMT BDNF SLC6A4
- $P = 124$ gene-Parkinson's data are similar so need to test all their genes which include three target genes (HDC, COMT, BDNF)
- Mapped number of genes in desired pathways = 3, i.e., (HDC, COMT, BDNF)
- now $v = 132$ in which three genes are target and are used for random walk over the v nodes.

  Similarly, the algorithm is executed for OCD, the result comes with interaction score, then updation and then prioritization of gene network for disease.

Table 9 Interaction score updation for mood disorder

mood	MAOB	AKT1	STAT3	BDNF	CREB1	PINK1	INTEACTION SCORE SUM
CHD8	0	0	0	0	0	0	0
PINK1	0	0	0	0	0	0	0
MTHFR	0.26	0	0	0.202	0	0	0.462
SHANK3	0	0	0	0.2	0	0	0.2
DISC1	0	0	0	0.379	0	0	0.379
TOR1A	0.385	0	0	0	0.208	0	0.593
HLA-DQB1	0	0	0	0	0	0	0
SYNGAP1	0	0	0	0	0	0	0
SLC22A5	0	0	0	0	0	0	0
IMPA1	0	0	0	0	0	0	0
CLOCK	0	0	0	0.2	0.318	0	0.518
ZNF41	0	0	0	0	0	0	0
CDKL5	0	0	0	0.243	0	0	0.243
MECP2	0	0	0	0.946	0	0	0.946
CLN3	0	0	0	0	0	0	0
CHAC	0	0	0	0	0	0	0
XBP1	0	0.35	0.271	0	0.333	0	0.954
SLC6A4	0.432	0.827	0	0.615	0.241	0	2.115
PD	0	0	0	0	0	0	0
AKT1	0	0	0	0.928	0.996	0.416	2.34
DRD4	0.569	0	0	0.884	0	0	1.453
CREB1	0	0	0	0.947	0	0	0.947
COMT	0.973	0	0	0.609	0	0	1.582
BDNF	0	0	0	0	0	0	0
HTR1A	0.411	0	0	0.609	0.307	0	1.327
STAT3	0	0	0	0.394	0.517	0	0.911
ANXIETY	0	0	0	0	0	0	0
DISC1	0	0	0	0.379	0	0	0.379
ADCY9	0	0	0	0	0	0	0
VGF	0	0	0	0.896	0.276	0	1.172
IMPA1	0	0	0	0	0	0	0
PPT1	0	0	0	0	0	0	0
HRH1	0	0	0	0	0	0	0
PDE4B	0	0	0	0	0	0	0
ZNF41	0	0	0	0	0	0	0
MAOB	0	0	0	0.34	0	0	0.34
CDKL5	0	0	0	0.243	0	0	0.243
CHAC	0	0	0	0	0	0	0
XBP1	0	0.35	0.271	0	0	0	0.621
FGFR2	0	0	0	0.368	0	0	0.368
OPRK1	0	0	0	0.21	0	0	0.21
OPRD1	0	0	0	0	0	0	0
PINK1	0.219	0	0	0	0	0	0.219
CLN3	0	0	0	0	0	0	0
DRD4	0.569	0	0	0.884	0	0	1.453
COMT	0	0	0	0.609	0	0	0.609

Table 10 Genes expanded sorting for mood disorder

S.no.	Mood	Interaction score sum
1	AKT1	2.34
2	SLC6A4	2.115
3	COMT	1.582
4	DRD4	1.453
5	DRD4	1.453
6	HTR1A	1.327
7	VGF	1.172
8	XBP1	0.954
9	CREB1	0.947
10	MECP2	0.946
11	STAT3	0.911
12	XBP1	0.621
13	COMT	0.609
14	TOR1A	0.593
15	CLOCK	0.518
16	MTHFR	0.462
17	DISC1	0.379
18	DISC1	0.379
19	FGFR2	0.368
20	MAOB	0.34
21	CDKL5	0.243
22	CDKL5	0.243
23	PINK1	0.219
24	OPRK1	0.21
25	SHANK3	0.2
26	CHD8	0
27	PINK1	0
28	HLA-DQB1	0
29	SYNGAP1	0
30	SLC22A5	0
31	IMPA1	0
32	ZNF41	0
33	CLN3	0
34	CHAC	0
35	PD	0
36	BDNF	0
37	ANXIETY	0

(continued)

Table 10 (continued)

S.no.	Mood	Interaction score sum
38	ADCY9	0
39	IMPA1	0
40	PPT1	0
41	HRH1	0
42	PDE4B	0
43	ZNF41	0
44	CHAC	0
45	OPRD1	0
46	CLN3	0

Table 11 Interaction score for OCD

ocd	CNTNAP2	SLC6A4	HTR2A	HOXB8	HDC	COMT	BDNF	SLC6A4
CNTNAP2	0	0	0	0	0	0	0	0
SLC6A4	0	0	0.75	0	0	0.752	0.615	0
HTR2A	0	0	0	0	0	0	0.411	0
HOXB8	0	0	0	0	0	0	0	0
HDC	0	0	0	0	0	0	0	0
COMT	0	0	0.563	0	0	0	0.609	0
BDNF	0	0	0	0	0	0	0	0
SLC6A4	0	0	0.75	0	0	0.752	0.615	0

Using gene–gene interaction score, we first find significant disease pathway and overall gene in the pathway network and then mapping our candidate gene, we find the highest correlated genes that are called the "target genes."

4.4.1 Interaction Score for OCD

In Table 11, the interaction score is calculated for each gene through RWR and each node (genes) is taken with equal probability. Distance score is minimized and interaction score is maximized for OCD.

4.4.2 Updated Interaction Score for OCD

In Table 12, the interaction score is updated and summed for each genes through RWR having interactions with the target genes for OCD.

The target gene HDC score is not taken as it is not interacting with other candidate genes. The target gene COMT score is taken for the candidate gene SLC6A1. The

Table 12 Interaction score updation for OCD

ocd	HDC	COMT	BDNF	INTEACTION SCORE SUM
CNTNAP2	0	0	0	0
SLC6A4	0	0.752	0.615	1.367
HTR2A	0	0	0.411	0.411
HOXB8	0	0	0	0
HDC	0	0	0	0
COMT	0	0	0.609	0.609
BDNF	0	0	0	0
SLC6A4	0	0.752	0.615	1.367

target gene BDNF score is taken for the candidate genes SLC6A4, HTR2A, and COMT.

4.4.3 Prioritized Genes for OCD

In Table 13, genes expanded sorting for OCD is done and the highly interacted genes are sorted with the gene names and prioritized in network generation resulting for OCD.

Table 13 Genes expanded sorting for OCD

S.NO.	OCD	INTERACTION SCORE SUM
1	SLC6A4	1.367
2	SLC6A4	1.367
3	COMT	0.609
4	HTR2A	0.411
5	CNTNAP2	0
6	HOXB8	0
7	HDC	0
8	BDNF	0

4.4.4 Results and Discussions

Firstly, Sect. 1.1.1.1 gives the interaction scores of the eight genes. Secondly, in Sect. 1.1.1.2, the target genes (three genes, i.e., HDC, COMT, and BDNF) are selected from the pathway interaction use from ENRICHNET tools and the interaction score is calculated with RWR method. Finally, in Sect. 1.1.1.3, the scores are updated according to the targeted. Here, it is total four genes to interact and fame the network for disease prioritization.

4.5 *Random Walk with Restart-Schizophrenia*

- L = 61 GENE-MTHFR PRODH HTR2A DRD3 RTN4R DISC1 SHANK3 BDNF DRD4 WFS1 ZDHHC9 NR0B1 MECP2 NPY FTL CNTF COMT SLC1A1 APOE ROGDI RSRC1 KIAA0513 KIAA0391 QKI NPAS3 HS6ST3 DBH DGCR8 AHI1 NCDN ABCA13 CAMK2B DAOA USP14 APOL6 APOL5 APOL4 APOL3 DTNBP1 GCLC FXYD6 MLC1 NOS1AP NRG3 GAD1 GPR85 YWHAE GSK3B FEZ1 HOMER3 HOMER2 HOMER1 PPP1R1B GRM2 GPHN APOL1 RAI1 ARSA MTHFR SHANK3 SYNGAP1
- $P = 124$ gene-Parkinson's data are similar so need to test all their genes which include three target genes (GAD1, GSK3B, BDNF)
- Mapped number of genes in desired pathways = 3, i.e., (GAD1, GSK3B, BDNF)
- Now $v = 185$ in which three genes are target and are used for random walk over the v nodes.

  Similarly, the algorithm is executed for schizophrenia, the result comes with interaction score, then updation and then prioritization of gene network for disease. Using gene–gene interaction score, we first find significant disease pathway and overall gene in the pathway network and then mapping our candidate gene, we find the highest correlated genes that are called the "target genes."

4.5.1 Interaction Score for Schizophrenia

In Table 14, the interaction score is calculated for each gene through RWR and each node (genes) is taken with equal probability. Distance score is minimized and interaction score is maximized for schizophrenia.

4.5.2 Updated Interaction Score for Schizophrenia

In Table 15, the interaction score is updated and summed for each genes through RWR having interactions with the target genes for schizophrenia.

The target gene GAD1 score is taken for the candidate gene NPY, DTNBP1, GCLC, MLC1, PPP1R1B, and GPHN. The target gene GSK3B score is taken for

Table 14 Interaction score for Schizophrenia

schizophenia	MTHFR	PRODH	HTR2A	DRD3	RTN4R	DISC1	SHANK3	BDNF	DRD4	WFS1	ZDHHC9	NR0B1	MECP2	NPY	FTL
MTHFR	0	0	0.291	0.26	0	0	0	0.202	0	0	0	0	0.2	0	0.246
PRODH	0.249	0	0.296	0.307	0	0.374	0	0.201	0	0	0	0	0	0	0
HTR2A	0	0	0	0	0	0	0	0.411	0	0	0	0	0	0	0
DRD3	0	0	0	0	0	0	0	0.896	0	0	0	0	0	0	0
RTN4R	0.229	0.283	0.281	0.367	0	0	0	0.49	0.259	0	0	0	0	0	0
DISC1	0	0	0.235	0.201	0	0	0.379	0	0	0	0	0	0	0	0
SHANK3	0	0	0	0	0	0.307	0	0.2	0	0	0	0	0.374	0	0
BDNF	0	0	0	0	0	0	0	0	0	0	0	0	0	0	0
DRD4	0.361	0.266	0	0.908	0	0	0	0.884	0	0	0	0	0	0.915	0
WFS1	0	0	0	0	0	0	0	0	0	0	0	0	0	0	0
ZDHHC9	0	0	0	0	0	0	0	0	0	0	0	0	0.339	0	0
NR0B1	0	0	0	0	0	0	0	0	0	0	0	0	0	0	0
MECP2	0	0	0	0	0	0	0	0.946	0	0	0	0	0	0	0
NPY	0	0	0	0.923	0	0	0	0.653	0	0	0	0.2	0	0	0
FTL	0	0	0	0	0	0	0	0	0	0	0	0	0	0	0
CNTF	0	0	0	0	0	0	0.839	0	0	0	0	0	0	0	0
COMT	0.468	0	0.563	0.655	0	0.54	0	0.609	0	0	0	0	0	0	0
SLC1A1	0	0	0	0	0	0	0	0	0	0	0	0	0	0	0
APOE	0.657	0	0	0.274	0	0	0	0.466	0	0	0	0	0	0	0.409
ROGDI	0	0	0	0	0	0.307	0	0	0	0	0	0	0	0	0
RSRC1	0	0	0	0	0	0	0	0	0	0	0	0	0	0	0
KIAA0513	0	0	0	0	0	0	0	0	0	0	0	0	0	0	0
KIAA0391	0	0.227	0.227	0.229	0	0	0	0	0	0	0	0	0	0	0

the candidate gene APOE. The target gene YWHAE score is not taken as it is not interacting with other candidate genes. Similarly, it is done for all candidate genes in respect of the target genes.

4.5.3 Prioritized Genes for Schizophrenia

In Table 16, genes expanded sorting for schizophrenia is done and the highly interacted genes are sorted with the gene names and prioritized in network generation resulting for schizophrenia.

4.5.4 Results and Discussions

Firstly, Sect. 1.1.9.1 gives the interaction scores of the 61 genes. Secondly, in Sect. 1.1.9.2, the target genes (six genes, i.e., GAD1, GSK3B, BDNF, YWHAE, CAMK2B, and COMT) are selected from the pathway interaction use from ENRICHNET tools and the interaction score is calculated with RWR method. Finally, in Sect. 1.1.9.3, the scores are updated according to the targeted. Here, it is total 32 genes to interact and fame the network for disease prioritization.

Taking five topmost genes that cause diseases from this chapter, the data are shown in Table 17.

Table 15 Interaction score updation for schizophrenia

schizopheni a	GAD 1	GSK3B	BDN F	YWHA E	CAMK2 B	COM T	INTEACTION SCORE SUM
MTHFR	0	0	0.202	0	0	0	0.202
PRODH	0	0	0.201	0	0	0.563	0.764
HTR2A	0	0	0.411	0	0	0	0.411
DRD3	0	0	0.896	0	0	0	0.896
RTN4R	0	0	0.49	0	0	0.228	0.718
DISC1	0	0	0	0	0	0	0
SHANK3	0	0	0.2	0	0	0	0.2
BDNF	0	0	0	0	0	0	0
DRD4	0	0	0.884	0	0	0.784	1.668
WFS1	0	0	0	0	0	0	0
ZDHHC9	0	0	0	0	0	0	0
NR0B1	0	0	0	0	0	0	0
MECP2	0	0	0.946	0	0	0	0.946
NPY	0.463	0	0.653	0	0	0.318	1.434
FTL	0	0	0	0	0	0	0
CNTF	0	0	0	0	0	0	0
COMT	0	0	0.609	0	0	0	0.609
SLC1A1	0	0	0	0	0	0	0
APOE	0	0.319	0.466	0	0	0.429	1.214
ROGDI	0	0	0	0	0	0	0
RSRC1	0	0	0	0	0	0	0
KIAA0513	0	0	0	0	0	0	0
KIAA0391	0	0	0	0	0	0	0
QKI	0	0	0	0	0	0	0
NPAS3	0	0	0	0	0	0	0
HS6ST3	0	0	0	0	0	0	0
DBH	0	0	0.347	0	0	0	0.347
DGCR8	0	0	0	0	0	0	0
AHI1	0	0	0.229	0	0	0	0.229

(continued)

Table 15 (continued)

NCDN	0	0	0	0	0	0	0
ABCA13	0	0	0.297	0	0	0	0.297
CAMK2B	0	0	0.43	0	0	0	0.43
DAOA	0	0	0.34	0	0	0	0.34
USP14	0	0	0	0	0	0	0
APOL6	0	0	0	0	0	0	0
APOL5	0	0	0	0	0	0.657	0.657
APOL4	0	0	0	0	0	0.679	0.679
APOL3	0	0	0	0	0	0.462	0.462
DTNBP1	0.307	0	0.364	0	0	0.563	1.234
GCLC	0.8	0	0	0	0	0	0.8
FXYD6	0	0	0	0	0	0	0
MLC1	0.203	0	0	0	0	0	0.203
NOS1AP	0	0	0	0	0	0	0
NRG3	0	0	0	0	0	0	0
GAD1	0	0	0.507	0	0	0.286	0.793
GPR85	0	0	0	0	0	0	0
YWHAE	0	0	0	0	0	0	0
GSK3B	0	0	0.429	0	0	0.229	0.658
FEZ1	0	0	0	0	0	0	0
HOMER3	0	0	0	0	0	0	0
HOMER2	0	0	0.241	0	0	0	0.241
HOMER1	0	0	0.462	0	0	0	0.462
PPP1R1B	0.229	0	0.425	0	0	0.307	0.961
GRM2	0	0	0.379	0	0	0	0.379
GPHN	0.34	0	0.317	0	0	0	0.657
APOL1	0	0	0	0	0	0.714	0.714
RAI1	0	0	0	0	0	0	0
ARSA	0	0	0	0	0	0	0
MTHFR	0	0	0.202	0	0	0	0.202

Table 16 Genes expanded sorting for Schizophrenia

S.NO.	SCHIZOPHRENIA	INTERACTION SCORE SUM
1	DRD4	1.668
2	NPY	1.434
3	DTNBP1	1.234
4	APOE	1.214
5	PPP1R1B	0.961
6	MECP2	0.946
7	DRD3	0.896
8	GCLC	0.8
9	GAD1	0.793
10	PRODH	0.764
11	RTN4R	0.718
12	APOL1	0.714
13	APOL4	0.679
14	GSK3B	0.658
15	APOL5	0.657
16	GPHN	0.657
17	COMT	0.609
18	APOL3	0.462
19	HOMER1	0.462
20	CAMK2B	0.43
21	HTR2A	0.411
22	GRM2	0.379
23	DBH	0.347
24	DAOA	0.34
25	ABCA13	0.297
26	HOMER2	0.241

(continued)

Table 16 (continued)

27	AHI1	0.229
28	MLC1	0.203
29	MTHFR	0.202
30	MTHFR	0.202
31	SHANK3	0.2
32	SHANK3	0.2
33	DISC1	0
34	BDNF	0
35	WFS1	0
36	ZDHHC9	0
37	NR0B1	0
38	FTL	0
39	CNTF	0
40	SLC1A1	0
41	ROGDI	0
42	RSRC1	0
43	KIAA0513	0
44	KIAA0391	0
45	QKI	0
46	NPAS3	0
47	HS6ST3	0
48	DGCR8	0
49	NCDN	0
50	USP14	0
51	APOL6	0
52	FXYD6	0
53	NOS1AP	0

(continued)

Table 16 (continued)

54	NRG3	0
55	GPR85	0
56	YWHAE	0
57	FEZ1	0
58	HOMER3	0
59	RAI1	0
60	ARSA	0
61	SYNGAP1	0

Table 17 Five topmost genes that cause diseases

S.NO.	ADHD GENE	Dementia	mood disorder	OCD	SCHIZOPHRENIA
1	DRD4	APP	AKT1	SLC6A4	DRD4
2	SLC6A3	LRRK2	SLC6A4	COMT	NPY
3	TPH1	SNCAIP	COMT	HTR2A	DTNBP1
4	ADRA2A	NOTCH3	DRD4	CNTNAP2	APOE
5	DRD5	SNCA	HTR1A	BDNF	PPP1R1B

5 Conclusion

In the above sections, we have found the RWR method useful in scoring the interactions with the help of both STRING database and ENRICHNET tool which covers the total allelic variant genes to be tested throughout the steps of initialization and getting scores for all the target genes in determining distance scores minimization and interaction score maximization from the reference genes availability. So, in this respect, RWR method helps us to find genes and to reach to the conclusion of the highly interacted genes network formation for the above disease prioritization. The prioritized genes can be used in any computational model for classification purpose.

References[1]

1. Broy, M. (2002). Software engineering—from auxiliary to key technologies. In M. Broy & E. Dener (Eds.), *Software pioneers* (pp. 10–13). Heidelberg: Springer.
2. Dod, J. (1999). Effective substances. In *The dictionary of substances and their effects*. Royal Society of Chemistry. Available via DIALOG. http://www.rsc.org/dose/title of subordinate document. Cited 15 Jan 1999.
3. Geddes, K. O., Czapor, S. R., & Labahn, G. (1992). *Algorithms for computer algebra*. Boston: Kluwer.
4. Hamburger, C. (1995). Quasimonotonicity, regularity and duality for nonlinear systems of partial differential equations. *Annali di Matematica Pura ed Applicata, 169,* 321–354.
5. Slifka, M. K., & Whitton, J. L. (2000). Clinical implications of dysregulated cytokine production. *Journal of Molecular Medicine*. https://doi.org/10.1007/s001090000086.
6. Dod, J. (1999). In *The dictionary of substances and their effects*. Royal Society of Chemistry. (Available via DIALOG, 1999), http://www.rsc.org/dose/title of subordinate document. Cited 15 Jan 1999.
7. Ibach, H., & Lüth, H. (1996). *Solid-state physics* (2nd ed., pp. 45–56). New York: Springer.
8. Preuss, S., Demchuk, Jr., Stuke, M. *Applied Physics A, 61.*
9. Slifka, M.K., Whitton, J.L. *Journal of Molecular Medicine*. https://doi.org/10.1007/s00109000 0086.
10. Smith, S.E. (1976). In E. Zaimis (Ed.), *Neuromuscular junction,* Vol. 42, p. 593. Handbook of Experimental Pharmacology. Heidelberg: Springer.
11. Calfee, R. C., & Valencia, R. R. (1991). *APA guide to preparing manuscripts for journal publication*. Washington, DC: American Psychological Association.
12. Dod, J. (1999). Effective substances. In *The dictionary of substances and their effects*. Royal Society of Chemistry. Available via DIALOG. http://www.rsc.org/dose/Effective substances. Cited 15 Jan 1999.
13. Harris, M., Karper, E., Stacks, G., Hoffman, D., DeNiro, R., Cruz, P., et al. (2001). Writing labs and the Hollywood connection. *Journal of Film Writing, 44*(3), 213–245.

[1]References may be *cited* in the text either by number (preferred) or by author/year (Make sure that all references from the list are cited in the text. Those not cited should be moved to a separate *Further Reading* section or chapter.). If the citatiion in the text is numbered, the reference list should be arranged in ascending order. If the citation in the text is author/year, the reference list should be *sorted* alphabetically and if there are several works by the same author, the following order should be used:

1. all works by the author alone, ordered chronologically by year of publication
2. all works by the author with a coauthor, ordered alphabetically by coauthor
3. all works by the author with several coauthors, ordered chronologically by year of publication.

The *styling* of references (Always use the standard abbreviation of a journal's name according to the ISSN *List of Title Word Abbreviations*, see http://www.issn.org/en/node/344) depends on the subject of your book:

- The *two* recommended styles for references in books on *mathematical, physical, statistical and computer sciences* are depicted in [1–5] and [6–10].
- Examples of the most commonly used reference style in books on *Psychology, Social Sciences* are [11–15].
- Examples for references in books on *Humanities, Linguistics, Philosophy* are [2, 16–19].
- Examples of the basic Springer Nature style used in publications on a wide range of subjects such as *Computer Science, Economics, Engineering, Geosciences, Life Sciences, Medicine, Biomedicine* are [2, 20–23].

14. O'Neil, J. M., & Egan, J. (1992). Men's and women's gender role journeys: Metaphor for healing, transition, and transformation. In B. R. Wainrig (Ed.), *Gender issues across the life cycle* (pp. 107–123). New York: Springer.
15. Kreger, M., Brindis, C. D., Manuel, D. M., & Sassoubre, L. (2007). Lessons learned in systems change initiatives: benchmarks and indicators. *American Journal of Community Psychology.* https://doi.org/10.1007/s10464-007-9108-14.
16. John, A., O'Connell, D. C., & Kowal, S. (2002). Personal perspective in TV interviews. *Pragmatics, 12,* 257–271.
17. Cameron, D. (1997). Theoretical debates in feminist linguistics: Questions of sex and gender. In R. Wodak (Ed.), *Gender and discourse* (pp. 99–119). London: Sage Publications.
18. Cameron, Deborah. (1985). *Feminism and linguistic theory.* New York: St. Martin's Press.
19. Suleiman, C., O'Connell, D.C., & Kowal, S. (2002). 'If you and I, if we, in this later day, lose that sacred fire…': perspective in political interviews. *Journal of Psycholinguistic Research.* https://doi.org/10.1023/a:1015592129296.
20. Brown, B., & Aaron, M. (2001). The politics of nature. In J. Smith (Ed.), *The rise of modern genomics* (3rd ed.). New York: Wiley.
21. Slifka, M. K., & Whitton, J. L. (2000). Clinical implications of dysregulated cytokine production. *Journal of Molecular Medicine.* https://doi.org/10.1007/s001090000086.
22. Smith, J., Jones, M., Jr., Houghton, L., et al. (1999). Future of health insurance. *New England Journal of Medicine, 965,* 325–329.
23. South, J., & Blass, B. (2001). *The future of modern genomics.* London: Blackwell.

Deep Learning Techniques Dealing with Diabetes Mellitus: A Comprehensive Study

Sujit Kumar Das, Pinki Roy, and Arnab Kumar Mishra

Abstract Deep learning (DL) is an emerging technology in solving various real-life problems in the most efficient way. The increasing computational power makes it capable to handle large amounts of data without much human interactions. The successful applications of the most popular DL models like convolutional neural networks (CNNs), autoencoder (AEs), deep belief network (DBNs), restricted Boltzmann machines (RBMs), and recurrent neural networks (RNNs) in various supervised and unsupervised tasks have opened doors to many information processing tasks. In recent years, the use of DL technique has helped in solving many healthcare-related problems. The capability of handling various types of data and providing abstract representation made DL one of the prominent tools to perform predictive analysis tasks in a disease like diabetes mellitus (DM). We have realized that a detailed discussion is required on these models along with their applications in various problem domains. This will help readers to understand their requirements in advancing health care. In this chapter, we have tried to cover each of the models and figure out how they handle various types of data in medical the domain and made our work easier. This leads us to the discussion on one of the most common diseases in the world "diabetes mellitus," which causes serious complications in the long run if diagnosis and various management measures are not taken on time. Thus, we have tried to give a deep inside view of DL models and algorithms which are helping in DM research problems like early stage detection (diagnosis), DM managements, diabetes retinopathy, and biomarkers identifications.

Keywords Diabetes mellitus (DM) · Deep learning (DL) · Health care · Convolutional neural networks (CNNs) · Restricted Boltzmann machines

S. K. Das (✉) · P. Roy · A. K. Mishra
Department of Computer Science and Engineering, National Institute of Technology, Silchar, India
e-mail: dassujit88@gmail.com

P. Roy
e-mail: pinkiroy2405@gmail.com

A. K. Mishra
e-mail: arnab.mishra.1992@gmail.com

R. Patgiri et al. (eds.), *Health Informatics: A Computational Perspective in Healthcare*,
Studies in Computational Intelligence 932,
https://doi.org/10.1007/978-981-15-9735-0_15

(RBMs) · Deep belief network (DBNs) · Autoencoders (AEs) · Recurrent neural network (RNNs)

1 Introduction

1.1 Deep Learning (DL)

Modern deep learning (DL) technique was first introduced by Hinton [1]. The concept of DL had been around for almost a decade. However, its importance and huge computational power in various research fields gained popularity in the machine learning research communities nearly around 7 years ago [2]. This is when convolutional neural networks (CNNs) achieved the state-of-the-art results on an object recognition challenge popularly known as ImageNet [3]. Hinton's research group had won the ImageNet challenge by achieving 10% more accuracy than the team in second place. Accordingly, after this huge achievement of DL in ImageNet, Google and Baidu have changed their image search engine's algorithms and started using Hinton's DL model. Another significant achievement of DL could be recognized in March 2016, when Google's AlphaGo player had beaten the world's strongest Go game player at that time Lee Se-dol by 4:1 in a game competition organized by Google's DeepMind (DL project) in South Korea [4].

DL is a subfield of machine learning (ML), which has successfully diminished ML's constraints by providing more computational power and capabilities to handle large data in a more precise manner. ML techniques require expertise and proper domain knowledge for better handling of input features through which algorithms can generate patterns and learn from data. It makes ML approaches more expensive, with respect to learning complexity, computational time and cost [5]. The layered and hierarchical structures of DL approaches have given more power to feature engineering [6, 7]. The algorithms allow the greedy approach to learn data representation in a more precise way [8, 9]. Studies have found that better representations of data play significant roles in the performance of classification modeling [10] as well as quality improvement in data samples (generative probabilistic models) [11]. To learn a complicated and more abstract representation of data, the consecutive layers of DL architecture provide the facility to perform nonlinear transformations on its input layer and produce a better representation in the output layer [12]. The layered architecture in DL is generally arranged in a sequence manner and each layer composed of a large number of primitive and nonlinear operations in such a way that the representation in one layer from raw data can be fed into the next layer as inputs. These operations and representations make the whole system quite complex. For classification and recognition tasks, DL models typically follow an unsupervised pretraining and supervised fine tuning strategy for feature engineering and representation of data.

The concept of DL and its different network architectures have evolved from artificial neural network (ANN) and hence working principles of any deep learning networks (DLNs) are similar to ANN. The basic differences between ANN and

DLN are the number of layers and numbers of nodes for each layer, which, in the case of DLNs are more as compared to ANN. The neural network consists of more than three layers of neuron including input and output layer is known as DLN and training of it is DL. Apart from this, DLNs have advantages in feature engineering, better representation, etc., as already mentioned above. There are many definitions of DL, but the most important aspect covered by each definition is it consists of multiple layers and a more abstract representation of features at higher levels of a layer. DL has shown its promise in many application areas like computer vision, natural language understanding, audio processing, phonetic recognition, information retrieval, etc. [13]. In recent years, it has found significant importance in medicine and health care due to the huge amount of data produced every day and the use of digital record storing systems in this domain. Again the capability of processing multiple types of data in a single network in a more efficient way makes it a choice of tool in designing expert systems for advancing health care. Figure 1 is a pictorial representation of DLN, which shows its capability of processing various data types in the same network. Further discussion on DL techniques in health care will be continued in later sections.

The network depicted in Fig. 1 above represents a large-scale network comprising of one input layer (left most), four hidden layers (intermediate layers), and an output layer (right most) with three output nodes. The network is capable of processing different types of data (image, temporal, and multimodal). The lower level hidden layers (HL1 and HL2) learn useful features for each type of data individually. The higher-level hidden layers (HL3 and HL4) take the merged data from the lower-level hidden layers as input and learn a more complex function in the network. Finally, output layer generates the final the output of the network.

Before going into further discussions on the use of DL techniques and tools in the biomedical domain, we have realized that the readers need proper knowledge of popular DL architectures and their application areas in recent times. We have found

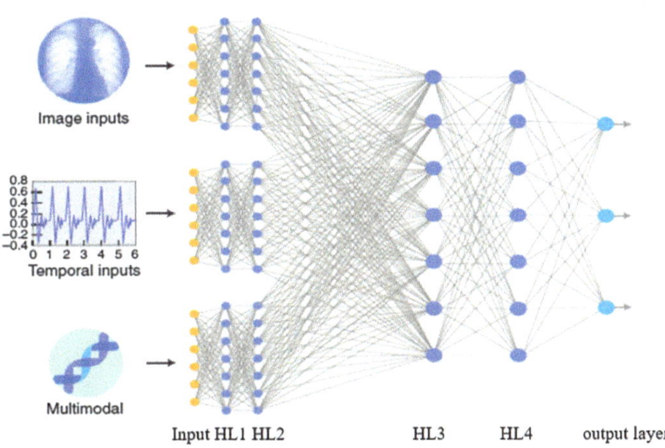

Fig. 1 DL architecture handling different data types

that there are mainly five DL models which are very useful in performing a complex task in various problem areas. These are CNNs, DBNs, autoencoders (AEs), restricted Boltzmann machines (RBMs), and recurrent neural networks (RNNs). Again there are different variations of these models which are designed to perform some specific tasks.

1.1.1 Convolutional Neural Networks (CNNs)

CNNs work based on the principle of conditional probability [14], which makes it fall into discriminative architecture [15]. The use of convolution instead of matrix multiplication in NN reduces the number of weights and makes the network simple and computationally more powerful. More precisely, the advantages of using convolution layers are parameter sharing and sparsity of connections (each output value depends on a small number of inputs). Along with these CNNs also require minimum preprocessing of data. Another unit of complete CNNs is the pooling layer, which can be used to reduce the size of data representation resulting in computation speed and providing considerable robustness to the system by recognizing important features. One of the most popular pooling techniques is max pooling [16] which will be discussed systematically later in this section. Other pooling method can be average (or mean) pooling and median pooling. Third unit of CNNs is a fully connected output layer, similar like any conventional NNs.

Figure 2 has shown a convolution operation of 6×6 input image and 3×3 filter. The filter will go through the entire image and produce a convolved image of 4×4 size. The reason of getting 4×4 convolved image is, only 4×4 positions are possible if a 3×3 filter move across a 6×6 image. More generally, if we have

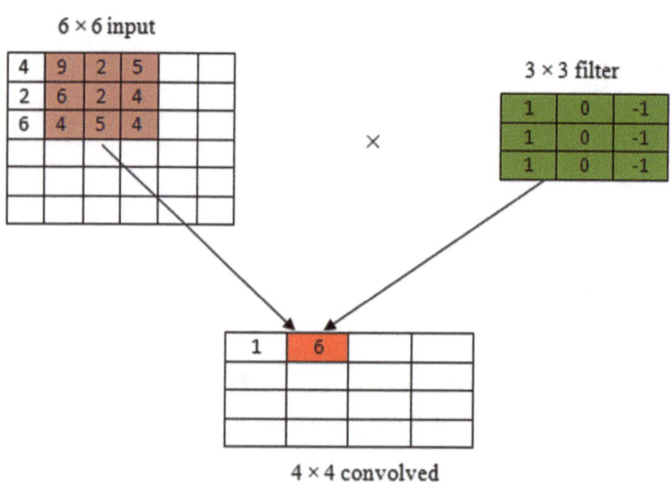

Fig. 2 Convolution operation

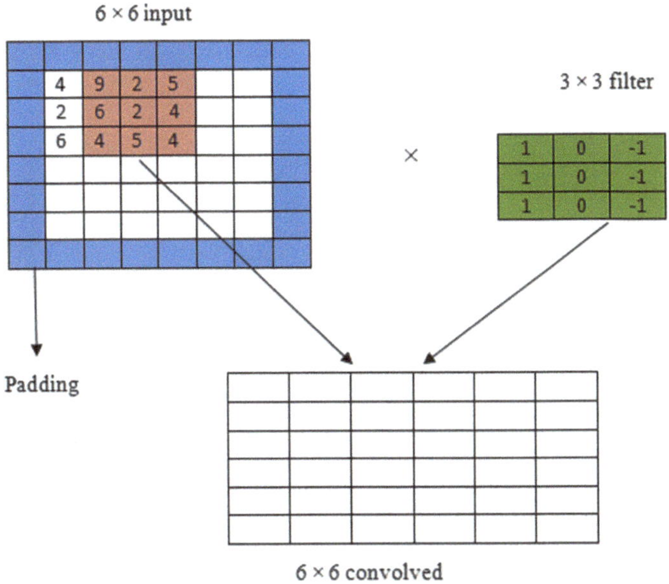

Fig. 3 Padding

$n \times n$ input image and $f \times f$ filter than the size of the convolved image is $(n - f + 1) \times (n - f + 1)$. The movement, how the filter will move across the image, can be considered as a parameter, for example, if it moves 1 pixel at a time, then it is known as stride of 1. Again if we consider the above example of convolution operation, we can easily understand that the pixels in the middle of the input image are covering more number of 3×3 regions compared to the pixels at the edge of the image. This may result in throwing out information from the image. Moreover, performing multiple convolution operations in the image can be a cause of image shrinking problem. Padding can be done before performing convolution to solve image shrinking problem. An example of padding is shown in Fig. 3.

The padding is amount of extra pixels added at the border of an image. In the above example of padding, we have shown of adding extra pixels around the input image. After padding, the resultant convolved image will have following dimension:

$$(n + 2p - f + 1) \times (n + 2p - f + 1)$$

In this case, $n = 6$, $p = 1$ and $f = 3$ therefore we will get 6×6 resultant image. The amount of padding divides the convolution in two categories: valid convolution, where no padding is done, and the other one is same convolution, where the padding is done in such an amount that the size of the input image and the size of the output image remain same. Sometimes to reduce the trainable parameters from a large input, image pooling is done in each depth dimension of image which makes depth of the image unchanged but it helps to reduce the size of the image. The pooling unit is

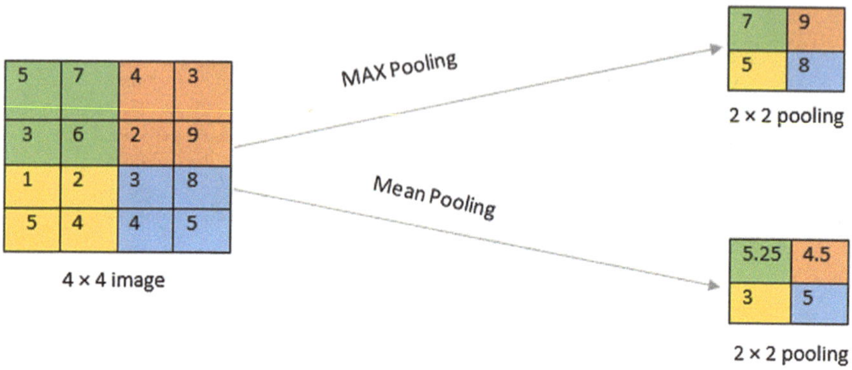

Fig. 4 Pooling operation

an optional layer in CNNs which is placed between two successive convolutional layers. There are many researchers who do not suggest pooling layers and instead of that they prefer using larger stride in convolution layer.

In the pooling operation shown in Fig. 4, a 4 × 4 convolved image has pooled into 2 × 2 after performing two kind of pooling operations. Initially the convolved image has been divided into four regions considering the pooling window. In max pooling, the maximum pixel value is taken and in mean pooling the average pixel values from each region are taken as a resultant pixel value. In the above example, the hyperparameters in the pooling operation are $f = 2$ (for 2 × 2 square in each region) and $S = 2$ (stride).

The output layer, i.e., the third unit of CNNs is a fully connected network which is responsible for generating final classes to be predicted in the output nodes. The output unit of CNNs is identical to basic NNs. The requirement of a fully connected network at the end of CNNs can be understand from the capability of convolution and pooling layers. These two units are responsible only to extract features and reduce parameters from the input image. Generally, a softmax activation function [17] is use in the output nodes of fully connected network. The activation function is responsible to distribute probabilities among the output class labels. Depending on the task needed to perform, in the output layer, a loss function [18] (binary cross-entropy and categorical cross-entropy) is used to compute error in predictions. The general CNN-based architecture is pictorially depicted in Fig. 5.

After many successful applications of CNNs, there are more versions of CNNs that have come out depending on tasks. Dynamic convolutional neural network (DCNN) [19] is such an architecture, which made a huge improvement in NLP tasks like question classification and sentiment classification. Human action recognition from video is another important task in surveillance. Both the spatial and temporal information handling have been done using 3D CNN architecture [20] by performing 3D convolution operation.

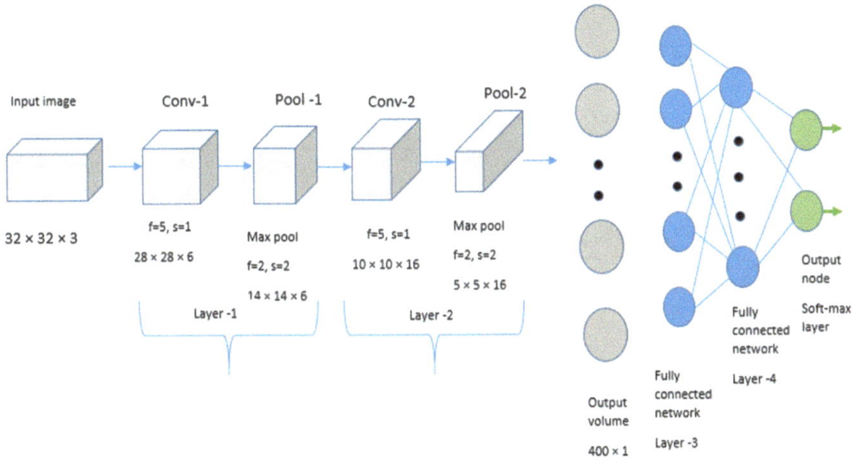

Fig. 5 Complete architecture of CNNs

1.1.2 Restricted Boltzmann Machine (RBM)

The model can be viewed as a stochastic neural network, and it is a probabilistic graphical model. RBM contains two layers: visible layer and hidden layer, where input layer is responsible for containing input nodes of the network and the nodes in hidden layer in responsible for taking care of latent variables or hidden variables of the data and can be viewed as a nonlinear feature detector [21]. RBM is a special category of Boltzmann machine (BM). In BM, the task of learning is performed by adjusting the network parameters. The connections in the processing units are bidirectional and considering the aspects of trying to learn unknown probability distribution makes learning BM difficult in practical approach. The problem in hand of simplifying learning gave birth to RBM, where each neuron in visible layer has a connection with all neurons in hidden layer. The restriction is not having any connections among the neurons in the same layer makes RBM is one of the best improved versions of BM. A typical RBM architecture with m visible nodes and n hidden nodes is shown in Fig. 6.

RBM represents an asymmetric bipartite undirected graph, where $V = \{v_1, v_2, \ldots v_m\}$ is "m" visible units for observable data and $H = \{h_1, h_2, \ldots h_n\}$ is "n" hidden units for capturing latent variables between observed data, $\{b_1, b_2, b_3, \ldots, b_m\}$ and $\{c_1, c_2, c_3, \ldots, c_n\}$ are bias used in visible variable and hidden variable respectively. In case for binary RBM (v, h) belongs to $\{0, 1\}^{m+n}$ and joint probability given by Gibbs distribution as below:

$$p(V, H) = \frac{1}{Z}\sum_{h} \mathrm{e}^{-E(v,h)}$$

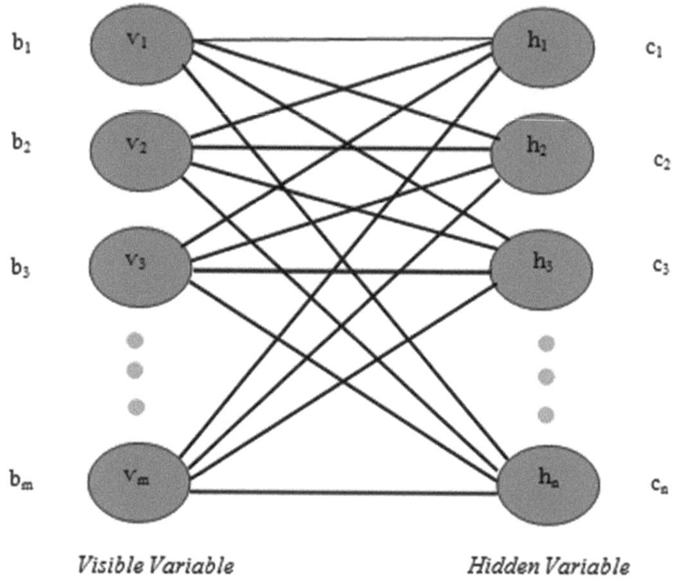

Fig. 6 RBM architecture with m visible and n hidden nodes

Here, "Z" is summation over all possible connections between two layers responsible for making sure that the sum of the entire probability distribution is equal to 1. The value of "Z" can be calculated as:

$$Z = \mathrm{e}^{-E(v_1,h_1)} + \mathrm{e}^{-E(v_2,h_2)} + \ldots + \mathrm{e}^{-E(v_m,h_n)}$$

Therefore, the energy function of the joint configuration (V, H)

$$E(V, H) = -\left(\sum_{i=1}^{n}\sum_{j=1}^{m} x_j w_{ij} h_i + \sum_{j=1}^{m} b_j x_j + \sum_{i=1}^{n} c_i h_i\right)$$

where w_{ij} is real weight associated with the edge connects visible node x_j to a hidden node h_i.

1.1.3 Autoencoders (AEs)

In the area of information processing in 1988, Bourlard and Kamp [22] were able to generate a MLP model in auto-association mode such that the model was capable of doing data compression and dimensionality reduction automatically [24, 25].The motivation of finding auto-association for dimensionality reduction gave birth to an unsupervised learning algorithm named "autoencoder" for code datasets in a more

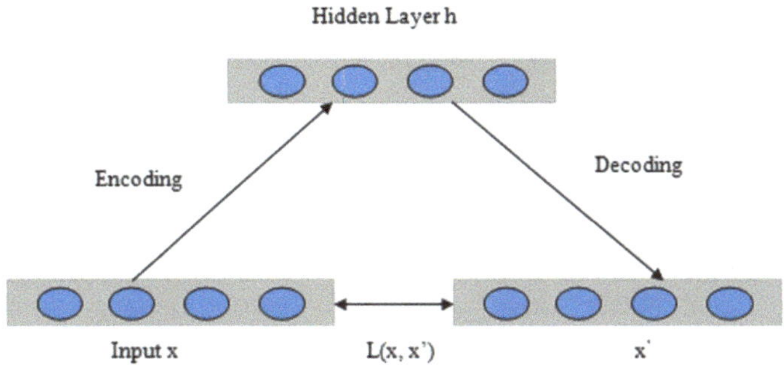

Fig. 7 Systematic diagram of autoencoder

efficient way. AEs have been found very successful in learning generative models of data [23]. The use of encoder and decoder in AE makes the model capable of encoding the input into some more precise representations and also original input can be reconstructed back from the representation without losing any information. Along with providing input into lower dimensions, its capability of extracting useful features and filtering out useless information makes AE a better learner. A pictorial depiction of simple autoencoder architecture is shown in Fig. 7.

Same like MLP, AEs are also a one hidden layer feed-forward neural network architecture. But AEs are for reconstructing the input and MLPs are for prediction of target values. The use of encoder in AEs is to encode the input "x" into hidden representation "h" using formula as below:

$$h = f(wx + b)$$

Similarly, the use of decoder is to decode the "h" representation back to input as below:

$$x' = f'\left(w'h + b'\right)$$

Here, "w" is the weights matrix while converting the input vector "x" to hidden representation "h" and w' is the weights matrix in decoding stage. In general w' is transpose to w matrix. Encoding and decoding function are nonlinear by making use of nonlinear activation functions. The most common nonlinear activation functions are sigmoid, tanh, softsign, and ReLU.

The primary goal is to minimize the reconstruction average error by parameter optimization. To minimize the error or the deviation from $\boldsymbol{x}'$ to x, the error is backpropagated through the network to adjust the weights. In general, standard mean square error (MSE) is taken to measure the reconstruction accuracy. This minimization is known as loss function $\boldsymbol{J}_\theta$ can be written as:

$$J_\theta = \frac{1}{M}\sum_{n=1}^{m}\left(x'^{(i)} - x^{(i)}\right)^2$$

where $x^{(i)}$ is ith training sample. The training of AE can be divided into two stages. In first stage, unsupervised learning is used to learn the features and in the second stage network is fine tuned in supervised manner.

After realizing the usefulness of autoencoder at several tasks in information processing, various attempts have been made to improve its computational power. These attempts have given birth to some new variations of AEs. To mention such variations, one approach can handle noises in the data. To identify the noise in data in 2008, Vincent et al. [26, 27] had come up with DAEs. Initially, they have added noises and trained the AE. It has been found that DAEs are capable of removing noises from the training data automatically makes it robust in nature. Another variation of AEs can be stacked architecture of AEs. The stacked architecture has made the implementation of DAEs easier because with a very little information about the noisy data (type and level), it was capable of removing noisy data from training set. In this era where amount of data generated everyday increasing exponentially shows sparsity in them. Dealing with this in 2006 Poultney et al. [28] have proposed a learning algorithm for AEs by adding nonlinear sparsity between a linear encoder and decoder.

1.1.4 Deep Belief Networks (DBNs)

The mutual dependency between the visible and hidden variables in RBM encouraged researchers to find dependencies between them. This goal had been achieved by Hinton in 2006 and introduced DBNs by stacking RBMs [29]. It composes several layers of stochastic and latent variables. A typical DBN architecture pictorially depicted in Fig. 8.

Here, "V" is visible layer and h_1, h_2, h_3, h_4, h_5 are hidden layers W_1, W_2, W_3, W_4, and W_5 are weights. For unlabeled data, DBNs have been found to be more effective. The training of DBNs is similar like stacked autoencoder which is in two stages. In the first stage, initial parameters are trained in greedy layer-by-layer approach. In the next stage, tuning of parameters is carried out in supervised manner using labeled data and a softmax function at final layer. Taking a stack of RBM in DBNs, it increases the upper bound of log-likelihood and accordingly improves learning abilities. In stacked of RBMs, the learning is done in bottom-up approach (in our example from left to right) and the features extracted by the topmost layer (right most) are then backpropagated to the lower layers for better learning [23].

There are some variations of DBNs based on tasks like for high-dimensional and highly structured data a Gaussian kernel had been used by Salakhutdinov and Hinton [30]. Due to the difficulty in modifying learning process in large-scaled datasets, Deep convex network (DCN) has been proposed by Deng and Yu [31], which consists of variety of layered modules. In DCN, the lowest module has two linear layers and

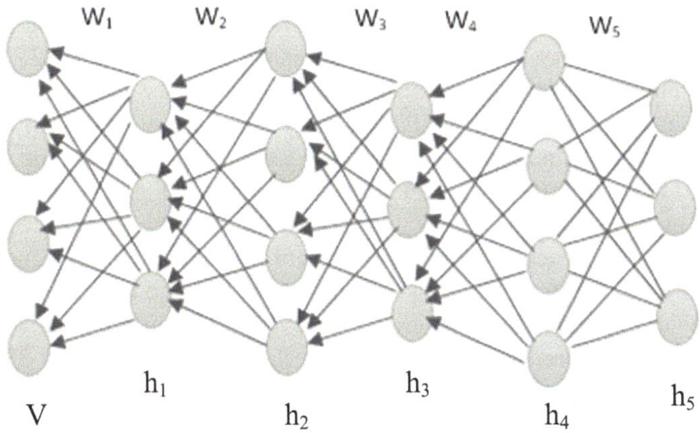

Fig. 8 Deep belief network (DBN)

a single nonlinear layer. The two linear layers are responsible for taking care of inputs and outputs. The single nonlinear layer contains input variables. DCN learns in a batch mode fashion, which makes it capable of parallel learning and hence scalability improves.

1.1.5 Recurrent Neural Networks (RNNs)

RNN is an unsupervised DL architecture, suitable to learn features for time series data. It is capable of learning features by considering the previous states stored in the internal nodes of the network. This time step-based unrolling is shown in Fig. 9.

Here, $(x_0, x_1 \ldots x_{t-1}, x_t, x_{t+1})$ are inputs and $(O_0, O_1 \ldots O_{t-1}, O_t, O_{t+1})$ are outputs at time step $(t_0, t_1 \ldots t_{t-1}, t_t, t_{t+1})$, respectively. To get the current hidden state, RNN uses the present input and previous hidden state.

$$s_t = f(x_t, s_{t-1})$$

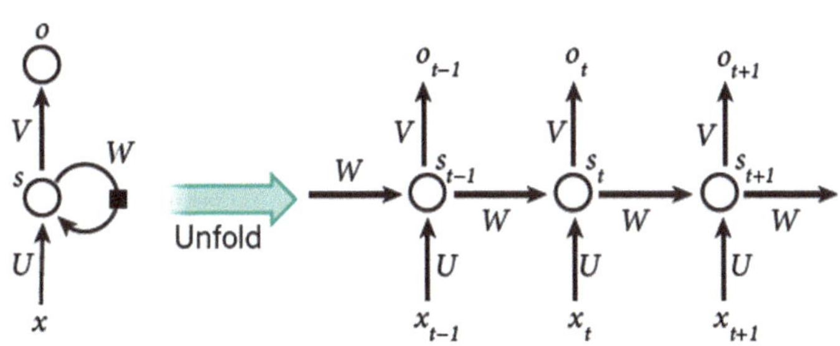

Fig. 9 RNN with unfolding view

where f is encoder function. RNN is a very powerful dynamic learning model but due to gradient vanishing or exploding its training becomes difficult [32, 33]. Thus, preserving long-term dependencies using RNN were not possible until the concept of augmenting the network with explicit memory had come into picture. Long short-term memory (LSTM) networks in which using special hidden units the inputs are remembered for long time [34]. Another memory module augmentation in RNN is "tape-like" memory where RNN has the ability to choose whether to "read from" or "write to" is known as neural turing machine [35]. The use of tape-like memory not only helped RNN to remember long-term decencies but also improved its abilities in reasoning and symbol manipulation tasks. RNN and its different variations have great success in many tasks like NLP, MT, speech recognition, etc. [36–38].

2 Diabetes Mellitus

Diabetes mellitus (DM) is a metabolic disorder having various causes, which can be characterized by chronic hyperglycemia [39] from defects in insulin (produced by pancreas of human body) production, utilization of insulin produced, or both. The defect in insulin disturbs carbohydrate, fat, and protein metabolism in body [40]. Focusing on DM in the late 1970, World Health Organization (WHO) [41] and National Diabetes Data Group [42] had introduced some new dimensions of classification and diagnostic criteria in front of the world. These new dimensions of looking at DM by the individual organization made more chaotic situations as disease categorization and use of oral glucose volumes for diagnostic purpose of the disease were not similar in their reports. Later, both the organizations had come to some similar conclusions by modifying their reports in 1985 [43]. But on the path of getting similar conclusions by two organizations, more and new findings were added in etiological information and DM data. They have also recognized some issues in disease classification and in diagnostic criteria which were immediately needed to be consider for re-examined. Later, in 1997 [44], American Diabetes Association (ADA) and WHO had resolved those issues and came to an acceptable conclusion. In 1980 [3], the experts' committee of WHO had suggested the classification of diabetes into two primary categories IDDM or type-1 and NIDDM or type-2. Five years later in 1985 [43], they have suggested again a few modifications in classifications. They have removed the terms type-1 and type-2. Along with removing these terms, they have introduced a new malnutrition-related diabetes mellitus (MRDM) and included other types and gestational diabetes mellitus [2]. This classification was widely accepted around the globe and makes it considered in the tenth revision of International classification of diseases (ICD) in 1992. Kuzuya and Matsuda [45] have suggested diabetes classifications based on clinical stages and etiological characteristics. Clinical stages have taken care of the characteristics of different stages during clinical tests and etiology categorized the disease from better understanding of causes. We have concluded all these classifications into final types of DM which

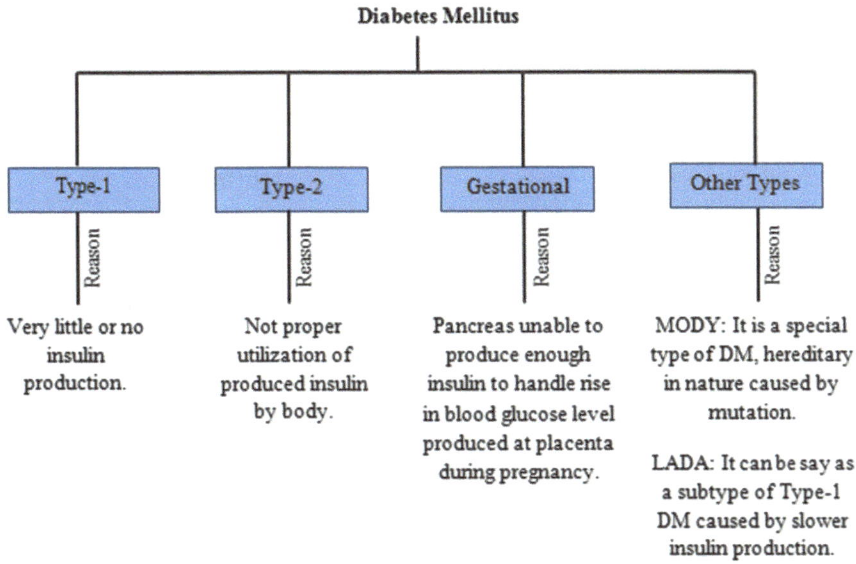

Fig. 10 Diabetes classification

are presently accepted throughout the world. The classification of DM is shown in Fig. 10.

Over time, if DM is left untreated, it may cause long-term damage, dysfunction, and failure of different organs [40, 46]. DM may lead an adult toward stroke and nerve damages. The damages of small blood vessels in retina may cause for a permanent blindness. Research has found that DM is one of the most leading causes of kidney failures. Some preventive measures can be taken to reduce the burden of DM. These include maintaining healthy body weight, involving in physical activities, having healthy diet, avoiding sugar, saturated fats, and use of tobacco. Classification of diabetes with reason of occurring is depicted in Fig. 10.

The International Diabetes Federation (IDF) Atlas edition in 2017 has come with an alarming statistics of DM in the world. It has reported that in 2017 the number of diabetes affected population is 425 million and this number will be increase to 629 million by 2045.

India comes in the region of Southeast Asia in IDF and it has been found the India's contribution in carrying diabetes-affected population is highest among all Southeast Asian countries. Each 1 in 12 adults in this region age of 18–99 of total 84 million populations is living with diabetes, and this figure is estimated to rise 156 million in 2045. It has been found that among this population about 58% people who are living with DM are undiagnosed, resulted 1.3 million deaths in 2017 [47] (Table 1).

IDF has reported that currently India carrying the largest population of people living with diabetes in Southeast Asia region. The mortality due to diabetes can be reduced significantly if early stage detection of the disease, better risk management

Table 1 Diabetes mellitus statistics of top five countries in Southeast Asia

Country name	Diabetes population
India	74,047,266
Bangladesh	7,349,526
Sri Lanka	1,248,310
Nepal	679,207
Mauritius	236,795

system, and proper monitoring can be done. However, for all these tasks, it is very important for physicians to have access of high-quality decision support systems with advanced technological tools. The recent advancement of DL techniques has shown exceptional results in the field of DM along with other healthcare-related problems for the development of robust data-driven automatic medical expert systems.

3 Challenges of Using DL in Health care

Supervised learning has always encouraged by many works in ML and DL. In recent years, scopes of unsupervised learning have extended due to the significant developments in the area of DL. These developments have come with some challenges and the opportunities for the DL research communities. In general, these challenges are almost similar in all kind of tasks where DL techniques are used, but in this section we will highlight a few of them which exist in solving problems of healthcare area.

Inadequate training data: DL models are known for handling huge number of parameters in a network. While estimation of these large parameters are to be done accurately, training of a model needs enough number of training samples. Although there is no specific mention about how much data is sufficient for training a DL model, but according to the thumb rule, the standard amount is 10 times to the number of parameters needs to be estimated. A major portion of the population in the world does not have access to primary health services. Therefore, getting sufficient amount of data, which can help in designing DL models is most of the time unfavorable situation. Moreover, considering the variability in diseases, understanding of healthcare domain becomes more complicated compared to other domain like image processing, computer vision, speech processing, etc. Consequently, availability of healthcare-related data to train a DL model, which can provide robust and significant results, is one of the first and the most complicated aspects.

Quality of data: The real-world medical data are not cleaned, sparse, unstructured like sequences of time series, DNA audio video signals, etc. Also, these are heterogeneous in most of the time. Any predictive model with the aim of good performance needs good quality of data. Thus, adequate domain knowledge and applying various preprocessing techniques like missing value handling, noise removal, irrelevant features elimination strategies, etc., are prerequisite before feed healthcare data into DL models.

Handling non-static data: The healthcare data can be received in real time from multiple sources, which may include blood glucose monitoring, blood sugar, brain activity signals, and so on. It is very important of DL to understand and process these time changing data. Learning from these continuous data is a challenging task. Although some of the DL architecture like LSTM and hybrid models are doing great in analyzing non-static data, further explorations are required to handle them which can contribute significantly.

Domain constraints: The medical domains are not completely explored yet. The causes and the progress of many diseases are not known yet in an exact way like other domains. DL models required large amount data to train. Sometimes unavailability of experts to label these data makes this process even more complicated.

Interpretability: The working principles of DL are often blackbox in nature. However, health care is a very sensitive area, where the working nature of an algorithm should be well explanatory to gain its acceptance by medical professionals and naive users. Moreover, requirement powerful hardware processing units to analyze large medical data makes it more difficult.

4 Deep Learning in Health care

In recent times, biomedical data are available in large volume. But most of these available data are unstructured in nature. To provide better facility in the area of health care, use of these data in an efficient way can play a significant role in the society. Advancement of technological development like in DL considering its tremendous success in other problem domains has encouraged researchers to make use of DL techniques in biomedical informatics. The ultimate goal to developed reliable medical tools will help medical practitioners for better decision making in terms of speed, accuracy, and cost. The use of data-driven approaches although applied in many ML applications in different problem domains, higher dimensionality, temporal dependency, and heterogeneity of medical data create very difficult path for traditional ML approaches [48, 49]. Therefore, without proper domain knowledge, it has become very difficult to use ML algorithm for these tasks. DL, a representation learning approach, is quite well suited in such situations with a little domain knowledge. The era of using DL techniques in health care had started with the announcement of solving healthcare-related problems using DL approaches by Google DeepMind [50] and Enlitic's deep intelligence approach for X-ray and CT scan [51] images. In this section, we will see the use of DL techniques in health care with respect to medical imaging, electronic health records (EHRs), and genomics.

4.1 Medical Imaging

The primary goal of using DL technique is to make the algorithms capable of learning features automatically and optimally from the data at hand. The traditional ML techniques have failed to do the task in most of the times considering the largeness of medical data. The use of images has given a new direction in performing various cognitive tasks in medical image analysis. The success of LeNet in the year of 1995 [52] for handwritten digit recognition task attracted DL research community for the first time to think about the use of DL techniques in clinical images. Later after a revolution of using CNN in ImageNet challenge in 2012, researchers started using CNN in medical image analysis and from then CNN has become a choice of DL model for the entire research community in context to image-based expert systems. The task of using medical image primarily includes segmentation, classification, registration, recognition, detection, etc. In this article, our primary goal is to give a comprehensive view of DL techniques in diabetes mellitus disease, and we are not highlighting all medical imaging tasks. To highlight a few recent works, we have searched PubMed by giving query "deep learning" and "medical image" and as a result we have found that a total of 57 articles has been published in the year of 2019. Among these articles, we have considered tasks specifics articles to cover maximum problem area of medical imaging data. Summary of the chosen articles is listed in Table 2.

In details, U-Net is considered as a significant network for image segmentation due to its low memory capacity. Moreover Li et al. [53] proposed an innovative structure, known as up-skip connection to enhance the information flow between encoder and decoder. Despite the success of this proposed architecture, further explorations in post-processing steps and data imbalance are required to improve significant segmentation performance. Rehman et al. [54] have combined traditional image processing methods with the latest DL approach in FU-Net to address the issue of vertebrae segmentation in CT image data. Further, use of this approach in multimodal dataset and training on larger samples requires more exploration. Limited data for training a model opens opportunities for data augmentation. Yang et al. [55] have successfully improved ultrasound image segmentation using dual path U-Net after generating real-time image augmentation. The use of data augmentation techniques like GANs [57] technique in medical imaging and CNNs architecture [58] shows a significant contribution in various segmentation and image classification tasks.

4.2 Electronic Health Records (EHRs)

EHR is an outcome of storing large patient-specific information generated in the healthcare sectors which are in computer-readable form [59]. Presently in the world considering the vast amount of structured (e.g., encoded diagnosis) and unstructured (e.g., clinical narratives by doctors) data contained by EHR system, there are

Table 2 Summary of articles on medical imaging data

Authors	Application	Model	Dataset	Result
Li et al. [53]	Brain tumor segmentation	U-Net with up-skip connection and inception module	BRATS 2015 BRATS 2016	BRATS 2015: 2.6%, 3.9%, and 5.2% BRATS 2017: 2.8%, 3.7%, and 8.1% higher than U-Net
Rehman et al. [54]	Vertebral bone segmentation osteoporotic fractures	FU-net (region-based label set with deep learning framework)	CSI 2014: lumber and thoracic CSI 2016: with 10 annotated CT datasets	CSI 2014: dice score 96.4 ± 0.8% no fractures and 92.8 ± 1.9% with fractured CSI 2016: dice score 95.2 ± 1.9% on 15 CT and 95.4 ± 2.1% on total 25 CT
Yang et al. [55]	Ultrasound image segmentation of arterial walls	Fully convolutional neural network-based dual path.	IVUS 40 MHz and 20 MHz B-mode 43 volumes	IVUS 40 MHz: 0.87 and 0.86 Jaccard measure (JM) for Lumen 0.82 mm and 1.07 mm Hausdorff distance (HD) for media IVUS 20 MHz: 0.90 JM and 0.92 JM for Lumen. 0.25 mm and 0.30 mm (HD) for media
Soomro et al. [56]	Segmentation of colorectal tumor in 3D MRI images	U-Net (DPU-Net) 3D multiscale densely connected CNN	T2-weighted 3D colorectal MRI images	Before post-processing: Dice similarity coefficient (DSC) = 0.8406 ± 0.0191 Recall rate (RR) = 0.8513 ± 0.0201
Guan and Loew [57]	Breast cancer detection form mammogram images	Generative adversarial network (GAN) and CNN	Digital database for screening mammography (DDSM)	After post-processing: DSC = 0.8585 ± 0.0184 RR = 0.8719 ± 0.0195 ASD = 2.5401 ± 2.402

(continued)

Table 2 (continued)

Authors	Application	Model	Dataset	Result
Alaskar et al. [58]	Automated ulcer detection	Convolutional neural network (CNN)	Wireless capsule endoscopy (WCE) images	Classification accuracy: 100%

various applications that have been made for providing better healthcare facilities like predicting future patients outcome, patient stratification, integrating genetics, disease co-occurrences, and many more. To give a more specific view to the readers, we have listed out some of the very recent works carried out in EHR systems. We have searched PubMed by giving queries "deep learning" and "electronic health records," "deep learning" and "electronic medical records," "deep learning" and "EHR." The summary of our findings is listed in Table 3.

Utilizing EHR data to answer some critical questions like chronic condition of patients' next hospital visit, learning time decay factors for medical codes, status of the disease progression, etc., was always fascinating and challenging tasks. Many researches have been carried out to studies that deal with these issues. Bai et al. [60]

Table 3 Summary of articles on electronic health records (EHRs)

Author	Application	Model	Dataset	Results
Bai et al. [60]	Prediction of the main diagnosis of a future hospitalization	Timeline with RNN	SEER-medicare linked database	Inpatients data: F1 score: 0.235 Mixed data: F1 score: 0.473
Li and Yu [61]	Single-domain and multidomain medication and adverse drug event relation extraction	MLP and CapNet. fully shared (FS), shared-private (SP), and adversarial training (ADV) modes	MADE1.0 cancer corpus and cardio corpora MADE1.0 and i2b2 challenges	CapNet gave 87.2% in F1 in MADE1.0
Li et al. [62]	Automatically classification of whether an EHR note sentence contains a bleeding event	Hybrid CNN and LSTM autoencoder (HCLA)	878 EHR notes: 76,577 sentences and 562,630 word-tokens.	HCLA achieved 0.957 area under receiver curve and 0.938 F1 score
Reddy and Delen [63]	Prediction of hospital readmission for lupus patients	Recurrent neural network (RNN)–long short-term memory (LSTM)	Cerner health facts EMR	AUC = 0.70, Sensitivity = 74.49%, Specificity = 56.61% Accuracy = 70.54%

have proposed a DL approach named timeline which outperformed state-of-the-art models based on RNN. The relation between medication and adverse drug events helps in management of diseases. Li and Yu [61] have proposed a DL approach by combining MLP and capsule network (CapNet) to find single-domain and multidomain relation extraction from EHR notes. In another work, Li et al. [62] have proposed a DL-based classification approach to find bleeding events from EHR notes. It may help in drug-safety surveillance and pharmacovigilance. Analysis of longitudinal EHR data and making use of them in answering various problems are challenging tasks. Reddy and Delen [63] have used RNN and long short-term memory (LSTM) to predict rehospitalization of lupus patients in 30 days. The EHR data itself make DL tasks very challenging, due to their unorganized structure. Therefore, to get significant performances in DL approaches, it is very important to explore data preprocessing techniques. Moreover, making use of the latest DL approaches may give better predictive capabilities to the models.

4.3 Genomics

The genomics data are increasing exponentially in recent years, and the task of finding hidden relationships or having a more demonstrative insight to data has become perplexed for traditional ML techniques. Demanding a more expressive model, DL has become a method of choice considering its vast contribution in related fields. The applications of genomics include finding associations between genotype and phenotype [64], discovering biomarkers for patient stratification [65], predicting the function of genes [66], and charting biochemically active genomic regions such as transcriptional enhancers [67]. To have a brief idea on the applications of genomics how DL techniques have been used in very recent time, we have listed some of the major research findings in Table 4.

To understand some biological processes like DNA damages, transcriptional activation and chromosome packaging detection of histone modification have become a demanding research area in recent years. To get efficient performance, traditional approaches require high cost and long procedures. Therefore, requirements of DL approaches fit in this situation to solve these issues. Yin et al. [68] have proposed a DL framework named DeepHistone using customized CNN to predict histone modification. Though they have achieved significant results, further improvement may be achieved by introducing embedding representation of DNA sequence, incorporating RNN architecture, and finding sequence patterns. Tian et al. [69] have proposed a CNN-based approach to identify genome-wide DNA methylation, which helps in the drug development process. Their approach successfully achieved methylation prediction of CpG loci from local DNA sequences. Therefore, it has overcome difficult pre-processing and at same time covered all the ranges of methylation values. In some other cancer-related research, the analysis of the association of genomic features [70] and drug response prediction, from integrated genomic profiles, [71] is significant.

Table 4 Summary of articles on genomics

Authors	Application	Model	Dataset	Result
Yin et al. [68]	Prediction of histone modification	DeepHistone: A DNN module consists of DNA module, DNase module, and joint module	ChIP-seq peak files regarding the 15 epigenomes and 7 histone markers	auROC score over 15 epigenomes is 0.9 For histone marker auROC score is 0.87
Tian et al. [69]	Determination of genome-wide DNA methylation	Methylation regression CNN	Whole genome bisulfite sequencing (WGBS) data (GEO, GSM432685) of H1 ESC	Regression error is smaller in hypermethylation CpG islands: accuracy = 93.2%, AUC = 0.96
Liu et al. [70]	Association analysis of deep genomic features for breast cancer	Denoising autoencoders (DA)	The cancer genome atlas (TCGA) and copy number alteration (CNA)	Non-CpG islands: accuracy = 93.8%, AUC = 0.97
Chiu et al. [71]	Drug response prediction of tumor from integrated genomic profile	DeepDR: three deep neural networks	Cancer cell line encyclopedia (CCLE) and the cancer genome atlas (TCGA)	DA can efficiently extract genomic features, which can improve significance of features in breast cancer MSE for testing 1.98 log-scale

5 Deep Learning in Diabetes Mellitus

The pathway of achieving significant success in developing cost-effective, widely acceptable, and reliable system makes it one of the primary research areas in current time. Along with disease prediction task, work on diabetes diagnosis and management system has its own progress focusing on identification of biomarkers which are strongly related with the onset and disease progress, identification of a person being at high risk of developing diabetes in future, detection of the disease at early stage to facilitate appropriate treatment, early intervention to predict risk of long run complications, providing the facility of selecting optimal treatment to the patients, monitoring glycemia [72]. In this chapter, we will focus on discussing DL techniques in context of different subtasks, which are helping in reducing diabetes mellitus proportion in the world population.

5.1 Early Stage Disease Prediction/Classification

We discussed in the earlier section how DM affected all over the world and its long-term complications on patients. Therefore, an early stage detection of the disease surely helps in reducing diabetes mortality. There are various attempts that have been already made to provide automated systems which are capable of predicting this disease at early stage. Among those highlighting, some of the recent works where DL techniques have been precisely used hopefully, able to give readers a constructive view on the use of advanced model in handling such problems in medical fields. The concept of information gain (IG) in dimensionality reduction helps by giving more importance to the relevant features and putting them into a ranking category shows a significance improvement in prediction accuracy with deep neural network architecture. The dataset has been used Pima Indian diabetes (PID) dataset having 768 female diabetes patients' records. There are total eight attributes and using IG ranked the attributes. Among eight attributes, best five attributes are chosen which are: plasma glucose, body mass index, Age, two hours serum insulin (muU/ml), and triceps skin fold thickness (μU/ml). DNN architecture contains 5-layer structure with 12, 30, 50, 30, 12 units ReLU activation function which is used to provide nonlinearity. The first rank attribute after IG found plasma glucose, which is given as input into the DNN to train other attributes. After 3200 iterations using 10-fold cross-validation the classification accuracy has been found 90.26% [73]. Data fuzzification to improve diabetes classification has been tried. Fuzzification of data converted the inputs into matrix form, where columns represent features and row represents fuzzy values. The fuzzy matrix then has fed into the CNN module for classification of the disease. It has been found that fuzzification gave better performance than classical NN and CNN structure [74]. MLP has been used for many predictive analysis tasks. The training and setting networks into a suitable one to improve prediction accuracy has taken its own place in solving this problem, four combinations by increasing nodes in hidden layers [75]. DNN architecture has been tried out in classifying diabetic and non-diabetic patients on PIMA diabetes dataset. Before training the DNN, network correlation has been found among the attributes of the dataset. The DNN architecture with four hidden layers of 12, 16, 16, 14 nodes, respectively, found the best combination with eight input nodes and one output node to gain good classification accuracy. The ReLU activation function has been used in the network model. Using fivefold and 10-fold cross-validation, the accuracy on the test sets along with other measurement parameters like sensitivity, specificity, F1 score, and MCC has been calculated for both validation schemes. Data overfitting seems to be an important factor which can reduce accuracy in a predictive task. To deal with overfitting use of dropout layer before fully connected network makes the network capable of learning multiple representations of data. The layers in the network having nodes are hindered from co-adapting well and reduce overfitting. Such architecture with three layers includes one input (64 nodes), one hidden (32 nodes), and one output (1 node) layers, and dropout layers have been proposed to improve prediction accuracy. In the input layer ReLU and in output layer softmax activation function

Table 5 Summary of diabetes diagnosis tasks on PIMA diabetes dataset

Authors	Model	Result
Huang and Lu [73]	Information gain DNN	Accuracy = 90.26%
Deshmukh et al. [74]	Fuzzification of data with CNN	Prediction accuracy better than classical NN and CNN Average accuracy = 86.67%
Kumar and Manjula [75]	8-128-128-1 MLP architecture	Fivefold cross-validation: Accuracy: 98.04, F1 score: 0.99 sensitivity: 98.80 MCC: 0.96 specificity: 96.64
Ayon et al. [76]	Four hidden layers DNN with 12,16,16,14 nodes, respectively	10-fold cross validation: Accuracy: 97.27, F1 score: 0.98, sensitivity: 97.80, MCC: 0.94, specificity: 96.27
Ashiquzzaman et al. [77]	DNN with dropout	Prediction accuracy: 88.41%

have been used. The dropout rate in the first two layers was 25% and in the final layer it has been increased to 50% to solve overfitting problem. Finally, this combination of DNN has given prediction accuracy of 88.41% on PIMA diabetes dataset [77]. Summary of articles on diabetes diagnosis is listed in Table 5.

To give a comprehensive view on other diabetes-related problems solved using DL techniques, we searched MedPub by giving query "deep learning" and "diabetes mellitus" one of the most popular search engines for articles on biomedical research. We have tried to cover research findings from 2016 to April, 2019, by selecting those articles based of various subdomains of DM. Among them one of the famous is diabetes retinopathy. It is a diabetes complication that damages the blood vessels of light sensitive tissue in retina. Early detection of these changes in retina can help in not occurring further complications like blindness. Microaneurysms (MA) are tiny red dot occurred in retina of a diabetic patient which lead to blot hemorrhages (HEM). These two are to indicate the beginning of diabetes. The summary table for detecting MA and HEM is given in Table 6.

Table 6 MA detection methods using DL

Authors	Model details	Dataset	Result and Discussion
Orlando et al. [78]	CNN ensemble Deep learning	MESSIDOR, DIARETDB1, E-Ophtha	Sensitivity 91.09% (MESSIDOR)
Dai et al. [79]	Multisieving CNN, image-to-text mapping	DIARETDB1	Precision 99.7%, recall 87.8%
Harangi et al. [80]	Ensemble-based NN (DCNN)	e-Ophtha and ROC	AUC 0.8335
Quellec et al. [81]	ConvNets with backpropagation	DIARETDB1, e-Ophtha	ROC 0.9542

Table 7 HEM detection methods using DL

Authors	Model details	Dataset	Result and Discussion
van Grinsven et al. [82]	Fast CNN, selective data sampling	KAGGLE, MESSIDOR	ROC = 0.894, ROC = 0.972
Khojasteh et al. [83]	CNN based	DIARETDB1, e-Ophtha	Accuracy 97.3% (DIARETDB1) and 86.6% (e-Ophtha)
Kar et al. [84]	Curvelet differential Evolution algorithm	DIARETDB1, MESSIDOR	Sensitivity 97.67%, specificity 97.74%

Combination of low-level handcrafted and high-level CNN-based features gives more predictive powers in decision making. In such a work, Orlando et al. [78] have proposed feature fusion method and random forest classifier-based approach to identify red lesion in diabetic retinopathy from fundus images. Harangi et al. [80] have proposed a decision fusion approach by taking multiple DCNNs and observed that it outperformed individual models' performances in red lesion identification in diabetic retinopathy. Some of the other microaneurysms identification using DL approaches have shown significant results. It creates opportunities for the research community to explore various DL architectures in this area.

For the management of diabetes, it is very important to track blood glucose status in the human body. The summary of HEM detection using DL is listed in Table 7.

Grinsven et al. [87] have proposed a hybrid approach by combining a multi-layer CNN and a modified RNN. CNN network has been used to capture the feature of multidimensional time series and the function of RNN was to analyze the previous sequential data to predict blood glucose. Although the proposed approach has achieved significant performances, they have observed that upon increasing prediction horizons the prediction of glucose decreased. In another work, to find the pathologic signs of diabetic retinopathy, Parham Khojasteh et al. [83] have proposed a CNN-based framework. The objective was to find exudate, microaneurysm, and hemorrhage from fundus images. The use of multiple datasets and testing strategy along with use of patch and image-based analysis of fundus was two significant strengths of this work. Although they have achieved significant performances, the overlapping situation between microaneurysm and hemorrhage made identification complex. This has been considered as one of the limitations of the dataset being used. Kar et al. [84] have proposed sequential and intelligent steps for automatic identification of lesions in diabetic retinopathy. Their approach has included step-by-step processes of vessel extraction and optic disk removal, preprocessing, candidate lesion detection and post-processing. Although this approach has outperformed state-of-the-art methods, it has shown weaker results in red lesion identification due to appearance of them in darker patches.

Along with these diabetes retinopathy prediction tasks, disease management by predicting patient state prediction is an important subtask of diabetes research. Blood glucose (BG) is an important biomarker for DM and the proper management of BG is essential to fight against the disease progression. Li et al. [85] proposed a hybrid system composing of CNN, LSTM, and RNN and names the proposed architecture as CRNN, which is used to monitor the BG for diabetes type-1 patients. High blood sugar level causes higher glycemic index in human body. Maintaining blood sugar level can be done by physical exercises and proper diet. Diagnosis of glycemic index is a difficult task. But advancement of DL techniques like DBN [86] with the help of sensor-based network made it possible to diagnose glycemic index of human body by food habits. It has been found that glycemic index can be reducing to 85% with such models. Hypoglycemia is a situation, where low blood glucose level is common in type-1 diabetes patients, especially in children. Recognition of this at the onset has become very important to reduce further disease complications. Physiological parameters like heart rate (HR) and correct QT interval are essential to the diagnosis hypoglycemia. Using these parameters, recently DBN-based idea has been proposed by San et al. [87] to diagnosis hypoglycemia, which has been identified as a significant finding in detection of the condition in children body.

6 Future Directions of DL in Health care

DL filed in solving real-life problems is very new and hence it warrants large research scope. Most of the time human and animal leanings are unsupervised in nature. The advancement of DL opens the door to explore unsupervised learning techniques. Particularly in medical domain designing advanced expert systems, developing new algorithms for learning from data, which can go neck to neck with human expertise. But an affordable cost and reliability of the facilities are challenging. Furthermore, with not having sufficient medical records to serve advanced models and algorithms is a matter of concern. There are no doubts on the achievement of existing DL models in solving problems of health care. But there are many scope and opportunities that have come up to design other advanced DL models or improvements in existing models. We hope DL models with advanced algorithms will work in feature enrichment by which overcoming limited data availability, it can perform well enough. In the same way considering the sensitive nature of patients' information, providing a federated interface using DL techniques has its own research scope. Another area of research can be incorporating expert knowledge in DL models in solving healthcare problems to give proper direction to achieve the solutions.

7 Conclusion

The advancement of technology brings an opportunity to extend its hands in solving biomedical problems by providing expert systems and algorithms to assist medical practitioners. In this chapter firstly, we have tried to give a deep inside view of popularly used DL technologies to solve real-life problems. The architectural representations, their working principles, and their developments during the course of time have been discussed. Secondly, to realize the current scenario of diabetes patients through the world, we have included a brief introduction of diabetes mellitus with its statistics and complications. We have also included problem areas in health care, where DL techniques have showed its interest and successfully implemented to provide assistance in solving them in cost-effective and reliable manner. After discussing the problems areas in a generalized way we have focused on different possible solutions to reduce the diabetes mellitus-affected population. We have found that just automatic diagnosis of the disease is not only problem area. The management of the disease is also a great concern, where DL has been used in recent years. We have tried to cover such many problems areas related to diabetes mellitus and their possible solution using DL. Along with these, we have realized researchers must understand the challenges those can be face during solving problems using DL. Therefore, we have also pointed out the challenges of DL in healthcare problems domains. Lastly, we have included the future directions of DL in a generalized way. We hope this chapter will give a detailed idea to the young researchers in the area of biomedical and more specifically in diabetes mellitus using DL.

References

1. Hinton, G. E., Osindero, S., & Teh, Y.-W. (2006). A fast learning algorithm for deep belief nets. *Neural Computation, 18.7*, 1527–1554.
2. Esteva, A., et al. (2019) A guide to deep learning in healthcare. *Nature Medicine, 25.1*, 24.
3. Krizhevsky, A., Sutskever, I., & Hinton, G. E. (2012). Imagenet classification with deep convolutional neural networks. In *Advances in neural information processing systems* (pp. 1097–1105).
4. Silver, D., Huang, A., Maddison, C. J., Guez, A., Sifre, L., Van Den Driessche, G., et al. (2016). Mastering the game of go with deep neural networks and tree search. *Nature, 529*(7587), 484–489.
5. Bengio, Y., & LeCun, Y. (2007). Scaling learning algorithms towards. AI. In L. Bottou, O. Chapelle, D. DeCoste & J. Weston (Eds.), *Large scale Kernel machines* (pp. 321–360). Cambridge, MA: MIT Press.
6. Bengio, Y., Courville, A., & Vincent, P. (2013). Representation learning: a review and new perspectives. In *IEEE transactions on pattern analysis and machine intelligence* (Vol. 35, No. 8, pp. 1798–1828).
7. Arel, I., Rose, D. C., & Karnowski, T. P. (2010). Deep machine learning-a new frontier in artificial intelligence research [research frontier]. *IEEE ComputIntell, 5,* 13–18.
8. Hinton, G. E., Osindero, S., & Teh, Y.-W. (2006). A fast learning algorithm for deep belief nets. *Neural Computation, 18*(7), 1527–1554.
9. Bengio, Y., Lamblin, P., Popovici, D., & Larochelle, H. (2007) Greedy layer-wise training of deep networks. In *Advances in neural information processing systems* (pp. 153–160).
10. Larochelle, H., Bengio, Y., Louradour, J., & Lamblin, P. (2009). Exploring strategies for training deep neural networks. *Journal of Machine Learning Research, 10,* 1–40.
11. Salakhutdinov, R., & Hinton, G. E. (2009) Deep Boltzmann machines. In *International Conference on, Artificial Intelligence and Statistics* (pp. 448–455). JMLR.org.
12. Najafabadi, M. M., Villanustre, F., Khoshgoftaar, T. M., et al. (2015). Deep learning applications and challenges in big data analytics. *Journal of Big Data, 2,* 1.
13. Markoff, J. (2012). Scientists see promise in deep-learning programs. *New York Times*, November 24 2012.

14. Lewis, David. (1976). *Probabilities of conditionals and conditional probabilities* (pp. 129–147). Dordrecht: Ifs. Springer.
15. Arel, I., Rose, D. C., & Karnowski, T. P. (2010). Deep machine learning-a new frontier in artificial intelligence research. *IEEE Computational Intelligence Magazine, 5*(4), 13–18.
16. LeCun, Y., et al. (1998). Gradient-based learning applied to document recognition. In *Proceedings of the IEEE* (Vol. 86.11, pp. 2278–2324).
17. Dunne, R. A., & Campbell, N. A. (1997). On the pairing of the softmax activation and cross-entropy penalty functions and the derivation of the softmax activation function. In *Proceedings of the 8th Aust. Conference on the Neural Networks, Melbourne* (Vol. 181).
18. Janocha, K., & Czarnecki, W. M. (2017). On loss functions for deep neural networks in classification. arXiv preprint arXiv:1702.05659.
19. Kalchbrenner, N., Grefenstette, E., & Blunsom, P. (2014). A convolutional neural network for modelling sentences. arXiv preprint arXiv:1404.2188.
20. Ji, S., et al., (2013). 3D convolutional neural networks for human action recognition. In *IEEE Transactions on Pattern Analysis and Machine Intelligence* (Vol. 35.1, pp. 221–231).
21. Hinton, G. E. (2007). Boltzmann machine. *Scholarpedia, 2*(5), 1668.
22. Bourlard, H., & Kamp, Y. (1988). Auto-association by multilayer perceptrons and singular value decomposition. *Biological Cybernetics, 59*(4–5), 291–294.
23. Deng, L. (2012). Three classes of deep learning architectures and their applications: a tutorial survey. In APSIPA Transactions on Signal and Information.
24. Hinton, G. E., & Salakhutdinov, R. R. (2006). Reducing the dimensionality of data with neural networks. *Science, 313*(5786), 504–507.
25. Hinton, G. E., & Zemel, R. S. (1994). Autoencoders, minimum description length, and Helmholtz free energy. In *Advances in Neural Information Processing System.*
26. Vincent, P. (2011). A connection between score matching and denoising autoencoders. *Neural Computation, 23*(7), 1661–1674.
27. Vincent, P., Larochelle, H., Bengio, Y., & Manzagol, P. A. (2008). Extracting and composing robust features with denoisingautoencoders. In *Proceedings of the 25th International Conference on Machine Learning* (pp. 1096–1103).
28. Poultney, C., Chopra, S., & Cun, Y. L. (2006). Efficient learning of sparse representations with an energy-based model. In *Advances in Neural Information Processing Systems* (pp. 1137–1144).
29. Salakhutdinov, R., Mnih, A., & Hinton, G. (2007). Restricted Boltzmann machines for collaborative filtering. In *Proceedings of International Conference on Machine Learning* (pp. 791–798). ACM.
30. Salakhutdinov, R., & Hinton, G. E. (2007). Using deep belief nets to learn covariance Kernels for Gaussian processes. In *Proceedings of the Conference on Neural Information Processing Systems* (pp. 1249–1256).
31. Deng, L., & Yu, D. (2011). Deep convex net: a scalable architecture for speech pattern classification. In *Proceedings of the Interspeech.*
32. Hochreiter, S., & Schmidhuber, J. (1997). Long short-term memory. *Neural Computation, 9*(8), 1725–1780.
33. Gers, F. A., Schraudolph, N. N., & Schmidhuber, J. (2002). Learning precise timing with istm recurrent networks. *Journal of Machine Learning Research, 3,* 115–143.
34. Hochreiter, S., & Schmidhuber, J. (1997). Long short-term memory. *Neural Computating, 9,* 1735–1780.
35. Weston, J., Chopra, S., & Bordes, A. (2014). Memory Networks. http://arxiv.org/abs/1410.3916.
36. Fu, T., Han, Y., Li, X., Liu, Y., & Wu, X. (2015). Integrating prosodic information into recurrent neual network language model for speech recognition. In *Proceedings of Asia-Pacific Signal and Information Processing Association Annual Summit and Conference* (pp. 1194–1197). IEEE.
37. Hermanto, A., Adji, T. B., & Setiawan, N. A. (2015). Recurrent neural network language model for english-indonesian machine translation: experimental study. In *Proceedings of International Conference on Science in Information Technology* (pp. 132–136). IEEE.

38. Zhang, X., Xie, G., Liu, C., & Bengio, Y. (2017). End-to-end online writer identification with recurrent neural network. *IEEE Transactions on Human-Machine Systems, 47*(2), 285–292.
39. Capes, S. E., et al., (2000). Stress hyperglycaemia and increased risk of death after myocardial infarction in patients with and without diabetes: a systematic overview. *The Lancet, 355.9206*, 773–778.
40. Alberti, K. G. M. M., & Zimmet, P. Z. (1998). Definition, diagnosis and classification of diabetes mellitus and its complications. Part 1: diagnosis and classification of diabetes mellitus. Provisional report of a WHO consultation. *Diabetic Medicine, 15.7*, 539–553.
41. WHO Expert Committee on Diabetes Mellitus. (1980). Second Report. Technical Report Series 646. Geneva: WHO.
42. National Diabetes Data Group. (1979). Classification and diagnosis of diabetes mellitus and other categories of glucose intolerance. *Diabetes, 28,* 1039–1057.
43. World Health Organization. (1985). Diabetes Mellitus: Report of a WHO Study Group. Technical Report Series 727.Geneva: WHO.
44. The Expert Committee on the Diagnosis and Classification of Diabetes Mellitus. (1997). Report of the Expert Committee on the Diagnosis and Classification of Diabetes Mellitus. Diabetes Care (Vol. 20, pp. 1183–1197).
45. Kuzuya, T., & Matsuda, A. (1997). Classification of diabetes on the basis of etiologies versus degree of insulin deficiency. *Diabetes Care, 20,* 219–220.
46. Kumar Das, S., Mishra, A. K., & Roy, P. (2019). Automatic diabetes prediction using tree based ensemble learners. *International Journal of Computational Intelligence & IoT*, *2.2*.
47. https://www.idf.org/our-network/regions-members/south-east-asia/diabetes-in-sea.html. Access details: 20-02-2020, time: 3.30 pm.
48. Jensen, P. B., Jensen, L. J., & Brunak, S. (2012). Mining electronic health records: towards better research applications and clinical care. *Nature Reviews Genetics, 13,* 395–405.
49. Luo, J., Wu, M., Gopukumar, D., et al. (2016). Big data application in bio-medical research and health care: a literature review. *Biomedical Informatics Insights, 8,* 1–10.
50. Google's DeepMind forms health unit to build medical soft-Ware https://www.bloomberg.com/news/articles/2016-02-24/google-s-deepmind-forms-health-unit-to-build-medical-software. Access Details: 20-02-2020 time: 1.30 pm.
51. Enlitic uses deep learning to make doctors faster and more accurate. http://www.enlitic.com/index.html. Access Details: 21-02-2020 time: 1.00 pm.
52. LeCun, Y., et al. (1998). Gradient-based learning applied to document recognition. In *Proceedings of the IEEE, 86.11*, 2278–2324.
53. Li, H., Li, A., & Wang, M. (2019). A novel end-to-end brain tumor segmentation method using improved fully convolutional networks. *Computers in Biology and Medicine.*
54. Rehman, F., et al. (2019). A region-based deep level set formulation for vertebral bone segmentation of osteoporotic fractures. *Journal of Digital Imaging*, 1–13.
55. Yang, J., Faraji, M., & Basu, A. (2019). Robust segmentation of arterial walls in intravascular ultrasound images using dual path U-Net. *Ultrasonics.*
56. Soomro, M. H., et al. (2019). Automated segmentation of colorectal tumor in 3D MRI using 3D multiscale densely connected convolutional neural network. *Journal of Healthcare Engineering.*
57. Guan, S., & Loew, M. (2019). Breast cancer detection using synthetic mammograms from generative adversarial networks in convolutional neural networks. *Journal of Medical Imaging, 6*(3), 031411.
58. Alaskar, H., et al. (2019). Application of convolutional neural networks for automated ulcer detection in wireless capsule endoscopy images. *Sensors, 19.6*, 1265.
59. Jensen, P. B., Jensen, L. J. & SørenBrunak. (2012). Mining electronic health records: towards better research applications and clinical care. *Nature Reviews Genetics, 13.6*, 395.
60. Bai, T., et al. (2018). Interpretable representation learning for healthcare via capturing disease progression through time. In *Proceedings of the 24th ACM SIGKDD International Conference on Knowledge Discovery & Data Mining.* ACM.

61. Li, F., & Yu, H. (2019). An investigation of single-domain and multidomain medication and adverse drug event relation extraction from electronic health record notes using advanced deep learning models. *Journal of the American Medical Informatics Association*.
62. Li, R., et al. (2019). Detection of bleeding events in electronic health record notes using convolutional neural network models enhanced with recurrent neural network autoencoders: deep learning approach. *JMIR Medical Informatics, 7.1*, e10788.
63. Reddy, B. K., & Delen, D. (2018). Predicting hospital readmission for lupus patients: an RNN-LSTM-based deep-learning methodology. *Computers in Biology and Medicine, 101*, 199–209.
64. Ozaki, K., et al. (2002). Functional SNPs in the lymphotoxin-α gene that are associated with susceptibility to myocardial infarction. *Nature Genetics, 32.4*, 650.
65. Golub, T. R., et al. (1999). Molecular classification of cancer: class discovery and class prediction by gene expression monitoring. *Science, 286.5439*, 531–537.
66. Oliver, S. (2000). Proteomics: guilt-by-association goes global. *Nature, 403*(6770), 601.
67. ENCODE Project Consortium. (2012). An integrated encyclopedia of DNA elements in the human genome. *Nature, 489*(7414), 57.
68. Yin, Q., et al. (2019). DeepHistone: a deep learning approach to predicting histone modifications. *BMC Genomics, 20.2*, 193.
69. Tian, Q., et al. (2019). MRCNN: a deep learning model for regression of genome-wide DNA methylation. *BMC Genomics, 20.2*, 192.
70. Liu, Q., & Pingzhao, H. (2019). Association analysis of deep genomic features extracted by denoising autoencoders in breast cancer. *Cancers, 11*(4), 494.
71. Chiu, Y.-C., et al. (2019). Predicting drug response of tumors from integrated genomic profiles by deep neural networks. *BMC Medical Genomics, 12.1*, 18.
72. Abramoff, M. D., & Suttorp-Schulten, M. S. (2005). Web-based screening for diabetic retinopathy a primary care population: the eyecheck project. *Telemedicine Journal & e-Health, 11*(6), 668–674.
73. Huang, L., & Lu, C. (2018). Intelligent diagnosis of diabetes based on information gain and deep neural network. In *2018 5th IEEE International Conference on Cloud Computing and Intelligence Systems (CCIS)*. IEEE.
74. Deshmukh, T., Fadewar, H. S., & Shukla, A. (2019). The detection of Prameha (diabetes) in Ayurvedic way with the help of fuzzy deep learning. In *International Conference on Intelligent Computing and Communication Technologies*. Singapore: Springer.
75. Kumar, N. M., & Manjula, R. (2019). Design of multi-layer perceptron for the diagnosis of diabetes mellitus using Keras in deep learning. In *Smart Intelligent Computing and Applications* (pp. 703–711). Singapore: Springer.
76. Ayon, S. I., & Md Islam. (2019). Diabetes prediction: a deep learning approach. *International Journal of Information Engineering & Electronic Business, 11.2*.
77. Ashiquzzaman, A., et al. (2018). Reduction of overfitting in diabetes prediction using deep learning neural network. In *IT convergence and security 2017* (pp. 35–43). Singapore: Springer.
78. Orlando, J. I., et al. (2018). An ensemble deep learning based approach for red lesion detection in fundus images. *Computer Methods and Programs in Biomedicine, 153*, 115–127.
79. Dai, L., et al. (2018). Clinical report guided retinal microaneurysm detection with multi-sieving deep learning. *IEEE Transactions on Medical Imaging, 37.5*, 1149–1161.
80. Harangi, B., Toth, J., Hajdu, A. (2018). Fusion of deep convolutional neural networks for microaneurysm detection in color fundus images. In *2018 40th Annual International Conference of the IEEE Engineering in Medicine and Biology Society (EMBC)*. IEEE.
81. Quellec, G., et al. (2017). Deep image mining for diabetic retinopathy screening. *Medical Image Analysis, 39*, 178–193.
82. van Grinsven, M. J. J. P., et al. (2016). Fast convolutional neural network training using selective data sampling: application to hemorrhage detection in color fundus images. *IEEE Transactions on Medical Imaging, 35.5*, 1273–1284.
83. Khojasteh, P., Aliahmad, B., & Kumar, D. K. (2018). Fundus images analysis using deep features for detection of exudates, hemorrhages and microaneurysms. *BMC Ophthalmology, 18.1*, 288.

84. Kar, S., & Maity, S. P. (2018). Automatic detection of retinal lesions for screening of diabetic retinopathy. *IEEE Transactions on Biomedical Engineering, 65*(3), 608–618.
85. Li, K., et al. (2019). Convolutional recurrent neural networks for glucose prediction. *IEEE Journal of Biomedical and Health Informatics.*
86. Kumari, S. K., & Mathana, J. M. (2019). Blood sugar level indication through chewing and swallowing from acoustic MEMS sensor and deep learning algorithm for diabetic management. *Journal of Medical Systems, 43.1*, 1.
87. San, P., Ling, S. H., & Nguyen, H. T. (2016). Deep learning framework for detection of hypoglycemic episodes in children with type 1 diabetes. In *2016 38th Annual International Conference of the IEEE Engineering in Medicine and Biology Society (EMBC).* IEEE.

Noval Machine Learning Approach for Classifying Clinically Actionable Genetic Mutations in Cancer Patients

Anuradha Thakare, Santwana Gudadhe, Hemant Baradkar, and Manisha Kitukale

Abstract Cancer is the most concerning disease since the number of patients diagnosing with cancer is increasing. Early diagnosis and prediction of a cancer type play a key role in cancer research. The treatment or prevention revolves around the same set of treatment processes for every person on the earth. It is possible that the same treatment may not work for every individual since cancer is the disease involving genes. Generally, by analyzing the genetic profile of patients treatment is advisable. During genetic profile analyses, most work is manual. Once sequenced, there may be thousands of genetic mutations in a cancer tumor, and classifying these mutations can help to identify tumor growth from the neutral mutations. Classifying genetic mutation is time-consuming work in which, reviewer has to classify and manually review every single mutation. So, to address the solution for this problem, classifying clinically actionable genetic mutations based on the clinical evidence is of prime importance. This article presents the hybrid genetic naive Bayes (Gen-NB) classifier as a solution to the above problem. In this work, the features from clinical text data are extracted with the Tf-idf method. The proposed algorithm extracts optimal features from genetic mutations and clinical text data which in turn help in strengthening the overall classification process. The proposed hybrid algorithm, Gen-NB has shown an increase in accuracy of 75.31% as compared to traditional naive Bayes which is found to be 60%.

A. Thakare (✉) · S. Gudadhe
Pimpri Chinchwad College of Engineering, Pune, India
e-mail: adthakare2014@gmail.com

S. Gudadhe
e-mail: s.santwana20@gmail.com

H. Baradkar
Jagdamba College of Engineering and Technology, Yavatmal, India
e-mail: hemant.baradkar@gmail.com

M. Kitukale
P. Wadhwani College of Pharmacy, Yavatmal, India
e-mail: Kitukalemanisha5@gmail.com

R. Patgiri et al. (eds.), *Health Informatics: A Computational Perspective in Healthcare*, Studies in Computational Intelligence 932,
https://doi.org/10.1007/978-981-15-9735-0_16

Keywords Classification · Hybrid genetic naive Bayes (Gen-NB) · Exploratory data analysis · Genetic mutation · Term frequency · Inverse document frequency

1 Introduction

Cancer is one of the diseases which include abnormal cell growths or tumors, results in a reversible effect to other parts of the human body. Diagnosis of cancer is very important as early stage detection increases the chances of survival of the patients. There are various therapy and diagnosis techniques that have evolved which helps to reduce the effect of cancer from the human body. Conventional cancer treatment which is mainly based on morphological appearances and gene expressions of the tumor.

Recently, cancer is treated by various treatments like surgery, chemotherapy, hormonal therapy, radiation therapy, personalized medicine, etc. Personalized therapy is one of the new evolving treatments which work on the concept of genetic profile understanding of patients. Precision medicine helps the doctor to give the treatment based on genetic understanding of the patient. In this treatment, a sample of the cancer is taken and gets tested to check genetic mutation that may be responsible for growth of cancer. The procedure used to check for genetic changes in cancer is called genes sequencing. Before personalized medicine evolved, many cancer patients get the same treatment over the certain type and certain stage of most cancers [1]. From the research study, researchers understand that cancer patients have genetic changes which cause cancer to grow and spread. Also study says that genetic changes occur in one person which may not occur in others one having the same type of cancer. Genetic mutation study helps the researchers to determine that there are variations in genetics profile those who suffer from cancer. This treatment helps the specific patient to recover from a specific cancer stage.

In the human body, genetic mutations happen often. A mutation may be harmful or neutral. Harmful mutation has an adverse effect on the human body. Some harmful mutations likely involve the cause of cancer. To identify the cancer genes, genetic mutation classification is an important task. Classifying genetic mutation involves manually reviewing every single mutation. So, to address the solution for this problem, classifying clinically actionable genetic mutations based on the clinical evidence is of prime importance.

In this work, a hybrid Gen-NB algorithm is proposed. This algorithm extracts optimal features from genetic mutation and clinical text data which in turns helps in strengthening the overall classification process. Extracted features are classified using logistic regression, random forest, naive Bayes, and proposed Gen-NB algorithm. In all, the proposed algorithm has shown improved accuracy over naive Bayes. In this article, related work discussed in Sect. 2, genome sequencing and genetic mutations discussed in Sect. 3, proposed Gen-NB classifier discussed in Sect. 4, result and analysis discussed in Sects. 5 and 6 presents the conclusion.

2 Related Work

Machine Learning is one of the prominent branches that contributes in the area of genome medicine. In various ways, machine learning helps to find out insights of genetic data. The queries like, how to interpret genome data, how to analyze the data, etc., are answered by machine learning techniques. Applying machine learning techniques in genetic study gives more findings which helps the researchers to find out many information link genome sequence, mutation, gene expression. From the survey it is observed that gene mutations are likely to affect cancer development. Understanding the genetic data is helpful to identify and predict the risk. Identifying the expression of genes, protein binding helps for accurate prediction. The large amount of genetic mutation information, gene expression and advanced machine learning strategies can help researchers for effective genomic medication [2].

Machine learning applications help in genome sequencing and analyzing genetic mutation data. By applying machine learning techniques on genetic data, it gives important insights which help to get better results [3]. Disease classification from genetic data is still one of the challenging tasks in genetic study. In this paper, [4] the author has presented genomic profiling evaluation by applying machine learning methods. From the result, it is observed that while classifying the disease odds ratio is one of the main factors. Also extra genes variants need to be observed to get important information in genome profiling.

Support vector machine [5] is one of the most suitable classification methods which will identify the patterns. From the survey, it is observed that SVM gives better accuracy in classification. In this paper, analysis of high-dimensional data by applying signature discovery techniques is done. Also, this paper mainly focused on identifying signature genes which help in disease prediction and the regulatory networks inference. In this paper [6], the author has presented a developed discovery engine (DE) as a new approach. This approach helps to identify the maximum characteristics of a patient which helps to predict the right diagnosis. These identified characteristics provide the best suitable remedy for the patients. Discovery engine is one of the robust techniques in terms of performance. Features that are extracted from the discovery engine are evaluated with clinical reference.

In prediction of breast cancer, the author has presented the three strategies. These strategies help to improve the response of the patients during chemotherapy drugs. These strategies are instant, hybrid selection method, and oversampling. In this work, all three strategies are evaluated against the baseline method under the ROC (AUC). From the result, it is observed that improved prediction accuracy [7].

Fig. 1 Genome sequencing

AGCTCCGGTTCCCAACGATCAAGGCGA
GGTTAGCTAATTCGGTCCTCCGATCGTT
ATGGTTATGGCAGCACTGCATAATTCTC
GTGACTGGTGAGTACTCAACCAAGTCA
ATCATTGGAAAACGTTCTTCGGGGCGA

3 Genome Sequencing and Genetic Mutations

3.1 Genome Sequencing

Identification of DNA nucleotide order or base in the genome is genome sequencing [8, 9]. As, Gs, Cs, and Ts order forms DNA organism's. In genes sequence, researchers are mainly identifying some important information about the presence of genes. Figure 1 shows the genome sequence.

3.2 Genetic Mutation

In genetic mutation, changes in DNA sequence are permanent. This changes differ from actual genetic sequences which are found in most of the people. Generally, these genetic changes start occurring from a single DNA building block to a large segment of a chromosome having multiple genes. Figure 2 shows the genetic mutation. Genetic mutations are further classified into two types, hereditary mutation and acquired mutation.

3.2.1 Hereditary Mutations

Hereditary mutations are inherited from parents. It is present forever in every cell in the human body. These mutations get inherited from the parent's egg or sperm cells into the child. It is also called a germline mutation. When an egg and a sperm cell combine, a fertilized egg cell gets DNA from both the parents. The child with fertilized egg will have the mutation in each of her or his cells, if this DNA has a mutation [10].

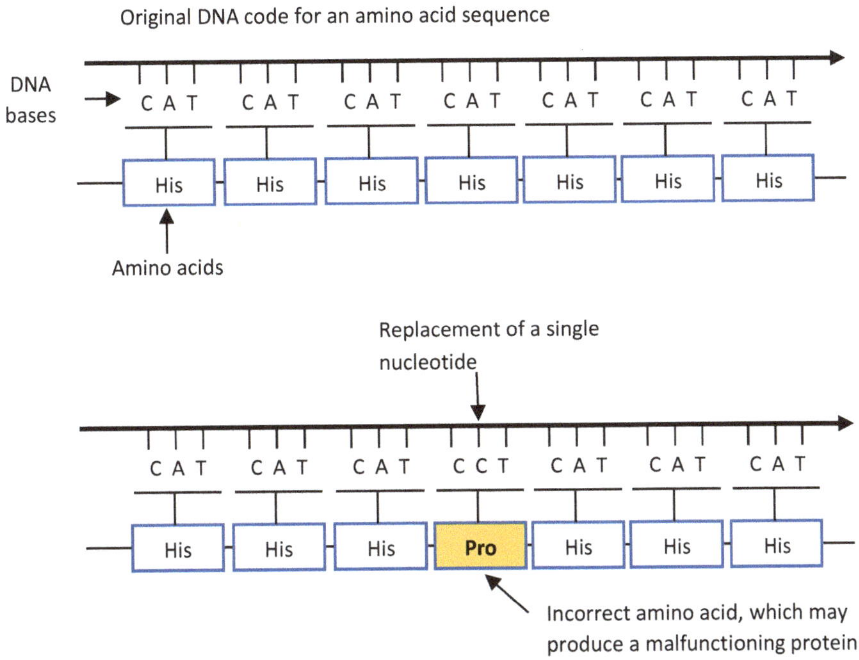

Fig. 2 Genetic mutation

3.2.2 Acquired Mutations

During a person's life, this mutation occurs at some specific time during a person's life. Acquired mutation is present in some cells in the body. Generally, environmental factors like ultraviolet radiation, error occurred while copying DNA during cell division is responsible for causing this type of mutation [10].

4 Proposed Gen-NB Classifier

This section discusses the architecture of the proposed Gen-NB algorithm. Proposed Gen-NB algorithm is a hybrid model of genetic algorithm and naive Bayes algorithm. The architecture for classification of genetic mutations based on clinical evidence for development of personalized medicine [11] is represented in Fig. 3.

This architecture has three major computational modules, namely input data, data preprocessing, and classification, whereas exploratory data analysis and result are the modules that produce analytical results. The modules are listed below:

1. Input data
2. Exploratory data analysis (EDA) method

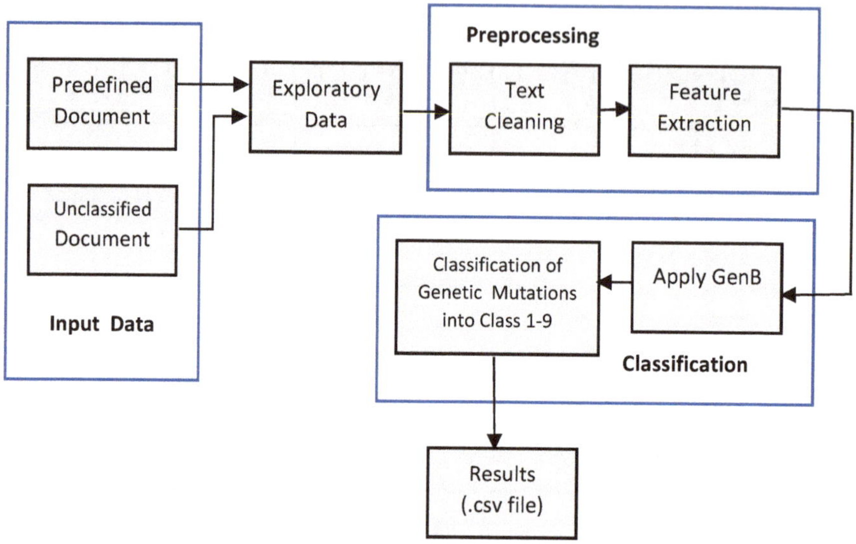

Fig. 3 System architecture

3. Data preprocessing:
   3.1 Text cleaning
   3.2 Feature extraction
4. Evaluation of feature against proposed classifiers
5. Classification of genetic mutations against proposed classifiers

   Results.

4.1 Input Data

From kaggle [12], dataset is collected. Genetic mutations are classified in nine different classes. There are two files—test and training file in dataset. Genetic mutation information is provided in one training/test variant. Whereas clinical evidence (text) is provided by another training/test text) file. Classifying the genetic mutations, this file is used. The ID field is used to link both the files. The files are described next.

Training variants—It is a comma separated file. It contains the descriptive information about genetic mutations which are considered for training. ID field (row id field link the mutation to the clinical evidence), gene (genes with present genetic mutation), variation (for mutations amino acid change), class (genetic mutation).

Training text—It is delimited file shown as double pipe (||). It consists of clinical evidence (text) which is considered for genetic mutations classification. ID field (row id link the clinical evidence to genetic mutation), text (classify the genetic mutation).

Test variant—It is a comma separated file. It contains information about genetic mutations. This information is used for training. ID is the field (row id link the mutation to clinical evidence), variation (for mutations amino acid change), and genes.

Test text—It is delimited file represented as double pipe (||). It has clinical evidence (text) which is mainly considered for genetic mutations classification. ID field (row id link clinical evidence to genetic mutation), text (classifying the genetic mutation).

4.2 Exploratory Data Analysis (EDA)

Exploratory data analysis method is used for data analysis. EDA includes the number of techniques (graphical); it helps to provide detail information inside the dataset, extract the specific variables, identify the outliers and anomalies, check given assumptions, uncover underlying structure, etc.

There are few quantitative methods available in EDA. Because of highly graphical, explored nature EDA is most commonly used. Graphics provide the incomparable power to analysts to do the analysis. The graphical EDA methods are more simple, and it has many techniques as given below.

- Raw data plot (probability plots, data traces, block plots, Youden plots, lag plots, histograms, and bihistograms)
- Simple statistics plot such as standard deviation plots, box plots, mean plots.
- Plot position such as maximizing the ability of natural pattern recognition, such per page different plots.

4.3 Data Preprocessing

4.3.1 Text Cleaning

The preprocessing of text data which includes to break out HTML characters, removal of stop words, data decoding, lookup apostrophe, eliminate punctuation, eliminate expressions, break attached words, word standardizing, slangs lookup, grammar checking, etc.

4.3.2 Feature Extraction

In the machine learning domain, features are extracted from input data which is measured one and generates the derived values (non redundant and informative value). It helps for subsequent learning and also supports better human interpretations. Main step in statistical NLP is to convert raw text into meaningful features. It helps to provide a detailed view of text. Frequency inverse document frequency (TF-IDF) method helps to identify how important a word is in a document. To get a vector space model from textual data, TF-IDF method is used. TF-IDF is specially used stop words filtering in subject filled. It includes classification and text summarization.

4.4 Evaluation of Feature Against Proposed Classifiers

Once a feature is extracted, these extracted features are evaluated against several classification algorithms. It will help to find out most correct combination of classifier and feature extraction. A performance measure is used to evaluate the features.

Performance measures: For training and validation, binary accuracy is used to calculate the correct classification rate, and it is calculated by the equation given in Eq. 1.

$$\text{Accuracy} = \frac{\text{TP} + \text{TN}}{\text{TP} + \text{FP} + \text{FN} + \text{TN}} * 100 \tag{1}$$

Here, TP is true positives, correctly labeled positive tuples; TN is true negatives, correctly labeled negative tuples, FN false negative, positive tuples mislabeled negative. FP false positive, negative tuples incorrectly labeled positive.

4.5 Classification of Genetic Mutation Against Proposed Classifiers

4.5.1 Classification of Genetic Mutations in Cancer Patients with Hybrid Genetic Naive Bayes Classifier

This section discusses classification of genetic mutations with newly developed hybrid genetic naive Bayes classifier called Gen-NB. The hybridization of genetic algorithm and naive Bayes algorithm is used for classification of genetic mutations. Genetic algorithm selects most optimal features from the extracted features. These optimal features are further classified with naive Bayes classifier. The genetic mutations are evaluated in terms of accuracy of classifying the genetic mutations as cancerous mutations or non-cancerous mutations.

4.5.2 Working of Gen-NB

The genetic mutations (G) and clinical text data (T) datasets are read and combined as a final dataset (D) such that $D = G + T$. Then, D is exposed to exploratory data analysis (EDA) which is an important step as discussed in the above sections. The data is cleaned considering the results of EDA. The text features (H) are extracted using vector space method and calculating term frequency and inverse document frequency. The genetic process is further applied on these extracted features to select optimal features.

In genetic search space, we have a random population of features extracted. Here, we are generating a random population $P(t)$ with features (H). Now, generate the fitness score F for each sample in a search space $P(t)$. The termination criteria for this hybrid algorithm are convergence point. Until the termination criteria, the genetic operators, selection, cross-over, and mutation are executed, and fitness of every candidate is evaluated. The roulette wheel strategy is used for selection with single point cross-over. Mutation strategy is bit flip mutation. This gives rise to a new generation. The final set of optimal features is selected when algorithm is converged that means there is no improvement in the fitness value.

The optimal feature selection gives rise to target oriented search. The naive Bayes algorithm classifies these features calculating the probability that every feature falls in the class cancer or non-cancer. Here, with optimal features, search is enhanced, and results are more accurate. Gen-NB algorithm discussed below.

Algorithm

```
Inputs: Genetic Mutations and Text dataset
Output: Classified Genetic Mutations
Steps;
Read Genetic Mutations (G) and Clinical text data (T ) datasets.
Combine the datasets (D) = G + T
Perform Exploratory Data Analysis (EDA)
Clean the dataset considering the results of EDA
Extract   text features (H) using TF-IDF method.

Initialization;
T = 0;
Generate random population (P(t)) from extracted features(H);
Calculate fitness function (F) score for each sample (P(t));
While not termination do
        Pp(t) = P(t).selectParents();
        Crossover/ Reproduction(Pp) = Pc(t) ;
        Mutate(Pc(t));
        Evaluate(Pc(t));
        P(t + 1) = (Pc(t), P(t)) next generation build from this;
        t=t+1;
        Apply Naive bayes classifier to (P(t + 1))
End
```

4.6 *Result*

Results are obtained in the form of a csv file. Discussed in the result section.

5 Result and Analysis Discussion

5.1 *Implementation Details*

Based on clinical evidence, genetic mutations are classified into 1 to 9 classes. The result and analysis are discussed in terms of implementation details and stepwise analysis of results. The implementation details are as: The implementation is carried out on the platform which includes system specification as; machine requirement with processor—Intel Core i5, RAM-16 GB, Storage-128 GB or Higher, System Type 64-bit operating system. Software specification with operating system—Windows/Ubuntu/MacOS. The experimentation is with Python 3.6 and tool Jupyter Notebook. The statistical results and related analysis are discussed in the next section.

5.2 *Result and Analysis*

This section discusses the results and analysis of Gen-NB. The experimentation results are presented here in Sects. 6.1 and 6.2. In first, the intermediate results of exploratory data analysis are discussed, whereas in the second subsection, the results of classification of genetic mutations are discussed.

5.2.1 Results of EDA and Data Preprocessing

Genetic mutations and clinical text datasets are taken as an input. There are 8989 instances. Experimental results are obtained using EDA. To analyze the input dataset exploratory data analysis method is used. To get the better result, EDA is performed. Also it helps to identify the correlation between various features. From the experimental result, it can be observed that distribution of data is quite random. No observable relationship is found between various features. In case of preprocessing of the data, EDA method is more useful. Result of exploratory data analysis shown below. Table 1 shows the genes with variant and class present in the sample input file as a testing variant.

Natural language processing technique is used. From clinical evidence, features are extracted; this step is performed after analyzing the data. clinical data is represented using a vector space model. Once tokenization of words is done, it is stemmed

Table 1 Genes with variant and class

ID	Genes	Variation	Class
0	FAM58A	Truncating mutation	1
1	CBL	W802*	2
2	CBL	Q249E	2
3	CBL	N454D	3
4	CBL	L399V	4
5	CBL	V3911	4

A	B	C	D	E	F	G	H	I	J
ID	class1	class2	class3	class4	class5	class6	class7	class8	class9
12	1	0	0	0	0	0	0	0	0
19	0	1	0	0	0	0	0	0	0
21	0	1	0	0	0	0	0	0	0
55	0	0	0	1	0	0	0	0	0
64	0	0	0	1	0	0	0	0	0
70	0	0	0	1	0	0	0	0	0
89	0	0	0	0	0	0	0	0	1
93	0	0	0	0	0	0	1	0	0
111	0	0	0	0	0	0	1	0	0
113	0	0	0	0	0	0	1	0	0
119	0	1	0	0	0	0	0	0	0
121	1	0	0	0	0	0	0	0	0
126	0	0	0	1	0	0	0	0	0
137	1	0	0	0	0	0	0	0	0
159	1	0	0	0	0	0	0	0	0
215	1	0	0	0	0	0	0	0	0
226	0	1	0	0	0	0	0	0	0
234	0	0	1	0	0	0	0	0	0
286	0	1	0	0	0	0	0	0	0
344	0	0	0	0	0	0	1	0	0
353	0	1	0	0	0	0	0	0	0
381	1	0	0	0	0	0	0	0	0

L	M	N	O	P	Q	R	S	T	U
ID	class1	class2	class3	class4	class5	class6	class7	class8	class9
426	0	0	0	0	0	0	1	0	0
469	0	0	1	0	0	0	0	0	0
535	0	0	0	0	0	0	1	0	0
542	0	0	0	0	0	0	0	0	1
545	0	0	0	0	0	0	1	0	0
552	1	0	0	0	0	0	0	0	0
562	0	0	0	1	0	0	0	0	0
564	1	0	0	0	0	0	0	0	0
602	0	0	0	0	0	1	0	0	0
617	0	0	0	1	0	0	0	0	0
630	0	0	0	0	0	0	0	0	1
638	0	0	0	0	0	1	0	0	0
651	0	0	0	1	0	0	0	0	0
663	1	0	0	0	0	0	0	0	0
667	0	0	0	0	1	0	0	0	0
677	0	1	0	0	0	0	0	0	0
681	1	0	0	0	0	0	0	0	0
683	0	0	1	0	0	0	0	0	0
703	0	1	0	0	0	0	0	0	0
704	0	0	0	0	0	0	1	0	0
762	0	0	0	0	0	0	1	0	0
766	0	0	0	0	1	0	0	0	0

Fig. 4 Sample output of filtered word

and filtered. The main purpose is to generate a distinct list of stems and frequencies. Figure 4 shows sample output of filtered word.

Table 2 shows the training variants. It includes the ID, genes, variants, and class. To extract the features from genes and their corresponding variations, one hot encoding technique is used. Changing categorical into the integer features is nothing but the one hot encoding. To get better prediction, these extracted features are given to classification algorithms. Logistic regression technique, random forest classifier algorithm, naive Bayes algorithm, and hybrid genetic naive Bayes algorithm are used to classify the genetic mutation.

5.2.2 Results of Classification of Genetic Mutations

Classification of genetic mutation with logistic regression algorithm, random forest classifier algorithm, naive Bayes algorithm, and hybrid genetic naive Bayes, Gen-NB algorithm is discussed in this section.

The logistic regression results in 46.00% classification accuracy. The random forest classifier and naive Bayes classifier results in 51.00% and 60.00% accuracy,

Table 2 Training variants

ID, gene, variation, class	ID, gene, variation, class
0, FAM58A, truncating mutations, 1	21, CBL, C396R, 4
1, CBL, W802*, 2	22, CBL, G375P, 4
2, CBL, Q249E, 2	23, CBL, S376F, 4
3, CBL, N454D, 3	24, CBL, P417A, 4
4, CBL, L399V, 4	25, CBL, H398Y, 4
5, CBL, V391I, 4	26, SHOC2, S2G, 4
6, CBL, V430M, 5	27, TERT, Y846C, 4
7, CBL, Deletion, 1	28, TERT, C228T, 7
8, CBL, Y371H, 4	29, TERT, H412Y, 4
9, CBL, C384R, 4	30, TERT, H876Q, 4
10, CBL, P395A, 4	31, TERT, promoter mutations, 7
11, CBL, K382E, 4	32, TERT, P704S, 4
12, CBL, R420Q, 4	33, TERT, Amplification, 2
13, CBL, C381A, 4	34, TERT, C250T, 7
14, CBL, P428L, 5	35, DICER1, G1809R, 4
15, CBL, D390Y, 4	36, DICER1, G1809K, 4
16, CBL, Truncating Mutations, 1	37, DICER1, D1709E, 1
17, CBL, Q367P, 4	38, DICER1, D1709A, 1
18, CBL, M374V, 5	39, DICER1, E1705A, 4
19, CBL, Y371S, 4	40, DİCER1, D1810A, 4
20, CBL H94Y, 6	41, DICER1, truncating mutations, 1

respectively. The hybrid Gen-NB algorithm results are found to be more promising with the accuracy of 75.31%. Table 3depicts the classifier with the accuracy for classifying genetic mutations.

The accuracy of hybrid genetic naive Bayes algorithm is observed with respect to the number of generations. With the increase in the number of generations, from 100 to 150, it showed improvement in the accuracy from 62.46 to 63.24%. In the generation 200, the accuracy is improved to 65.32%. Finally, in the generation 250 onwards, the improvement in accuracy was reached to 75.31% and got stable. Here, Gen-NB converged at 250 generations with the used dataset. Table 4 shows the result and analysis of the proposed Gen-NB with respect to the number of generations.

Table 3 Classifiers with the accuracy for classifying genetic mutations

S. No.	Classification algorithm	Accuracy (%)
1	Logistic regression	46.00
2	Random forest	51.00
3	Naive Bayes	60.00
4	Proposed Gen-NB	75.31

Table 4 Result and analysis of proposed Gen-NB with respect to no. of generation

S. No.	Number of generation	Accuracy (%)
1	100	62.46
2	150	63.24
3	200	65.32
4	250	75.31
5	300	75.31

6 Conclusion

Genetic mutations classification is mainly built on the medical literature. Classifying the genetic mutation is not an insignificant task, as clinical evidence decoding is much strenuous. To achieve the better result of the proposed technique, modeling of clinical evidence and classification of genetic mutations into its correct class is essential.

In this implementation, the features are extracted from clinical text data by applying TF-IDF natural language processing techniques. The proposed genetic naive Bayes algorithm extracts optimal features from genetic mutations and clinical text data which in turn helps in strengthening the overall classification process. The result of proposed Gen-NB in terms of accuracy compared with logistic regression, random forest, and naive Bayes algorithm. These results showed how optimal feature selection helps in classifying genetic mutations more accurately. The proposed hybrid algorithm, Gen-NB results in improved accuracy of 75.31%, as compared to traditional naive bayes which is only 60%. This work further will be enhanced for improvement in accuracy by modifying the hyper parameters of the Hybrid Genetic Naive Bayes (Gen-NB).

References

1. Chen, Y., Sun, J., Huang, L.-C., Xu, H., & Zhao, Z. (2015). Classification of cancer primary sites using machine learning and somatic mutations. PubMed, PMCID: PMC4619847.
2. Nijeweme, W. O., Leung, M. K. K., Delong, A., Alipanahi, B., & Frey, B. J. (2016, January). Machine learning in genomic medicine: A review of computational problems and data sets. In *Proceedings of the IEEE* (Vol. 104, No. 1).
3. Libbrecht, M. W., & Noble, W. S. (June, 2015). Machine learning in genetics and genomics. *Nature Reviews Genetics, 16*(6), 321–332.
4. Zhang, Z., & Lin, H. (November, 2011). Genomic profiling by machine learning. In *IEEE International Conference on Bioinformatics and Biomedicine Workshops (BIBMW)*, Atlanta, GA, USA, pp. 12–15.
5. Mart´ın-Navarro, A., Gaudioso-Sim´on, A., Alvarez-Jarreta, J., Montoya, J., Mayordomo, E., & Ruiz-Pesini, E. (2017). Machine learning classifier for identification of damaging missense mutations exclusive to human mitochondrial DNA-encoded polypeptides. *BMC Bioinformatics*.

6. Yoon, J., Davtyan, C., & van der Schaar, M. (July, 2017). Discovery and clinical decision support for personalized healthcare. *IEEE Journal of Biomed Health Informatics.*
7. Kourou, K., Exarchos, T. P., Exarchos, K. P., Karamouzis, M. V., & Fotiadis, D. I. (2015). Machine learning applications in cancer prognosis and prediction. *Elsevier Computational and Structural Biotechnology Journal, 13,* 8–17.
8. https://www.genomenewsnetwork.org/resources/whats_a_genome/Chp2_1.shtml. (Last Referred on April 16, 2020).
9. Kurkure, M., & Thakare, A. (2017). Lung cancer detection using Genetic approach, Computing Communication Control and automation. In *2016 International Conference on, Publication in IEEE Digital Library*: 23 February 2017, pp. 1–5, ISBN: 978-1-5090-3291-4.
10. https://ghr.nlm.nih.gov/primer/mutationsanddisorders/genemutation (Last Referred on 15th April 2020).
11. Waykole, R. N., & Thakare, A. D., Intelligent classification of clinically actionable genetic mutations based on clinical evidences. In *Fourth International Conference on Computing Communication Control and Automation (ICCUBEA).* New York: IEEE. ISBN: 978-1-5386-5257-2
12. https://www.kaggle.com/datasets. (Last accessed on July 20, 2019).

Diagnosis Evaluation and Interpretation of Qualitative Abnormalities in Peripheral Blood Smear Images—A Review

K. Suganya Devi, G. Arutperumjothi, and P. Srinivasan

Abstract The computer and the digital camera have given proven opportunities to improve the hematology research and education with patient service. Peripheral Blood Smear (PBS) images of high quality can be obtained quickly and smoothly from the Peripheral Blood Smear with the help of a modern, high resolution digital camera and a high quality microscope. A PBS or blood film is a thin layer of blood coated on a microscope slide. PBS are usually examined to analyze the blood related problems and occasionally, to find parasites within the blood. PBS image examination is a part of the daily work of every testing laboratory. The manual examination of these images is difficult, takes more time and faces human intervention and observation error. This has motivated researchers to develop different algorithms and methods to automate peripheral blood smear image analysis. The interest of computer aided decision making has been identified in many medical applications such as automatic detection, classification and analysis of objects in hematological cytology. Image analysis itself consists of a sequence of steps consisting of image segmentation, features extraction and selection and pattern classification. The aim of this review article is to summarize the qualitative abnormalities of the blood cells, viz., Red Blood Cell, White blood Cell and Platelets. This aids the researcher, for ease interpretation and common diagnosis of the peripheral blood smear images. Also, this helps the researchers to propose more relevant image processing and machine learning tools for developing a complete automated PBS analysis system that can reduce the time spent for slide examination.

Keywords Morphological abnormalities · Hemoglobin · RBC · Leukocytes

K. Suganya Devi (✉)
Department of CSE, National Institute of Technology, Silchar, Assam 788010, India
e-mail: suganya@cse.nits.ac.in

G. Arutperumjothi
Department of Computer Science and Engineering, University College of Engineering, Tindivanam 607106, India

P. Srinivasan
Department of Physics, National Institute of Technology, Silchar, Assam 788010, India

R. Patgiri et al. (eds.), *Health Informatics: A Computational Perspective in Healthcare*, Studies in Computational Intelligence 932,
https://doi.org/10.1007/978-981-15-9735-0_17

1 Introduction

The development of automated methods for classification of blood cells from digitized blood smears started in 70s decade and becomes a current research in pattern recognition. As of now, complete automated microscopy systems are under development by combining recent developments in machine learning and image processing to reduce the human intervention in the process. Traditionally, visual microscopically examined blood smears are used for diagnosing many diseases by analyzing it quantitatively and qualitatively. Examining these smears by human is very difficult, time consuming, recursive with less statistical reliability [1]. Thus, methods that automate visual analysis tasks have been developed in order to enhance the performance in hematological laboratories. So, Peripheral Blood Smear (PBS) examination is used for analyzing the blood disorders.

A PBS testing is a procedure, in which a special stain is used in the drop of blood spread over the glass slide. Later it is studied under a microscope for examining the blood cells. The drop of blood used for a Blood Smear test contains numerous Red Blood Cells or erythrocytes (RBCs), White Blood Cells or leukocytes (WBCs), and platelets or thrombocytes. A Blood Smear test provides information on the number, shape, and general appearance of the blood cells [2]. It also helps to diagnose a range of deficiencies, diseases, and disorders involving blood cell production, function, and destruction. Analyzing the PBS manually under microscope for detecting several blood disorders is still considered as a gold standard. By this, various cell types is counted (quantitative) and analyzed for structural (qualitative) disorders, etc. But, it involves labor-intensive and time-consuming procedure that requires intensive training and there is a need of technical expertise to interpret the observations in the blood smear. Also, examination of slides by humans has a number of problems. Firstly, it takes lots of time for interpretations [1] thereby it is expensive. Secondly, it is subjective and easily prone to human error, which means that it is very hard to get consistent results from the examination. Both of this has implications for both laboratory resources as well as diagnostic accuracy. So there is a need of automating the process, which enhances reproducibility of the results and reduces cost [3]. To be useful, a fully automated computer-based qualitative and quantitative analysis of blood cells is needed which is faster than a human observer, and at least as accurate as a human observer. As a result, many researchers have addressed problems related to microscopic image analysis of PBS, and indeed developing image analysis systems for computer-assisted interpretations of peripheral blood smears.

The diagnostic importance of PBS are bountiful. The PBS uncovers the structure of peripheral blood cells by which it is ensuring its importance in structural diagnosis of different blood disorders caused by different types of cells. Its diagnostic importance has not been reduced by progression in automating the molecular and hematological examining methods [4]. Structure of the blood cells on a PBS slide can be best discussed in line with each hemopoietic cell lineage. The scattering of cells, its dimensions, structure, and color, inclusion bodies of the RBCs and structure of the other major cell lines should be carefully assessed. Still, few deformities should be considered when reporting like smear or smudge cells that may be artifacts [5].

The following sections of this paper is organized as follows by defining classifications in blood disorders: Sect. 2 discusses and describes various morphological abnormalities of RBCs that lead to anemia; in Sect. 3 various morphological abnormalities of WBCs are discussed; in Sect. 4 various abnormalities in platelets have been discussed followed by conclusion in the last section. The various abnormalities in RBCs have been tabulated for easy understanding.

Qualitative deformities in PBS

The abnormalities in PBS can be categorized into two main categories, Viz., qualitative and quantitative disorders. The quantitative abnormalities is the one in which the count of cells seems to be abnormal either in excess or less but seems to be normal. The qualitative defects are the one in which the cells seems to be abnormal in shape, size or in function, or extrinsic cells are found in circulation.

Qualitative strangeness may involve the morphology of RBC, WBC and plate-lets [3]. RBC morphology examination includes difference in shape, hemoglobin, size, distribution, color and inclusion appearance. WBC morphology evaluation includes abnormalities in nucleus, cytoplasm and inclusion which tells about the diseases [6]. The count of Platelets must be checked in addition with a review of size and shape of blood smear and clumping.

2 Morphological Abnormalities in RBC (Erythrocytes)

Red Blood Cells (RBCs) are the vital element of blood (see Fig. 1). Mature RBCs are in the shape of bi-concave discs with absence of nucleus and cell organelles such as lysome, endoplasmic reticulum and mitochondria. RBCs are seen with diameter of 7.2 μm, but the range is between 6.2 and 8.2 μm for normal. Their width is 2.0 μm, however it can be between 2.0 and 2.5 μm. There is no nucleus [7].

Abnormal RBC structure can be found in different pathological conditions such as:

(1) Anisocytosis: Variations in size
(2) Variations of color

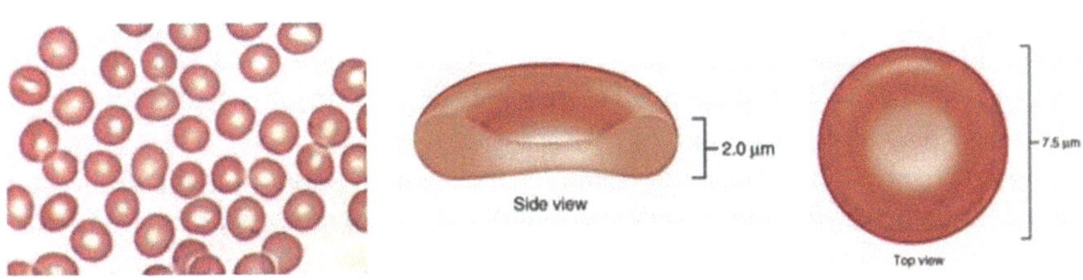

Fig. 1 Normal red blood cells

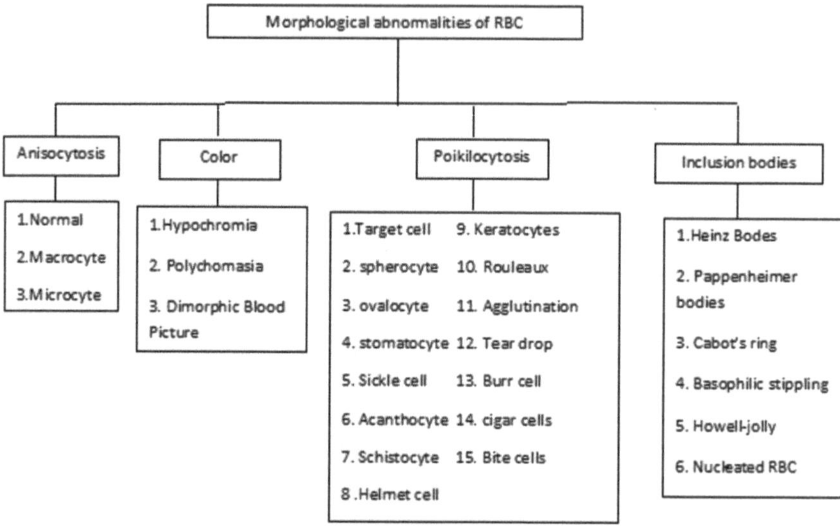

Fig. 2 Morphological abnormalities of RBC

(3) Poikilocytosis: Variations due to shape change
(4) Appearance of inclusion bodies (Fig. 2).

(1) **Anisocytosis**: Difference in the dimensions of the RBCs is called as **anisocytosis** and the degree of anisocytosis in a blood sample is called as the **Red Cell Distribution Width (RDW).** Normally, the size of RBC is 7.5 ± 0.2 μm in diameter. Based on this appearance the abnormalities may be termed as Normocytic, Macrocytic and Microcytic. When the RBC morphology is appeared to be normal, then it is called as normocytic and reported as normochromic [2]. RBCs that appears smaller than the normal size is termed as Microcytes (see Fig. 3a) and reported as Microcytosis. Simply, a microcyte, is a RBC with a small (micro-) mature cell (-cyte). This can be found in the diseases like: Iron deficiency anemia, thalassemia, lead poisoning, side roblastic anemia and anemia due to chronic disorders

RBCs that is greater than the normal size is termed as Macrocytes (see Fig. 3b) and reported as macrocytosis. Simply, a macro-cyte is RBCs with a large (macro-) mature cell (-cyte). Macrocytes are either oval or round [6, 7]. This can be found in the diseases like Liver diseases, hypo-thyroidism, mega loblastic anemia, Deficient in Vit B-12 and Folic acid, Aplastic Anemia, Neonates, chemo therapy, post splenectomy and some other causes of elevated erythropoiesis.

Figure 4 the reference range for Mean red Cell Volume (MCV) in fem to liter for normocytes, microcytes and macrocytes. MCV can be given as

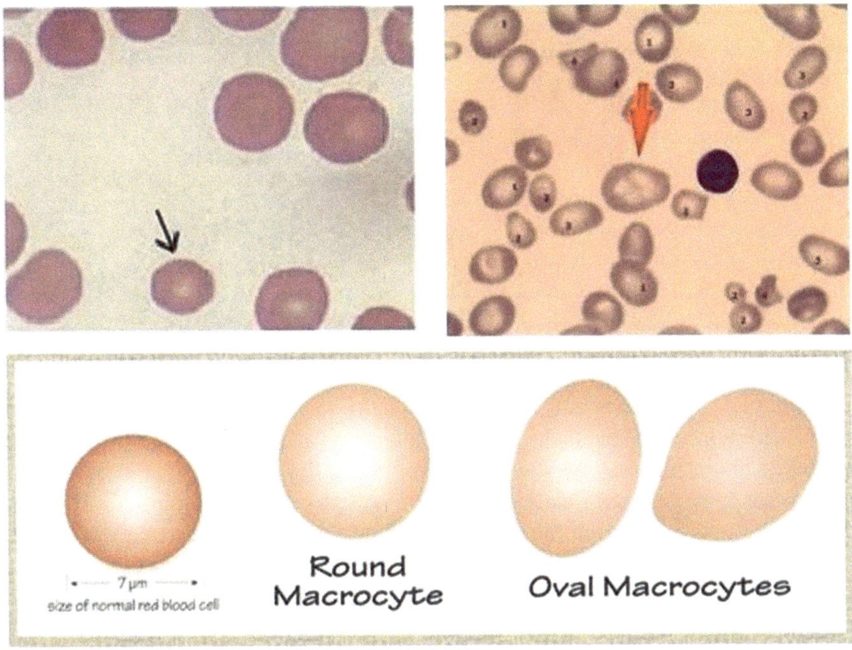

Fig. 3 Microcytes and macrocytes

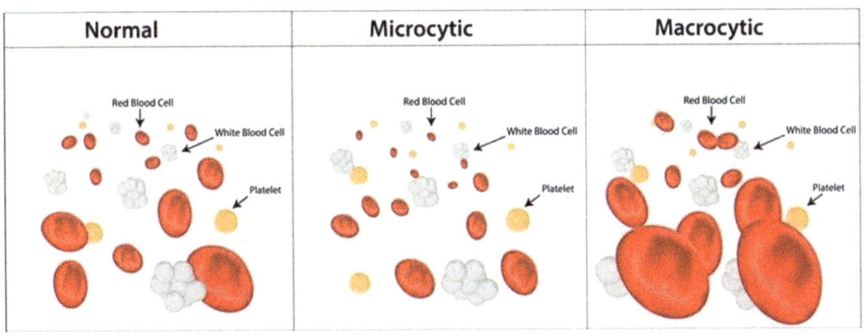

Fig. 4 The reference range for Mean red Cell Volume (MCV)

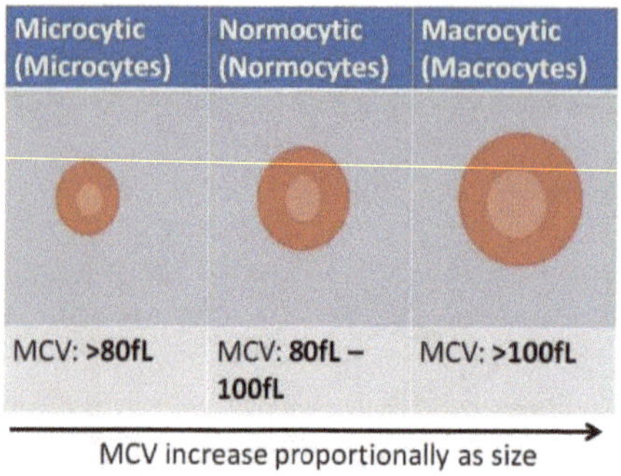

$$\frac{\text{Total Packed RBC}}{\text{Total RBC number}}\, X\, 10 = \text{MCV}$$

(2) **Variation in color**: RBCs that seems to be in bi-concave shape and having an area of central pallor that occupies approximately one-third (normal amount of hemoglobin) of the cell's diameter are called as normo-chromic RBCs. The hemoglobin amount gives the color to the RBCs. Increase in hemoglobin is termed hyper-chromia and decrease in hemoglobin is hypo-chromia [6]. The RBCs contains hemoglobin that can be either in oxygenated state or in deoxygenated state; in the former case it is called oxy-hemoglobin and in the latter case it is called de-oxyhemoglobin. In short, oxy-hemoglobin and de-oxyhemoglobin are nothing but the different shades of red. Oxy-hemoglobin is a brilliant scarlet-red, while de-oxyhemoglobin is a darker burgundy-red.

(i) **Hypo-chromia**: Hypo-chromia is the prevalent abnormality found in color that occurs in RBCs. Hypo—means "less" and chromic means "color". So, hypochromic cell can be described as 'a cell with less color'. In other words, RBCs that have a pallor area that is bigger than the normal are called hypo-chromic [8]. Hypo-chromic RBCs (see Fig. 5a) are pale in color (due to lose their red coloration) as they lack hemoglobin within them. Some of the abnormalities due to Hypo-chromia: IDA, Thalassemia, Side-roblastic anemia, Lead poisoning, some cases of chronic inflammation and any of these conditions leading to micro cytosis.

(ii) **Poly-chromasia**: This lacks central pallor; RBCs stain gives the shades of blue-gray due to absorption of both basic dyes and Eosin by RNA and hemoglobin

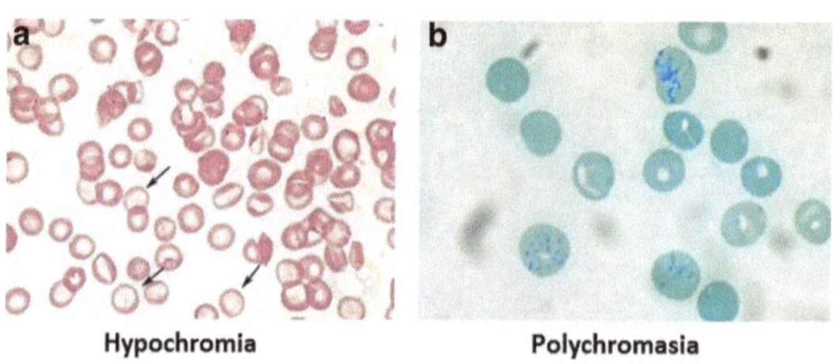

Fig. 5 Polychromasia

respectively. Often it seems to be slightly bigger than normal RBCs and round in shape - round macro cytosis. Poly-chromasia literally translates to poly- "many, chrome- "color," because of many immature RBCs being released into the blood stream with different shades of bluish gray (See Fig. 5b). Poly-chromasia often indicates the symptom of bone marrow stress as well as the presence of immature RBCs [9]. Some of the diseases associated with poly-chromasia include: Acute and Chronic Hemorrhage, Hemolysis, Effective treatment for anemia and neonates.

(iii) **Di-morphic Blood Picture** are the two different groups of red cells. These groups may vary in their dimensions, structure or hemoglobin content [1]. These can be seen in Anemic patient after transfusion, Iron deficiency patient's taking supplements, Combined B12 / folate and iron deficiency, Side-roblastic anemia.

(3) **Poikilocytosis**: The difference seen in the structure of RBCs is called Poikilocytosis and any abnormally shaped RBC is known as Poikilocyte. RBC appears as bi-concave disk in large blood vessels but their shape changes due to change in capillaries. Poikilocytes occurs due to abnormalities in membrane or by traum. Poikilocytes that are caused because of abnormalities in membrane are: Acantho-cytes (Spur Cells), Codo-cytes (Target Cells), Echino-cytes and Burr Cells, Sphero-cytes, Stomato-cytes (Mouth Cells), Drepano-cytes (Sickle cells), Degma-cytes ("Bite Cells"). Poikilocytes that are caused due to trauma are: Dacro-cytes (Teardrop cells), Blister Cells and Kerato-cytes, Microsphero-cytes and Pyro-poikilocytes, Schisto-cytes, Semilunar Bodies.

(i) **Acantho-cytes (Spur cells)**: The word acantho - means "thorns". Thus, acanthocytes is the cells that are having a membrane with spikes as shown in Fig. 6, due to irregular thorny projections that varies in width, length and count [10]. In particular, there is no central area of pallor and simply, they are RBCs with improperly spaced projection. Projections are varies in size (normally width) but normally contains a round. Spherical cells with two to twenty spikes of uneven size (length) are distributed unequally in the red cell surface. Acantho-cytes can be seen in: liver diseases, post splenectomy, anorexia nervosa and starvation,

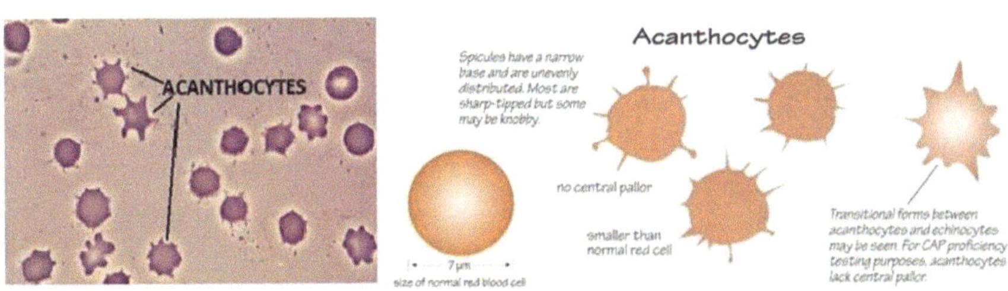

Fig. 6 Acanthrocytes (see the thorn like projections which are uneven, and of varying distribution, length and width)

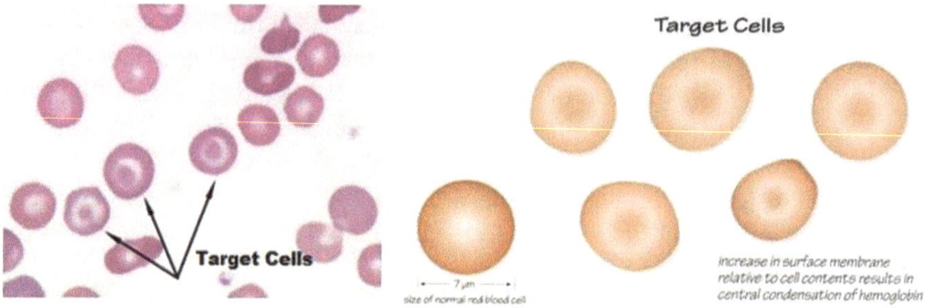

Fig. 7 Target cells

Hypothyroidism, Malabsorption, alcoholism, Vit-E deficiency. They are also found in an inherited disorder called a beta lipoproteineimia.

(ii) **Target cells (codocyte)**: Codo-cytes, otherwise called as Target cells, looks like typical RBCs, with a central area of pallor with proper size. They seems to have a dark, red spot in the middle and hence they are also known as **bull's eye** cells [10, 11]. Red cells have an area of increase in stain that appears in the area of central pallor as shown in the Fig. 7. Target cells can be seen in these diseases like: Obstructive Liver Disease, severe IDA, thalassemia, Hemoglobinopathies (S and C), post splenectomy, LCAT (Lechitin-Cholesterol AcylTransferase) Deficiency.

(iii) **Echinocytes or Burr Cells**: Echino—means hedgehog, or sea urchin (Greek word *echinos*). Echnino-cytes are burr-like erythro cyte with properly spaced, short blunt projections. It is a RBC having an abnormal membrane with thorny projections as like acanthocytes. The dissimilarity between the acantho-cyte and the echino-cyte can be seen in the structure of their thorny projections [11]. Acantho-cytes have unevenly spaced projections with varied dimension size and numbers whereas Echino-cytes have evenly spaced projections that are small in size (see Fig. 8). Also, under the Wright Stain (as shown in Figure), echinocytes appears to have a central area of pallor but Acantho-cytes show little to no central pallor. Both acantho-cytes and echino-cytes

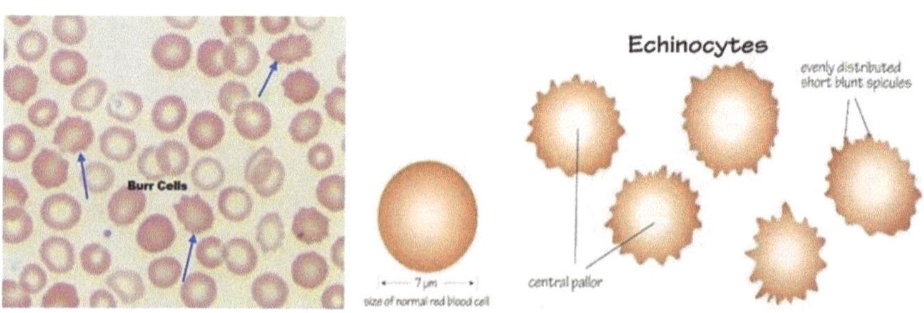

Fig. 8 Echinocytes

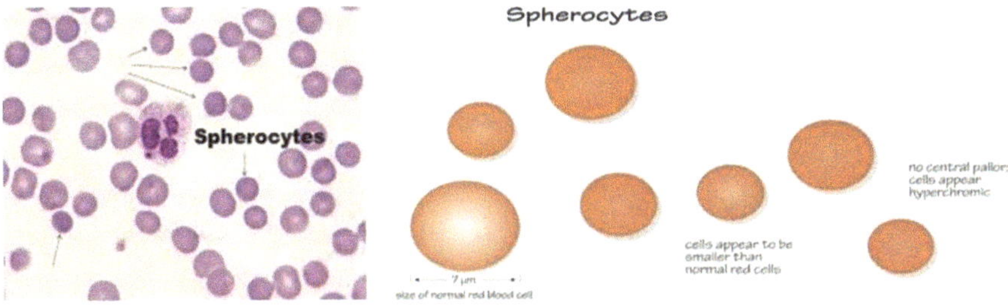

Fig. 9 Spherocytes

occurs due to the malformation in the cell membrane of the RBC. Red cells are covered with ten to thirty short spikes of regular form. These cells can be in the diseases like: Uraemia, Pyruvate Kinase Deficiency, Neonates, Hemolytic anemia, severe burns, EDTA artifact, Liver disease.

(iv) **Sphero-cytes**: RBCs do not have the bi-concave disk shape of the normal cell and seems to be more spherical with absence of Central pallor (see Fig. 9). It has increased hemoglobin content. The sphero-cytes are actually small in size than the normal RBCs, and therefore cannot be macro cytes. In contrast, micro cytes shows a central area of pallor whereas sphero cytes do not have central polar [10]. These are seen in the diseases like: hereditary sphero-cytosis, immune hemolytic anemia, Transfused cells, Zieve's syndrome.

(v) **Stomato-cytes (Mouth cells)**: Red cells seen with a central linear slit or stoma that looks like mouth shaped form in peripheral blood smear [12]. In short and simple, they look like coffee beans as shown in the Fig. 10. Stomato-cytes can be seen in the diseases like: excess alcoholism, alcoholic liver disease, hereditary stomatocytosis, Hereditary spherocytosis, Rh Null Phenotype for Blood.

(vi) **Sickle cells (Drepanocytes)**: These are the RBC that shaped like cresent or sickle blade, or a crescent. Sickle cells (see Fig. 11) can be seen in Hb-S disease/sickle cell anemia [6].

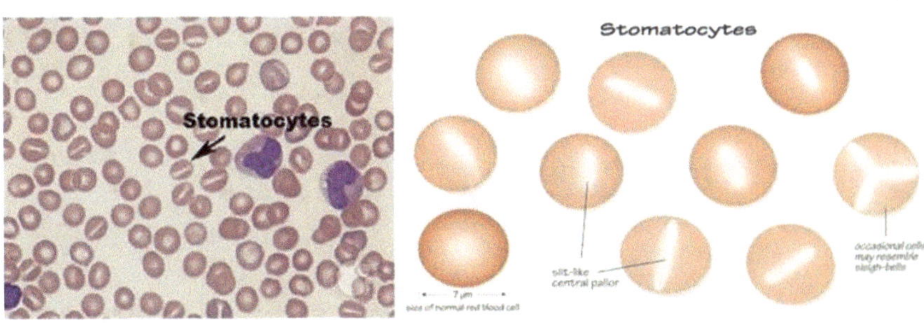

Fig. 10 Stomatocytes

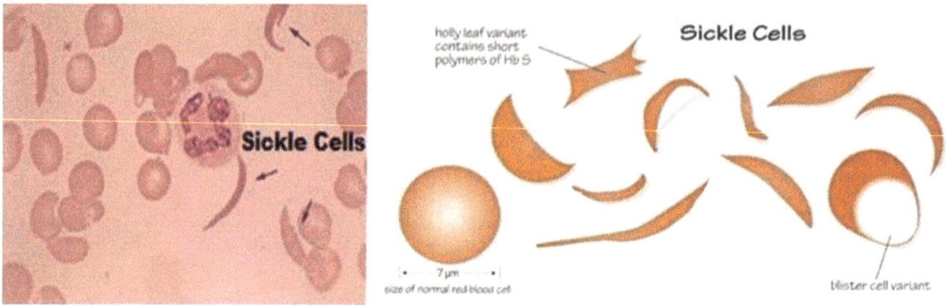

Fig. 11 Sickle cells

(vii) **Ovalo-cytes (egg-shaped) and Ellipto-cytes (Cigar shaped)**: RBCs that differ in structure from elongated to oval or even like a cigar or pencil (see Fig. 12), and rich in hemoglobin, are called ovalo-cytes and ellipto-cytes, respectively. They can be seen in the diseases that comes by hereditary disorders, such as hereditary elliptocytosis, or in acquired disorders, such as iron deficiency anemia, infectious anemias, thalassemia, and in new born babies, sickle cell anemia.

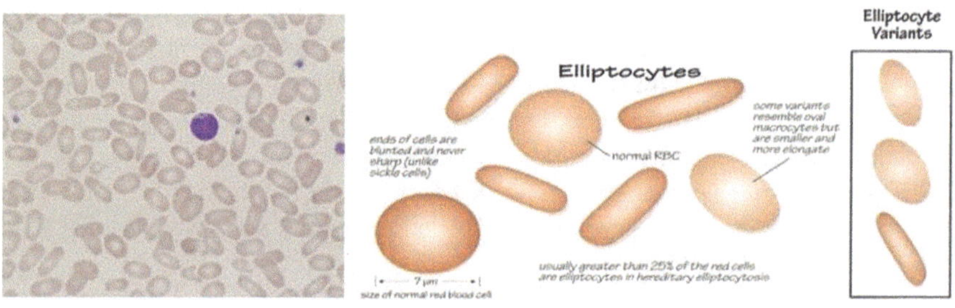

Fig. 12 Ovalocytes

Fig. 13 Bite cells

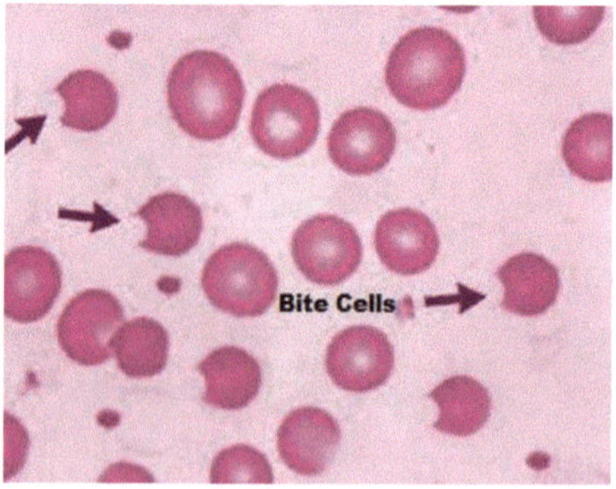

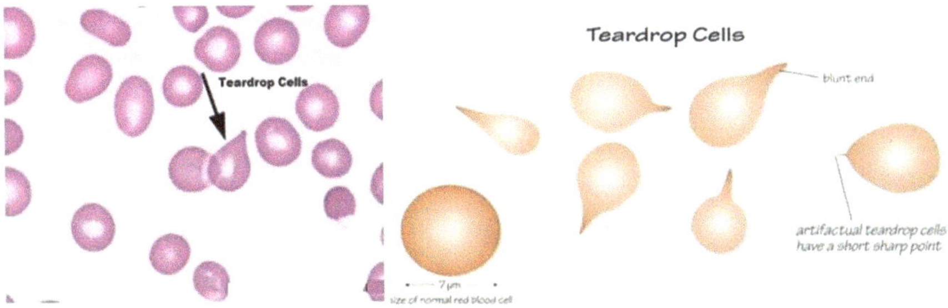

Fig. 14 Teardrop cells

(viii) **Degmacytes (Bite cells)**: It is an abnormally shaped RBC (shown in Fig. 13) with one or more semi-circular portions removed from the cell margin which looks like a bite. These "bites" formed as a result of removal [13] and can be seen in the denatured hemoglobin by macrophages in the spleen.
Glucose-6-Phosphate Dehydrogenase deficiency (G6PD) is a common disorder [14] in which uncontrolled oxidative stress causes hemoglobin to denature and form Heinz bodies that leads to the formation of bite cells. It can be seen in: Glucose-6-phosphate Dehydrogenase Deficiency (G6PD).

(ix) **Dacro-cytes (Teardrop cells)**: These are RBCs that looks like teardrop or pear (see Fig. 14) and are usually microcytic and are often hypo-chromic [15]. Teardrop cells can be seen in the diseases like: myelo-fibrosis, mega-loblastic anemia, IDA, Beta thalassemia, Myelophthisic anemias, Extramedullary Hematopoiesis.

(x) **Blister Cells and Kerato-cytes**: Blister cells are RBCs with vacuoles or markedly thin areas at outer region of membrane. These cells shows the sign of deficiency in G6PD and other conditions imposing oxidant stress on the erythro-cyte [16]. Cells with pseudo vacuoles are called "blister" cells or pre-keratocytes (see Fig. 15a). When the vacuole breaks (usually within minutes), the balance cell resembles like a helmet with straps or a horned cell which is designated as a kerato-cyte (see Fig. 15c). Otherwise these cells looks like half-moon with two or more spicules. Simply, Kerato-cytes are damaged cells

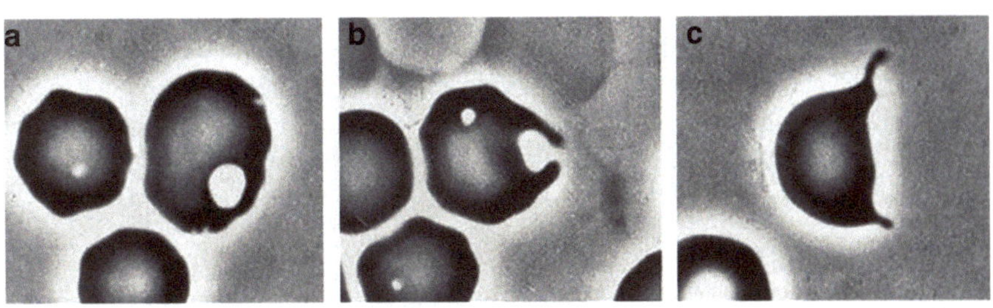

Fig. 15 **a** Blister cell, **b** blister cell bursts, **c** final Keratocytes

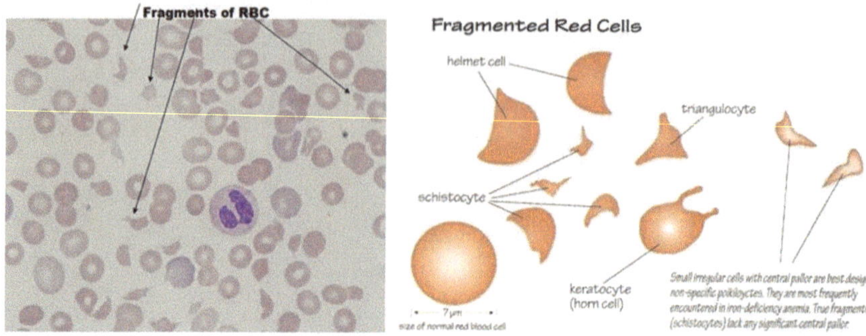

Fig. 16 Schistocytes

and it can be seen in the diseases like G6PD deficiency, pulmonary embolism, disseminated intravascular coagulation.

(xi) **Schisto-cytes**: These are helmet or triangular shaped, fragmented or greatly distorted RBCs smaller than normal size (see Fig. 16). It is literally a broken piece of a RBC and they are unevenly shaped, jagged and have pointed extremities, that is, usually 2 pointy ends. There is no central pallor area since they are simply fragments of RBCs [18]. Schisto-cytes can be seen in diseases like: Thalassemia, micro-angiopathic hemolytic anemia, mechanical hemolytic anemia, uremia, artificial heart valves, Thrombotic thrombocytopenic purpura.

(xii) **Red cell agglutinate**: These are improper clumps of RBCs which are found in cold agglutinations, warm autoimmune hemolysis [19].

(xiii) **Rouleaux Formation**: In this, the RBCs are arranged in a Stack which looks like a stack of coins. These are found in hyper globulinemia, hyper fibrinogenaemia [19].

(Xiii) **Unique cases of poikilocytosis**: These distinctive cases of poikilocytosis are classified into two vital hemoglobinopathies Viz., Hemoglobin SC disease and Hemoglobin C Crystals [20].

Hemoglobin SC Disease

Hemoglobin S-C disease is a hemoglobinopathy that shows symptoms that are similar to sickle cell disease, but milder than sickle cell. In this condition, only one allele of the autosomal sickle cell trait is present in patients [21]. Though they are not exactly "sickle cells" they still produce some abnormality in cell morphology. Therefore they are called as "mitten-shaped" cells with one or two finger like projections as shown in the Fig. 17.

Hemoglobin C Crystals

Hemoglobin C (reduced as Hb C or HbC) is an unusual hemoglobin that has occurred by glutamic acid residue and a lysine residue substitution at the sixth position of the β-globin chain. The softness of host erythro-cytes is changed to mutated form and

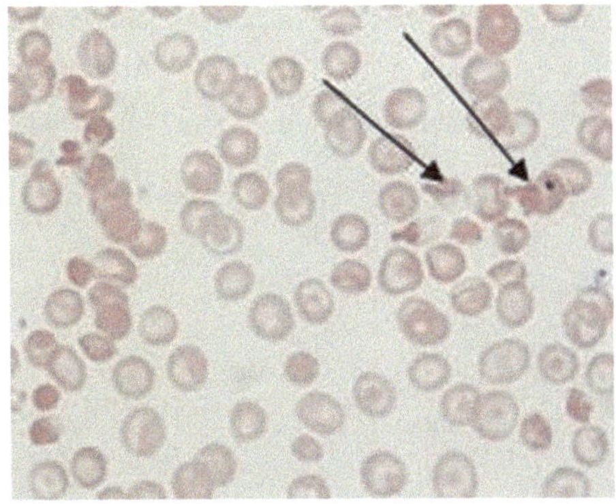

Fig. 17 Hemoglobin SC disease

thereby causes a hemoglobinopathy [21, 22] Target cells, micro sphero-cytes and HbC crystals are found in a blood smear of a homozygous patient. They look like pills. Hb C crystals are the notable cell seen in this condition, and is shown in the Fig. 18.

(4) **RBC inclusions**: Inclusion bodies are the idle things that are inactive in the cells. They are just included inside the cell, for some purpose. These are nuclear or cytoplasmic aggregates of stainable substance, normally proteins [23]. These inclusions in RBCs shows some indications on pathology, and so it is good to know about these inclusions that are seen within a RBC. Some of the Inclusion Bodies within RBCs are Howell-Jolly Body, Heinz Body, Nucleated RBC, Pappenhemier Body, Basophilic Stippling, Cabot Ring (Table 1).

(i) **Howell-Jolly bodies**: These are small round cytoplasmic red cell inclusion (see Fig. 19) with the same staining characteristics as that of nuclei and these are nothing but fragments of DNA [24]. These are found in post splenectomy, Severe Megaloblastic Anemia, sever hemolytic anemia, Hyposplenism.

(ii) **Heinz bodies**: These are formed by the damage caused probably by oxidative stress but also by genetic abnormalities and losing its characteristics of the hemoglobin component of RBCs (methemoglobin) [25]. With a supra vital stain

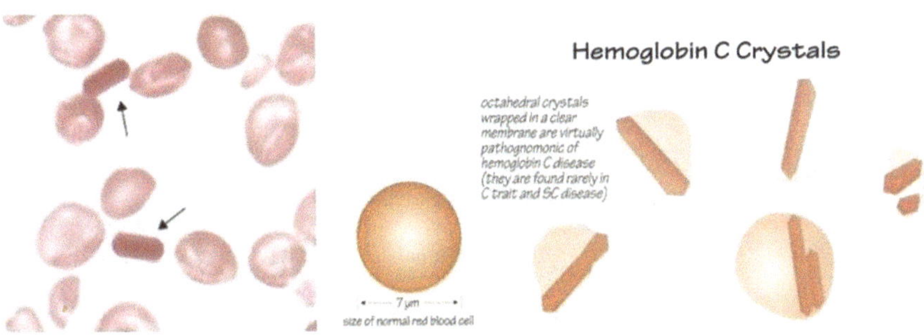

Fig. 18 Hemoglobin C crystals

Table 1 Summarize abnormalities of RBC (Poikilocytes)

S. No.	Poikilocytes	Appearance	Key Features
1	Acanthocytes [10]	Crenated RBC with very spiny, irregular projections	Size: diameter smaller than normal cells (like spherocytes) Shape: 3–20 irregular membrane spikes, **unevenly distributed** Cytoplasm: **no central pallor**
2	Echinocyte (Burr Cell) [11]	Similar to crenated RBCs but projections are less pointed and more regular than acanthocytes	Size: normocytic Shape: 10–30 evenly distributed short, blunt or pointed spicules; projections uniformly sized Cytoplasm: normochromic; retains central pallor (unlike acanthocytes)
3	Elliptocytes (Oval, Pencil Cell) [11]	elongate with round ends (cigar, egg, pencil shapes)	Size: variable; usually longer than normal red cell and much more narrow Shape: uniform, symmetrical rod shape; sides nearly parallel Cytoplasm: often retain central pallor
4	Teardrop Cells (dacrycocyte)	Round ells with elongated tail or point; resembles a teardrop	Size: microcytic to normocytic Shape: teardrop or pear-shaped RBC with single tapered end (tail) that is blunt or round Cytoplasm: normochromic to hypochromic
5	Stomatocyte (Hydrocyte) [12]	RBC with a slit-like central pallor	Size: normocytic Shape: round; uniconcave disk Cytoplasm: normochromic; central pallor appears slit-like, straight, fish mouth, or curved rod-shaped; a few cells may have tri- polar pallor creating cells that resemble sleigh bells
6	Spherocytes	Cells appear perfectly round and have no central pallor; often smaller than normal RBCs	Size: slightly microcytic Shape: round to spherical Cytoplasm: no central pallor

(continued)

Table 1 (continued)

S. No.	Poikilocytes	Appearance	Key Features
7	Schistocytes (helmet cell, triangulocyte, keratocyte, horn cell, fragmented RBCs) [18]	Pieces of RBCs that can have a vast variety of shapes and sizes	Size: irregular cell sizes; usually microcytic Shape: shapes vary from helmetto triangular to unclassified fragments Cytoplasm:small fragments **lack central pallor**; horn cells can be normochromic
8	Target cells (Codocytes) [10]	RBCs have a bullseye appearance	Size: normocytic to slightly macrocytic Shape: round Cytoplasm: increased surface membrane to volume ratio results in a central, darker hemoglobin region within the area of central pallor creating the appearance of a target or bulls-eye
9	Target cells (Codocytes) [10]	RBCs have a bullseye appearance	Size: normocytic to slightly macrocytic Shape: round Cytoplasm: increased surface membrane to volume ratio results in a central, darker hemoglobin region within the area of central pallor creating the appearance of a target or bullseye
10	Sickle cells (drepanocyte) [6]	Usually a thin, crescent shaped cell	Shape:sickle shaped with at least one pointed end; may also be crescent shaped, boat shaped, filament shaped, holly leaf form (rarely) and envelope shaped Cytoplasm: no central pallor; very dense hemoglobin concentration (normochromic to hyperchromic)
11	NRBCs	RBC with a small, pyknotic nucleus with dense chromatin	Size: 8–10 μm size; slightly larger than a mature RBC Cytoplasm: varies depending on stage of maturation; usually more blue-gray

(continued)

Table 1 (continued)

S. No.	Poikilocytes	Appearance	Key Features
12	Howell-Jolly Bodies (nuclear fragment, HJ bodies, Ho-Jo's) [25]	Large, singular dark purple inclusion	Size 1 μm; sometimes as small as 0.5 μm Shape: spherical or oblong blue-purple or blue-black inclusion Cytoplasm: normochromic or hypochromic Location: eccentrically located (off center); usually a single inclusion, but multiple can be present
13	Basophillic Stippling (punctuated basophilia) [27]	Medium-sized, blue- black dots (granules) evenly distributed throughout the RBC	Size of granules: numerous small coarse or fine granules: uniform in size and shape, 0.5 μm in diameter Cytoplasm: uniformly filled with deep blue or blue-gray dots
14	Pappenheimer Bodies [26]	Small dark blue-purple staining hemoglobin iron granules; seen on Wright stained smear and confirmed with iron (Prussian blue) stain	Size: Usually less than 1 mm (Sometimes <0.5 mm) Shape: blue-purple granules with irregular, sharp edges (not round) Location: usually found along the periphery of the cell; one or two irregular, small blue- purple-green granules; if present in multiples, they form irregular closely aggregated clusters
15	Hemoglobin Crystals [22]	dense staining, angular crystalline forms that vary in shape; may be rectangular, rod-shaped, tetragonal, octahedral (Washington monument, gold bar), spherocytic, rhomboid, or hexagonal	Size: variable since crystals may markedly distort the cell Shape: a normal disk shape is distorted by the crystal; cytoplasm contains the crystal, which is a precipitate of hemoglobin C or SC Cytoplasm: often pale or colorless; there is generally a clear area around the crystal

like crystal violet, these Heinz bodies appears as round blue precipitate. Seen in G6PD Deficiency, Chronic Liver Disease, Alpha Thalassemia, splenectomy.

(iii) **Pappen-heimer bodies**: These are basophilic erythrocytic inclusions that are usually located at the outer region of the cell. They contain iron content and stain with Prussian blue as shown in Fig. 20. This stain is used to identify that

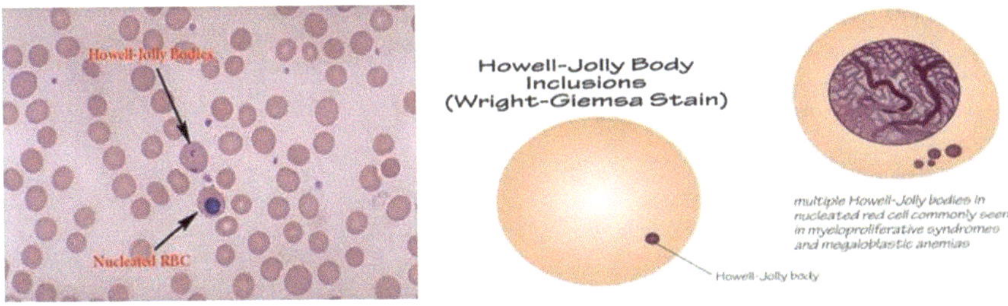

Fig. 19 Howell-Jolly body inclusions

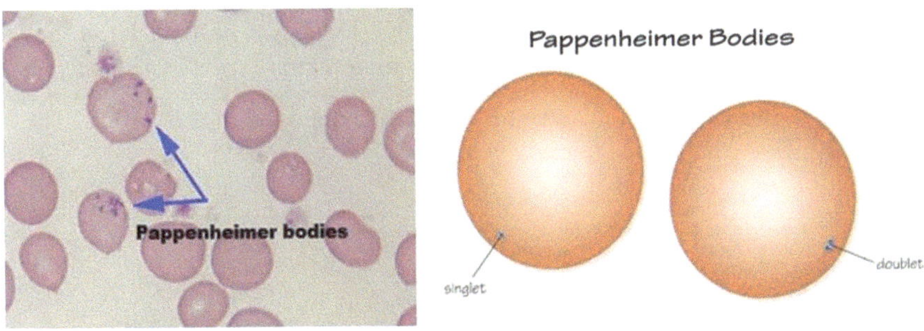

Fig. 20 Pappenheimer bodies

these inclusion bodies are pure iron deposits, and not heme as in Heinz Bodies [26]. These represent iron deposits in Wright Stain that turns into dense blue with uneven granules. Cells that contains these inclusions can be confused with late reticulocytes. Prussian blue stain, which is not taken up by reticulocytes, is helpful in differentiating these two inclusions. Pappen-heimer bodies are found in RBCs of patients with hemolyticanemia, splenectomy, side-roblastic anemia, Megaloblastic anemia, Hemoglobinopathies.

Basophilic Stippling: Basophilic stippling is also referred to as punctuate basophilia (shown in Fig. 21) that comes in fine and coarse granules located in a fairly evenly distributed manner [27]. These granules are nothing but accumulations of ribosomes and RNA. This can be found in hemoglobinopathies thalassemia, side-roblastic anemia, megaloblastic anemia and a rare inherited condition, pyrimidine 5′nucleotidase deficiency, severe infections, hemolytic anemia, liverdamage, heavy metal (lead or arsenic) poisoning.

(iv) **Cabot's Ring**: These are rings, loops or number '8′ type structures (see Fig. 22) that are located within the cytoplasm of the RBC. They look like beads on a string. They are typically red purple colored when it is stained by Wright Stain [28]. Red purple colored thread-like rings are seen in RBCs of severe anemias. These are the reminants of nuclear membrane. Some of the disorders linked with Cabot's Ring are: Myelodysplastic Syndrome, Megaloblastic Anemia.

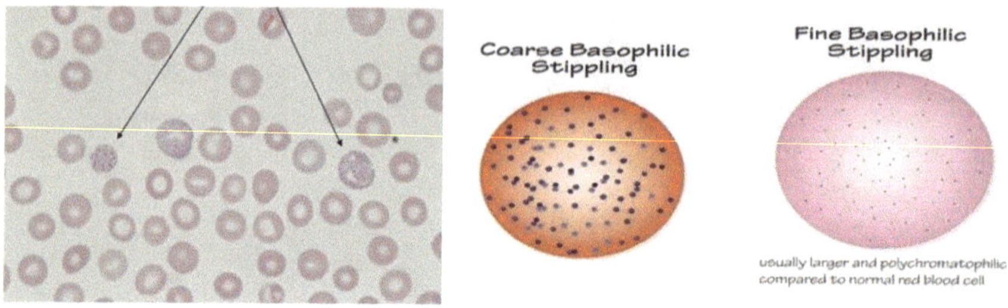

Fig. 21 Basophilic stippling

(v) **Nucleated RBCs**: These are immature RBCs appears to have nuclei as shown in Fig. 23 and are not normally seen in the outer region except in neonates [29].

The following figure summarizes the qualitative abnormalities of RBCs. These structure of RBC can be used to classify anemia.

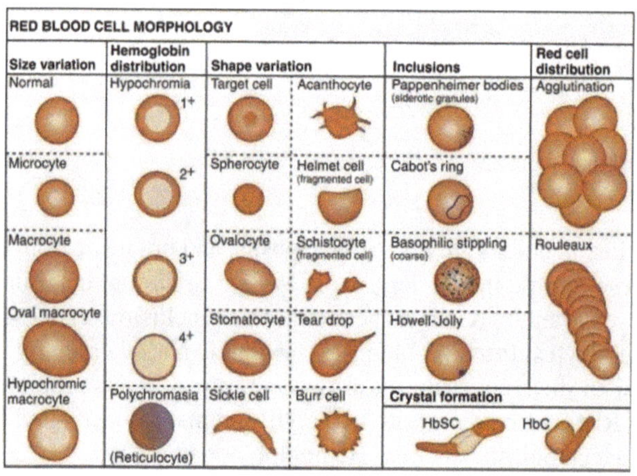

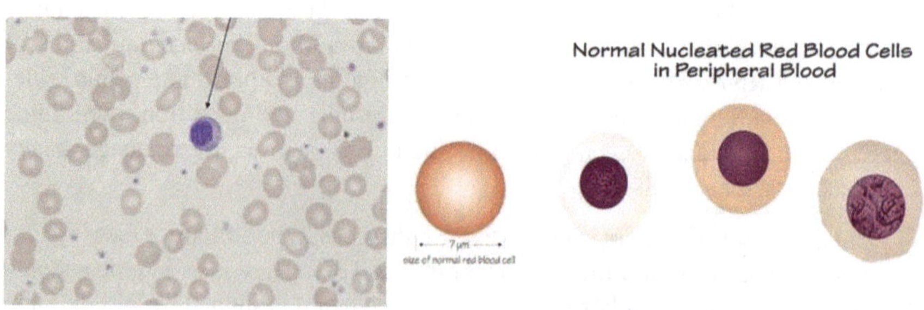

Fig. 23 Nucleated RBC's

3 Morphology of White Blood Cell (Normal Leukocytes) and Its Abnormalities

White Blood Cells (WBCs) will have a nucleus surrounded by cytoplasm as shown in Fig. 24. And they are derived from bone marrow stem cells. In the bone marrow, these are differentiated into two groups: granulo cytic and lymphoid cells [28]. Morphologic appearances of WBC's on a peripheral blood smear includes:

1. ***Polymorpho nuclear neutrophil***: Neutrophil measures 14–15 μm in size. Its cytoplasm is colorless or slightly eosinophilic and contains multiple, small, fine, mauve granules. Nucleus has two to five anatomical classifications that are interconnected by fine chromatin strands. Nuclear-chromatin is condensed and has dense purple color staining [31]. A partitioned neutrophil has at least two anatomical classifications (lobes) interconnected by a chromatin strand. A band neutrophil shows unpartitioned U-shaped nucleus of equal size. Usually band neutrophil contains less than 3% of all leukocytes. Majority of neutrophils have three anatomical classifications, but less than 5% have five anatomical classifications. In females, 2–3% of neutrophils shows a small projection (called drumstick) in the nuclear lobe which represents one inactivated X chromosome.
2. ***Eosinophil***: These are a bit bigger than neutrophils in the range of 15–16 μm. The nucleus is many a time bi-lobed and the cytoplasm is packed with numerous bright orange red granules that are large in size. On blood smears, some of the eosinophils are often broken [2].
3. ***Basophils:*** These are seen infrequently on normal blood smears. These are small in the range of 9–12 μm, round to oval cells with deep purple granules that are very large in size. It is hard to see the nucleus as it covered by granules [31].
4. ***Monocytes:*** these are the largest of the leukocytes appears in the range of 15–20 μm. They are improper in structure, with oval or clefted (kidney-shaped) nucleus and fine, delicate chromatin. Cytoplasm is ample enough with blue gray aspect and often contains fine azurophil granules and vacuoles. After getting moved from blood to tissues they are referred to as macrophages [8].

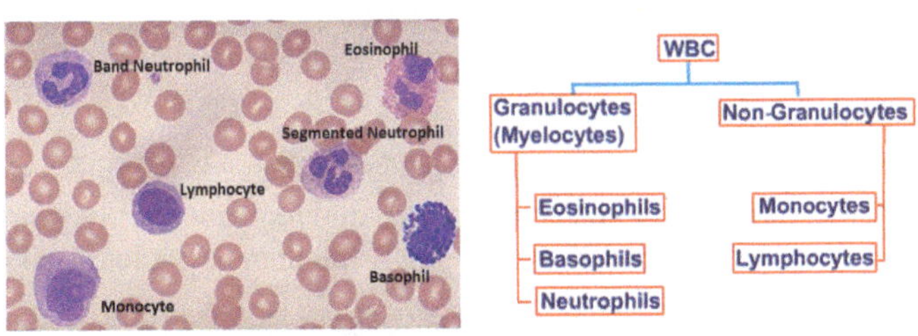

Fig. 24 Normal white blood cell

Structure component	Nucleus Appearance	Function	Example
Neutrophil [31]	Multi-lobed	These are the usual and prime responders to microbial infection	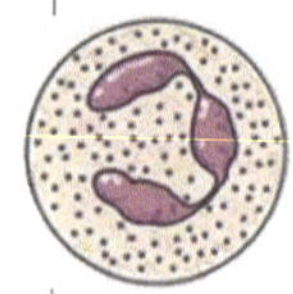
Eosinophil [2]	Bi-lobed	Inflammatory(all ergic reaction and parasitic)	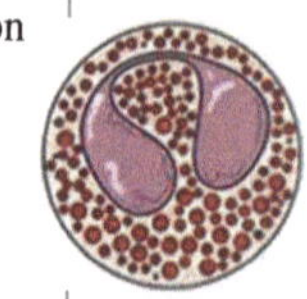
Basophil [31]	Bi/Tri-lobed	Allergic and antigen response	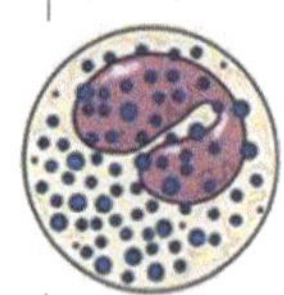
Lymphocyte [28]	Deep staining, Eccentric	Include B cells, CD4 cells, and CD8 + cyt cells. Operate primar lymphatic system	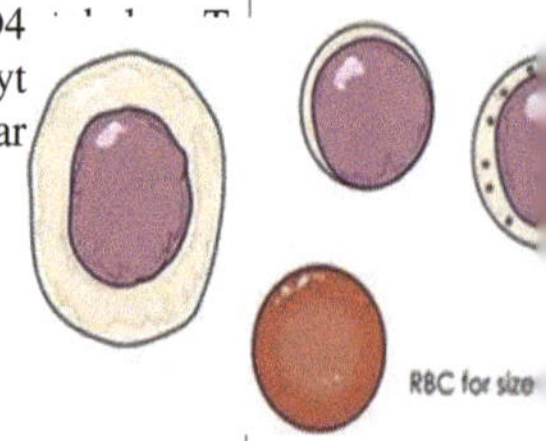
Monocyte [8]	Kidney shaped	Phagocytosis of pathogens Presentation of antigens to T cells. It removes dead cell debri and attack Microorganisms	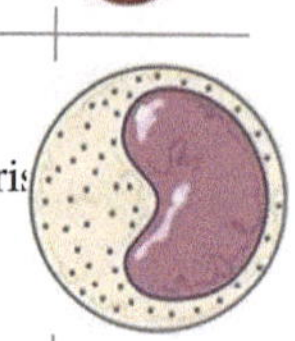

5. ***Lympho-cytes***: On PBS, one can see small and large lympho-cytes. The large numbers of lympho-cytes looks small in size in the range 7–8 μm. These cells have a high nuclear cytoplasmic ratio with a thin rim of deep blue cytoplasm. The nucleus seems to be round or slightly clefted with coarsely clumped chromatin. Large lympho-cytes are in the order of 10–15 μm and have a more pale blue cytoplasm in plenty in addition with some azurophil granules. Nucleus is oval or round and mostly placed on one side of the cell [28].

Abnormalities in Leukocytes

(i) **Toxic Granulation**: Leukocytes having enlarged granules with more basophilic. These have coarse granules and dark stains of blue purple in the cytoplasm of neutrophils. They are usually found in severe bacterial infections and are shown in Fig. 25a [9, 27].

(ii) **Dohle inclusion bodies (Amato Bodies)**: They looks like small oval shaped light blue cytoplasmic inclusions usually found in the outer region of

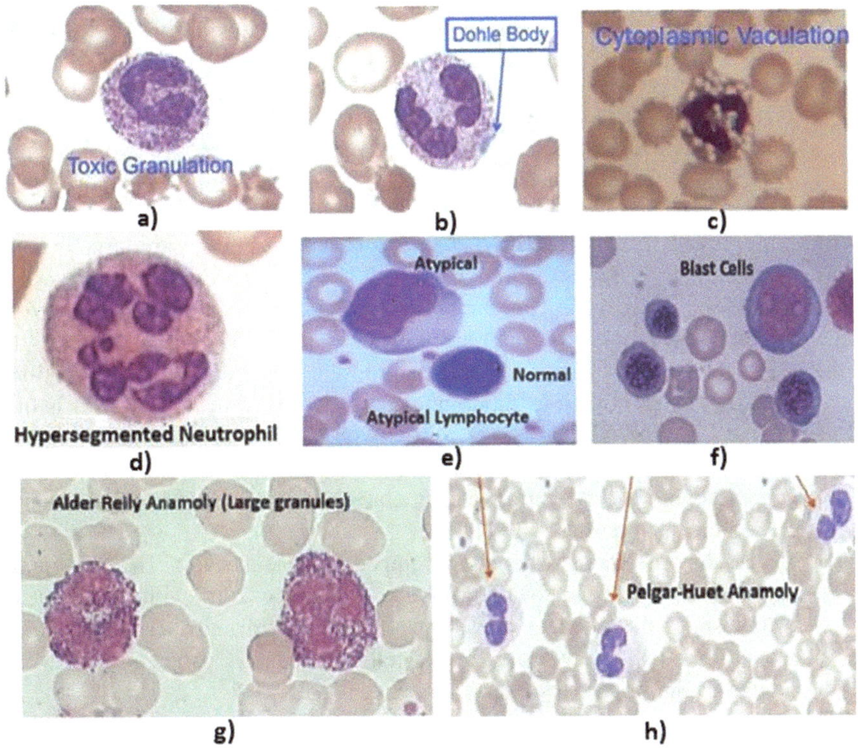

Fig. 25 **a** Toxic granulation **b** Dohle body **c** Cytoplasmic Vaculation **d** Hypersegmented Neutrophil **e** Atypical Lymphocyte **f** Blast cells **g** Alder Reilyanamoly **h** Pelgar-HuetAnamoly

neutrophils (see Fig. 25b). They represents reminants of ribosome and rough endoplasmic reticulum. They usually have toxic granules and are found in bacterial infections [30] like: Inflammatory and infectious states, severe burns, Tuber culosis, Post chemo-therapy, Pregnancy.

(iii) **Cytoplasmic vacuoles**: Vacuoles in neutrophils (cytoplasm of granulocytes) are indicators of phago cytosis and are seen in bacterial infections, Toxic effect of ethanol, and Jordan's anomalyas (Refer Fig. 25c).

(iv) **Shift to left of neutrophils**: This denotes the presence of under developed cells of neutrophil series (band forms and meta myelocytes) in peripheral blood and occurs during infections and inflammatory disorders [31]. This can be seen during pregnancy or neonate, Infections, Bone marrow fibrosis and infiltration by malignancies. Severe neutrophilia with left shift is coined as leukaemoid reaction.

(v) **Hyper segmented or right shift of neutrophils**: Hyper segmentation of neutrophils is said to be present when greater than 5% of neutrophils have five or more anatomical classification (see Fig. 25d). These are seems to be bigger in size and are so called as macro polycytes [32, 33]. They are found where there is deficiency in folic acid or vit B-12 denotes one of the earliest signs.

(vi) **Pseudo Pelger Huet cells**: It is a bilobed neutrophil with condensed chromatin as shown in Fig. 25e).In this, there is failure of nuclear segmentation of granulocytes so that nuclei are rod-like, round, or have two segments [34]. These granulocytes are also observed in myelo proliferative disorders (pseudo-Pelger-Huet cells).

(vii) **Alder Reilly granules**: These coarse azurophilic granules are large in size with dark purple stains (as shown in Fig. 25f) which mostly found in the cytoplasm of granulocytes. These are characteristically found in the AlderReilly anomaly and in patients with muco polysaccharides [35].

(viii) **Atypical lymphocytes**: They are found in the smear during viral infection, in particular in infectious mono nucleosis (as shown in Fig. 25g). It is big in size, unevenly shaped lympho-cytes with ample cytoplasm and irregular nuclei. Cytoplasm shows bead like structure that decorates the borders and deep basophilia at the edges. Nuclear chromatin is less dense and occasional nucleolus may present [36].

(ix) **Blast cells**: They are most under developed of the leukocytes. They are big in the range of 15–25 μm, oval to round cells (see Fig. 25h), with high nuclear cytoplasmic ratio. Nucleus shows one or more nucleoli and nuclear chromatin seems to be under developed. These cells are found in patients with severe infections, infiltrative disorders, and leukemia.

4 Morphology of Platelets and Its Abnormalities

Platelets are small in size (1–3 μm in diameter) and purple structures with tiny uneven projections on surface. These occurs in clumps in the blood films that are prepared from non-anticoagulated blood (i.e., direct finger stick) [37]. The platelet count is the prime evaluation criteria in many of the lab tests as it shows the function of the hemostatic system. Platelet defects can be classified either by their clot formation location in the three phases say, initiation, extension, and cohesion or aggregation or by the deficiency found in their structure or function.

(i) **Platelet Satellitism**: Platelets crumped around Neytrophils (see Fig. 26a). This describes the phenomenon of adherence of platelets to white Blood Cells [37]. They are seen in intravenous EDTA that has no clinical symptoms other than false low platelets counts.(in vitro).

(ii) **Giant Platelets**: Platelets seems to be larger than the Red cells (see Fig. 26b). This can be seen in increased platelet turnover, Myelo proliferative disorders, Myelo dysplastic disorders.

(iii) **Large Platelets**: These are larger than one-third of normal platelets, but smaller than the RBCs as shown in Fig. 26c [38]. This can be seen in increased platelet turn over, Myelo proliferative disorders, Myelo dysplastic disorders.

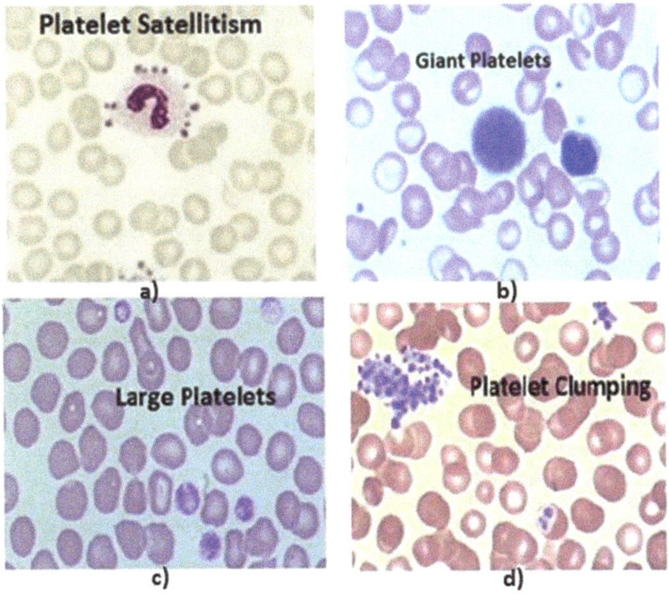

Fig. 26 **a** Platelet Satellitism **b** Giant Platelet **c** Large Platelet **d** Platelet clumping

(iv) **Platelet Clumping**: These are small Clumps of platelets (see Fig. 26d). These are found in Invitro artifact due to EDTA or cold and causes false low counts of platelet, difficult vene section [38, 39].

(v) **Micro clots**: These are combinations of Fibrin strands, platelets and white cells (in this case–neutrophils) [40].

5 Conclusion

Though investigation of primary haemopathies especially anemias and hematological malignancies goes beyond cellular hematology, morphology remains the initial (baseline) tool for diagnostic evaluations. Specific morphologic abnormalities of red cells correspond to numerous differential diagnoses. From the above literature survey it is shown that traditional method are very tedious, have less accuracy and depend on the patience of the human in pathology. Thus it may be possible to have many errors. Therefore a rapid image processing and segmentation method has been proposed. In this discussion the image analysis has been done on the Morphology of Blood cells (digital image).Various qualitative abnormalities of the blood cells have been discussed is by no means exhaustive and the same has been tabulated. Future work on image analysis of peripheral blood smears should emphasize building an automated software tool utilizing the best performance image segmentation algorithms along with data mining techniques, which has a strong influence in automating the process of the peripheral blood smear image analysis.

References

1. EsanAyodele, J. (2016). Complete blood cell count and peripheral blood film, its significant in laboratory medicine: A review study. *American Journal of Laboratory Medicine., 3,* 34–57.
2. Adewoyin, A. S., & Nwogoh, B. (2014). Peripheral blood film—A review. *Annals of Ibadan Postgraduate Medicine, 12,* 71–79.
3. Riley, R. S., James, G. W., Sommer, S., & Martin, M. J. (2013). *How to Prepare and Interpret Peripheral Blood Smears, 82*(4), 449–453.
4. Tefferi, A., Hanson, C. A., & Inwards, D. J. (2005). How to interpret and pursue an abnormal complete blood cell count in adults. *Mayo ClinProc, 80*(7), 923–936.
5. Munster, M. (2013). The role of the peripheral blood smear in the modern haematology laboratory. *SEED Haematology Sysmex, 33,* 839–845.
6. Tkachuk, D. C., & Hirschmann, J. V (2007). Approach to the microscopic evaluation of blood and bone marrow. Wintrobe Atlas of clinical haematology. *Lippincott Williams & Wilkins, 4*(1), 37–40.
7. Bain, B. (2005). Current concepts: Diagnosis from the blood smear. *The New England Journal of Medicine, 353* (5), 498.
8. Pagana, K., Pagana, T., & Mosby's. (2006). *Manual of Diagnostic and Laboratory Tests* (3rd ed., pp. 447–448). St. Louis Mosby Elsevier.
9. Janz, T. G., Johnson, R. L., & Rubenstein, S. D. (2013). Anemia in the emergency department: Evaluation and treatment. *Emergency Medicine Practice, 15*(11), 1–16.
10. Bolton-Maggs, P. (2004). Guidelines for the diagnosis and management of hereditary spherocytosis. *British Journal of Haematology, 126*(4), 455–474.
11. Percy, M. J., Zhao, Q., Flores, A., et al. (2006). A family with erythrocytosis establishes a role for prolyl hydroxylase domain protein 2 in oxygen homeostasis. *Proceedings of the National Academy of Sciences of the United States of America, 103*(3), 654–659.
12. Percy, M. J., Furlow, P. W., & Lucas, G. S. (2008). A gain-of-function mutation in the HIF2A gene in familial erythrocytosis. *New England Journal of Medicine, 358*(2), 162–168.
13. Perrotta, S., Nobili, B., Ferraro, M., et al. (2006). VonHippel-Lindau-dependent polycythemia is endemic on the island of Ischia: Identification of a novel cluster. *Blood, 107*(2), 514–519.
14. Gale, D. P., Harten, S. K., Reid, C. D., Tuddenham, E. G., Maxwell, P. H. (2008). Autosomal dominant erythrocytosis and pulmonary arterial hypertension associated with an activating HIF2 alphmutation Blood *112*(3), 19–921.
15. Stefanini, M., Urbas, J. V., & Urbas, J. E. (1978). Gaisböck's syndrome: its hematologic, biochemical and hormonal parameters. *Angiology, 29*(7), 520–533.
16. EsanAyodele, J. (2014). Severity and prevalence of malaria infection and effect of anti-malaria drugs on gender differences using some haematological parameters. *International Journal of Haematological Disorders., 1*(1), 1–7.
17. Bain, B. J., Blood cell Morphology in Health and Disease in Dacie and Lewis Practical Haematology, (11 ed), *5*, 69–10.
18. Qaseem, A., Humphrey, L. L., Fitterman, N., Starkey, M., & Shekelle, P. (2013). Treatment of anemia in patients with heart disease: A clinical practice guideline from the American College of Physicians. *Annals of Internal Medicine, 159*(11), 770–779.
19. Bhutta, Z. A., Das, J. K., Walker, N., et al. (2013). For The Lancet Diarrhoea and Pneumonia Interventions Study Group. Interventions to address deaths from childhood pneumonia and diarrhoea equitably: What works and at what cost? *Lancet, 381,* 1417–1429.
20. Schaefer, M., & Rowan, R. M. (2000). The Clinical relevance of nucleated red cell counts. *Sysmex Journal International, 10*(2), 59–63.

21. Constantino, B. T., & Cogionis, B. (2000). Nucleated RBCs-significance in the peripheral blood film. *Laboratory Medicine, 31*(4), 223–229.
22. Berend Houwen, B. (2000). Blood film preparation and staining procedures. *Laboratory Haematology, 6,* 1–7.
23. Shagana, J. A. (2014) Diagnostic cells in the peripheral blood smear. *Journal of Pharmaceutical Sciences and Research, 6*(4), 213–216.
24. Alhadidi, B. (2012). Diagnosis of iron deficiency anemia using image processing techniques. *Research Journal of Applied Sciences, Engineering and Technology, 4*(23), 5144–5148.
25. Alhadidi, B., & Fakhouri, H. N. (2008). Automation of iron deficiency anemia blue and red cell number calculating by intestinal villi tissue slide images enhancing and processing. Proceeding of the In *International Conference on Computer Science and Information Technology* (pp. 407–410).
26. Alhadidi, B., Zu'bi, M., & Suleiman, H. (2007). Mammogram breast cancer edge detection using image processing function. *Information Technology Journal, 6*(2), 217–221.
27. Chen, P., Yan, X., & Zheng, C. (2006). Recognition of blood and bone marrow cells using kernel-based image retrieval. *IJCSNS International Journal of Computer Science and Network Security, 6,* 29–34.
28. Hamghalam, M., Motameni, M., & Kelishomi, A. E. (2009). Leukocyte segmentation in giemsa- stained image of peripheral blood smears based on active contour. In *International Conference on Signal Processing Systems* (pp. 103–106).
29. Hirimutugoda, Y. M., & Wijayarathna, G. (2010). Image analysis system for detection of red cell disorder using artificial neural networks. *Journal of Biomedical Informatics, Sri Lanka, 1*(1), 35–42.
30. Karunakar, Y., & Kuwadekar, A. (2011). An unparagoned application for red blood cell counting using marker controlled watershed algorithm for android mobile. In *Fifth International Conference on Next Generation Mobile Applications and Services* (pp. 100–104).
31. Liao, Q., & Deng, Y. (2002). An accurate segmentation method for white blood cell images. In *Proceedings of the IEEE International Symposium on the Biomedical Imaging* (pp. 245–248).
32. Miswan, M. F., Sharif, J. M., Ngadi, M. A., Mohamad D., & Abdul Jamil, M. M. (2011). An overview: Segmentation method for blood cell disorders. *BIOMED IFMBE Proceedings, 35,* 596–599.
33. Mohapatra, S., Patra, D., & Kumar, K. (2011). Blood microscopic image segmentation using rough sets. In *International Conference on Image Information Processing (ICIIP)* (pp. 1–6).
34. Mu, J., Liu X. M., Kamocka, M. M., Xu, Z. L., Alber, M. S., Rosen, E. D., & Chen, D. Z. (2009). Segmentation, reconstruction, and analysis of blood thrombi in 2-photon microscopy images. In *22nd IEEE Symposium on Computer-Based Medical Systems (CBMS)*, Albuquerque (pp. 3–4).
35. Nguyen, N., Duong, A., & Vu, H. (2010). A new method for splitting clumped cells in red blood images. In *Second International Conference on Knowledge and Systems Engineering* (pp. 3–8).
36. Sadeghian, F., Seman, Z., Ramli, A. R., Kahar, B. H. A., & Saripan, M. (2009). A framework for white blood cell segmentation in microscopic blood images using digital image processing. *Biology Proceedings Online, 11,* 196–206.
37. Savkare, S. S., & Narote, S. P. (2011). Automatic classification of normal and infected blood cells for parasitemia detection. *IJCSNS International Journal of Computer Science and Network Security*, 11(2).
38. Sharif, J. M., Miswan, M. F., Ngadi, M. A., Salam, M. S. H., & Mahadi bin Abdul Jamil, M. (2012). Red blood cell segmentation using masking and watershed algorithm: A preliminary study. In *International Conference on Biomedical Engineering (ICOBE)* (pp. 258–262).
39. Wang, R., & McCane, B. (2008). Red blood cell classification through depth map and surface feature. In *International Symposium on Computer Science and Computational Technology* (pp. 339–342).
40. Zahir, S., Chowdhury, R., & Payne, G. W. (2006). Automated assessment of erythrocyte disorders using artificial neural network. In *IEEE International Symposium on Signal Processing and Information Technology* (pp. 776–780).

Gender Aware CNN for Speech Emotion Recognition

Chinmay Thakare, Neetesh Kumar Chaurasia, Darshan Rathod, Gargi Joshi, and Santwana Gudadhe

Abstract Audio and speech analysis have been in focus for a while, with which comes many features at hand; feature selection has to be taken in account. Also a lot of advancements have been in the machine learning front, so we performed a detailed analysis of features as well as model selection. Using the SAVEE dataset for initial work and RAVDESS dataset for final proposed system, the proposed system uses mel-frequency cepstral coefficient with SVM for gender bias and CNNs for emotion recognition.

Keywords Speech emotion recognition · Convolutional neural network · Gender information

1 Introduction

Emotion recognition systems help bridge the gap in human machine interaction. As the advancements in the field of human machine interaction, the emotions come into play. The speech input doesn't only pack the information in word form to understand the emotion but also the intonation and accent; the same words can pack a different emotion. This makes speech emotion recognition an interesting field of work. To

C. Thakare (✉) · N. K. Chaurasia · D. Rathod · G. Joshi · S. Gudadhe
Pimpri Chinchwad College of Engineering, Pune, India
e-mail: chinmay0598@gmail.com

N. K. Chaurasia
e-mail: nkc512@gmail.com

D. Rathod
e-mail: rathoddarshan56@gmail.com

G. Joshi
e-mail: gargij16@gmail.com

S. Gudadhe
e-mail: s.santwana20@gmail.com

R. Patgiri et al. (eds.), *Health Informatics: A Computational Perspective in Healthcare*, Studies in Computational Intelligence 932,
https://doi.org/10.1007/978-981-15-9735-0_18

make the problem definitive and limit the problem, we are using the Ekman model [1] of six emotions. As the same words can reflect different emotions, on the other hand, speech signal's acoustic features require less processing for extraction in terms of time as well as computational complexity.

Communication between humans and machines can be made more effective and natural with machines understanding emotions like humans. With many ways to express emotion in communication, few ways being posture, gesture, speech, and facial expressions. Communication of emotions through speech signals is the most natural method [2].

In depth knowledge of the domain is required to understand features and choose the ones to work on, for the problem. Machine learning serves as the basis of emotion recognition systems. So, the type of features selected plays a major role in model selection; the certain type of feature works well with a few specific types of models.

In order to make the system usable in real time, it is necessary that the system must be quick at extracting features. Although this is with the assumption that machine learning models in the system have low latency in result generation. Hardware affects the performance, but not that significantly apart form during training.

This paper presents a system which takes into account the gender of the speaker and then predicts the emotion based on the acoustic features. Everything is experimented with and documented properly, for ease of understanding. All the features and the machine learning algorithms are under consideration which are recorded.

Emotion recognition system performs the task of classifying the sample input into the emotion classes. The machine learning algorithms considered here are support vector machine, random forest classifier, XGBoost, and convolutional neural network. The features mentioned are all considered in combination with the algorithms.

2 Related Work

Gender aware speech emotion recognition (SER) systems have been in the picture for a while. In [3, 4] gender recognition and SER combined systems have performed better than SER without gender information. In [4], CNN-BLTM with deep neural network was used, which performed better than the baseline model. 2D spectrogram is given to CNN, which is computationally expensive. Different gender driven features are shown to perform well.

While in [5], the dependent vs. independent features are compared. The text dependent system is shown to have very slightly better performance. In [6], the pitch median (energy) is used as a feature for the gender recognition system. PCA with KNN is used and generated significantly good results.

The recent work in [7, 8], the results are as high as 85% on RAVDESS. But this work uses only four emotion classes (angry, joy, neutral, and sad) [7]. In [8], they used six emotions (angry, fear, happy, neutral, sad, and surprise) on Chinese speech dataset. The system uses CNN-RFC to produce 75.57% accuracy.

3 Proposed System

There is a need for two machine learning models. First, for emotion recognition from the acoustic features and second, for gender recognition. For both the models required for the system proper selection of model and feature combination are to be studied. In depth exploration has been done to find best results, the models under consideration are paired with all the features at hand.

To find the best combination of the models and features, the metrics used are accuracy and categorical cross-entropy as loss function. There are seven classes one for each emotion (angry, disgust, fear, happy, neutral, sad, surprised.) to be considered for this classification system.

The emotion recognition system has gender aware nature, meaning it uses gender bias for emotion recognition. In Fig. 1, the basic flow of the system is shown. The system is basically divided in three phases.

First phase uses the gender recognition system to detect gender of the speaker in the audio clip. This is important as a simple attribute specifying the gender as an attribute is not very effective for the overall accuracy of the system. So the gender recognition system splits the data into male and female, which is later fed to emotion classifier model. This is shown in Fig. 1.

3.1 Features

Feature and model selection are very important parts of the whole system. While the feature leads the reason for the better working of the system, the combination of the both is to be considered for best possible results. The problem at hand is that there are too many possible combinations. So to work this out, features will be limited and so

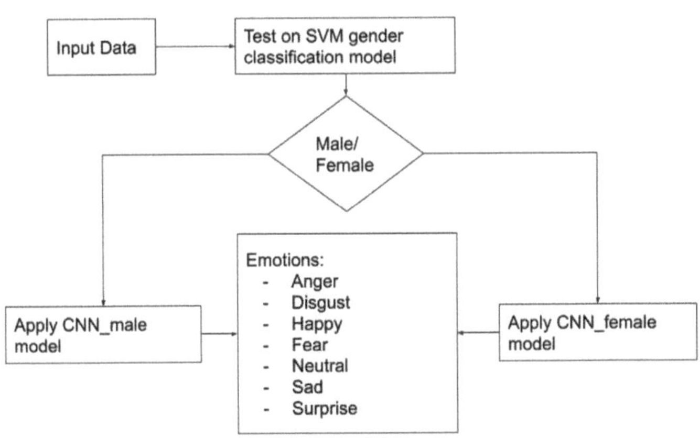

Fig. 1 Block diagram of proposed emotion recognition system

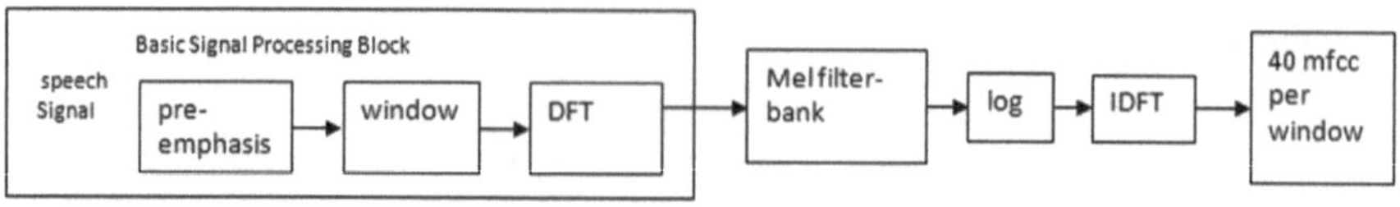

Fig. 2 Stages in MFCC extraction

will be the machine learning models. There are many "natural" (Acoustic–phonetic) features available: Formant frequencies, intensity, duration, articulations, etc., and there are not-so-natural features as well: cepstrum, linear spectral frequencies, vocal tract area function, delta, and double-delta coefficients, etc., [8]. The features used in the experiment are all acoustic, even though the utterance type of features has proven to be useful [3]. The reason for this is that the utterance level features are specific to the language, meaning a different model, and knowledge base for each language.

3.1.1 Mel Filter Bank

Pre-emphasis: The weaker higher frequency components are boosted in the pre-emphasis phase. It balances the frequency spectrum since high frequencies have lesser magnitude in comparison with low frequency spectrum.

Window: Audio file is split into shorter time frames of length 2048, and window function is applied. We used the hamming window out of the available windows.

DFT: Each of the window frames is converted into a magnitude spectrum on application of discrete Fourier transform.

Mel filter Bank: Mel spectrum is calculated by passing the signal through mel filter bank. Human ear perceived frequency is measured in terms of mel scale. Energy is extracted by applying a mel space filter bank to the power spectrum [9, 10].

3.1.2 MFCC

Discrete Cosine Transform: Take the DCT of the log of filter bank energies to obtain MFCC [9, 10]. The steps involved in MFCC extraction are shown in Fig. 2.

3.1.3 Tonnetz

It is the harmonic content of an audio signal [11].

3.1.4 Spectral Contrast

The contrast energy of each sub-band obtained frames from spectrogram is taken by calculating the difference between mean energy in higher quantile range to mean energy in low quantile range [12].

3.1.5 Chroma STFT

These spectrographs determine how musical chords are changing over time. It consists of twelve element vectors in which each element is the intensity of a particular semitone [13].

3.2 *Preprocessing*

The proposed system is implemented in three stages as shown in Fig. 3, preprocessing, feature extraction, and recognition system. The system is a gender aware, which utilizes both the gender recognition system as well as the emotion recognition system.

The voice recording when given to the system, first operation is preprocessing. In this two operations are performed. Firstly, trimming operation is performed; this removes the silent parts of the audio recording from the start of the clip. This helps by removing the non-useful parts of the audio.

And second operation is pre-emphasis, the weaker higher frequency components are boosted balancing the frequency spectrum. This makes the audio more balanced for more effective feature extraction.

The effect of the trimming and pre-emphasis can be seen in Fig. 4a, b, respectively.

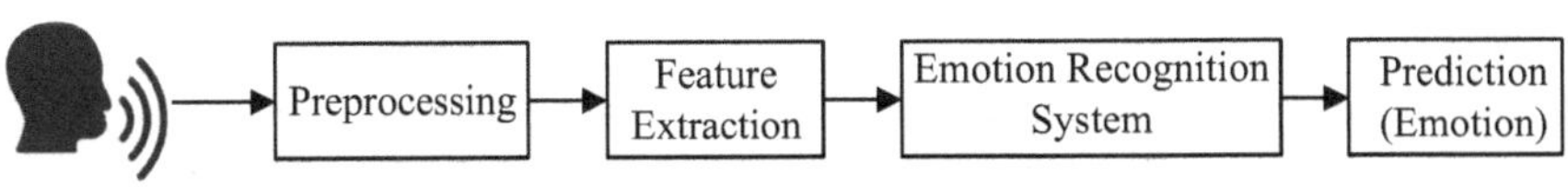

Fig. 3 Proposed system's block diagram

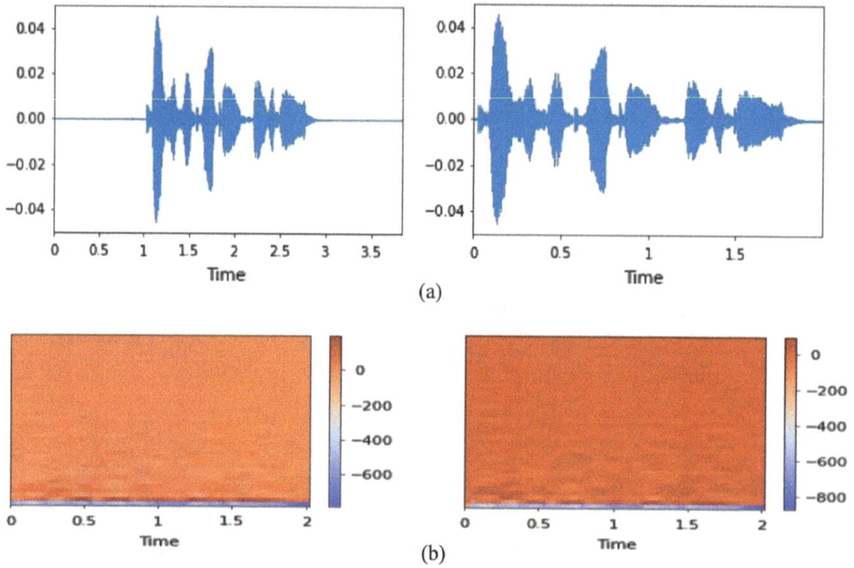

Fig. 4 Preprocessing visualization **a** Trim effect on signal input and **b** MFCC without pre-emphasis and with pre-emphasis

4 Experimental Evaluation

4.1 Dataset

4.1.1 SAVEE

The database consists of speech recordings representing seven different emotions, by four male actors. The recordings are British English utterances. The data is categorized in four actors and seven emotions for each actor. The clips consist of 15 sentences per emotion. Ten subjects assessed the dataset under audio conditions, in order to maintain the quality [14].

4.1.2 RAVDESS

The database is made of speech samples spoken in English. It consists of 24 actors and is gender balanced. The speech samples are labeled for seven emotions including angry, calm, fearful, happy, sad, surprise, and disgust. Two levels of intensities for each type of emotion are included. This is recorded in a North American accent. The dataset contains three types of representation of the same data audio-only, video-only, and audio video combined [15].

For our work, we worked exclusively with audio data only from RAVDESS. Gender diversity helps in better generalization.

4.2 Feature Extraction

The feature extraction being an important part of the system, we are extracting only the features that have been proven useful from the exploration done and tabulated earlier. So MFCC values are extracted in two phases as seen in Fig. 5a. Firstly, 40 MFCC values are extracted per window shown in Fig. 5b; each window has a fixed

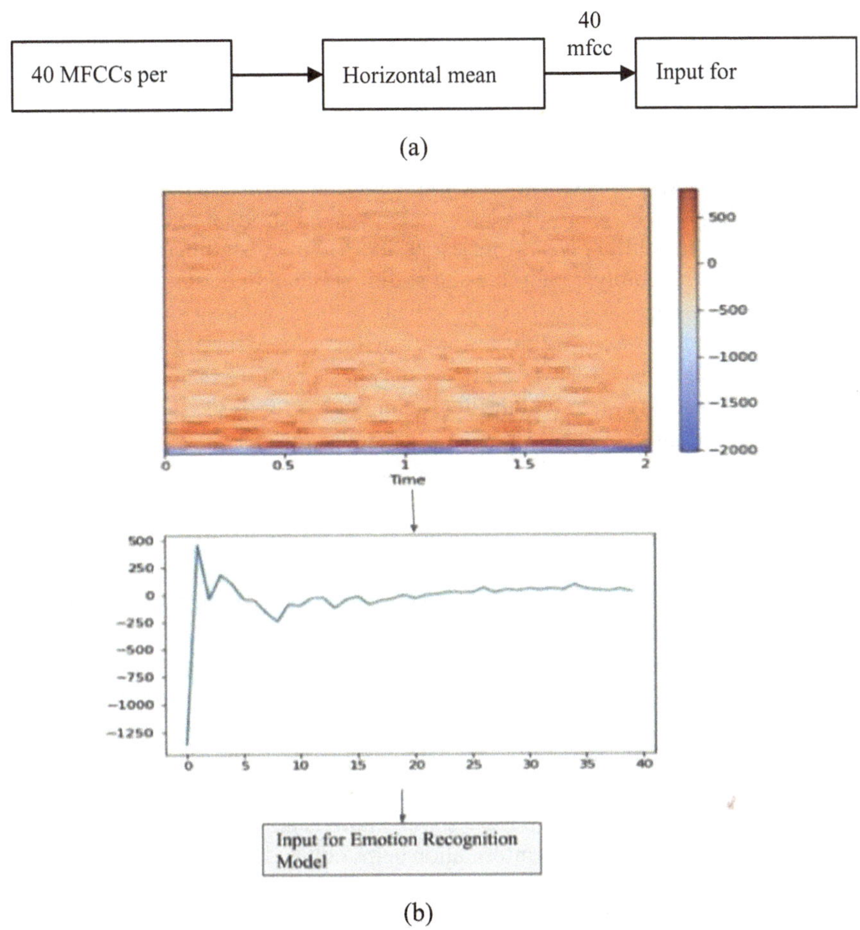

Fig. 5 **a** Block diagram of feature extraction and **b** visualization of the data at phases in feature extraction

Table 1 Accuracy (in %) of the gender biased vs. unbiased system

Model/Feature	MFCC
CNN (biased)	77.93
CNN (unbiased)	73.01

Table 2 Accuracy (in %) of the feature and model combination in gender recognition system

Model\Feature	MFCC	Mel filter bank	Contrast	Tonnetz
RFC	96.82	96.82	92.85	71.82
SVM	98	79.5	87.5	63

length of 93 ms spaced by 23 ms which corresponds to 2048 frame length and 512 hop length at sampling rate of 22,050 Hz.

Further, in the second phase, horizontal mean is taken to convert it into 40 values, one for each frequency group. This makes sure that irrespective of length of the audio clip exactly 40 MFCC values is produced. The taken mean value plot can be seen in Fig. 5b. This is later fed to the prediction model. Since both gender and emotion recognition use the MFCC for prediction, only MFCC is needed to be extracted.

The gender recognition system increases the accuracy significantly as can be seen from Table 1. Simply adding it as an additional feature doesn't seem to show a significant difference. Also with CNN at hand a single value doesn't make much difference to the model. So to tackle this problem, this system simply only recognizes the gender of the speaker. This being the only task of the system, again all the combinations are tried out, to find the best combination for this system.

For the exploration of this system, we used the RAVDESS database. As the gender recognition system needs both male and female actors voice clips. Also as this database is larger and has 12 male and female voice actors each.

Table 2 shows the accuracy in percentage (%) of each combination in tabulated. Since this system is just supposed to be supporting the main emotion recognition system, only models with low complexity are used. So, only support vector machine and random forest are used for comparison.

After looking at the results in Table 2, it can seen that MFCC with SVM shows the most promising option. SVM works with low computational cost and latency, which is very favorable for the application.

The exploration is performed on the SAVEE dataset. As this system performs only emotion recognition, it didn't matter if the database has only male voice actors.

In Table 3, the performance of every combination is tabulated. The values are of accuracy in percentage (%). This information helps out in selection of the best model and feature combination.

The data from Table 3, we can conclude that the combination of CNN and MFCC gives the best results in terms of accuracy on the classification task. The mel filter banks also show promising results but the processing for the machine learning model

Table 3 Accuracy (in %) of the feature and model combination for emotion recognition system

Model\Feature	MFCC	Mel filter bank	Contrast	Tonnetz
CNN	79.16	65.63	36.46	27.08
RFC	67.96	70.62	52.08	29.16
SVM	68.75	44.79	49.47	27.08
XGBOOST	62.5	64.58	48.95	21.87

Table 4 Accuracy (in %) for feature and gender-based CNN models

Model\Feature	MFCC	MFCC + Pre-emphasis + Energy
CNN_male	76.19	74.6
CNN_female	71.87	79.68

is high as compared to MFCC. So CNN and MFCC are selected for the final proposed model.

5 Discussion and Analysis

CNN_male has only 40 MFCC values as a feature. While CNN_female has the same features as CNN_male with addition of energy. This is done as we have found that log of mean of energy is also an important feature for classification of female emotion recognition. As can be seen from Table 4, the pre-emphasis and energy feature proved successful for female audio clips, but it didn't prove useful for male audio clips.

The models have slightly different architectures; this is done in order to capacitate models to handle different features. So to maximize the accuracy both models tuned, thus have different hyperparameters. This helps in making sure that the accuracy of the overall system is as high as possible.

Figure 6a, b shows the confusion matrix of CNN_male and CNN_female, respectively. These confusion matrices show class-wise performance.

The overall accuracy of the system is 76.37% as compared to 73.01% of the initial unbiased system (base model). This can be seen from the confusion matrix of the overall system in Fig. 7.

6 Conclusion

The results show that classification of gender has improved the emotion recognition model using CNN. The accuracy of 77.93% in the gender biased system as compared

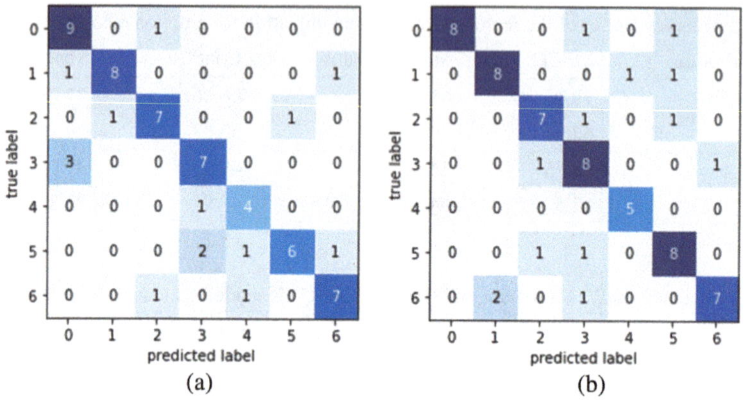

Fig. 6 Confusion matrices for emotion recognition models **a** CNN_male **b** CNN_female

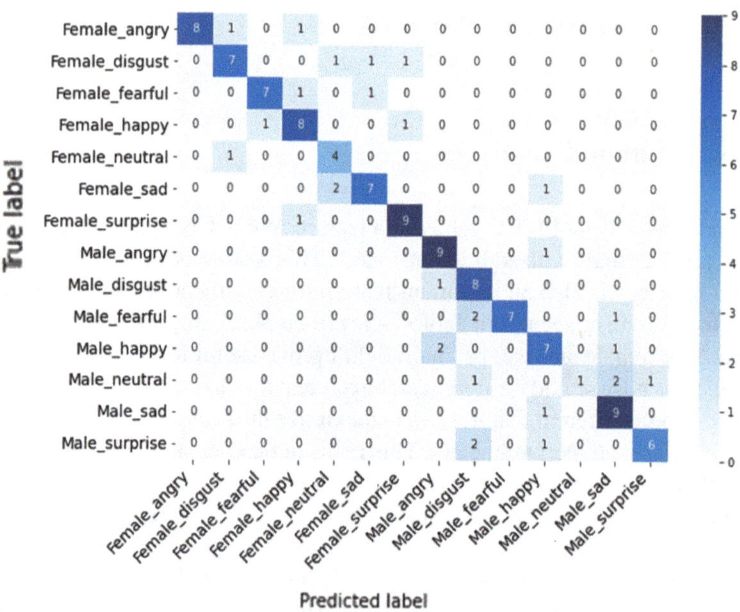

Fig. 7 Confusion matrix for the complete gender aware SER system

to 73.01% in unbiased systems is considerable and can be used for emotion recognition systems. Despite the accuracy and its improvement from previous implementation, it can still be improved as it has been tested with limited datasets of SAVEE and RAVDESS. Our future work would be to extract more effective features and combine it with models containing emotion recognition from videos to develop even more robust systems.

References

1. Ekman, P., & Power, M. J. (1999). *Handbook of cognition and emotion.* Sussex: Wiley .
2. El Ayadi, M., Kamel, M. S., & Karray, F. (2011). Survey on speech emotion recognition: Features, classification schemes, and databases. *Pattern Recognition, 44*(3), 572–587.
3. Vogt, T., & Andre, E. (2006). Improving automatic emotion recognition from speech via gender differentiation. In: *Language Resources and Evaluation Conference*, Genoa.
4. Zhang, L., Wang, L., Dang, J., Guo, L., & Yu, Q (2018). Gender-Aware CNN-BLSTM for Speech Emotion Recognition. In V. Kurkova et al. (Eds.) *ICANN 2018*, LNCS 11139 (pp. 782–790). https://doi.org/10.1007/978-3-030-01418-6_76.
5. Nayak B., & Pradhan, M. K. (2016). Text-dependent versus text-independent speech emotion recognition. In Satapathy, S., Raju, K., Mandal, J., Bhateja, V. (Eds.) *Proceedings of the Second International Conference on Computer and Communication Technologies. Advances in Intelligent Systems and Computing* (vol 379.). New Delhi: Springer.
6. Chen, C., You, M., Song, M., Bu, J., & Liu, J. (2006). An enhanced speech emotion recognition system based on discourse information. In Alexandrov, V. N., van Albada, G. D., Sloot, P. M. A., Dongarra, J. (Eds.) *Computational Science – ICCS 2006*. ICCS 2006. Lecture Notes in Computer Science (vol. 3991). Berlin, Heidelberg: Springer.
7. Koduru, A., Valiveti, H. B., & Budati, A. K. (2020). Feature extraction algorithms to improve the speech emotion recognition rate. *International Journal of Speech Technology, 23,* 45–55. https://doi.org/10.1007/s10772-020-09672-4.
8. Zheng, L., Li, Q., Ban, H., &Liu, S. (2018). Speech emotion recognition based on convolution neural networks combined with random forest. In *2018 Chinese Control and Decision Conference (CCDC)*, Shenyang (pp. 4143–4147).
9. Das Mandal, S. K. (2020). NPTEL courses: Digital speech processing, NPTEL: National Programme on Technology Enhanced Learning. Retrieved at April 10, 2020. From the website https://nptel.ac.in/courses/117105145/.
10. Davis, S., & Mermelstein, P. (1980, August). Comparison of parametric representations for monosyllabic word recognition in continuously spoken sentences. *IEEE Transactions on Acoustics, Speech Signal Processing, 28*(4), 357–366.
11. Harte, C., Sandler, M., & Gasser, M. (2006). Detecting harmonic change in musical audio. In *Proceedings of the 1st ACM Workshop on Audio and Music Computing Multimedia* (pp. 21–26). Santa Barbara, CA: ACM Press. https://doi.org/10.1145/1178723.1178727.
12. Jiang, D.-N., et al. (2002). Music type classification by spectral contrast feature. In *Proceedings. IEEE International Conference on Multimedia and Expo* (vol. 1, pp. 113–116).
13. Ellis, D. P. W. (2007). Classifying music audio with timbral and chroma features. ISMIR.
14. Haq, S., Jackson, P. J. B., & Edge, J. D. (2008). Audio-visual feature selection and reduction for emotion classification. In *Proceedings of the International Conference on Auditory-Visual Speech Processing* (pp. 185–190).
15. Livingstone, S. R., & Russo, F. A. (2018). The Ryerson audio-visual database of emotional speech and song (RAVDESS): A dynamic, multimodal set of facial and vocal expressions in North American English. *PLoS ONE, 13*(5), e0196391. https://doi.org/10.1371/journal.pone.0196391.

FSC
www.fsc.org
MIX
Papier | Fördert gute Waldnutzung
FSC® C083411

Kolibri 360 GmbH
Ferdinand-Jühlke-Straße 7
99095 Erfurt, Deutschland
produktsicherheit@kolibri360.de